My Journey to Rec[...]

Part One

Debbie Armstrong had ME/CFS for over nine years and is now fully recovered.

In this booklet Debbie shares her frustrations, struggles and moments of inspiration with you. She also includes quotations, poems, definitions, journal extracts, top tips to take away and practical tasks for you to try on your journey to recovery.

This publication is the first in a series of four. They explain in more detail the ingredients in Debbie's Recipe for Recovery, which you will find in this booklet.

Published by Debbie Armstrong

Publishing partner: ipeace

First published in 2019
This edition published in 2021

Copyright © Debbie Armstrong 2019

ISBN 978–1–8383494–2–4

Book design, layout and production management by
Debbie and Marcus Armstrong

Hand-drawn illustrations by Gemma Scott

For my parents, Margaret and Norman,

with love.

By the same author

My Journey to Recovery

Part Two

first published in 2020

revised edition to be published in 2021

Parts Three and Four

due to be published in 2022

Aching limbs
Aching head
Stupid brain
All is dead

Noise too loud
Music worse
Nothing rhymes
Except this verse

Banging door
Hurting head
If only I could
Get off this bed

I have a life
I am a wife
And mother
And need other

Things to do
Than be ill and ache
And lie and take
Your contempt for

My 'laziness'

Janice Earls, 1984

Today my life will change forever.

Today will be the start...

...the moment when I begin to lose everything that matters.

All those things that make me who I am will be ripped away...

...until my helplessness, and my desperation, and my loss become too huge, and I am swallowed up.

But I do not know this yet.

I only know that I have woken in this bed, with bones of lead.

And a head that weighs so, so heavy upon my pillow.

Fear devours me with sharpened teeth.

Abigail Watkin, 2019

MY JOURNEY TO RECOVERY
Part One

Taking responsibility

Finding acceptance

Making decisions

Maintaining commitment

Initiating action

Evaluating beliefs

Contents

In this booklet, the abbreviation 'ME' is used to include myalgic encephalomyelitis (ME), also known as chronic fatigue syndrome (CFS) and fibromyalgia (FM).

'Life is a gift, and it offers us the privilege, opportunity, and responsibility to give something back by becoming more.'

Tony Robbins

Coddiwomple:
To travel in a purposeful manner
towards a vague destination.
(colloquial verb)

Debbie volunteering at a school in India, 2013.

Don't let your illness define you;
create your own definition of life.

My story

In February 2004, I woke up one morning in agony, too weak to lift my head off the pillow. It felt as though the marrow in my bones had turned into lead piping. I felt breathless exhaustion within me and a black fog surrounding me.

I was shocked. I was scared.

For the preceding twenty years I had been getting slowly and steadily ill. My illnesses included irritable bowel syndrome (IBS); anxiety and depression; Tietze syndrome; migraines; chronic cystitis and sinus infections; insomnia; and muscle pains so severe that I was unable to turn my head and, on occasion, unable to open my mouth.

What was happening to me?

I assumed that I had caught flu from people at work. It took many blood tests, hospital investigations, and well over a year to get a diagnosis. The painful truth was that my body had crashed with ME, and I would remain ill for over nine years.

During that time, my partner left me. I was dismissed from my job. On many occasions, I was bed- or house-bound. It was a terrifying experience. I lost my life as I had known it. Everything that I valued and cared about was gone. I felt isolated and utterly alone. I discovered that there was, and still is, no traditional medical cure.

I finally recovered using a combination of alternative approaches, hard work and dedication.

As I write this in 2019, I've been fully recovered for over seven years. I have a different, wonderful partner. I have another job and a life that I truly love.

Several major traumas, as well as a long-term relationship that was emotionally and physically abusive, caused chronic stress. This stress led to an intense lack of self-care, which finally manifested as ME. Amazingly, my body had kept going for a long time before screaming 'STOP'! Developing ME didn't happen overnight, nor did my recovery.

Chronic stress over an extended period could have led to a heart attack, a stroke or some other life-threatening illness. ME is not fatal. It severely diminished my quality of life but did not cut short my time here.

I do believe that full recovery is possible, although there is no magic pill or 'one size fits all' solution. It's a personal journey of self-healing. ME was the vehicle that took me to a new life and a new way of being in the world.

In this book I want to share my story of recovery with those who are living with ME, people in recovery, and those who have friends or family with this debilitating condition.

I tried to write about my experience of ME many times without success. Then, in 2016, I felt inspired to write my story in the form of a Recipe for Recovery, and finally it all came flowing out!

On pages 44–45, you will find my Recipe for Recovery. I have taken the first group of ingredients and written about them in detail in this booklet.

Recovery has been a very personal voyage of discovery for me, and I wanted to share my frustrations, struggles and moments of inspiration with you. I have even included some extracts from my journals here. These will give you an insight into my feelings, and show how and when things began to change. Journal extracts are easy to find because they look handwritten and are on scraps of yellow paper!

I hope that reading about my experience will help to reassure you. However isolated your illness makes you feel, you are not alone.

While I genuinely believe that recovery is possible, having lived through the trauma and turmoil of ME, I understand that it might seem unreal to you right now.

Please read on.

I hope that my experience will inspire you to know that you too can make changes in your life that can lead to recovery from ME.

There is so much for me to tell you.

Each ingredient from my Recipe for Recovery begins with a cover page that includes a definition and a quotation. Each section ends with top tips for you to take away, followed by something practical for you to try.

The rest of the ingredients are in my other booklets.

Before you go any further, if you only have the time and energy for one thing, then please take a moment to read through my Recipe for Recovery. It's my gift to you.

To get in touch about this booklet, to talk about your recovery journey or to join my mailing list, please email me at:

myjourneytorecovery1@hotmail.com

or visit my website:

myjourneytorecovery.online

This booklet contains extracts from fifteen years of personal journals that I have written about my experience of ME and recovery. Where possible, I have credited sources of information, but it has not always been possible to recall the specific source.

Responsibility:
The state or fact of being responsible, answerable or accountable for something within one's power, control or management.

'Self-realisation is the sweetest thing. It shows us how we are fully responsible for ourselves, and that is where we find our freedom.'
Byron Katie

This chapter relates to responsibility in my Recipe for Recovery.

Imagine getting in your car and starting on a crazy roller-coaster of a journey with no idea what your final destination will be. That was my experience of going from being bed-bound and house-bound with ME to making a full recovery. During those nine years, I experienced depression and suicidal thoughts – and manic, adrenaline-fuelled highs. The journal extract below shows just how bleak I often felt.

> *Back early from a retreat.*
> *Couldn't even get out of bed.*
>
> *What a total waste of time.*
>
> *So much shame.*
>
> *What a total waste of space I am. Burnt out.*
>
> *Why do I keep thinking things will be different?*

Alone, terrified, and in desperation at my situation, I began to read a book by M. Scott Peck, *The Road Less Travelled*. The insights it contained about my responsibility for my recovery unsettled me, and I felt a mix of confusing, conflicting emotions. I felt a crushing sense of deflation; secretly, I had hoped for a fairy godmother to come and take away my unbearable pain and my sense of isolation.

The poem on the next page was written for me by my friend, Abigail Watkin. These words, and my journal extract that follows, show how lost I was feeling.

I am alone and drowning.

Screaming silently ...

... pinned inside this strait-jacket life ...

... this waking nightmare.

I struggle.

I kick.

I fight.

I choke.

I am never, never, never, strong enough to push my head above the water...

And no one is waiting to catch my hand.

I am the fading. I am the shadow. I am the ripple.

I am the falling light upon the water ... all gone out.

I've been told I've got to stop blaming other people for my crashes and take responsibility for my wellbeing!

Other people – with their healthy lives and normal problems – have no idea what's going on for me.

Feel full of rage ... crying, crying, crying.

What else is there for me?

As I read more of M. Scott Peck's book, I felt strangely liberated, and I realised that perhaps my recovery was something I could control.

Prompted by ideas about self-responsibility, I began to explore my thoughts, emotions* and behaviours.* Even though I felt guilty at first about what it might mean for those around me, I was inspired to change many of the things I was doing. In particular, I focused on all the emotions and behaviours that were linked to my view of myself as a 'helper'** and an 'achiever'.**

*You will find a chapter on emotions and behaviour in *My Journey to Recovery, Part Three*. **On pages 54–55 you will find information on psychological subtypes.

With this new road map, I started to feel more secure. I glimpsed a brighter road ahead. I was able to be kinder to myself: this, in turn, allowed me to feel more confident about recovery and adopt a more optimistic approach to life.

The poem by Portia Nelson, 'Autobiography in Five Short Chapters',* neatly summarises what I was going through. The poet's 'I walk down the street [...] I am lost ... I am hopeless' becomes 'I walk down another street' by the end of the poem.

Fuelled by my new awareness of self-responsibility, I stopped labelling myself as 'selfish' when I met my own needs or 'lazy' when I needed to rest. I cautiously allowed myself to be more self-focused. As my responsibility for each pit stop and diversion along my route grew, so did my self-confidence.

I started to inch my way towards my final destination: recovery.

*https://www.mindfulnessassociation.net/words-of-wonder/autobiography-in-five-short-chapters-portia-nelson

own your
recovery

read a self-help
book

write a
journal

Have a go at writing a journal

I started to keep a journal a long time before I began my recovery journey, and I highly recommend it.

My emotions* were repressed, and masked by anger. I didn't know what I was feeling or how to name or express my feelings. By writing down what was happening to me, I was able to free some of the emotions that were trapped inside, which helped me to put things in perspective. Spending long periods alone, especially when bed-bound, meant that my life seemed a little unreal.

I dedicated a special notebook to my thoughts, emotions and anything else that I thought was important. I kept it private.

If you'd like to start writing a journal, here's how to give it a go:

- find something to write on

- write about how you feel today

- write about your health

- write about you.

It doesn't matter what you discover; the important thing is that you are looking. Write down everything that comes to mind.

You could treat yourself to a special notebook for your journal. You may find it surprisingly liberating. I did!

*You will find a chapter on emotions in *My Journey to Recovery, Part Three.*

Acceptance:
Acknowledging the reality of a situation
without attempting to change it.

'Grant me the serenity to
accept the things I cannot change;
courage to change the things I can;
and wisdom to know the difference.'
Reinhold Niebuhr

This chapter relates to acceptance in my Recipe for Recovery.

Taking responsibility for my recovery was a positive first step for me. The next step was challenging. I had to try to accept that I had ME, with all its pain, limitations and frustrations. Acceptance didn't mean that I agreed with or liked what was happening. I just had to acknowledge things precisely as they were at that time.

These extracts from my journal show some of my frustrations.

I'm feeling strange today, like I'm living in a dream. Hope I wake up to be a new me, not this me.

I'm struggling to be where I am, who I am. If I do accept what's happening, does that mean I'll stay stuck like this forever?

I feel invisible, useless, pathetic. Getting jittery. Best not to think about it. I don't want another panic attack.

Battling these feelings of defeat and frustration took all my strength. I had to turn and face what was happening in my life. I had no choice but to confront the endless pain, as well as all the things I didn't like about myself.

Lying here, too weak to get up.

Feeling unnaturally disconnected from my body. I know I'm trying to control what I can't control; I just can't seem to help it.

I feel powerless, not able to accept how different my life is now.

Desperate to get my old life back, but not sure what to do about it. Seems like there's no way out.

Cautiously, I surrendered myself to my situation, deliberately leaving behind my judgements of how my life was meant to be, and my need to push hard to change or fix everything.

From this point of acceptance and surrender, I was able to move forward towards recovery, one step at a time. No longer fighting the reality of my situation, I was also no longer trying to run away from it. I knew there was no magic pill that would cure me, even though I was taking more than ten different medicines at that time. Although I continued to oscillate between feeling optimistic and pessimistic for many years, I also felt more confident that I would find a way forward.

The following poem, written for me by my friend Abigail Watkin, reflects how much my feelings changed as I began to have the courage to accept my condition:

The future is a beating, breathing, golden thing,

An orb of fragile dreams that shimmer, float, and tantalise,

Just a little further off,

Stretch out then, generously,

With every fibre, sinew, cell,

With every pulse of blood,

With every thought,

With every breath of mind and love,

Reach quickly, lest your dreams be lost.

Now cradle this precious thing that you have taken.

Hold it carefully,

With eager fingertips made tender by this hope,

Let us taste our future,

Let us taste our dreams,

For they are new and sweet and pure.

My experience with ME has shown me that when we resist the negative things that happen to us, we only give them greater strength.

'What we resist, persists.' *(Carl Jung)*

I now believe that our point of power starts at the moment of acceptance. When we permit ourselves not to need to know, or understand, or achieve, when we allow things to be what they are, then we can begin to heal.

Before I reached acceptance, my motivation had been on getting my old life back. Afterwards, healing became my focus.

Wherever that path led, I was determined to follow.

be where
you are

move past blame
and guilt

accept
yourself

Have a go at accepting yourself

Acceptance helped me to live with what I was going through, which meant looking at myself with objective eyes and seeing what was really there.

Even in the depths of despair about having ME, I tried to find one small thing I liked about myself as a starting point for self-acceptance.

Since I felt so worthless, it helped me to write down three things I liked about myself, e.g. 'I like the colour of my hair, I like my ability to listen to people, I like that I am often kind to others'.

It's not always easy to find things we like about ourselves, is it? If you're struggling, ask someone who knows you well to tell you three things they like about you. Write them down in the present tense, e.g. '**I am** kind to others'.

Keep looking back at what you have written. As you become more comfortable with the list, add to it.

I also enjoyed Louise Hay's affirmations* and, as part of my desire to feel more valued, I listened to them regularly.

Saying something positive about myself increased my sense of wellbeing.

*On pages 49–53 you will find information on the alternative therapies I used during my recovery.

Making decisions

Decision:
A cognitive process resulting in the selection of a course of action.

'Don't ever make decisions based on fear.
Make decisions based on hope and possibility.'
Michelle Obama

This chapter relates to decisions in my Recipe for Recovery.

Making a conscious decision to recover was essential, and also very difficult. I felt tremendously anxious about my illness and my recovery. If I said I was going to try to recover (even to myself) and then I didn't, I would have failed, and this triggered anxiety within the 'achiever'* part of me. If I focused on my recovery, I would have to put my needs before the needs of others, and this triggered anxiety within the 'helper'* part of me. Also, my fear of not being 'good enough' to deserve to recover was off the scale!

It felt as though ME had stripped me of my ability to make decisions, as you can see from this journal extract.

> *Just can't decide about the 90 Day Programme.*
>
> *I'm so annoyed with myself. I've already asked three people if I should go and, even though they said 'go for it', I still can't make a decision.*
>
> *I HATE this! I'm driving myself NUTS!*
>
> *Will it be worth it? Will it be a waste of money? Will other people think it's my fault if it doesn't work?*
>
> *Feel like my head is going to burst.*

*On pages 54–55 you will find information on psychological subtypes and you will find a chapter on behaviour in *My Journey to Recovery, Part Three*.

In my experience, ME 'Magnifies Everything'. Even the most straightforward decisions can seem overwhelming, so I started making small decisions before working up to bigger ones.

I soon began to find that making any decision was better than making no decision at all. The poem 'The Road Not Taken'* by Robert Frost summarises my feelings about making decisions.

The poet says:
'Two roads diverged in a yellow wood,
And sorry I could not travel both
And be one traveller, long I stood...'

The endless flow of anxiety-driven** thoughts in my head began to ebb as I stopped simply letting things happen and managed to take some control. You can see this from my journal extract below.

Finally decided to call the Optimum Health Clinic for a free 15-minute chat about joining their 90 Day Programme.

It added to my faint but growing confidence, and I've decided to sign up.

Wow! How unlike me to be so bold and so decisive.

Can't quite believe it.

*https://www.poetryfoundation.org/poems/44272/the-road-not-taken
**On pages 54–55 you will find information on psychological subtypes.

Avoiding decision-making in the past had played havoc with my emotions.* I tried to address this by not allowing the fear of making a wrong decision paralyse me. By making a conscious decision to take charge of my recovery, I found new strength. I was able to view myself as actively 'in recovery', rather than passively 'ill'. Although this was scary at first, it became easier over time.

This shift in my thinking helped me to have a more optimistic outlook about my life, as I took a brave step forward on my journey to recovery.

*You will find a chapter on emotions in *My Journey to Recovery, Part Three.*

start with
small decisions

keep it
simple

do a cost/benefit
analysis

To help me make decisions, particularly challenging ones or ones that might impact negatively on my recovery, I asked myself a question. For example, 'Is it right for me to go away at the weekend, or is it right for me to stay home alone and have some quiet time?'

Then I followed this process:

- pause

- take some deep breaths

- write down reasons 'for' and 'against' on a sheet of paper

- consider the points I have listed

- set a time limit to do the above

- make a decision.

Once I'd done this, it helped to talk my decision through with someone I trusted, someone who had my best interests in mind.

This process supported me to make informed decisions and assess the cost and benefit of every choice I made.

Commitment:
A willingness to give your time and energy to
something in which you believe.

'Desire is the key to motivation, but it's
determination and commitment to an unrelenting
pursuit of your goal that will enable you
to attain the success you seek.'
Mario Andretti

This chapter relates to commitment in my Recipe for Recovery.

Once I'd decided to recover, finding the commitment to see it through was the next challenge. This meant staying dedicated to the 'cause', no matter what. I had some good days and some bad days. At times, I felt as though the world was opening up for me. At other times, I just wanted to crawl into bed and give up. I learned that the key to success is to keep going, even when that seems impossible.

The first line of the poem 'Breaking Surface'* by Mark Nepo, 'Let no one keep you from your journey', is how I began to see my commitment to recovery.

Sometimes, keeping going meant letting go of things that weren't working, or that were too hard at that moment. I began to understand that letting go was not the same as giving up or giving in. Recovery became my main priority, though, at times, I still felt incredibly anxious. The following journal extracts show how I felt.

I'm going to be starting the 90 Day Programme in two days. Now my friend can't give me a lift to the station. I'm too weak to drive myself and too anxious to take a taxi.

What am I going to do? I feel my anxiety spiralling out of control. Can't believe I've signed up to do this. What was I thinking?

Maybe best to cancel...

*https://marknepo.com/poems_breaking.php

I realised that my friend not being able to give me a lift triggered my anxiety.

I feel so stupid, but it brought up all my old fears of being let down, rejected, abandoned.

After a day of feeling exhausted and crying on and off, I'm feeling a little stronger.

I'm committed to going, so I'm going to go.

At times, committing to my recovery was unbelievably hard – for me, and for those around me. The cost was too high for some relationships* to survive, and I lost people along the way. Almost everything that didn't help with my recovery took second place.

For those in my life who had known me as a long-term 'people pleaser', it was a significant challenge. I had changed the dynamics of my relationships.

I once heard someone talk about their recovery from ME, explaining that if he came across anything (or anyone) that wasn't helpful to him, he moved on quickly. At the time, I was shocked at such selfishness. Eventually, though, I learned to be more discerning in my own choices.

My commitment was not to one thing, or one way; it was solely to do whatever it took to recover.

*You will find a chapter on relationships in *My Journey to Recovery, Part Three*.

don't give up

prioritise
your recovery

do something
every day

Have a go at doing something every day

It is exceptionally difficult to commit to something huge, intangible and difficult to attain, such as recovering from ME.

Doing one thing every day towards my recovery helped me to move forward. I kept in mind the question, 'How do you eat an elephant?'

The answer is 'One chunk at a time!'

The first commitment I made to my recovery was to take an hour every day for myself, usually in the afternoon, when I would listen to a guided relaxation.* Having this hour every day reinforced the commitment I had made to my recovery, and gave me some much-needed time out.

Try it for yourself. Think of one thing, no matter how small, that you could commit to doing every day that will help your recovery.

It doesn't matter what you do. The important thing is that you are doing it.

*On pages 49–53, you will find information on the alternative therapies I used during my recovery.

Action:
A conscious process of doing something
that has an intention and a goal.

'And the day came when the risk to remain
tight in a bud was more painful than the
risk it took to blossom.'
Attributed to Anaïs Nin

This chapter relates to action in my Recipe for Recovery.

After spending five years in a boom-and-bust cycle with little hope of recovery, I knew I had to take decisive action. The things I had been doing weren't working. Just waiting for a miracle to happen wasn't an option. I wasn't living; I was barely existing. I was in emotional and physical turmoil. In my heart, I knew I needed to do something – anything – to shift me forward.

Action became a matter of survival.

Although talking and thinking both helped, I also needed to take action to implement my intention to recover. This journal extract shows how taking action helped me to feel more determined.

> Well, today's the day. I'm going to the Optimum Health Clinic to start the 90 Day Programme. Got a friend picking me up in an hour. I feel sick.
>
> I can't tell if it's anxiety or excitement, but either way, I know that I need to do this for myself, and by myself.
>
> This could be it! MY turn to recover.

Initiating action became the key to change. This is reflected in the words of the first line of the poem 'The Journey'* by Mary Oliver:

'One day you finally knew what you had to do, and began...'.

*https://www.mindfulnessassociation.net/words-of-wonder/the-journey-mary-oliver

My goal was my recovery, and I became accountable for my actions. I started to improve my diet,* go for a gentle walk* on my activity days,* and take time out for me. After trying it for a reasonable length of time, I stopped any action that I felt had proved ineffective, and replaced it with something new. Eventually, taking action became empowering in itself.

However small the step I took, it was still a step forward rather than no step at all. I made many mistakes along the way to recovery. After a time, I came to see these mistakes as opportunities to learn new information that would be useful to me in future, and would stop me making the same mistake again. My journal extract below shows you how encouraged I was feeling after completing the 90 Day Programme:

> *I did it! Made it to London and back on my own and managed the whole three days!*
>
> *The course has been an encouraging starting point. The overarching message I've taken away is that I'm going to have to do the work to recover – and I'm strong enough to do it.*
>
> *Amazing! I feel hopeful.*

Completing the 90 Day Programme was a significant step forward. It was uplifting and informative. There are, however, many routes to recovery, and it's essential that you find one that is right for you.

*You will find chapters on eating healthily, exercise and pacing (where I talk about activity days) in *My Journey to Recovery, Part Two*.

start
today

do one thing at
a time

take a self-help
course

Have a go at a self-help course

There are many self-help courses out there and, over the years, I've attended quite a few. The self-help course that kick-started my positive action for my recovery was the 90 Day Programme* run by the Optimum Health Clinic.

It is a psychology-based training course. It states: 'ME is a process where multiple systems, both psychological *and* physical, are interacting together in a dysfunctional way, resulting in the symptoms of ME.'

The three-day course took an integral approach and helped me to understand what had happened to me, and what was currently happening. It also gave clear pointers about what was necessary for recovery.

If you're struggling to take action, try asking yourself the following:

- What will I gain from recovery?

- What is likely to happen if I don't recover?

- What will improve my ability to take action? (This can include practical, emotional and physical factors.)

*Please note that I am not recommending or endorsing this course as a means of recovery. It is just something that was of benefit to me.

Belief:
A firm thought that something is true.

'He who knows others is wise.
He who knows himself is enlightened.'
Lao Tzu

This chapter relates to beliefs in my Recipe for Recovery.

I found it hard to write about beliefs for this booklet. The exercise touched on several complex areas – theory, psychology, philosophy, spirituality and, of course, my own beliefs.

Before I had ME, I had no idea that my beliefs played a part in my life, or even what they were. I went to work, came home and looked after my children. There wasn't much time for me to review what was happening in my life, or the part my beliefs played.

During my recovery, I discovered that **what I believed** was not the same as **the truth**. My beliefs lay beneath the patterns of my behaviour, and I was acting as though they were true. I also learned that my thoughts are in line with my beliefs.

My journal extract reflects my confusion and distress.

I'm feeling fragile today. Not sure what to make of all this stuff about beliefs.

It seems a bit weird. Can it be true that what's inside my head is shaping what's out in the world?!

If that's true, does that mean that what's in my head has made me ill?

Feeling deflated. Will it always be my fault?

I first read about beliefs in Louise Hay's book, *You Can Heal Your Life*. It was a difficult read for me because I was able to see, for the first time, how I had contributed to finding myself in this place.

Louise Hay says: 'We may not have control over events in our lives, but we do have control over our experience of those events… Change your thinking, change your life.' I found this statement unsettling, as I believed that my life had been taken away by ME.

Many years later, I had the opportunity to identify my own self-limiting beliefs and set about changing them. At this time, these words by Mahatma Gandhi began to make sense:

> '*Carefully watch your thoughts, for they become your words.*
>
> *Manage and watch your words, for they become your actions.*
>
> *Consider and judge your actions, for they become your habits.*
>
> *Acknowledge and watch your habits, for they shall become your values.*
>
> *Understand and embrace your values, for they become your destiny.*'*

*https://www.azquotes.com/citation/quote/453692

Finally, I saw that if changing my beliefs could change my life, then I had some agency over my healing. I could take back power.

I liked that idea!

Take a look at my journal extract below:

> Did my first homework today from the 90 Day Programme. It's about beliefs.
>
> No wonder I got ill. What's in my head is a mess!
>
> I don't think it's all my stuff, though. Some of it belongs to other people – their beliefs, not mine.
>
> I'm proud of myself for tackling this challenging stuff, and hopeful that I'm heading in the right direction.

As I learned that it was possible to transform myself past my limiting beliefs, I began to make a new map of my inner world.

Slowly, one step at a time, I started to heal from the inside out.

don't let your beliefs limit your life

what we believe, we perceive

evaluate your beliefs

To help me become aware of my beliefs, I took a blank sheet of paper and wrote a subject heading at the top. Then, one subject at a time, I wrote down all the thoughts that came up for me. This enabled me to uncover unhelpful self-limiting beliefs that may have contributed to me staying stuck in ME.

I found it hard to do this exercise, but persevering was worth it! My new awareness allowed me to make changes, as you can see in the example on the next page.

Try this yourself. Start with the following subjects. Ask yourself, what do I believe about this?

Family   Health   Life   Money   Recovery   Work

Try not to censor what you write. It's private and for your eyes only. It's essential that you are as honest with yourself as possible, so you know where you are on your journey. Then, for each unhelpful belief you identify, ask yourself the following questions:

- Where did this belief originate? Is it true for everything?

- What does this belief mean to me?

- What evidence is there to support this belief now?

- How do I feel about having this belief? How would I feel without this belief?

Repeat for any other subjects that are important to you.

How to change an unhelpful limiting belief

Current belief: 'I will never recover'

Thoughts and self-talk*: 'I am useless and worthless', 'I am powerless', 'People think I am pathetic and stupid', 'They think I'm faking it, and not really ill'.

Emotions: anxiety, sadness, guilt, shame, humiliation, disappointment, anger, hopelessness.

Behaviours: not being bothered to get out of bed ('What's the point?'), not taking steps towards recovery, apathy, depression, isolation, lack of self-care.

You can change this limiting belief into something more positive and helpful by changing your thoughts and self-talk.

New belief: 'I think I can recover, although it will take effort and time'

Thoughts and self-talk*: 'There is a chance that I can recover', 'I will need help', 'Other people have recovered, so why not me?', 'I am not alone'.

Emotions: calmness, happiness, worthiness, pride, excitement, hopefulness.

Behaviours: having a helpful routine, researching options for recovery, trying new things, getting support, engaging with positive people, improving self-care.

*You will find a chapter on communication, including self-talk, in *My Journey to Recovery, Part Three.*

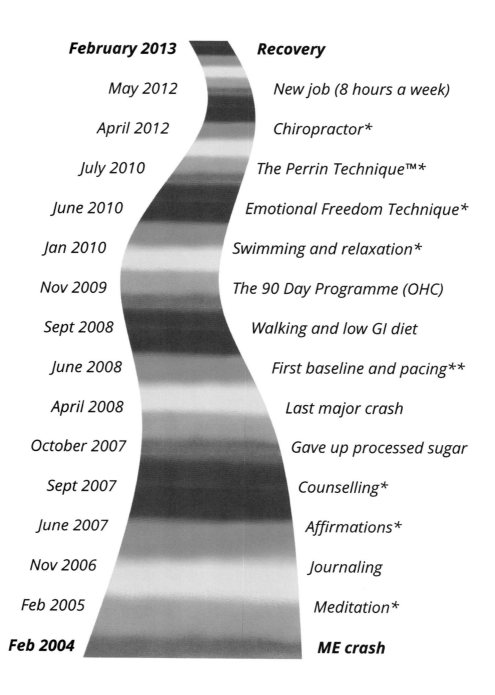

February 2013	Recovery
May 2012	New job (8 hours a week)
April 2012	Chiropractor*
July 2010	The Perrin Technique™*
June 2010	Emotional Freedom Technique*
Jan 2010	Swimming and relaxation*
Nov 2009	The 90 Day Programme (OHC)
Sept 2008	Walking and low GI diet
June 2008	First baseline and pacing**
April 2008	Last major crash
October 2007	Gave up processed sugar
Sept 2007	Counselling*
June 2007	Affirmations*
Nov 2006	Journaling
Feb 2005	Meditation*
Feb 2004	ME crash

*On pages 49–53, you will find information on the alternative therapies I used during my recovery. **You will find chapters on baseline and pacing in *My Journey to Recovery, Part Two.*

Congratulations: you've reached the end of Part One. I hope you've found it helpful.

On the following pages you will find my Recipe for Recovery. Please feel free to take another look. It's not necessary to use the ingredients in any particular order. The recipe is just a fun way of summarising the chapters in all four of my booklets. The bowl needed to mix these ingredients is doing the work.

On page 46, I've listed the practical top tips from this booklet. Keep them handy for times when you are feeling lost and need to get back on track.

In my experience, the road to recovery is long and littered with unexpected twists and turns. My nine years of ME were the most traumatic and challenging of my life. However, having recovered, I see that my experience was an opportunity to take time for myself, to slow down, to focus on my health and my personal growth. As a result, I have a new-found confidence and joy in life.

What I've written is a guide. I believe the answers are already inside us and, with the right support, recovery is possible.

Sending warm wishes to you,

A self-help guide with an easy-to-follow, step-by-step approach to recovery from ME/CFS/FM.

INGREDIENTS

RECIPE FOR RECOVERY

PREPARATION

- Responsibility
- Acceptance
- Decisions
- Commitment
- Action
- Beliefs

METHOD for preparation

1. Put **responsibility** into a large bowl, then gently fold in **acceptance**.

2. Measure your **decisions** and combine with **commitment**.

3. Blend a tablespoon of **action** with helpful **beliefs** and put to one side.

THE BASE

- Boundaries
- Baseline
- Pacing
- Eating healthily
- Exercise
- Self-discipline

METHOD for the base

1. Whisk **boundaries** with a **baseline** to make your recovery sweet.

2. Measure **pacing** guidelines and heat gently with **eating healthily**.

3. Warm up some **exercise**, then stir in **self-discipline**.

Quantities needed will vary.

A self-help guide with an easy-to-follow, step-by-step approach to recovery from ME/CFS/FM.

INGREDIENTS

RECIPE FOR RECOVERY

THE FILLING

- Communication
- Balance
- Emotions
- Relationships
- Behaviour
- Trust

METHOD for the filling

1. Weigh **communication** with a large handful of lightly seasoned **balance**.

2. Extract juice from your **emotions**, pour over **relationships**, then stir.

3. Leave your **behaviour** to cool in the fridge. Sprinkle with **trust**.

THE TOPPING

- Calm
- Love
- Self-esteem
- Forgiveness
- Success
- Staying well

METHOD for the topping

1. Create a **calm** topping, then add a generous helping of **love**.

2. Scatter **self-esteem** and finely grated **forgiveness** round the edge.

3. Drizzle a level teaspoon of **success** over **staying well**.

Quantities needed will vary.

Top Tips: Part One

- read a self-help book

- write a journal

- do a cost/benefit analysis

- do something every day

- take a self-help course

- evaluate your beliefs

COMING SOON!

My Journey to Recovery

Part Two

revised edition

To join my mailing list and be notified when Part Two is published, please email me at: myjourneytorecovery1@hotmail.com

ME

The most widely used definition of ME/CFS, in research, is the Fukuda definition (1994), which is as follows:

'Clinically evaluated, unexplained chronic fatigue cases can be classified as chronic fatigue syndrome if the patient has:

1. Clinically evaluated, unexplained persistent or relapsing chronic fatigue that is of new or definite onset (has not been lifelong), is not the result of ongoing exertion, is not substantially alleviated by rest, and results in a substantial reduction in previous levels of social, occupational, educational, or personal activities.

2. The concurrent occurrence of four or more of the following symptoms:

   - substantial impairment in short-term memory or concentration;

   - sore throat;

   - tender lymph nodes;

   - muscle pain;

   - multi-joint pain without swelling or redness;

   - headaches of a new type, pattern, or severity;

   - unrefreshing sleep; and

   - post-exertional malaise lasting more than 24 hours.

These symptoms must have persisted or reoccurred during six or more consecutive months of illness and must not have predated the fatigue.'

Dr Keiji Fukuda, The CDC (Fukuda 1994) Definition for Chronic Fatigue Syndrome, www.cfids-me.org/cdcdefine.html

Useful books

M. Scott Peck, *The Road Less Travelled* (Ebury Digital, 2012)

Louise Hay, *You Can Heal Your Life* (Hay House, Inc., 1995)

Tony Robbins, *Awaken the Giant Within* (Simon & Schuster, 2012)

Bruce Lipton, *The Biology of Belief* (Hay House, Inc., 2015)

Byron Katie, *Loving What Is* (Ebury Digital, 2008)

Alex Howard, *Why ME?* (Cherry Red Books, 2015)

Poems

Mary Oliver, 'The Journey'

Mark Nepo, 'Breaking Surface'

Robert Frost, 'The Road Not Taken'

Portia Nelson, 'Autobiography in Five Short Chapters'

Useful websites

www.louisehay.com

www.theoptimumhealthclinic.com

I have used the resources listed above and found them beneficial at different stages of my recovery. However, I do not recommend or endorse these resources as a guaranteed means to recovery.

Alternative therapies

Alternative therapies are a group of diverse health care systems, practices and products that are not generally considered part of conventional medicine.

One specialist consultant informed me that there was no medical cure for ME and only a 10% chance of recovery, so I searched for alternatives. I found answers from different sources, such as friends, therapists, workshops and books.

I did a lot of the work for my recovery on my own. However, there were times when I needed extra support from qualified professionals. I sought help when I hit a block, felt stuck, or when things got too tough to handle by myself.

On the following pages I have listed the alternative therapies mentioned in this booklet which were beneficial at different times on my journey to recovery. I give a short definition of each, followed by a few words about my experience and the benefits I felt from each therapy.

Affirmations are positive statements, written or spoken, that we repeat to ourselves out loud or in our thoughts.

I found out about consciously using positive statements when I discovered Louise Hay. At first, I listened to her affirmations on a CD. These days, you'll find them on Louise's website. As I had more than enough negative self-talk going on, taking time out to repeat positive statements about myself was a welcome break. As part of my recovery, I often listened to, and wrote down, affirmations. I also made up my own, such as 'It doesn't always have to be me', which was a useful reminder when my 'helper'* trait started to kick in. I also used 'I don't need to fix this', which was a useful reminder for the 'achiever'* in me.

In addition, I did Louise Hay's 'mirror work', which involved sitting in front of a mirror and looking into my eyes, then saying affirmations, such as 'Well done, Debbie. You did it! I'm so proud of you.' Over many years, repeating positive statements created an environment for self-healing by slowly replacing my self-limiting thoughts and beliefs with more helpful ones.

Chiropractic is 'a pseudoscientific complementary and alternative medicine that is concerned with the diagnosis and treatment of mechanical disorders of the musculoskeletal system, especially the spine'(Wikipedia).

I tried several chiropractors during my years of ME and recovery. For me, beyond the formal education and training needed to qualify as a chiropractor, many chiropractors have the valuable skill of being able to relate to people, particularly when they are feeling vulnerable. As a result, some of the treatments I received were more beneficial than others, even though they all provided the same level of physical improvement. I continued treatment with the chiropractor with whom I felt most comfortable for over a year.

*On pages 54–55 you will find information on psychological subtypes.

Counselling is a therapy that 'provides a safe and confidential space for you to talk to a trained professional about your issues and concerns. Your therapist will help you explore your thoughts, feelings and behaviours so you can develop a better understanding of yourself and of others' (https://www.bacp.co.uk/about-therapy/what-is-counselling).

I tried several different counsellors before I found one who was right for me – and before I was in the right place to do the work. It was an uncomfortable process, and the emotional distress I felt got worse before it got better. My counsellor was skilled at supporting me as I struggled to find my way through a maze of suppressed and conflicting emotions.

Over several years, I reviewed traumas from my past and present. My healing took time and commitment. I often felt like giving up when things got too tough. In the end, the work I did in counselling contributed to my recovery from ME. Without it, I'm not sure I would have been able to sustain my recovery in the long term, as I would have been carrying too much emotional baggage.

Emotional Freedom Technique (EFT) is also referred to as 'psychological acupressure. The therapy aims to release emotional blockages within the body's energy system. [...] When these energy channels become blocked or unbalanced, it is believed to lead to emotional and physical illness. Using tapping techniques, EFT looks to correct these imbalances' (https://www.therapy-directory.org.uk/articles/eft.html).

Experience has shown me that emotional health is directly linked to physical health, and it is essential to have a holistic approach to recovering from ME. I was introduced to EFT, also known as tapping, when I attended the 90 Day Programme at the Optimum Health Clinic. Using my fingertips to tap all over my face and body felt very strange at first, and I didn't start to use the technique for over six months.

Once I got going, tapping became part of my daily routine and worked well with using positive affirmations. Whenever I felt an emotion that I wanted to shift, I started to tap and I started to feel better. I also found EFT helpful in working on historic emotional issues. I worked with a skilled EFT practitioner, who helped me to deal with more deep-rooted traumas.

Meditation is 'a practice where an individual uses a technique to train attention and awareness to achieve a mentally clear, emotionally calm and stable state' (Wikipedia).

As my brain swung from being overactive to being clouded with brain fog, I found meditating difficult in the beginning. Focusing on my breath was impossible, so I used guided meditations instead. I often became impatient waiting for the track to finish and, as I was too weak to sit up, I always did them lying down. After some months, I began to enjoy the experience of meditation. It was a time just for me and time out of my mind. I also found that my sleep started to improve, and I was able to handle life's challenges more easily. At the same time meditation gave me the chance to see what was going on in my inner world, away from the hustle and bustle of everyday life. A daily meditation helped to calm my stressed nervous system.

The Perrin Technique™ is 'an osteopathic approach that manually stimulates the fluid motion around the brain and spinal cord. Manipulation of the spine further aids drainage of these toxins out of the cerebrospinal fluid. Massage of the soft tissues in the head, neck, back and chest direct all the toxins out of the lymphatic system and into the blood, where they are eventually detoxified in the liver' (https://theperrintechnique.com).

On my journey to recovery, I met someone who was seeing improvements using the Perrin Technique™. I decided to give it a go, and luckily there was a practitioner close to my home.

I had treatments every week for the first six weeks, then every other week and finally once a month. I continued to have sessions for about two years. The massage helped to increase the flow of my sluggish lymphatic system, and aided the removal of toxins from my body. In between treatments, I continued with a basic massage routine myself, which I did every day.

Relaxation is 'any method, process, procedure, or activity that helps a person to relax; to attain a state of increased calmness; or otherwise reduce levels of pain, anxiety, stress or anger'(Wikipedia).

I was often frustrated when trying to relax, thinking of all the other things I had to do. It took months before I was able to enjoy the experience and stay in the moment. Eventually, I looked forward to having this time to myself as part of my daily routine. I enjoyed lying down, popping in my headphones and letting a guided relaxation take me to a more peaceful place. This also helped to calm my stressed nervous system.

Psychological subtypes

Alex Howard from the Optimum Health Clinic has described the following psychological subtypes in the context of ME:

Anxiety: 'where we have a tendency towards lots of mental busy-ness, and trying to create a sense of being okay and being safe by running through all the scenarios and all the problems [we are dealing with] many, many, times.'*

'Repetitively going over a thought or a problem without completion' is defined, in psychological terms, as rumination. (https://www.psychologytoday.com/gb/blog/depression-management-techniques/201604/rumination-problem-in-anxiety-and-depression)

Achiever: 'where we're always driving ourselves to do more and be more, defining our self-worth by how much we do and how much we achieve.'*

'Personality type Three is named *The Achiever* because when they are healthy, Threes really can and do achieve great things in the world. [However], they want success because they are afraid of disappearing into a chasm of emptiness and worthlessness: without the increased attention and feeling of accomplishment which success usually brings, Threes fear that they are nobody and have no value.' (https://www.enneagraminstitute.com/type3#:~:text=We%20have%20named%20personality%20type,their%20graciousness%20and%20personal%20accomplishments)

*https://www.theoptimumhealthclinic.com/2018/11/the-story-behind-psychological-subtypes/, OHC Live EP 028, 'The story behind psychological subtypes', 28 November 2018. You will find a chapter on behaviour in *My Journey to Recovery, Part Three.*

Helper: 'where we're constantly placing other people's needs as being more important than our own, [...] and ignoring our own needs.'*

'The psychoanalytical approach describes that the origin of the [Helper] syndrome lies in early childhood. Parents do not sufficiently respect essential emotions and needs of the child [...] As a consequence, children have a very low self-esteem, and they develop rigid expectations of themselves [...] The typical self-exploitation of people with helper syndromes in the long run puts them at risk of exhaustion, depression and burnout.'
(https://casework.eu/lesson/helper-syndrom-when-helping-becomes-a-problem)

*https://www.theoptimumhealthclinic.com/2018/11/the-story-behind-psychological-subtypes/, OHC Live EP 028, 'The story behind psychological subtypes', 28 November 2018. You will find a chapter on behaviour in *My Journey to Recovery, Part Three.*

Praise for

Recipe for Recovery

'Simple, sound and, I think, rather beautiful.'
Linda Hall, Personal Development Coach and Meditation Teacher (lindahallmeditation.com)

'I think the idea and design are very clever, and the content witty and insightful. Debbie has included many important points that CFS/ME sufferers should know. I think getting this message out to people who are newly diagnosed with CFS/ME will save them a lot of time and heartache.'
Alex Bazargan

'Loved your recipe! So beautifully and thoughtfully done. I'll be coming back for more inspiration – your story and message can help so many.'
Victoria Ausonio

'Tears came to my eyes when I read your recipe as it is so succinct, so wise, so loving ... it simply blew me away. Thank you so much for this; it is invaluable.'
Susan Ashmore

Praise for

My Journey to Recovery, Part One

'I'm enjoying it. I really like the format – bite-size pieces that won't intimidate someone who is already feeling exhausted.'
Brad Yates, Personal Development Consultant (tapwithbrad.com)

'You have simplified and focused Part One readers on the key points for embarking on the road to recovery from ME. It is succinct, clear and simple to follow. If a person is sincerely searching it will stir curiosity about what each ingredient means in their lives and lead from there, as it did you.'
Charmaine Kemps

'Wow! I sure wish I'd had this when ME knocked me down. It's absolutely perfect, just the right amount of information. The balance of visuals and text is brilliant. For those of us further along, it's a great reminder of the priorities in recovery. It's empowering to read this and it gives such hope. You hit all the right notes. Fantastic resource. Excellent work.'
Maggie Sanders

Acknowledgements

My heartfelt thanks go to the following people, who encouraged me so much on my journey to recovery:

Marcus for his love, care and being by my side throughout six years of ME and seven years of recovery. I would not be where I am today without him. For all this, and for helping me to shine, I'm genuinely grateful.

My friends who gave their support willingly and offered reassurance when I needed it most: Cathy, Charmaine, Emma, Helen, Jan, Janice, Kay, Michael, Peter, Richard, Tracey and Trish.

The therapists, counsellors, practitioners and other health care professionals who assisted me at different times and in different ways.

A special thank you goes to:
Abi, for working with me on Part One and for her beautiful poems; Gemma, for her fun, creative hand-drawn illustrations; James, for retouching the photographs; Janice, for her beautiful poem; Marcus, for helping me go from draft to final print; and Jane Hammett, for her careful editing and proofreading.

I feel blessed for all we have shared.

Printed in Great Britain
by Amazon

THE RECURRING NIGHTMARE

You're in a hot grotto of some sort, or perhaps a medieval dungeon. You smell niter and soil and you can see water bleeding through walls of uneven bricks lit by wan firelight. The fire gently crackles…

And the woman raises the cup…

She's robust, beautiful, and nearly nude. The only clothing she wears is hardly clothing at all but the black and white wimple of a nun. She seems parched, her lambent skin glazed with sweat, and the firelight lays moving squiggles on it, like faint tongues of light. And the cup—

Not a cup, really. It's cereal bowl–sized but of dull brown clay. You can't see what's in it. The woman's breasts jut as she raises it high, as if in offering. Three gemstones mounted on the bowl sparkle, one black, one green, one red.

Behind her, the firelight on the wall…changes. Soon the bricks are squirming with wavering lines of black, green, and red, slowly writhing, snakelike. When the nun lowers the bowl just below her bare breasts, you see its contents: blood.

The luminous black, green, and red lines behind her begin to churn in a fury and then her eyes go wide and she turns her head to gaze right through the mirage—

Right at you—

—and grins, showing two long, narrow, and very sharp fangs…

EDWARD LEE

BRIDES OF THE IMPALER

LEISURE BOOKS NEW YORK CITY

For Wendy Brewer, my infernal angel.

A LEISURE BOOK®

September 2008

Published by

Dorchester Publishing Co., Inc.
200 Madison Avenue
New York, NY 10016

ISBN 10: 0-8439-5807-3
ISBN 13: 978-0-8439-5807-2

Visit us on the web at www.dorchesterpub.com.

ACKNOWLEDGMENTS

Above all, I need to thank Jess Franco, Amano de Ossorio, Paul Naschy, and Jean Rollin, whose macabre and brilliant films have enthralled me for years and whose manipulation of imagery and atmosphere have proven a polarizing influence. Also, very special thanks to Dallas Mayr for NYC data and fifteen years of friendship. And, in no particular order: Tim McGinnis, Dave Barnett, Don D'Auria, Bob Strauss, Monica Kuebler, Tony and Kim, Mary Tutty of Mary's Cabin, Julie Ahrens (for the very cool shirt!), Thomas Deja, John Mahoney and his parents, Nanci Kalanta, Mark Justice, Michael Lohr, Nick Cato, Chris from Insidious, Tom Weisser, Tom Moran, Charlie Meitz and Nina Zwaig (for Romanian stuff), Tim Shannon (for crab-infested water), and Anda for med stuff, Rich Chizmar, Tess, Pam, Ashley and Trey, Crystal and Alicia and Gus, Stephanie Shiver for *Cadaverettes*, Megan Dipo (for the wonderful Infernal Angel illo), Robert from Sweetbay (whom I hope likes this book), Dave and Liz Bolter, Kathy, Kirt, Tony, and Audrey, Sascha Mamczak, Ian Levy, and Ioana Mitea.

Lastly I must acknowledge the excellent and indefatigable historians Radu R. Florescu and Raymond T. McNally for their superlative book, *Dracula: Prince of Many Faces*. This book provided much historical data crucial to my novel. Any historical inaccuracies are solely my fault.

E.L.

BRIDES OF
THE IMPALER

PROLOGUE

Romania, Thirty years ago

Fredrick flinched like a sudden chill, and behind his closed eyes he saw a nude woman impaled upside-down through the mouth on a twenty-foot pike . . .

Sweet Jesus . . . When he opened his eyes, there was nothing but drab stone walls.

"Are you all right, Professor?"

Fredrick shook out of the vertigo. *Just the power of suggestion*, he knew. In truth, he had no interest in Romania's archeological history after 100 or so A.D. "Yes, yes. Just an odd chill . . ."

Janice Line, his postgrad teaching assistant, beamed at the ancient church's rock walls. "This entire place is so mythic. I can't believe I'm finally here." It was with awe that she looked at the great altar. Janice was twentysomething, with shining, dark-copper hair and overly enthusiastic eyes. She stood shorter than average and would be described as "plush" rather than overweight. Cutoff demin shorts, work boots, and a T-shirt that read CARTER FOR PRESIDENT; she possessed all the idealism of any proverbial archeology student. Fredrick knew he was over-the-hill now; his assistant's burgeoning breasts scarcely gave him cause to glance.

"So this is the legendary Nave of Snagov," he said, looking down with her. A deep, jagged hole had been dug directly at the foot of the ornate stone altar.

"And the even more legendary 'Table of the Lord,'" added Janice. An excited hush seeped into her voice. "The supposed grave of Vlad Tepes, aka Dracula. But when they originally dug this hole, they didn't find Dracula's body, they found—"

"Everyone knows the story, Janice," Fredrick complained. "They found the skeleton of a dog instead."

"A *headless* dog. Just as Dracula himself was said to have been buried headless, after his assassination in 1476."

Headless . . .

The word echoed in the airy chancel.

"He was so reviled by the Turks that they bartered for his head and took it to Istanbul. They displayed it in the public square . . . on the end of a pike."

"Come on," Fredrick said almost testily. He took her back outside. *Kids* . . .

In spite of the summer heat, a breeze seemed to slice cool air off the water beyond, the treacherously deep Lake Snagov. It was in the middle of this immense lake that the wooded island sat, and in the middle of *that* loomed the monastery itself, one of the oldest in Romania. The buildings stood curiously—a complex, actually—chapels, rectories, serfs' quarters, etc., part fortress, part house of God, and, yes, the coincidental final refuge of a fifteenth-century prince named Vladislav Dracula. Fredrick was tired of the morbid legend and even of the truth intermingled with it. His request for permission to excavate had nothing to do with that drivel.

But he could see the gleam in his young assistant's eyes . . .

The chapel they'd just exited had been refurbished off and on over centuries and appeared nearly pristine, along with selected other edifices, while others stood in varying degrees of ruin. "I can't believe the government let me make this survey," Fredrick voiced his thoughts.

Janice bounced along beside him, passing an old iron forge. "I hope they grant the rest—that would be wonderful. No one's excavated here to any significance since the earthquake in 1940." Janice subconsciously touched her elder's shoulder and squeezed. "With your egghead savvy? I'm *sure* you'll be able to talk the commission into authorizing another full dig."

Fredrick had to laugh. *Egghead savvy?* "Yes, that or the simple fact that the university has offered to pay the government twenty thousand dollars for the privilege."

"I'll bet that's worth a million here," she giggled.

Now they traced an inner fortress wall. Could the faint dark stains on it really be blood spilled almost six centuries ago? There were more stains, too, on the bricks beneath their feet.

"These are newer bricks, probably put here in the 1600s," Janice corrected. "The old ones were considered cursed, so they were dumped in the lake."

"What on earth for?"

"This is the inner fortress, Professor. In Dracula's time this entire quadrangle was filled with impaling pikes, probably hundreds of them—"

"I really don't want to hear any more about that, Janice," he interrupted.

"—on which the condemned were staked alive. Criminals, Turkish prisoners, and ethnic Germans mostly. Dracula was never content unless every single pike in the square was occupied."

"Enough," Fredrick insisted.

"Every morning when he woke up, the first thing he'd do is look down here and revel at all the corpses held aloft by the pikes—" and she turned quickly, pointing upward to a second-story window in one of the old rectories. "From there, Professor. That window right there."

Fredrick frowned—*What a sucker I am*—when he looked

up at the glassless window. Had the defender of Wallachia and the infamous impaler of thousands really done as Janice claimed?

Am I looking at his ghost right now?

Janice's tone descended to a studied seriousness. "We're walking on *history*, Professor."

"Yes," he snapped, "and the history you should be most concerned with is that of the Daco-Roman variety. I shouldn't have to remind you—we're here solely to investigate why brooches, jupon clips, and coins from 400 B.C. have been found on these grounds. We're *not* here to investigate Vlad Dracula. That's already *been* investigated, quite exhaustively."

"Oh, I know," she said, "but still . . ." Her beaming eyes scanned the half ruins once more. "It's just so . . . cool."

Cool. My God . . .

Janice wandered up stone steps to a rampart; Fredrick, along with his frown, followed her. "What are you coming up here for?"

"I just have to see it."

"See what? The lake? You already have. It's just a lake."

"No, no, Professor. I want to see the *other side* of the lake."

Exasperated, he nearly trotted after her. Janice was gazing between two stone merlons, at the dense forest across the water.

"It's a forest, Janice. Just a *forest*."

"Not just any forest," she intoned. "It's the Vlasian forest. One of Dracula's many Forests of the Dead. He impaled ten thousand prisoners, boyars, and Transylvanian Saxons in those woods, just to scare the Turks away. In fact, over the course of his guerrilla campaigns, Dracula impaled over ten times that many, all over southern Romania."

Had it really been that many? Of his own citizens?

When she turned, she stood starkly silhouetted by the

sun, a curvaceous, pitch-black cutout. "And down there. Do you know what that is?"

Fredrick looked back down into the quadrangle. She was pointing to the stream that coursed across the yard. "The monastery's water supply?" He wanted to yell now. "It's a stream, Janice. Just a *stream*."

"It's where Dracula may have secreted his most valuable booty as well. While most archival testaments from the 1470s claim that Dracula protected his spoils in iron drums and dumped them in the middle of the lake, several other statements insist that he merely paid peasants to spread that rumor."

"So the spoils are actually buried in the stream," Fredrick groaned.

"Yes! Only weeks before his murder, he forced his remaining boyar slaves to dam the stream and dig deep pits. It's a rumor that's been passed down for over five centuries. Dracula's true spoils are most likely buried there, and probably his body as well." She paused. "His *headless* body, I mean."

"If there was even a remote chance of that being true, someone would've dredged the stream in short order."

"Nope," she said, assured. "No one would dare, for two reasons. One, it would be against church law because any stream that passes through a House of God is considered sacred—it's holy water."

Fredrick's frown was now deepening the creases in his fifty-year-old face. "And the second reason?"

"Because this entire monastic complex is cursed."

It was Fredrick himself who felt cursed. He didn't believe in the supernatural; he was a scientist of the art of unlocking the secrets of ancient civilizations. He came from a long line of archaeologists; his brother, in fact, was the dean of archaeology at Harvard. *He'd laugh in my face if I told him I was coming here . . .*

The idea was to compel the Romanian Commission of

Historic Monuments to grant Fredrick twenty more work
visas so that he could bring his best students here to dig.
Hopefully they'd be able to identify the age of the sedi-
mentary layers here that held a plethora of ancient coins
and tools of Roman design. This would prove a Roman influence in the land several hundred years earlier than anyone had previously thought: a groundbreaking discovery
the likes of which all scholars longed for. *I could write my
own ticket if I proved that*, Fredrick knew. It would be the
same as a zoologist discovering a new species.

But here? *Five to ten feet above my academic gold mine is all
this Dracula nonsense . . .*

His younger colleague couldn't have been more trans-
fixed, but Fredrick guessed he could understand, if only in
part. Such supernatural legends never died due to the
power of their intrigue. *Ghosts, vampires, curses . . .* Fredrick
knew it was the same intrigue that caused protohumans to
etch such phantoms on their cave walls 100,000 years ago.
Obsession with the occult was a part of human nature.

As they went back down, Fredrick caught himself asking, "Who exactly killed Dracula, Janice?"

His question thrilled her. "No one knows for sure but it
was either a Saxon assassin hired by one of his many pro-
Turkish political rivals, or an actual Turkish spy hiding in
the ranks of Dracula's militia. Either way it was by a contract issued by the Ottoman Empire. They hated Dracula
with a passion because of the atrocities he committed
against them in battle. Dracula fought many campaigns
trying to reclaim parts of the Romanian heartland that
the Turks had overtaken after the capture of Constantino-
ple in 1453. Dracula was very much a tit-for-tat kind of
guy, and it's ironic that his infamous art of atrocity was actually taught to him by the Turks themselves."

"How's that?"

"Back in those times, enemies would often trade their
children to each other, to ensure peace treaties. When

Dracula was a child, he spent at least five years in the custody of the Turkish emperor, this to guarantee that Dracula's father, a powerful Christian warlord, didn't break the current peace accord he'd signed. Anyway, it was in these Turkish courts that young Dracula watched European prisoners be sawed in half, burned alive, eye-gouged, scalped and skinned, genitally mutilated, boiled in oil, and—last but not least—impaled." Janice winked at him. "How's that for a happy childhood?"

Fredrick felt shell-shocked and irked simultaneously. "I guess that's the *long* version of the answer to my regrettable question."

Janice giggled. "You asked. But my point is the irony that Dracula learned his penchant for *impaling* from the Turks themselves, his sworn enemies. Can you imagine, growing up and looking out your window to see *that*? What an effect it must've had on Dracula's young mind. Another thing Dracula had to witness were the Turkish guards forcing prisoners to eat each other, often their own family members—"

"Janice!" Fredrick yelled, nauseated now. "I only asked who killed the man!"

"Oh, sorry. I guess I digressed—"

"Yes, I'd say so!"

The young bosomy woman calmed down from her gruesome historical zeal. "Dracula was assassinated in late 1476 somewhere nearby, probably the woods just beyond the lake. He was forty-five. An abbot from this monastery discovered the decapitated body and had it brought here to be buried somewhere in the chapel we just looked at. Exactly where, no one knows. But it was hoped that the property's sanctity would serve a talismanic effect. Back then they believed that burying an evil person on church grounds was the same as Christ himself wielding the shovel, and personally tamping down the grave dirt."

Fredrick felt winded by the morbid dissertation. *Next*

time . . . don't ask. At the front gate, his colleague spoke with the military driver who'd driven them here from town. He smoked a rank filterless cigarette while sitting in a '50s-era Russian jeep. As the soldier spoke, his eyes never left Janice's considerable bosom. *How rude, these Communists,* Fredrick thought. He'd specifically brought Janice on the survey, however, because she spoke the native language.

"*Frebuie sa merg inapoi la comjemata acum,*" the soldier said, "*dor ma voi intoarce mune la amiajaah.*"

"*Multumesc joarte mult.*"

Only now did the scruffy conscript's gaze rise from Janice's chest to her eyes. "*Erti sujur ca nu frei sa mergi ar mime?*"

"*Da, oom ji bine.*"

The soldier flicked his cigarette over the bridge abutment. He shook his head with a half smile. "*Nimine niciodota nusi petrece nooptea in locul acesta,*" he said, then started his jeep and drove away, leaving a trail of blue exhaust.

"What did he say? I mean, when he *wasn't* staring at your chest?" Fredrick asked.

Janice grinned coyly. "He wanted us to go back with him. He said 'No one ever spends the night in this place . . .'"

It had been Janice who'd practically pleaded to spend the night in the monastery. *She played me like a piano,* Fredrick thought now, in the upstairs hall of the main rectory. *Those big puppy-dog eyes and those big—*

"This is so exciting, Professor, I really can't thank you enough," she said, still bouncing along more than walking. "I'll be a sport and let you have the honors."

"What honors?"

She stopped in the stone hall. "We know that Dracula lived on the monastery grounds many times during his life;

in fact, he occupied the area repeatedly, reinforcing its walls and turning it more into a garrison than an abode for monks. But it's not clear exactly *where* he stayed—which rooms, that is—save for one instance." She placed her hand on a doorframe. "This room here, the one we viewed from outside. We know *for a fact* that the Impaler Lord resided in this room with his Hungarian wife and two sons in the summer of 1475. So, unless you're scared . . . you can have this room tonight."

Ridiculous. "Very funny, Janice. But what's funnier is that we could've stayed at the guest house in town for the equivalent of five dollars but instead we're staying here. There's no electricity, the water barely trickles, and the windows have no glass. Tonight we'll probably get eaten alive by mosquitos."

"Not bats?"

Fredrick fumed. "Revel in your youth, Janice. It's full to bursting"—*Like your T-shirt,* he thought—"with naivety and idealism. If I'd known you were so obsessed with this Dracula nonsense, I probably wouldn't have brought you along."

"Of course you would've," she challenged, laughing.

"Really? And why is that?"

"Because I'm the smartest arch student you've ever had—"

Well . . . she's got me there, he admitted.

"—and I speak Romanian. You don't."

"Fine, but just to show you that I'm *not* afraid of this drab, silly monastery, I'll *happily* sleep in this room tonight."

"Not just any room," Janice added just to be dramatically redundant. "*Dracula's* room."

They spent the rest of the afternoon arranging their effects in their respective rooms. There were no beds, of course, so the floor sufficed for their sleeping bags. Fredrick read *Archaeology Review* by the light of a Coleman lantern. Every so often, he turned to face the window—*Dracula's window*, he reminded himself in jest—only to swear he heard a wolf howling across the lake. If anything, though, the stone-walled room couldn't have been less scary.

"Dinnertime, Romanian style," Janice announced after barging in. She carried her backpack in one hand and a candle in the other.

"I have Twinkies," Fredrick offered.

"No, no, we'll eat authentic tonight." She pulled some cans and jars from the pack and placed them on an old blond-wood table. "I wouldn't be surprised if Dracula himself ate the very same things in this room in 1475."

He definitely didn't eat Twinkies, Fredrick thought. "You got this at the deli in town, I presume."

"Yep. You'll like it." Now she lit another candle and began to open the cans and jars, preparing two paper plates. Fredrick noticed that her shadow on the back wall seemed to shift.

"Canned *bread?*" he questioned of one item.

"It's called lokum. It's kind of like nut bread—all Romanians eat it. In fact all of the dishes here are commonplace staples." Janice slid Fredrick a plate.

The lokum reminded him of rum cake, and there was also some sort of medley of beans and sliced beets. He took a bite of some manner of meat marinated in chopped olives and found it delicious.

"That's excellent. Is it beef?"

"Sort of. It's beef *tongue*."

Fredrick slid his plate away and reached for the wine.

She ate a piece of the lokum, mentioning, "Dracula liked to dip *his* lokum in the blood of enemies he'd executed. And he sometimes mixed the blood with his wine. He claimed it gave him extra strength on the battlefield."

"Thanks for telling me that, Janice." Fredrick hastened to change the subject. "With any luck, the commission will give us their answer tomorrow. They're supposed to be sending someone out—a woman from the district curator's office. If I could just get twenty more students here—I'm sure we'd make a lot of progress."

"I guess the only thing going against us is the fact that we're Americans."

"Yes . . . the so-called *Ugly* Americans. We're capitalistic pigs as far as they're concerned."

"But they'll take our money just the same," Janice said confidently.

"Whether they do or they don't, we have to be very careful what we say."

She looked wistfully out the window. "Maybe we're overreacting to all this Cold War stuff, Professor. The folks at the archaeology department seemed pretty cool if you ask me."

"*Cool* doesn't matter, Janice." Suddenly, Fredrick longed for a Big Mac. "Don't forget, this is a *Communist* country and a satellite of the Soviet Union."

"Yeah, sure, but Snagov isn't the same. No one comes here, the *soldiers* don't even patrol here." Janice uplit her face with a candle. "Remember, the island and everything on it has been cursed for five hundred years. The villagers won't even fish in the lake because that's where Dracula dumped so many corpses."

Fredrick sighed a useless resignation. When they were done eating, Janice cleaned off the table. "I don't know about you, but I'm exhausted," she declared. "I'm going to take a bath—or at least try to—and then go to bed."

"Good idea. And hopefully when you wake up, you'll forget about all this Dracula business." But as Janice reached for her backpack, Fredrick noticed a book sticking out of it. He snatched it up.

"Janice! You're hopeless!"

The book was entitled *Dracula: Prince of Many Faces.*

"That's the Holy Bible of Draculean history, Professor.

It's probably the most authoritative text that exists on the subject."

Fredrick wanted to scream. "We're not here for this monastery's relation to Vlad Dracula! We're here for relics from a millennium earlier!"

"Yeah, yeah," she dismissed. "I'll leave the book with you. I can't think of anything more appropriate than a nonbeliever reading all about Vlad's atrocities in the very room he slept in so many centuries ago."

"Good night, Janice!"

She paused at the door, and it was probably deliberate the way she turned at the waist to elucidate her bosom. "Oh, and if you want any more wine, I left the other bottles outside to cool."

Fredrick frowned. "To *cool?* Where?"

"In the stream, of course. You know—the stream where Vlad's *real* body is probably buried . . ."

"Go to bed!" Fredrick yelled.

Janice scooted away, an echoic laugh in her wake. Fredrick thumbed his eyes, then got ready for bed himself.

He tried to sleep but found himself totally jinxed now by the residual imagery of Janice's banter. He caught himself wondering exactly where in the room Dracula had slept. *A madman*, he thought. *A butcher.* Had the prince of Wallachia and savior of Transylvania actually murdered anyone in this room as well?

Fredrick slept in snatches, then dragged himself up. *Damn it!*

He lit a candle to push back some of the darkness. Sleep was impossible under these conditions.

He knew he was nervous about tomorrow, when the Romanian representative would come to tell him about the additional visas. *I don't suppose I'd want any Romanians digging in our historical sites*, he considered. Was there really a difference?

He redressed, tamped his pipe, and went downstairs and

back outside. There were no night-sounds at all—save for the infrequent wolf-bays. No peepers, no cricket trills. The moonlight made the stagnant night look icy. He lit his pipe and rewalked the inner quadrangle. The fortress walls, twenty feet thick at some points, seemed monolithic now, the twilight cutting the ramparts in stunning black. He knew there were torture chambers on the grounds, below some of the older edifices or their ruined foundations. *How many people had died here?* he kept wondering. Only silence here now, but in the mid-1400s?

Fredrick knew this fortress yard must've run rampant with screams—

The academician's hand flew to his heart when a shriek wheeled out into the night.

Jesus! He turned and looked up, heart hammering. Candlelight flickered in one of the second-story windows, then a shadow moved.

"Janice!" he bellowed. "Are you—"

The younger woman appeared in the stone window frame, a sheepish smile on her face. She held her hands to her overspilling bare breasts.

"Sorry," she echoed down. "I hope I didn't scare you."

"Well you *did* scare me! What's wrong?"

"I got in the bath too fast," she admitted. "The water's ice-cold."

"For pity's sake!" Fredrick continued to yell. "You almost gave me a heart attack!"

She smiled down. "Thought it was a specter, huh?"

Fredrick scowled.

"I can't sleep, either," she said. "Being here is just . . . too exciting."

What am I going to do with her? he bemoaned. He relit his pipe and let himself calm down. "Go to bed," he gruffed.

Her voice floated and she pulled back from the window. "Pleasant dreams . . ."

I will not let her spook me, he determined. Hadn't she said something about chilling some wine out here? *The stream*, he recalled. *I guess a few slugs of that would calm me down . . .*

He retraced his steps and found it; he presumed the stream was spring-fed, since its source didn't appear to extend past the north wall. A long sip of the icy wine quenched him, a strong fruity aftertaste glowing in his mouth. *Just don't get drunk*, he warned himself. He took the bottle to a stone bench with cruciform inlays and sat down, but after another sip, he frowned, recalling Janice's morbid remark at dinner. *Vlad Dracula dipped his bread in blood? I doubt it . . .*

The alcohol buzzed him in minutes. *Strong stuff.*

Or was it?

It occurred to him that the monk's bench was, almost imperceptibly, moving . . .

He rubbed his face, then stared up at the rectory.

My God . . .

It seemed to be moving, ever so slightly.

Either the Romanians make very *strong wine or—*

The rumbling came next, felt first in his diaphragm, then much more obviously. *Tremor*, he thought, sitting poised. *This area's known for them—it'll pass.*

The tremor didn't pass; it magnified, and the rumbling grew to a grinding cacophony. All around him now the moon-tinged fortress began to visibly shake. The bench was vibrating.

"Janice!" he yelled up at the rectory. "Come outside! We're having an—"

There was a grinding roar. The bench was lifting, and that's when Fredrick noticed that a fissure was forming just a yard to his right, and nearly half of the inner courtyard was rising out of the ground. He jumped up, about to race to the center of the yard, but—

"Jesus!"

The grinding roar exploded. Another angle of the

ground he stood on levered upward. Fredrick lost his footing and fell . . .

Right on his head.

smack!

He was unconscious before the fact could register, as the entire north wall collapsed . . .

I'm dead, he seemed to think, but if so, how could he think at all? He floated through blocked-out darkness, and at the furthest fringes of his senses he thought he heard the faintest screams, layers of them, wavering like surf, and then another sound, like the noises of a butcher's mart only on a grand scale. But gradually the sounds receded, to be replaced by something much more resolute:

A hiss.

Like a cracked steam pipe.

It was actually hours later—just before dawn—when Professor Fredrick regained consciousness, to a blazing throb of pain at the side of his skull. He rose to hands and knees, blinking incognizance for full minutes before he realized what happened. *An earthquake—a doozy* . . . And what was that hissing?

The rumbling had ceased. He wobbled, getting on his feet, and reached for the small flashlight in his pocket. When he switched it on—

Good Lord . . .

Steam, indeed, was hissing out of the fissure that all but bisected the quadrangle, the fissure being inches wide. *This island must be sitting on a seismic plate* . . . Several of the outer walls were rented, marked by great gaps ragged with stone rubble. But even more amazing . . . was the stream.

When the plate had lifted—nearly a yard—it cut off the narrow stream's flow; Fredrick now stood on a ledge, and below it on the other side, the spring now formed a meager pool that spread nearly to the outer walls. His feet splashed when he stepped off the ledge.

Then he stared at what existed at the end of his flashlight beam.

Several feet below what used to be the stream's bed, several casks jutted. When he reached over and tapped one, his knuckles came away rusted. *Iron,* he surmised. Each cask bore proportions similar to a five-gallon gasoline can.

Dracula's booty? something forced him to wonder.

Then the rest of his awareness snapped on.

My God! Janice!

He splashed through more water, then moaned when he noticed half of the rectory had toppled.

Damn it! "Janice!" he shouted. *Please don't be*—His flashlight carved slices through the darkness inside the rectory's vestibule. It appeared that the room he'd intended to sleep in had fallen through the ceiling, for he could see some of his belongings. But Janice had been in a closer room, hadn't she?

He wended through turned-over furniture and piles of bricks, to the stairwell—

"Oh, no, Janice . . ." he groaned.

Janice lay half-clothed amid the collapsed stairwell. A great swath of blood stained the bricks. Fredrick knelt to discern what he already knew. There was no pulse to be found at Janice Line's throat. The avalanche of bricks had left her partially crushed.

"Damn it all to hell," he muttered.

There was no retrieving any of his gear; what would be the point? *And there'll be no excavations now,* he knew. The authorities would surely restrict the entire complex as a hazard perimeter. Fredrick cursed himself for his own selfishness: even as his loyal assistant lay dead at his feet, what he regretted foremost was the fact that he'd never get to find out once and for all just how early Roman influence had infiltrated this macabre country . . .

Wait—

The rive in the stream . . .

Those casks . . .

Through plumes of rising dust, Fredrick jogged back to the upheaved stream—

And stopped cold.

A woman stood in the center of the yard, as if waiting for him.

"Who are you?" Fredrick raised his voice.

She seemed to be wearing a long raincoat of some sort, with a hood. It was still dark. Fredrick rudely shined his light in her face, but she didn't flinch. It was a youthful, attractive face with Slavic features. Her lips barely moved when she replied in a refined accent, "My name is Mrs. Pallus—"

"You're the woman from the commission? This site is unsafe. Were you here when the earthquake hit?"

"You are an interloper," was the only answer she gave. "Take care that your mistakes do not prove your destiny."

Fredrick stared back at her.

"There is much destiny here," she said. Her large dark eyes seemed amused at his dismay. Then: "Listen, and look—"

Fredrick *did* hear something; it was unmistakable: the sound of shovels biting into earth.

The casks! Someone's digging them out! He trotted past Mrs. Pallus and turned at the corner of the rectory to see the dimly lit scene. Several figures, indeed, were digging around the iron casks.

"You got an excavation team out here that fast?" Fredrick was nonplussed. "How could you possibly know what . . ."

When he looked back, the woman was gone just as the first streaks of morning light began to tint the horizon. *She* was gone, yes, but her voice seemed to sift through the air like remnant smoke.

"Consider yourself one of a privileged lot . . ."

"Where are you!" he shouted, but the protestation was drowned by a sudden rumbling much more violent than before. He noticed the figures at the dig glancing warily over their shoulders as they hastened to dig. Several casks had already been dislodged, while one figure took to prying off their lids. He seemed to inspect the contents with disappointment. All the while the trembling increased.

"You idiots!" Fredrick yelled as bricks and chunks of mortar fell all around him. "Run! We're having another earthquake!"

But only one of the figures even gave Fredrick a glance. Then the rest of the rectory wall collapsed—

On Fredrick.

One great slab crushed his leg at once. He was half-buried beneath rubble as the earth shook harder around him. The pain stupefied him, and he began to fade in and out of consciousness. But even as the tremor ensued, the mysterious figures continued with their frantic excavation.

"For God's sake, help me!" Fredrick screamed.

The figures seemed satisfied with one of the casks—not a coffin, just a cask. Two of them put it on a hand truck and wheeled it away.

"Help . . ."

A third figure approached as the tremors faded along with Fredrick's sentience. Morning light leaked over the ramparts. The man knelt, touching for a pulse. Fredrick managed to discern that the man was a priest.

In Latin, the priest read Fredrick the last rites, and then walked away.

CHAPTER ONE

New York City, Now

(I)

Cristina Nichols stalled at the ritzy bar's sign—DEMARNAC'S—and caught herself staring. Three lines composed the sign's border, the outer line black, then green, then red.

Black, green, red, she thought in a drone.

Just like the dream . . .

She snapped out of the fugue, then rushed into the bar.

She was nearly fretting when the revolving door emptied her into the hostess area. *This city is just . . . wild . . .* She'd left the clamor of West 67th Street as if fleeing muggers. Now she saw her own reflection in the mirrors behind the front bar and felt dismayed by her appearance. Outside, the vacuum drag from all those cars, trucks, and roaring buses had completely disheveled her butterscotch-blonde hair, making her look as though she'd just gotten out of bed.

What a mess . . .

New York Power Lunchers filled the brass and wood-stained eatery, their chatty din almost as nerve-racking as the car noise outside. *This is NOT my element,* she knew. Several uppity patrons seemed to smirk at her slapdash attire: faded jeans a bit too large, old white sneakers, and a baggy T-shirt bearing an incomprehensible print by Mark Rothko. The print was utterly black. She tried to fix her hair, sputtering. *Snobs in the big city—my favorite people.*

Britt Leibert, her sister, waved from a booth. Cristina edged past crowded tables and servers bearing trays of chocolate martinis and twenty-dollar appetizers.

"Little sister?" Britt complained. "You look like you just got off a Greyhound bus."

"I probably smell like it, too. I cut through the alley to get here." Cristina plopped down and feebly pushed more hair out of her face. "I'm really trying hard to like it here but sometimes it's just so crowded, and all that *traffic*. The city's like a labyrinth of cement and glass. The buildings look a mile high."

Britt shook her head, exasperated. She sipped something chichi that looked like wine in a highball glass. Both women were attractive but thirty-year-old Britt was the one with the refined features; she was the perfect cosmopolite with her wavy brunette hair, jewelry, and salon-pampered nails. Cristina was taller and more bosomed but she always felt ragtag whenever they were together, like an oblivious dorm girl at some liberal arts college. Britt had lived in Manhattan with her fiancé, Jess, for five years now, while Cristina's beau—co-owner of the same law firm— had commuted for just as long from the suburbs of Stamford, Connecticut, barely twenty miles away. Cristina knew this was a big step for her.

"You've only lived here a week," Britt dismissed. "A month from now, you'll love this city, and it really is better for your career."

"My career's fine." Cristina leveled her eyes. "Don't repeat this, but I made more money than Paul last quarter."

Britt's brow fluttered, as if surprised. "All the more reason for you to live in the country's artistic nerve center. Successful artists don't live in Connecticut, darling. They live here. And we'll get to see each other *all the time* now. It'll be great!"

"I know," Cristina agreed. In her life of semi-seclusion, Britt was her only confidante. "I am happy about that. The thing about my job—and Paul commuting—is I never had anyone to talk to."

Britt waved her hand. "Well we'll be regular Manhattan chatterboxes from now on. But, seriously, when you live in New York City, you have to *dress* New York City. That stuff you've got on now?" She scrinched her nose. "It ain't gonna cut it."

"I do look a little bummy."

"You look like you slept in a cement mixer, Cristina. Look. This weekend I'll take you clothes shopping. We'll have a ball!" Britt hesitated for some arcane reason, then leaned over her drink. "Did you really make more than Paul last quarter?"

"Yeah. The new line was a big success and my contract for the next one was huge. I don't really care about that, though—the money, I mean."

"After a couple months in this town? You will. And that's really impressive, too, you know? Paul's a managing partner of a big-time law firm and you're out-earning him, which means you're out-earning Jess, too, because they're *both* managing partners. That's serious moolah, Cristina. And you're only twenty-nine."

The compliment seemed jaded. Another thing Cristina didn't like about New York City mentality was the whole rat-race for money. *That's what it's all about here. Who's making what, who drives what, who gets reservations at such and such restaurant and who doesn't.* Cristina just wanted to ply her craft and be happy with Paul.

As appetizers were being placed, Cristina's gaze drifted back and forth to the window. Throngs of well-dressed businesspeople hurried this way and that; buses roared. Cristina felt a chill.

"Don't you want a drink?" Britt asked.

"No, thanks. I hate drinking during the day."

"Then at least have some stuffed squid—" Britt pointed to a plate on which sat a pile of tiny deep-fried squid mantles stuffed with some crabmeat concoction. Cristina just smiled and shook her head.

"It's going to take you a while to get in the Big Apple's groove," Britt laughed. She kept finnicking with the corner of an eye. "Damn. My eyelash is all screwed up. I'll be right back." She rose, pointing to another plate. "If you don't want any squid, try a cuttlefish fritter," she said, then sauntered to the ladies' room.

Cristina watched after her. *Yeah, she sure fits in all right*, she noted of her sister's poise and attire. Tan leather pants by Dolce & Gabbana, Tod's heels, and a gorgeous silk Ombre wrap-blouse, the color of a margarita. *The thing is I DON'T fit in, and am perfectly happy with that.* Cristina's last line of macabre figurines—Cadaverettes—had been a roaring success on the collector's market, and the next line promised to be even bigger. It was strange, though, how different she and Britt were, considering the sameness of their upbringings. They called themselves sisters but weren't really; they'd been raised in the same foster house, and were subject to the same influences during their formative and adolescent years. Yet, Britt was a psychologist for social services and Cristina was—

A creepy-doll designer. It was almost funny, but she did understand that the darkness of their mutual childhoods was probably the guiding force in the careers they later pursued, however different.

Without much forethought, she began to doodle on a napkin, sketching a frolicky caricature of a nun. The nun held a bowl of some sort, and possessed a great comic-bookish grin highlighted by long, thin vampiric fangs.

"So which one is that?" Britt asked, noticing the sketch. She sat back down, inspecting her nails.

"It's called the Noxious Nun," Cristina related. "It's the first figure in the next line. The line is called the *Evil Church Creepies* collection. First, the nun, then there'll be a priest, a deaconess, an altar boy, a choir girl, parishioners, of course, and Sunday school teachers. The last figure will be the Putrefactive Pope."

Britt daintily crunched on a fried squid. "That's some imagination you have."

"So you've told me. I know, I'm a cliché. Gloomy Insecure Artist."

"You're not *that* insecure," Britt laughed, chopsticking a slice of seared hamachi. "And don't worry. No psychology today, I promise."

Cristina was grateful, at least usually. Given Britt's profession as a therapist—and their horrendous upbringing—it was too easy for her to psychoanalyze Cristina. But at least Britt was fair enough to psychoanalyze herself at the same time.

"But something *is* bothering you. I could see it when you walked in."

Cristina seemed surprised. "Really?"

"And don't tell me it's the shock of moving to New York."

Cristina reflected. "I guess you're right." She severed eye contact. "I thought I saw Goldfarb the other day. And he even looked older, like he would now."

"Where? Here?"

"I was walking near the Julliard School, and there he was—Andre Goldfarb."

Britt's eyes turned stern. "You know that's impossible, right?"

"Oh, yes, yes—don't worry, I'm not seeing things."

"Our dear old foster daddy and his wife won't even be up for parole for another ten years. I monitor that very carefully."

Cristina nodded, and even felt pretty good about her ability to raise the issue. "It was just weird. He'd be in his mid-fifties now, and this guy I saw was a dead ringer."

"There's eight million people here, Cristina. Every now and then you're going to see someone who looks just like someone else. Last week I saw a woman who looked just like *me*."

"Really?"

Britt toned down to a whisper. "Yeah, and it really pissed me off—because her boobs were three times bigger than mine."

Cristina was amused by her sister's vanity. Actually, her body looked magnificent, like a runway model's. But she always complained about her petite breasts.

A moment stretched by, then Cristina had to ask: "You never told Jess the whole story, did you?"

"About the Goldfarbs?" She seemed shocked. "No way—just bits and pieces. I didn't tell him about the porn thing or the drugs."

"I told Paul everything," Cristina admitted.

"And so you should have. Paul's a lot more real-world than Jess—Jess couldn't have handled it. I'll probably *never* tell him everything, and not because I'm uncomfortable about what happened. He simply wouldn't know how to deal with it."

Cristina doodled augmentations over her sketch. "I guess the amazing thing is that *we* both could."

"You're right, and that's all that matters," Britt augmented. "We had gross, shitty childhoods but we overcame it all. We're fine. Lots of girls don't turn out so well. You wouldn't believe what's happened to a lot of the women who come through my office. Stuff that makes our experiences look like patty-cake." Britt speared another piece of squid. "But you're still not telling me what's wrong, and it's got nothing to do with Goldfarb or his scumbag wife."

"I'm just tired," Cristina said, rubbing her eyes. "I haven't slept well in the last month. Oh, I know it's part worrying about the new line of figures, and it's part shock from moving from Stamford to the middle of the Upper West Side."

Britt cast her an angled glance. "Any other *parts*?"

"Yeah, one, I guess." Now she reglanced at the Noxious Nun doodle. "Since Paul first showed me the house over a month ago, I have this recurring nightmare."

"About what?"

"About this." Cristina held up the doodle, then shrugged. "It's just a . . . bizarre dream."

"Well, you're an artist, and you're obviously using some image from the dream in your work. Catharsis, right? Isn't that what artists do?"

"I guess. At least that's what my shrink said."

"So. You dream about that kooky nun-sketch. That's it?"

Cristina briefly closed her eyes . . . and saw the flowing swirls. "The dream's set before a swirling background of black, green, and red. A naked woman is holding a crude clay bowl, like a halved coconut. And the bowl has three gemstones on it—one black, one green, one red."

Britt chuckled a sigh. "A naked girl holding a bowl. That's a *nightmare?*"

Cristina shared the chuckle. "Don't even go there, sister. No Freud today. See, in the dream, the woman's wearing a wimple."

"A what?"

"A wimple. It's that thing nuns wear on their heads. Like a white sock with an oval cut out for the face, and a black hatlike thing over it."

"All right. I'm following you now. Nude nun, in a *wimple,* holding a coconut."

"A bowl, really. Like a clay bowl or something. But here's the nightmare part. In the dream, she shows me the bowl, and it's got blood in it. Ad then the weird lines of color in the background get more intense, and then—"

Britt seemed bored. "Yeah?"

"Then the nun grins—and she's got fangs."

"And that's why you're losing sleep? Jeez, Cristina. You ought to have one of my tidal-wave nightmares. I *wish* I had dreams about nude women."

"With *fangs?*"

"Maybe I'd have fangs, too." Now Britt ate a crab puff. "You know what you're problem is, sister? You're just a worrywart. You're a successful artist, with a successful fiancé who wants you to move into his new house with him. These are very positive things but, yeah, they represent change, and the prospect of change can be stressful. It's this stress that's triggering the nutty nightmare, along with your natural-born . . . worrywartdom." Britt almost seemed berating now. "You're not traumatized, you're not suffering from some delayed reactive disorder, and you're not having flashbacks from the drugs the Goldfarbs used on us. Neither of us are having any of that crap."

Cristina squeezed her sister's hand and smiled. She always felt better after talking to her, even when she didn't incite the conversation. "You're a gem, you know that?"

"Actually, I'm a vain label-whore and an absolute *bitch* when I see someone like that prissy woman over there with a Gianni dress that looks better than mine," Britt said, and then scowled past Cristina's shoulder.

Cristina took a quick glance and shook her head. "You're a gem *and* a nut."

"Yeah, and thank God I'm engaged to a New York City attorney who's head over heels for me. I couldn't afford to shop at Salvation Army on what social services pays me."

"But that's proof of your character, isn't it?"

Britt gaped. "What, that I'm engaged to a rich lawyer?"

"Well, yeah. On what he makes, you wouldn't have to work at all, and neither would a lot of women. But you do. You work your butt off for low pay helping the abused and the victimized when you could be sitting in a lounge chair all day sipping Dom Perignon and fanning yourself in a Bill Blass bikini."

"Since you put it *that* way . . . yes! You're absolutely right!" Britt pushed some plates over to Cristina. "Now would you *please* eat some of this? If you don't, I'll eat it all myself, then I'll get fat, Jess'll get sick of me and kick me out for a skinny girl—probably that one over there in the Gianni dress—and then I *will* have to shop at Salvation Army."

"All right," Cristina conceded. "I'll have some."

"Good." Britt got up. "I'll be right back."

"Where are you going?"

Britt whispered. "I just *have* to ask that floozy where she got that dress."

"You're not serious!"

"Oh yes I am." Britt bit her lower lip. "Pretty sick, isn't it?"

Cristina chuckled, then started on the appetizers.

The bus-roar and heel-tapping clamor of the sidewalk didn't bother her when she left. Cristina declined a ride home from Britt; she liked to walk, and she wanted to get used to the city. The skyscrapers on either side of the street loomed so high, it seemed impossible for them to have even been built. Lunch hour was winding down, and the street was even getting a bit more sane.

"Hot dog, miss?" a gruff voice asked aside.

She looked to see a rugged street vendor in a Yankees hat and a Jets shirt. "Cheese, mustard, mayo?"

"Mayo?" Cristina exclaimed. "On *hot dogs?*"

"Don't knock it, toots." He had a chewed-down cigar between his teeth as he presumed to sell food. "It's New York *deli* mayo, from Artie's."

"Maybe next time . . ."

"You sure? Only two bucks. They're Sabrett's—the *genuine* New York dog."

"Actually, I'm full of cuttlefish, but thanks just the same," she said, and then slipped away.

What a pain in the . . .

She eyed the divergent crowd, which seemed to beat along the sidewalks like blood in arteries. It was the ultimate cross-culture here: every nationality mixed with every economic status, all pulsing together in tandem. *Maybe I could get used to this*, she considered. Or did the sudden tolerance stem more from feeling better after her talk with Britt?

She slowed by a comic/novelty shop, noticing several of her competitor's products in the window. Living Dead Dolls, Gurl-Goyles, Fantasmic Fishies. *But no Cadaverettes!* she fumed. She edged into the store, at once hesitant. *I've got to stand up for my product*, she knew, but she also knew she was 100 percent nonassertive. When her well-done burger came to the table medium, she never sent it back. Passivity was as much a part of her as her blonde hair.

All comic shops seemed to possess the same musty smell, and usually only a quarter of the floor space existed for comic books and graphic novels. Novelties comprised the rest: toys, action figures and figurines, T-shirts, etc. Cristina checked the shelves and found no trace of Cadaverettes there, either.

Bastards!

A long line congregated at the checkout. One man in a pricey suit waited to buy an armload of some comic called *Hell Tramp*, while an obese girl with multiple facial piercings sputtered as she held a copy of something called *Mr. Torso Part VII*. A man with spiked blond hair and a leather vest hypertensively manned the register. He looked like Billy Idol's grandfather.

"Excuse me, sir," Cristina peeped over the line. "I have a question if it's not too much inconvenience . . ."

The blond man sneered at her. "I'm a little busy here, if ya couldn't tell. Got no time for chitchat."

Cristina felt stultified. "Well . . . I've noticed that you carry Living Dead Dolls and Gurl-Goyles but no Cadaverettes. Do you not *like* Cadaverettes?"

The man shook his head as he frantically rang the next customer. "I like 'em fine, honey!" he snapped. "Reason we ain't got 'em is 'cos they sell out faster than I can put 'em on the shelves! Now gimme a break! I'm busy!"

Cristina stood wavering. *What should I do?* "Well . . . excuse me again, sorry, but would it be possible, do you think, if you could maybe reorder them?"

His glare struck her like an arrow in the face. "I'm busy! Have some fuckin' courtesy! Come back later, will ya?"

Cristina shivered but managed to mutter, "This isn't a very nice store," and then hurried away.

"Hey, bonehead," the suited man addressed the spiked clerk. "That was Cristina Nichols. She *created* Cadaverettes."

Alarm. "Hey—uh, I mean, Ms. Nichols?" the cashier pleaded after her. "Sorry! Don't leave! Can I book you for a signing?"

Cristina slipped back onto the street. *Why can't people just be nice?* Everyone seemed so manic here, so type A. But ultimately she left satisfied. They hadn't neglected her line at all; they'd simply sold it out, which was terrific. *It means I'm still selling.*

An alley tangented the corner of 67th and Dessorio Avenue. "Never cut through alleys, Cristina," Paul had emphasized the first day. "Never. This is *New York*, not Petticoat Junction. You can never be too careful." Cristina was touched by the tenor of his concern, but she saw no harm. The alley was only fifty or so yards long, and she could see it was clear save for a few garbage cans.

Which was why she jumped, when a scratchy voice drifted toward her from one side.

"Hey, lady?"

Cristina had only proceeded fifty feet. A homeless girl in pink sweatpants, a men's white T-shirt, and mismatched flip-flops stood right behind her.

Where did she come from? Cristina thought.

Scrubby tendrils of hair hung over her face like black

spaghetti. Some ghost of youth struggled beneath wasted features. *These homeless people always look so much older than they really are.* But at least Cristina didn't feel threatened now.

"Can I have, like, two dollars so I can buy a hot dog from the guy you didn't buy one from?"

Cristina couldn't calculate how the girl could've witnessed her encounter with the vendor. "I think so . . ." She reached in her pocket.

The girl sniffled and rubbed her nose. "And like maybe another one or two dollars so I can buy a soda?"

"Sure." Cristina gave the girl a twenty-dollar bill. "You can use the rest to go to the shelter on Henry Street. I read they added a lot of beds."

"Oh, I ain't homeless."

"That's good. Where do you live?"

"Here." The girl twitched. "We even have a TV. It doesn't work but we watch it anyway."

Cristina could think of nothing to say.

"And-and, like, I saw on the TV today that you were cutting your throat but then you blinked and it wasn't your own throat you were cutting, it was the man's."

She's probably delusional from drugs, Cristina realized. *And that's what she's going to buy with the money I just gave her . . .*

Then she winced when she saw scars on the girl's wrist.

The girl giggled, staring at the alley's brick wall. "That sounds kooky, doesn't it, but that's what I saw on the TV when the nun turned it on. Thanks for the money, and don't worry, I ain't gonna buy any rock with it. I'm gonna get some hot dogs. 'Bye." Then the girl oddly shuffled backward several steps, turned, and headed out of the alley.

But Cristina hadn't yet surfaced from her mute stare. *The nun?* "Hey, wait! What did you say about a nun?"

"Maybe I'll get mustard on mine instead of cheese—er, no, I'm gonna get one with cheese, or maybe . . . a bunch!"

The girl flip-flopped away as if off balance and left the alley.

The nun, Cristina's mind clicked. *She said something about a nun . . .*

How bizarre.

She retraced her steps back out the alley and peeped around. *How do you like that? She wasn't lying . . .* She watched the homeless girl buy a bunch of hot dogs from the vendor. Then, still twitchy and off balance, she flopped off in the opposite direction.

The poor thing's crazy. Mostly gibberish she was talking, Cristina considered. Just a coincidence.

But where had she actually come from?

An out of business Banana Republic was what sat on the corner, its rear wall forming one side of the alley. The place had finally been bought out by developers a few weeks ago, Paul had told her, and it wouldn't be long before contractors either leveled it or refurbished the structure for condos. Cristina walked back slowly, checking. There was a locked metal door and a locked garage on the loading bay but that was all.

Wait . . .

She stooped.

Between two garbage cans, street level, was a hole in the wall, not even the diameter of an old vinyl record album. *Could she have . . .* But, no. It would be hard even for the slightest person to squeeze their shoulders through such an aperture. *And—whew!*

Cristina backed away from the uric stench that gusted out.

Nobody could live in there . . .

When she headed home, she didn't notice the three objects lying near the hole.

Magic markers: one black, one green, and one red.

CHAPTER TWO

(I)

Forty-year-old Paul Nasher looked out his office window from the twentieth floor of the Mahoney Building. He stared through his smile down at Beekman Street and watched the orderly chaos of Financial District traffic. *God, I'm lucky*, he realized. Paul and his best friend, Jess Franklin, owned the firm outright now. They were among the most exclusive real estate lawyers in the city.

Yeah, we own this place, he mused. *And now I own the house*. It was the next step he'd succeeded in—the next step in cementing his life with Cristina.

Though Paul didn't have the build for a high-powered attorney—he was stocky, broad-shouldered like a power-lifter—he had the brains and the inclination. Real estate law came innately to him; he could "feel" the future pulse of the market, and due to this he made just as much money during the downs as the ups, the annex house he'd bought being a prime example. He didn't feel that he'd exploited the diocese at all—*Not with a million in cash, I didn't*—but it was just another of those circumstances that had landed in his jurisprudential lap. *I have the Midas touch. I wonder why . . .*

He sat down at the desk, wearing a gratified smile along with his charcoal-gray Z Zegna suit. What he wore at any given time cost more than the average person made in a week, or in a year if one counted his Lange & Sohne Flyback watch. It was all part of what he worked for, and he didn't take it for granted. What he wore was an extension of his sense of communication.

He communicated very well. His attire went hand in hand with his business acumen: it spoke the language of a winner.

Now if I could only get Cristina to marry me . . .

The door clicked open and in walked his partner. Jess Franklin, though he dressed just as well as Paul and, if anything, had more cosmopolitan taste, looked more accountant than attorney, a little mussed with the unruly brown hair and pointy goatee that seemed perpetually in need of a trim. Paul winced when Jess lit a Marlboro.

"You should get a haircut and quit smoking. That shit's not cool in our business. It's kind of . . . redneck."

"Hey, I *am* a redneck," Jess countered, "and damn proud of it. I'm the ground-pounder here, remember? You're the Face—"

"It's good you know your calling," Paul laughed.

"—in *spite* of the clear and present fact that I order better in a restaurant than you."

"Amen. And go ahead, tap the ashes on my floor. Good for the carpet, right? Isn't that what they say in the trailer park?"

"Carpet *tiles*, man," Jess prodded.

Paul found it difficult not to guffaw. "It must kill you that whenever you drop a grand for lunch at the Four Seasons, you can't smoke."

"Tell me about it. Whatever happened to America? Oh, and I let Ann go early. She said she had a date."

"Who's the lucky girl?"

Jess and Paul cracked laughs. Then Paul glanced at his Lange & Sohne. "Let's have a drink at Harry's. We don't have anything else going today, do we?"

"Mind like a steel trap, Paul. I've got that pile of summary judgment briefs to FedEx for the Mayr land-deal, and you've got that call coming in."

Paul straightened in his leather chair. "What call?"

"Do you ever look at your scheduler? You got a call at one from Panzram and Cartlon." Jess looked at his own watch, a Breitling Chromatic. "Five minutes."

"Ann never told me."

"Yes, she did. Yesterday. You weren't paying attention because you were too busy trying to see if she wasn't wearing panties beneath that little Cavalli skirt."

Paul smirked. "You're out of your—"

"She wasn't, by the way. And you know who Panzram and Carlton are, don't you?"

Paul looked fuddled. "I've heard of them, sure. East Side ambulance chasers, aren't they?"

Jess chuckled Marlboro smoke. "They're more than that as far as you're concerned. Change the air in your head."

Paul nodded. "I'll admit, I'm a little distracted lately, with Cristina here and all."

"Yeah, yeah, great, but we're attorneys, remember? Good attorneys forget about their squeeze the second they step into the office." Jess looked disapproving. "After you finagled the diocese to sell you the annex house for five times less than it's worth, they fired the lawyer they had on retainer—"

"But the monsignor named his price and I paid!" Paul objected, but only half in earnest.

"The monsignor's *eighty*, Paul."

"Fine, but what's this got to do with Panzram and Cartlon?"

Jess eyed the lengthening ash on his cigarette. "They're the firm the diocese hired after they shitcanned their regular guy."

Damn, Paul thought. "The contract's ironclad—you saw it yourself. If they try to sue me, they're gonna think a stone quarry fell on their heads."

"Well, just get ready 'cos—"

The phone rang.

Jess winked. "There they are, and good luck. I'll meet you at Harry's Bar when I'm done at FedEx."

"Right," Paul said.

"And, Paul?"

Paul glanced up. Jess, ever so meticulously, tapped an inch-long ash on the carpet and winked.

"Redneck." Paul sighed, waited two more rings, and picked up the phone. "Nasher and Franklin, Paul Nasher speaking."

"Ah, Mr. Nasher," issued a crisp, calculated voice. "I'm Vic Winner at Panzram and Carlton. I've recently been retained by the diocese to examine some of their legal affairs and I've come upon a discrepancy in the sales contract for the old annex house on Sixty-seventh Street."

"You mean *my* annex house," Paul corrected. "And I can't imagine what discrepancy you're referring to, because there is none."

A pause, then, "Really, Mr. Nasher, I'm sure you realize that the price you paid for the property was, shall we say, invidious."

"The diocesan legal representative wrote the contract, and the monsignor happily signed it. And then he *even more* happily took my million dollars. In cash."

A longer pause this time. "Monsignor Romay, as you know, is on in his years, and he was badly advised on the property's true market value—"

Paul stared at the gold-framed picture of Cristina on his desk. "I'd have to say that if the monsignor was badly advised about anything, it was in replacing his previous attorney with your crew. I know your firm, Mr. Winner, and it's not exactly topflight. Weren't you the guys who blew that huge asbestos case in Queens? A lot of innocent people got fucked up for life by those contractors. How could you botch a rainmaker like that?"

"That's outrageous!" the caller yelled. "You've got a lot of gall saying that after what you've done!"

"What *I've* done, Mr. Winner?"

"You hoodwinked the Catholic Church! You *stole* from them! This is actionable and you know it!"

Paul actually chuckled. "The only thing I know, Mr. Winner, is that you and your firm are second-rate. I'm sure the diocese approached much more bankable firms than Panzram and Carlton, and I'm sure they all turned the diocese down. Why? Because a *good* firm would know in a half a second that my sales contract for the Sixty-seventh Street property is 100 percent legal and binding. You wouldn't find a judge in a million years who'd hear the case after he looked at that paperwork. So go ahead and sue me, Mr. Winner. It would be my pleasure to bury you in court and embarrass you so bad you'll never get work again."

"You're unmitigated, Mr. Nasher!"

Paul unconsciously wiped at a scuff on his $300 shoe. "Let me put it as politely as I possibly can. If you fuck with *me*, I'll fuck you back so hard you'll be walking like a cowboy for the rest of your chump-change career."

Paul hung up. My God, *I LOVE confrontations like that,* he thought. *It makes my blood pressure go down . . .*

He stood up, tweaked his Luigi Borrelli silk tie, then smiled down at the picture of Cristina on his desk. *None of it means anything without her. Yeah, I'm REALLY lucky, all right.*

He called the floor janitor to report that a cigarette ash needed to be cleaned from his carpet.

Some guys got it, and some guys don't, he thought and left for the bar.

(II)

Twentieth Precinct Homicide on 82nd Street sat stone-silent. Vernon felt awkward; he squirmed in his seat with nothing to do. *Has the damn phone even rung in the last hour?* They were covering burglary, too, since the administrative shake-up last winter, but there was nothing there, either. *All our cold cases are solved, and we've only got three ongoing investigations. Twenty-fourth Precinct's got FIFTY!* Howard Vernon was a senior inspector with twenty-five years on the force and more commendations and valor medals than he could remember. *Somebody give me something to do!*

He spent his time getting fresh coffee and looking at the Byzantine-looking Ukranian cathedral out the window.

"This must be what retirement's like," he muttered.

"What's that, How?" someone asked. "You're retiring?"

Vernon turned to see. It was Slouch who'd made the remark, a fifteen-year vet in good standing. They called him Slouch because he slouched whenever he sat down. He was hard to make as undercover; he looked like some happy-go-lucky deadbeat who hung out in strip joints and actually thought the girls were attracted to him. His shaggy hair was always half in his face, dicing the permanent lazy shuck-and-jive smile.

"I feel irresponsible," Vernon said. "We're getting paid money to do a job, but—"

"But there's no job to do? Sounds good to me."

"Nothing ever happens in this precinct," he grumbled and sat back down. "I spend more time walking to and from the coffee machine than writing up DOR's."

"You're complaining like that's a bad thing, How," Slouch pointed out. "It means the crime rate is going down. And don't forget, the Comm's office transferred you here as a *reward* for outstanding service. Don't complain."

"Jesus Christ, Slouch, there's nothing to *do*. We're tits on a bull. The Twentieth doesn't get homicides so the boss has us double-timing on B&E's and nobody's even breaking and entering here."

Slouch stretched back with his feet up on his desk. He smiled big. "Maybe it's your karma—it makes people peaceful. It drives the bad guys off to the Twenty-fourth."

Where's Bed-Sty when you need it?

When Slouch's phone rang, Vernon glared. "Why your phone and not mine?" he yelled.

Slouch laughed. "Because you're the head of the unit and I'm the flunky, remember? Lemme do some grunt work for ya." When Slouch picked up the phone, he said, "Yeah? When? Okay," and hung up.

"What is it?" Vernon pleaded.

"Treat yourself to a cartwheel, How. Worden's Hardware Store got busted into last night."

"I'm on it," Vernon said, jumping up.

"Sit back down, How. Taylor did the work on it an hour ago. That wasn't the store calling—it was Vice."

"What the hell's Vice got to do with a B&E at a hardware store?"

Slouch paused at the door, grinning. "They got a witness . . . A *hooker*."

"Yeah?"

"I'm picking her up at booking and bringing her in. I hope to God she's hot. Meanwhile, Taylor's on the way with the lowdown."

Slouch loped out, leaving Vernon anxious and frowning. Now he was alone. *What could be duller than a hardware store burglary?* But he supposed it was better than nothing.

Vernon's second in charge was Jake Taylor. Good cop. Drank too much. "But only on Sundays," he once told Vernon. His curly brown hair and fat mustache, plus shabby tweed sports jackets made him look like a reject from the early seventies when every cop in the department was trying to look like Bruce Dern and be "hip."

When Taylor came in, he said, "Did you hear about the—"

"Worden's Hardware Store, B&E," Vernon responded to at least *sound* like he was a leg up. "Let me guess. A truck-job. They cleaned the place out."

"Not even close." Taylor dropped his case notes on Vernon's desk and sat down. "Somebody ripped off four Sloyd-brand wood-carving knives. Total value of the heist? $39.80."

Vernon glared. "That's the dumbest-ass thing I've ever heard! Nobody busts into a fuckin' hardware store and steals four cheap knives! You steal power drills and diamond-tipped saw blades and air compressors!"

"Right, and if you're looking to fence knifes, you go for Gerbers and the Al Mars and the bowies, the ones that go for two bills a pop."

Vernon's anger spilled over into his incredulity. "How'd they break in?"

"Front window, bold as brass. Don't know what time last night. They knew what they wanted, they went in, got it, and split. We got some prints but—" Taylor shrugged. "You might not wanna waste Tech Service's time on a forty-dollar heist."

"Four cheap knives?" Vernon just didn't get it. "That's the dumbest-ass thing I ever heard," he repeated.

Taylor eyed him. "I know you've had a few more birthdays than me, How, but is any of this ringing a bell? You said the same exact thing last winter . . ."

Vernon stared back at his partner. "Worden's . . . Yeah. The place near Greenflea, right? Around Seventy-seventh?"

"The cogs are turning."

Then the memory snapped back. "That's right. Somebody B&E'd Worden's last December, and stole . . ." *Ridiculous*, he recalled. "They stole a bunch of Christmas tree stands."

"Yep. Over a dozen of them, and that's *all* they ripped off. And do you remember who did it?"

Vernon pointed like a gun. "A bunch of homeless

women! Yeah, now I remember. They got them on the security camera, and we even busted one of them a few days later."

"Exactly. And you said it was the dumbest-ass thing you ever heard for somebody to pinch a bunch of Christmas tree stands. Gotta say I agree with you on that."

"Don't tell me it was the same homeless girls," Vernon ventured.

"Got no idea."

"But they got a security camera."

"Yeah, and the guy who closed last night forgot to put a new disc in. But Vice called me on the wire and said they got a witness."

"Slouch is bringing her up from booking," Vernon told him and then the door clicked open.

"Well, what have we here?" Taylor trumpeted. "Looks like a thirteen-year-old hooker."

"She's twenty-five, no lie," Slouch said. "Got a legit state ID and a rap sheet for soliciting. She's also got an associate's degree from the city college . . . Sit'cher tush down right there, Shirley Temple," he told the handcuffed girl. "Inspector Vernon wants to rap with ya."

Tears smeared the girl/woman's garish eye makeup. The physique facing Vernon was reed-slim, nearly breastless and hipless, and she looked back at him with huge, watery Little Bo Peep eyes. She dressed like a little girl in Catholic school: knee-high white socks, black tap shoes, plaid knee-skirt, veiling blouse, but the image was made outrageous by the loud, whorey lipstick and eye makeup.

"You're really *twenty-five?*" Vernon asked, astonished.

She nodded, sniffling.

Slouch laughed, "Hey, How—we ought to give her back to Vice so they can make her a controlled decoy. Young as she looks, we'd have half the perverts in New York behind bars in two weeks. Oh, and her name's *Cinzia*."

"Cinzia, huh? What's your gig, Cinzia? Crack, pills, meth?"

"I don't do drugs," she peeped.

"Bullshit," Vernon said stiffly. "Why else would you be doing *this*?"

She even tried to sit like a little girl, hands in lap. "For the *money*," she insisted. "There are guys out there who pay a *lot* because—"

"Because you *look* like a little kid," Vernon smirked, "and that means instead of working a job like the rest of us stiffs, you strut your skinny tush as chicken bait. Honey, believe me, there are better ways to get the things that you need than being a meat-magnet for scumbags who like to fuck kids."

The expletive jolted her; more tears welled. "I know."

"You give those freaks a taste, then they'll go out and rape *real* kids. You ought to be ashamed."

"Time Magazine Woman of the Year," Slouch laughed.

"I'm sorry!" she sobbed. "I know it's a shitty thing to do but I've got to make a living! It's hard out there. I'm paying nineteen hundred dollars a month to rent four hundred square feet."

"Welcome to New York," Vernon said. "Move to Minnesota and take your sob story with you."

Now she was crying like a genuine child. "I-I can't go to jail—I can't stand it—"

"This is her second strike," Slouch informed.

Taylor jerked her chair around—Good Cop/Bad Cop time. "We're just a precinct, *Cinzia*. We're not like a division in one of the boroughs. There's nothing we can do to help you stay out of the lezzie-tank. You'll be the hit of the cell block to all *those* Big Bertha mamas." Then he jerked her chair back to face Vernon.

"Maybe, maybe not. Give us a solid crack contact, and we might be able to help you out a little."

The girl began to blubber. "I don't have any *crack* contacts—I told you. I don't do drugs. Please! I screwed up, I'm sorry. You got no idea what it was like for me when I had to do time."

"We can all imagine, little girl," Taylor said.

But she's not lying about the drugs, Vernon could tell at a glance. The women always sung like canaries after a second or third bust. "Did you agree to a blood test when you got booked?"

"That she did, How," Slouch offered. "Makes ya wonder."

Vernon watched her intently, assaying body language and eye movement. "Maybe I *can* do something for you, Cinzia, but you know how life is. To get something, you have to give something."

The girl groaned. "Jesus, you gotta be kidding me; you guys are *cops*."

"Relax, I'm not talking about *sexual* somethings—"

"Shucks!" Slouch laughed.

Taylor jerked her chair back. "You give us the make on your johns so we get an assist from Vice—"

The girl groaned.

"And, you give us some info that leads to a bust on the hardware store," Vernon ganged up. "A little bird says you saw something last night."

For once, the girl seemed enthused. "Oh, yeah, I saw the whole thing near Seventy-seventh. The hardware store near Greenflea. It was like three in the morning."

"That's a bit late for a *little girl* to be wandering around," Taylor said, then shoved her chair back toward Vernon.

"Did you see the perpetrators?"

"Yes, four or five of them. They'd broken the front window. Right when I was walking by after a—well, you know. They all jumped out the hole in the window and ran away."

"Four or five of them? They didn't happen to be—"

"It's these nutty homeless chicks I see all the time hanging out around Broadway, near—what is it? Dessorio Avenue?"

Vernon and Taylor traded raised brows.

"But last night they were up around Seventy-seventh busting into the hardware store," she went on. "The reason I recognized them is I see 'em all the time during the day panhandling on Sixty-eighth."

"Homeless girls . . ."

"Yeah, crackheads. They're pains in the ass. They live place to place to place. You know."

"No, we don't know," Vernon said. "*What* place? The shelters south of town?"

"No, no, a building gets sold or a restaurant goes under, lots of the bums will squat there until someone comes in to start work on the place and throws 'em out. But they hang around this area. Upper West Side's a good place to beg for change. You want to see 'em, go down to where that guy sells off-brand hot dogs and says they're Sabrett's."

"That's half the vendors in New York, honey," Slouch said.

"It's the guy who's always around Dessorio and Sixty-seventh," she added. "I see them all the time, bumming change around there."

"Pretty interesting, huh, How? The *bum* part?" Taylor remarked.

"Just like those girls last December."

"And they're real nutty and silly," the prostitute complained. "Giggling and jabbering. They're worse than the damn pigeons."

"Have some compassion, Cinzia," Vernon told her. "They're probably all schizophrenic. What's *your* excuse for being a noncontributor?"

The girl put her head down.

Vernon rubbed his hands together. "What you gotta understand is this is about the cushiest precinct in the city.

These girls stole a pissant forty bucks' worth of knives last night and a bunch of *Christmas tree stands* last December."

The girl gave him an odd look.

"That's right. Christmas tree stands. Not exactly the crime of the century, huh?" Vernon went on. "But because our jobs are so easy here, if we don't solve this real fast— like in *one* day—we'll be the laughingstock of the department. So here's the deal. If your blood test comes up negative for drugs, and you show us where these nutty homeless girls hang out, I'll call the magistrate and have him drop your charges, if you agree to do some informant work for the Vice unit. That way, you stay out of jail, and we get something to do that makes us look like we're earning our pay for a change."

"All right," the girl said.

Vernon uncuffed her. "And clean that silly makeup off your face. It makes you look asinine."

"Thanks . . ."

"You're going to go with Detective Taylor now and show him where these girls congregate."

"I'm almost off-shift," Taylor complained.

"Such are the hardships of public service." Vernon cracked a smile.

"Hey, Jake, make sure you got your vest on," Slouch sniped. "These nutty homeless chicks are tough customers."

"You're going with him," Vernon said.

Slouch glared. "Why?"

"To pick up some hot dogs from that street vendor. I'll be able to tell if they're really Sabrett's. False advertising's a crime, too, you know."

Slouch wasn't happy. "And what are *you* doing, Inspector?"

"I'm going home," Vernon said. "I'm off-shift."

CHAPTER THREE

(I)

"It's Brazilian rosewood," Paul said with pride. The dining table shined with such luster it nearly seemed possessed of some dark inner light.

"I'll bet it cost a fortune," Cristina said.

"Sure, but we're successful, remember?"

"You've really done a spectacular job," she complimented, still dazzled by the visual impact of the foyer and dining room. "And look at these banisters!"

"That's knurled mahogany, honey." He ran his hand around the wood's corkscrew configuration at the end. "It's one piece of wood, believe it or not. They *steam* the wood so they can shape it to match the curvature of the stairs."

Cristina looked up the steps, marveling at the plush, black-red carpet. "These are the most beautiful stairs I've ever seen in a home, Paul."

"Yeah? And now it's *our* home."

When she turned, she was jolted by the stunning reflection of the stairwell's banister in a great circular mirror hanging in a quaint niche.

Paul's tie hung loosened, his jacket off, as he sipped a small scotch. Cristina could tell how excited he was to finally be unveiling the house to her. *He did all this for me,* she knew. *And it's beautiful.*

"Unfortunately, for now," he added, "these are the stairs to nowhere."

Cristina agreed with the tactic. "There's no reason to fix the whole place up right away."

"I'm going to do it a floor at a time, and I don't even have a timetable. This floor is more than we need anyway." He took her hand. "Now it's time for you to see the rest."

Each room waylaid her. Cristina wasn't much of a materialist but even she had to admit how much she loved what he'd done. She tended to like new things that looked old, and this nailed the sentiment. The barrel-vaulted ceiling in the living room lent a neoclassical air with its arched transoms and mosaic wainscoting. A fireplace as high as she stood graced one wall, faux logs burning gently. Tuscan pilasters formed a colonnade across the foyer—highlighting the pointed, double-paneled entry door—the end of which was dedicated to a mirrored wet bar.

"You want a drink for the rest of the tour?" he asked, freshening his own.

"No! I'm too excited!"

Dark hardwood floor segments alternated with shining slate the color of jade. Another room functioned as a lanai leading to a tiny but meticulous garden arranged on the balcony. *I'll be able to brainstorm out here!* Next came the den, which Paul informed was actually the "sitting room": cupolas full of bookshelves, a simple silver chandelier, and darkly upholstered armchairs—the feel of an exclusive club. Furniture, sconces, and shelving all resonated old-world craftsmanship, which continued along a butter-cream wall of arch-topped windows and exotic maroon drapes. In the kitchen, peacock-green African marble topped an expansive island counter.

"Get ready," he said. "Here's the master suite . . ."

More maroon and gold tones accentuated the cozy room where they'd be sleeping. A great, veiled poster bed, more dark old-world furniture, and angled into the corner was the bathroom and vanity, complete with a spa appointed by more decorative columns. Cristina felt winded, taking it all in.

"The interior decorator called it neo-Baroque," he said.

"I love it," she whispered.

When she snuck a peek at him, she could tell that he loved it too, but what he loved more was her approval. *What kind of guy would do all of this just to make a woman happy?* she had to ask herself. *He cares more about what I think than anything else.* It made her feel more special than she'd *ever* felt.

"I knew you'd like the style. The guest room's similar but I didn't do much to your work room, which is right in here," he said and opened two more double-paneled doors.

He obviously had the windows expanded to provide more light, and kept the style pretty basic.

"I know how artists are about their work space," he went on. "You'll want to tune it up your own way."

He was quite right about the "work space" thing; creative types had their own eccentricities regarding the work environment. They went back to the bedroom. "It'll be perfect," she said and hugged him. A tear slipped from her eye. "You did all this for me—"

"Well, you moved here for *me*," he said, tightening his embrace.

"It's for both of us." The sudden surge of excitement left her feeling hot, even prickly. *What's this all about?* she tested herself. Her nipples pressed against his chest seemed to spark.

When was the last time she'd felt such a sensation?

She tried to distract herself. "You must've spent so much redoing these rooms," she said, but kept hugging him. Suddenly the feel of his chest pressing her breasts began to spread.

"Honey, you probably could've swung it on what *you* made last year. Remember, we're *both* successful now, not just me."

"I know, but—"

But what? Why did she feel so pleasantly strange now?

His hot words blew against her ear. "You have no idea how happy I am that you like the place."

Her hand slipped around the back of his neck and pulled. The kiss was so sudden and desperate she couldn't figure it. She slipped her tongue in his mouth and pressed against him even harder.

"Yeah, I guess you *really* like the place," he remarked when the kiss broke.

"No, I love it, and I love you . . ."

He took her hand. "Come on, you haven't seen the game room yet. I've got a fifty-inch plasma that lowers out of the ceiling, and twelve speakers hidden in the walls. All that classical stuff you listen to? Wait'll you hear it on *this* system."

But his words sounded far away. Instead of following him out, she was backing away until her hands came away from his.

"Paul . . ."

He turned, eyes narrowed. "Don't you want to see—"

Cristina kept back-stepping, then slid her rump up on the vanity's marble top.

"Honey?"

Her voice suddenly sounded parched. "Come here . . ."

She reached out to him as he approached, then wrapped her legs around him, to seize his groin against hers. It was almost rough the way she grabbed his collar and pulled him down again to kiss her, this time more ravenously. It was a wild heat, like steam, that seemed to spiral inside of her, from her breasts, to her belly, to her sex. She could tell Paul didn't know what to make of this but she didn't even give him time to contemplate; she kept her mouth locked to his, nearly whining.

"Paul, I'm so sorry," she managed to pant, then frantically undid the top buttons of her blouse.

"Sorry for *what?*"

"You know." And then, frustrated, she yanked her blouse out of her jeans, and pushed one of his hands up against her skin.

He was so taken aback, he chuckled.

"Baby, I don't know. You're kind of throwing me for a loop but . . . I like it."

She locked her ankles behind his back, vising him harder. She felt in a low frenzy when she blurted, "I'm sorry I haven't been very sexual for a while. I haven't considered your needs at all."

"Honey, that's not true—"

"Yes, it is!" she panted. "I've been nervous about the new line and about moving and being in New York and—"

"Cristina! I haven't exactly been Mr. Stud for a while myself, not with all that's been going on at the office with Jess . . ."

She kept trying to sort her thoughts against the rising gust of lust. "For most of the last year you probably thought I lost my sex drive, that I wasn't attracted to you, but I need you to know that I *am*. I've always been so hot for you I can't stand it—I just don't show it a lot—"

His hands slid up her blouse even as he weighed his own perplexion. "Cris—"

"I want us to do it right here," she breathed. Finally she tore open the rest of her blouse and flipped her bra up over her breasts so his hands could find them. "Right now . . . I need you in me right *now* . . ." And as she made the unbidden plea, she cupped his crotch and rubbed, then ran her hand against her own crotch. She could feel her own heat building beneath the denim, and suddenly she thought she'd scream if she didn't have her pants off.

"Baby, you're really a trip today."

She unsnapped her waist button, pulled his hands off her breasts and put them on her waist. "Take these off." She kicked her shoes across the room, then lifted her butt up to help him.

She didn't even think about it while he was pulling her jeans off her legs: she caressed her own breasts and moaned out loud . . .

They both flinched at a loud, even pounding on the door. Her eyes darted to his.

"Don't answer it—"

He paused, then continued peeling her jeans off.

More knocking, louder, and also the doorbell.

"Damn it!" Paul looked crestfallen. "It's the movers with more of our stuff."

"Shit!"

"Baby, believe me, there's nothing I'd like better than to keep going here but if I don't get that, they'll probably leave . . ."

Cristina crumpled back against the vanity wall. "I know." And then she laughed, looking at herself. "That's what I call getting caught with my pants down . . ."

Paul stood her on her feet and pulled her jeans back up. "We'll pick up where we left off once they leave." Then he laughed at her buttonless blouse. "Maybe you better get something else on."

"Yeah. What would the movers think?"

"Come out whenever you're ready. I'll let them in now," he said, straightening himself up. "I think they've got my office stuff and law books, and most of your work stuff. That's pretty much all that's left."

She kissed him one more time, hard, as the doorbell rang again. "I'll be out in a minute."

Paul smiled, wiped his brow, and left.

Jeez, what's getting into me? she thought. *I feel absolutely slutty—I practically raped him!* She supposed everyone was subject to their moods, but this was uncanny. *It must mean that all my worries about moving here are over—just like Britt said earlier.* She couldn't remember the last time she'd felt so sexually charged. *And it's still there,* she realized, that lusty heat still spiraling. She took a moment to splash her face with cool water from the sink, catching her breath. The temptation was so great, she actually cosseted herself again through the jeans, then contemplated searching for her vibrator. But most of the moving boxes were still unpacked. *It would take me forever to find it*, she thought, and then winced when she realized how outrageous the idea was in the first place. *The movers would probably walk in . . . I'm sure Paul would love that.* "That's some girlfriend you got there, buddy." Instead she simmered herself down and put on a different blouse.

But, still, her ponderings continued. *Maybe this is the NEW me*, she hoped. She'd always felt that her sexual self had been shortchanged, stifled by her past and buried further by her introversion as an artist. It made her feel awful at times, because she knew that her own romantic moods were so few and far between that Paul must be left so unsatisfied as to wonder if their relationship was even right. *But he's hung in there for three years now*, she reminded herself. *I hope I feel like this every day, so I can really make it up to him . . .*

She hoped she wasn't still flushed when she finally ventured to the foyer. Blank-faced movers nodded to her as they hand-carted in more boxes. When none of them were looking, Paul silently mouthed *I love you* to her.

Just you wait, she mouthed back, then mockingly cleared her throat and said, "Is it okay for me to look around the upper floors? I mean, is it safe?"

"Oh, sure, everything's up to code if that's what you mean." He seemed to turn toward the bar, then thought better of it, which pleased Cristina. She wouldn't exactly say that he drank *too much*, but she felt much better when he refrained. "Third and fourth floors aren't even Sheetrocked yet, but the second floor is, and it's all wired. Go ahead and check it out if you want. You might get some ideas about how we should refurbish the rest."

"Okay," she said and skipped up the dark-scarlet carpet.

From the landing she could see unfinished doors standing
open, filling the hall with fading daylight. She browsed
around each empty room amid the scent of newly cut
Sheetrock, but instead of thinking about redecorating she
found her mind locked on her new line. *Evil Church
Creepies*, she mused. *The Noxious Nun . . .*

Would she have the same dream tonight?

It didn't matter how bizarre the dream might be, nor
how disturbed she was by it. *I used it to my creative advantage*, she knew. *Now I just need it to sell—BETTER than
Cadaverettes.* Bruno von Blanc, the owner of the development company, assured her that *Evil Church Creepies* would
outsell everything else on the market. "Your creative visions are right on the pulse of the marketplace, Cristina,"
he'd insisted. "You thought we were taking a chance on
Cadaverettes, remember? You thought they'd been branded
as derivative. But I knew before we even signed you up
that they were exactly what the market had been waiting
for. Everything *else* is derivative, Cristina. Cadaverettes are
the only original figurines coming out now, because they
mix the old with the new. And *Evil Church Creepies* isn't
just an extension of that; it's a new avenue. The preorders
alone will be through the roof."

Cristina hoped so, and it had nothing to do with the
money. If anything, she still couldn't relate to that part of
it. She'd made a phenomenal amount off the last line, yet
most of it was stuck in the bank, somehow defying her
awareness of it. She merely needed her creations to per-
petuate, to be enjoyed by others—preferably *lots* of others.

Semi-immortality, she thought, and wandered into more
rooms.

The *front* room. What looked immediately back at her
from the great bow window was another window: a great
wheel-window of stained glass, accented by intricate trac-
eries. *The church across the street*, she recalled. So far she'd
scarcely noticed it but now, from this higher vantage

point, it appeared quite grandiose, almost a mini Notre
Dame, with buttresses, pointed iron crockets, even a bel-
fry. It looked drab, though, unused. Cristina understood
that the house in which she and Paul now lived was originally some sort of an annex building for the same church.

Staring at it now reminded her that she hadn't been to
church in over ten years.

She left the room in a rush, electing not to confront the
subtle guilt.

Oh, wow. Now this is something . . . She'd drifted into
the rearmost room, as wall-patched and unfinished as the
others, but found herself spellbound. High lancet windows
made the room appear galleryish, and let in radiant blocks
of late-afternoon light. *This room is it,* she knew at once,
and in her mind she already envisioned how it would be
painted, carpeted, and arranged. *I doubt that Paul will be
hurt that I like this room better than the studio.* It was the feel
of the room, even in its denuded state, that instantly ap-
pealed to her artist's perceptions. The view looking down
wasn't much—just the boring alley—but it was the way
the windows let in all that light that made her fall in love
with the room.

My new studio, she thought.

It was exciting just to think about, but after some unde-
finable moments, her thoughts had drifted elsewhere and
she wasn't sure why. Suddenly she felt flushed again,
prickly with desire. *God . . .* A warm, delicious flash broke
her out in gooseflesh as she imagined Paul's hands on her
skin, sculpting the contours of her body. Her eyes closed
by themselves as further images poured into her head.
She stood boldly naked before him, in this same room, before this same window, her nudity displayed to the sun as
he knelt at her feet and—

It's been so long since he's done THAT, her thoughts
slurred. But even longer since she'd done much of anything for him. *That all changes tonight,* she felt certain.

The fantasy doubled then. She closed her eyes harder to see it more clearly, and to *feel* it. Paul was on his knees, his mouth tending to her sex. The sensations rushed. Soon she'd actually opened her blouse for real, to let the sun pour on her breasts as her own hands caressed them . . . Yes, if she only had the vibrator; that would really send her off. One hand eventually opened her jeans and slipped down. The hand was now Paul's mouth, working the delicate flesh to a hot, pulsing craze. Did she moan out loud? Her belly sucked in and her thighs quivered as her first climax in over a month broke and nearly brought her to the floor. Her fingers teased out the last sensations as her upper teeth crimped her lip . . .

I can't believe I just did that . . . She let her breath come back, let the tensions lift off from her muscles; then she opened her eyes.

Oh my—

She brought her hand to her mouth to keep from shrieking in embarrassment. Her heart seemed to swell twice its size—

Because when she'd opened her eyes, her head had been bowed down toward the window, and a woman was standing there on the alley street looking right back up at her.

Grinning.

Cristina stepped back in the corner, shivering. She rebuttoned her blouse so fast she'd lined it up wrong. *This is so embarrassing! What if I see that woman again?*

But—

Something occurred to her. Cristina was fairly certain she'd seen the woman before, on the street. One of the homeless waifs that loitered around 67th Street and vicinity, panhandling.

But she had to be sure.

She inched forward along the wall. As the edge slowly crossed her line of sight, she inched even more slowly, peeping down. Eventually the entire alley street came into view and there, for just a second, she thought she could make out the woman's features: holey jeans, barefoot, a baggy, stained T-shirt full of holes and hair hanging down like an oily mop. The woman—or girl—was walking away and a second later was out of the window frame completely.

Yeah, one of those homeless girls. Thank God. Who could she tell? And had she even been able to seen Cristina's face clearly enough to recognize her later?

I doubt it . . .

She sighed out the rest of the shock and buttoned her blouse up right this time. But something compelled her to take one last look at the girl as she was walking away.

Ever so careful, Cristina took off a window latch and angled the window open enough for her to stick her head out.

The girl wasn't to be seen.

Must've been walking really fast to be on the street by now . . . But before Cristina pulled her head back in, she stopped to squint.

Wait . . .

A figure stood at the end of the alley but it certainly wasn't the same girl. In fact, the figure looked almost like a nun.

(II)

They were whittling.

scritch scritch scritch scritch scritch . . .

The sound filled the dirty, brick-walled room like rats skittering—a sound they were well accustomed to. Empty cans had been heaped to the farthest corner—the garbage corner, where they sometimes went to the bathroom, too, and old empty boxes for makeshift walls. A dead Sylvania television sat askew in another corner; they watched it a lot, and sometimes even saw things. There were four of them tonight; others came and went but it was mostly just these four: Francy, Sandrine, Scab, and Stutty. Shoplifted candles burned to give them light. It was Stutty who'd just crawled in through the hole that was almost too small for them to squeeze into.

"I just saw the lady in the house," she said, "and she was playin' with herself."

"She was not," Francy scowled.

"She was too! In a window upstairs, and she saw me-saw me-saw me-saw—"

"Be quiet!" Francy yelled. Most of Francy's teeth were missing, and her pink glasses always slid down her nose. Her breasts sagged in an orange halter she stole from a store, and she wore baggy men's jeans and flip-flops. "We're working, we're whittling. You could be helping, Stutty, but we can't find the fourth knife we stole last night."

Stutty's obsessive-compulsive mind stalled. *Knife?* She sat down in a corner on a plastic storage bin that read BANANA REPUBLIC. She put her feet up on the old kerosene heater they found in the garbage last year that still worked, and watched the other three continue whittling. Stutty wished she could whittle too because it looked like fun. Stutty's breasts itched beneath the stained white T-shirt that said THE DAMNED on it, and it had a blue picture of a woman with a crown of thorns; she'd taken it off of a dead crackhead in the Meatpacking District. The color of her hair was indeterminate due to dirt and head oil, but it didn't really matter what color it was. She rarely wore shoes, often leaving black footprints.

The knife? she thought again, then said, "Oh, I know where it is!" and she pulled it out of her back pocket. It was a simple whittling knife.

"So you took it," Sandrine said, smirking in her stained, pink sweatpants, and white T-shirt. Her black-spaghetti hair hung over most of her face. "Is that . . . blood on it?"

All the girls looked. Stutty turned the knife and touched the smudged blade. "Oh, yeah! I got money—I got five dollars-five dollars-five—"

"Be quiet!" Francy yelled.

"Stutty got a trick," Scab said, as if jealous. She was the most quiet of the bunch, and probably the least mentally defected. Her large, dirty breasts swayed in the kind of sleeveless T-shirt that people called a wifebeater, and she wore cutoff army pants. Very short black hair covered her head, but she had lots of bald spots and scabs from some disease or hair blight. She wanted to grow her hair out long like the other girls but it just never grew. "But that was a shitty trick if all you got was five dollars."

"Why ya think the knife's got blood on it?" Stutty retorted with a wisp of pride in her voice. "Some fat guy in a little car, said he'd pay twenty but only gave five."

"Did ya kill him?" Sandrine asked, looking up from her whittling.

"No, but I stuck him right in the bag. Twice." Stutty laughed. "He had a wedding ring on!"

"Good," Francy approved. "Let the fucker go home to his wife and explain why he's got two knife holes in his nut-sack."

The four girls burst into a round of giggling.

"Oh, and I got some sardines, too," Stutty added.

The other three looked up with expectation in their eyes as Stutty took the narrow cans out of her pocket and gave them one each.

"King Oscar, I hope," Scab said, but then she frowned at the can.

"These are anchovies, not sardines!" Francy complained.

Sandrine cranked open her can and first drank the oil out of it. "But anchovies are better, they're easier to steal, and they're salty, and I don't even like sardines 'cos they remind me of my fucked-up childhood."

"Sardines?" Scab questioned, picking a narrow fillet from the can.

"Because my name's Sandrine so when I was a kid the other kids called me Sardine."

"Oh," someone said.

Stutty's eyes popped open. "And look at this real expensive eye shadow I stole!" She reached down the front of her pants and withdrew a small jar with a gold lid. "It cost five hundred dollars, the sign said."

"Huh?" Francy, Sandrine, and Scab said in unison.

"Yeah. It's the best. I reached around and stole it when the guy wasn't looking. They had red ones and white ones, too, but I think the black looks better."

"Gimme that!" Francy said and snatched the little jar. She opened it and smeared some over her eyelids, but then winced. "This stuff stinks! You sure this is eye shadow?"

"Well, yeah, I think-I think-I think-I—"

"Be quiet!"

Scab took the bottle; she could read better than the others.

"Only thing was weird is they had it in a refrigerator," Stutty remembered.

"Eye shadow?" Sandrine said.

Scab read the tiny words on the lid, chuckling, "Product of the Ukraine. Beluga caviar—"

"You didn't steal eye shadow, you dick! You stole fish eggs!" Francy grimaced, wiping her eyes. Scab shook her head and threw the $500-per-half-ounce jar against the wall.

Stutty liked to talk, so she kept talking, "Oh-oh-oh-oh—"

"Be quiet!" Francy yelled.

"I saw the hooker from last night—in a car," Stutty finally said.

"Who?"

"You know, that ho who saw us run out of the hardware store last night-last night-last—" But then she pinched her lips shut.

"So what?" Sandrine huffed. "We got away with it, and the New Mother'll be happy with us."

But Francy seemed concerned. She picked at a scab on her foot. "You saw her . . . in a car? Was it . . . a *police* car?"

"I think it was. It was unmarked but the two guys in it looked like plainclothes cops, and they were all looking around, like the ho was telling them to."

Francy smelled like fish eggs now. Her eyes locked on Stutty. "Did they see you?"

"Nope-nope-nope-nope——"

"Be quiet!"

"They didn't see me 'cos I hid behind the newsstand."

"Good."

"And then I saw the New Mother—"

"You did not!" Sandrine insisted.

"The New Mother only comes out at night," Scab corrected in a singsong voice.

"I only saw her for a second, in a shadow!" Stutty challenged this affront to her credulity. "She can do that, she told us she could!"

"Sub . . . cuh-poor," Francy began, her lips struggling. "Subcor—Shit! I can never pronounce the word!"

"Subcorporeal," Scab said. "So Stutty really did see her."

Stutty fumed, "Then don't call me a liar-a liar-a—"

Francy pointed a finger at her.

Stutty calmed down again, but kept talking. "I saw her right after I saw the hooker with those cops, and right after that, that's when I saw the woman in the house friggin' herself in the window."

"She gave me hot dog money today," Sandrine said. "She seemed nice."

"Then where's the hot dogs?" Francy complained.

"I . . . ate 'em . . ."

"Shit-wad!"

Scuffing could be heard. The four girls' eyes widened in the candlelight as they all turned their heads toward the hole.

"It's the New Mother," someone whispered.

"Aw, no it ain't!" Francy griped. "It's just Virginia . . ."

"Hi," the dirty-elbowed girl peeped when she crawled in and sat up. She had one ear cut off from a crack dealer who didn't like her, and wore cutoff sweatpants and a Yankees shirt. She switched from crack to smack, depending on availability but more often than not—and like a lot of them—the one component in her existence that was even less available than drugs was money. Her looks were far too gone now to get many tricks. "Ya got any food?"

"Sardines," Stutty said.

"Anchovies!" Francy yelled. "You think anchovies are sardines and fish eggs are fuckin' eye shadow!"

Scab and Sandrine laughed.

"I do not-do not-do-do—"

"Be quiet!" Francy yelled so loud her glasses flew off.

"You're not one of us, Virginia," Scab said, "so we can't give you our food—"

—but then they all froze as a shadow like smoke seemed to sift around them. Soon they could see something standing near the candles.

And the voice flowed, *Virginia is welcome in our convent, girls. All are welcome, and just as our generous lord shared with honest peasants, we too follow his example. We share with our sisters, don't we?*

Stutty gave Virginia a can of anchovies.

Let my love be upon you, the sweet voice fluttered, hovering. The girls all looked up in awe . . .

Such a righteous flock . . .

Then the voice, and the shadow, was gone.

"Give Virginia your knife," Francy ordered Stutty. "She's one of us now."

The girls all looked at each other and smiled, and then—

scritch scritch scritch scritch scritch—

—continued to whittle.

CHAPTER FOUR

(I)

John Rollin absently turned the ring round and round his finger—a fat silver ring with the strangest crest: a dragon strangled by its own tail. He was still doing this when he got out of the cab and looked up. *Unbelievable*, he thought. The cab drove away.

Just about the worst thing that could possibly happen . . .

Inside, the familiar walls of his home seemed alien now. He'd only been gone for six months, his first hiatus in a decade. It had been the best of his life—

—and I come back to this . . . this calamity.

He didn't even take his bags to his room; instead, he was upstairs in the front reading room, reaching for the binoculars. It was almost funny. *Over forty years of training have led me to this: peeping in windows . . .*

How could they have sold the annex house without consulting Rollin first?

He let his eyes acclimate, made sure the hall light was off so not to be detectable from outside. He carefully swung open the window, and in leaked the distant sounds of the city at night. Car horns, a siren, a late bus roaring by on 67th. One of the street lamps on Dessorio flickered on and off. It seemed to tranquilize his quiet rage.

And his fear.

A scuffing noise came from the street. Footsteps? Rollin raised the binoculars and looked.

Yes. Two girls. They wore ratty clothes and flip-flops. *Addicts*, he presumed. *Or homeless*. Often the two were synonymous. The optics of the binoculars seemed to magnify the meager available light to something surreal. He watched the two women shamble away, carrying their shrill chatter with them.

Now the street stood dead.

Rollin lifted the binoculars to the annex house . . .

Dim yellow lights burned on the first floor (which was actually raised half a floor above the street); the remaining three stories were dark. *Close to midnight*, Rollin observed. Were they still up at this hour? An attorney had bought the house; that's all Rollin knew. *One very HAPPY lawyer*, he thought, considering the price he'd paid. Paul Nasher was the man's name. But did he have a wife? Children?

Rollin gulped at the consideration. *Good God, I hope he doesn't have children with him in there . . .*

Drapes were left open on the elaborate, pointed windows fronting the house, but the designer blinds hung down, open to slits. The slits provided enough open space for Rollin to effectively continue his voyeurism. He spied an indulgent living room on one side, and an equally overopulent kitchen on the other. *He must've converted one of the back rooms for the bedroom . . .* Rollin manipulated his slightly elevated vantage point, then—

Ah. There's something.

The center pane of glass on the fanlight over the front door was keystone-shaped and clear, while the glasswork on either side was multicolored. Rollin found that when he moved over several inches, the binoculars could be zoomed right through that center glass. A door stood open at the end of a hall. The room was dark yet the bathroom door could be seen standing open, some lights on.

Movement in the bathroom urged Rollin to zoom closer.

A glittery shower curtain flung back, and now an attractive blonde woman, wet and naked, could be seen. *I'd say that's definitely NOT Paul Nasher.* So he *did* have a wife or significant other. Rollin struggled with some shame, trying to attain an optimum focus as the woman dried herself with a black towel. When she turned and bent over, Rollin winced at the exotic sight, then—worse—she reversed her pose and stretched upright, displaying a flat stomach and dark blonde pubic area. Rollin closed his eyes and sighed.

He didn't feel like so much of a pervert when the woman donned a robe, then strode out to the kitchen. He noticed a stunning tamber cabinet topped with crystal against one wall, and then recognized a kitchen nook with flooring made of herringbone Waterfall maple. He only knew this because he'd been to a billionaire's home once in Barcelona, trying to convince the magnate to contribute to some European orphan charities. Rollin groaned as more of his own material lust cringed. *Travertine marble, good Lord! These people have a lot of money . . .*

His thoughts reengaged when a man walked into the kitchen, boldly naked, and came up behind the blonde woman. He caressed her from behind, gave her a smiling start. *Pretty girl,* Rollin noted when she grinned over her shoulder. The man stood trim but stocky, well-muscled, had short dark hair, clean shaven. *Mr. Paul Nasher, attorney-at-law, I presume.* He and the woman laughed silently as some cat play ensued. *Oh, please,* Rollin thought, groaning: Paul Nasher had removed a can of whipped cream from the double-doored refrigerator and was now cornering the woman with it. Nasher mock-muscled her against a dining table, shucked the robe off of her, and began to lay her back as she halfheartedly objected. Rollin frowned when Nasher kneed right up on the table, which probably cost five or ten thousand dollars, and began applying lines of the whipped cream around the woman's breasts and belly.

I guess I really shouldn't be looking at this . . .

He peered more closely at the rest of the floor, then examined the dark windows upstairs. Some moonlight filtered in through a rear window on the second floor, and Rollin noticed stacks of moving boxes. *What do they even need a house that big for, especially if it's just the two of them?* But then he frowned at his own oversight. *But of course, he's a LAWYER who deals in REAL ESTATE. To him the house is an investment that will turn into a cash cow . . .*

Then, Rollin aimed the binoculars down toward the basement. *Good,* he thought. The sidewalk-level basement windows remained securely covered by iron bars . . .

But tomorrow I'll have to check the windows in the back . . .

There was no conscious thought when he roved the glasses back to the dining room table and saw at once that the previous whipped-cream frivolity had now been abandoned in favor of full-blown and rather frenetic sex. Nasher had the woman on her hands and knees on the sumptuous table, he behind her, thrusting. The look on Nasher's face appeared focused, determined, very much like an attorney in court. *How hackneyed,* Rollin thought. *He makes love like he's deliberating over a lawsuit.* And the woman . . .

She shined in sweat now, her full breasts rocking beneath her. Her head rocked as the muscles of her lithe physique tensed, highlighting a raw, primal beauty. Rollin knew he shouldn't be watching, because he knew it was from something primal in him as well. Now the woman's head arched back, her blonde hair disarrayed as her climax became evident. Rollin actually heard her ecstatic shriek through the windows . . .

The woman collapsed on the table, a cheek flat against the expensive wood. Her eyes closed and she made a sated grin.

Rollin had a feeling he knew what Nasher was about to proceed with next, and that's when he pulled the binoculars from his eyes.

But how much of his deeds had been motivated by sin? *Forgive me, God,* a thought whispered. It was a test—something God was known to do to him quite often, a real-world circumstance that his duties had forced him to see, and then the notion that threatened to be the saddest regret. What he'd been watching on the table was an act he'd never in his life performed himself. He felt better when he recalled the crucial words from his ordination:

Thou art a priest forever . . .

A moment later, Father John Rollin, the custodian and pastor of St. Amano's Church, walked out of the room and back down to the chancel, to pray.

Forgive me, God. Sometime's it's REALLY DIFFICULT being your servant . . .

But what would happen now? How much of it was actually true, and how much myth? *Those people across the street have no idea what they've moved into . . .*

Nor did Rollin have any idea that Paul Nasher and the blonde weren't the only ones in the house. Instead of allowing his binoculars to drift to the ribald scene on the table, he should've looked more attentively at the second-floor windows. There he would've seen those two homeless women lurking about in the shadows, as well as a third figure, who looked like a nun . . .

(II)

Paul felt about as masculine as he ever had when he carried Cristina in his arms and put her to bed. *Three times tonight,* he thought. *Not bad for forty.*

Or maybe it was simply her . . .

The new Cristina, he considered.

Whatever had gotten into her was fine with Paul. She murmured in his arms, made a luxurious stretch when he laid her down on the bed's black satin sheets.

Her eyes looked up at him, as if beseeching. "Thank you," she said.

Paul laughed. "For what? Sex?"

"No, silly. Thank you for giving me the time I needed. Most guys would've dumped a moody ditz like me by now."

How odd. He tried to joke back, "Well this lawyer ain't gonna be dumpin' nothin' except maybe some clients who pay lousy retainers."

Cristina curled atop the sheets, perfect white skin glowing against the luxuriant fabric. "I've haven't felt this good, this complete, since . . . well, ever. And I know it's because you convinced me to move here. This environment, plus *you*, has made me a new person, and I just know it's the person I've always been inside but could never . . . show."

This was getting deep, not that he objected. He sat down and stroked her thigh, which felt as satiny as the sheets. "You've always made me happy, and I want you to be *just* as happy. All that's going to happen now. We have our lives together, and now we both have the careers we've wanted more than anything."

She kept looking at him. "I owe you so much . . ."

"Quit talking like that. People in love don't owe each other anything." Seriousness in the bedroom often duped him; he didn't know how to respond. "What you owe yourself is a good night's sleep. You've got your meeting with that developer guy coming up."

"Bruno—"

Paul buffed off some of the seriousness. "Is he as good-looking as me?"

"He's gayer than Liberace, and, no . . ."

Paul splayed a hand over her breast. She was so *arousing* like this. *I could probably do it again* . . . He felt the large, warm nipple between his fingers; it seemed to get firmer in seconds.

"And I guess this sounds pretty crude," she added, "but you're the best lay of my life."

"Crude works."

"And if I wasn't so tired right now . . ."

"Ah, I wore you out?" he chuckled.

"No shit."

"You really know how to pump a forty-year-old's ego."

"Crude-ism Number Two. I'll pump more than your ego tomorrow." Then she brought a hand to her mouth. "I can't believe I said that."

"Believe it. So this is the new *crude* you, huh? I have no objections . . ."

"I love you, Paul . . ."

He kissed her, a kiss that lingered. *Give her a break, she's tired,* he told himself, even as his arousal became more apparent. *I love you, too,* he thought.

She was asleep. He carefully got up and slipped out. *A nightcap seems in order . . .* Naked, he walked boldly to the bar and poured a small scotch. The mirror reflected back his nakedness, his broad shoulders and well-defined chest. *Nope. Not bad at all.*

He browsed around the living room, then the kitchen. *Can't think of a single reason why I shouldn't be able to walk around my own house buck-naked.* The freedom made him feel unrestrained; it made him feel much more human than he generally did at his job. *Damn,* he thought. *There's one reason not to.* He sidestepped to the front window, noticing the blind's walnut louvers open an inch. *Good job, Paul. Give everyone on the street a show.*

Before he closed them, he noticed the church across the street. The place looked abandoned.

He kept wandering, sipping his drink. He examined a Pollock print on the stairwell—*Eyes in the Heat,* it was called. Even the painting's dozens of eyes seemed to look at him with approval, or even envy. *All the cards are starting to come up aces,* he realized. *Now that I've got Cristina out of her shell, I've got damn near everything.*

An undefined curiosity took him up to the next floor. Blocks of moonlight and street light jagged here and there from the high undraped windows. He stepped into one small room, sniffing those familiar scents of new plaster, carpet, and paint. Then he tensed—

click . . .

creak . . .

It sounded like a door opening, then a careful footfall creaking the old wood. *Impossible. The house is locked, and I checked the bars on the basement windows myself.* It was just a house noise, he resolved but remained mildly perturbed.

Then, very faintly, he heard the oddest words:

"Singele lui traieste . . ."

What the hell? and then he stalked out of the room and across the hall to where he swore he heard the words.

A woman's voice . . .

He was surprised by how fearless he felt, even knowing that he'd heard a voice, but in the next barren room, he relaxed. He could hear a television squawking through the wall. The next building, he knew, was all condos for wealthy retirees. *They're hard of hearing,* he reasoned, *and keep the volume up.* He made a mental note to look into soundproofing down the road.

He froze again when he stepped back into the hall and faced the back room . . .

Now he *did* feel a twinge of fear.

The shadow of a figure lay across the bare floor between moving boxes.

Holy shit . . .

The shadow seemed starkly tapered. A woman wearing a floor-length dress? And the jet-black shadow of the head was just as peculiar: angled upward with triangles of some sort hanging down.

"All right," he said with a stout voice. "I don't know how you got in here, but you better leave the way you came, and I mean right now. I've already called the police on my cell phone . . ."

The shadow didn't move.

What now? Retreat for a weapon, go back downstairs and call the police for real? It seemed the most sensible tactic, but . . . *That's got to be a woman*, he reasoned. His muscles tensed when he tightened his fists. *Someone's in my house so I better take action*. Unfaltered by his nakedness, then, he stepped boldly into the room.

The shadow had jagged during his final steps, and disappeared. Immediately, Paul's eyes darted out the window, and he exhaled long and hard. *Idiot*, he told himself. He could see the buildings across the alley, and higher up on one of the balconies a woman was watering plants. It had obviously been *her* shadow that had briefly played into the room.

All right. So much for that.

He chuckled at the afterthought. For a split second, the shadow had reminded him of that of a nun.

He looked about the room, which was cluttered with boxes that the men had brought earlier. Cristina had opted to use this room for her studio instead of the den downstairs. Better light, she'd said. *Whatever she wants . . .* Her work desks and computers were half set up now. A large drawing table and brace-frame sat in one corner, and on some walnut shelving she'd already arranged the figurines she'd created in the first two releases.

Cadaverettes, he thought with a tight smile and, *Plastic Surgery Botchies*. Paul had fronted the production cost for the latter, the first line of figurines. It was about thirty grand, no big deal, and once they'd gotten a distributor, the line, however limited, had sold out. *That's some bizarre stuff, all right*, he thought, peering at the row of figures. The line's motif was plastic-surgery disasters, the grim theme clashing with the "cuteness" of the figurines themselves, each about four inches high. They were little troll-like toys that each displayed some outrageous mistake of cosmetic augmentation, and had equally cute/macabre names, like Liposucked Lisa, for instance, a cute little cherubic woman with a smile on her plastic face, naked with her arms out to highlight fleshy grooves up and down her legs, belly, and buttocks—grooves from a botched liposuction job. Botox Bonnie grinned below huge bright eyes, her lips and face lopsided from inept injections. There were others: Rhinoplasty Robin, Grafted Greta, Facelifted Felicia, etc., which all displayed the most outrageous malpractices of each procedure. Implanted Isobel was the most notable entry in the line: another curvaceous nude kewpie with one breast huge and the other empty. Amused, Paul shook his head. *How could Cristina even THINK of things like this?*

But it had been the Botchies that had gotten Cristina's foot into the door of the market. After the line had sold out completely, a doll manufacturer by the name of Von Blanc Toys had offered Cristina a contract for her next line, Cadaverettes. Paul perused the second shelf where they all stood, a dozen of them, with names like Incinerated Ilsa, Over-Embalmed Oscar, Eviscerated Evan, Torso'd Trisha, Electrocuted Ellen, and the like. *Damn*, he thought, squinting. *They even look freakier in the moonlight.* Paul wasn't into this cult-market at all, but he was all for supporting Cristina's creative endeavors. *To each his own . . . or hers.* Ultimately he realized that her creation of these macabre toys was an important outlet of release, or, as Cristina's therapist had put it, "An all-too-crucial creative purgation of the emotional traumas of Cristina's past."

Paul knew all about that, and to this day, it made him furious. *Those goddamn Goldfarbs . . .* He swigged the rest of his drink. *All they got was twenty years. You fuck up kids like they did you sure as shit should get life with no parole. I wish to hell I'd been the prosecutor on that one . . .*

He let it go out of his head. It was all over anyway, and things were good. *So why dwell on it?* He found himself looking once more at the row of Cadaverettes and eventually was chuckling at the grotesque whimsey. *Runover Rhonda, Floater Frank, Crushed Cassandra, Headless Helen . . . And lots of people BUY these things*, Paul realized. *But what the hell do I expect her to do? Knit sweaters? She's found a niche market for these dolls—more power to her. And let's not forget—she made a SHITLOAD of money on these things last year.*

At least that's how he tried to deal with it. Sometimes he'd get a snicker or two from some opposition attorney— "Hey, Paul, isn't your girlfriend the one who makes those ridiculous dolls?" or "Man, that's one morbid fiancée you got there, pal."

To hell with them, Paul always reasoned.

He was about to leave but caught himself snagged by something.

The shelves . . .

He didn't seem to see several of the figures that were most memorable to him. Gutshot Glen, Hypothermia Harriet, and Leprosy Linda.

Hmm, he thought. *I guess Cristina hasn't put those up yet . . .*

CHAPTER FIVE

(I)

Jesus Christ. And yesterday I was complaining that nothing ever happened in this precinct . . .

Vernon was stupefied by what he stared up at in the Dumpster cove behind the brewing company on 76th and Amsterdam. Alleys in New York tended to reek of urine but this one stank of hops and barley, the combination of which stung his eyes like CS gas. Beat cops were cordoning the perimeter while TSD techs snapped pictures that caused Vernon to wince.

"This is some shit, huh, Inspector?" a tech asked.

Vernon opened his mouth to respond but nothing came out. Instead, someone else said, "This is fuckin' ghastly . . ."

And someone else: "Hell of a thing to have to look at at five in the morning."

You got that right, buddy.

Slouch shuffled up, his hair a mess from the sleep he'd just been jolted from. "You know, How, when you rang my phone a half hour ago, I was really pissed 'cos I thought sure it'd be another namby-pamby call."

"This look namby-pamby to you?" Vernon asked, still stifled by the visual shock. "Looks like a hardcore psycho job to me."

Slouch huffed the grimmest laugh. "I hope the M.E. gets here quick and gets the stiff out of here. Can you imagine what the papers are gonna do with this?"

"You don't have to tell me. Maybe we can hold them off for a few days but eventually . . ."

Slouch nodded. "We're gonna look like the Keystone Cops. I can see the headlines already. 'Woman *Impaled* in Twentieth Precinct.'"

Vernon got dizzy from the words.

Impaled, he thought.

The victim was a white female of indeterminate age. She'd been stripped naked, and then her body had been mounted upon a two-inch-thick wooden rod—six feet long and sharpened at one end. The rod ran completely through her body, from crotch to mouth, its point terminating at the roof of her mouth. Her clothes formed a small pile where the rod had been planted, and by now they were sodden with the blood that had poured down from the entrance wound. The woman looked starved, the insides of her elbows pocked with scabs. Yellowed eyes remained open in a death stare, the mouth open, too, an eternal gape that displayed the impaling rod's sharpened point. When a Technical Services photographer snapped a picture from behind, the bright silvery flash stretched the crime's shadow all the way down the alley.

"One dead junkie," Slouch commented. "Must've been a snitch. Lately the dope gangs have been hanging them upside-down and gutting them, but this . . ."

"Definitely a new twist," Vernon said. "Might be that new skag gang—Z-Mob, I think they're called. Narcotics said their stoolies are scared shitless of them, a hardcore crew. We'll have to check out those lines on the body. Probably a gang label."

Slouch hadn't noticed it initially but now he saw that the dead woman's body had been crudely adorned with waving lines running down her entire body. The lines alternated in color. "Black, green, and red," Slouch said. "Looks like magic marker, for Christ's sake."

"Not looks like—it *is*," one of the techs informed. He

held up a sealed plastic baggie that contained one El Marko red magic marker.

Slouch sighed through a smile. "Let's start praying to every god on the deity list that there's a decent fingerprint on it."

"Amen."

Yeah, Vernon thought, encouraged. *It's got to be a gang label.* Every so often they'd mark their turf with the bodies of sniffed-out informants, just . . . not this elaborately.

Vernon finally yanked his gaze from the corpse. Amid the photographic flashes, at times he couldn't see the pole, which made it look as though the woman were hanging in midair.

"Inspector?" one of the evidence men bid. "Back here. Something written on the body."

Vernon walked around, part queasy, part curious. Across bony shoulder blades, someone had magic-marked: **SIN-GELE LUI TRAIESTE.**

"A foreign name?" someone guessed. Someone else: "Probably some new gang-speak. They make up their own words to throw off wiretaps."

Vernon scribbled the odd words in his notebook. "Well. Looks like we get to do something we haven't done in a while. Detective work."

Slouch offered a lazy smile. "Right on."

Vernon's eyes played downward, where the rod had been planted in the ground. *Asphalt back here. There must be a hole in the asphalt,* Vernon considered. "Hey, Sarge," he asked one of the techs doing the initial workups. "Is it all right if I pull those bloody clothes off the bottom of the rod?"

The tech, ever blank-faced, passed Vernon a plastic evidence glove. He got down on one knee, and very carefully peeled the sodden clothes away.

Vernon stared.

"What the hell is that?" Slouch asked.

The evidence technician paused, then popped a brow. "Looks like a friggin' Christmas tree stand."

(II)

You're in a hot grotto of some sort, or perhaps a medieval dungeon. You smell niter and soil and you can see water bleeding through walls of uneven bricks lit by wan firelight. The fire gently crackles . . .

And the woman raises the cup . . .

She's robust, beautiful, and nearly nude. The only clothing she wears is hardly clothing at all but the black-and-white wimple of a nun. She seems parched, her lambent skin glazed with sweat, and the firelight lays moving squiggles on it, like faint tongues of light. And the cup—

Not a cup, really. It's cereal-bowl-sized but of dull brown clay. You can't see what's in it. The woman's breasts jut as she raises it high, as if in offering. Three gemstones mounted on the bowl sparkle, one black, one green, one red.

Behind her, the firelight on the wall . . . changes. Soon the bricks are squirming with wavering lines of black, green, and red, slowly writhing snakelike. When the nun lowers the bowl just below her bare breasts, you see its contents: blood.

At first you think the nun will drink the blood but she never does. She simply holds the bowl low, so that you can look at it, and then she speaks:

"Singele lui traieste . . ."

The accent-tinged words echo about the chamber while her flawless flesh shines with sweat. She holds the bowl like a prize. Eventually her intonation is replied to, the gruff but fading voice of a man, who says:

"Kanesae . . ."

The woman nearly swoons. Where did the male voice come from? The woman—this obscene nun—seems to grin aside, to a dark corner where the light barely reaches.

The luminous black, green, and red lines behind her begin to churn in a fury and then her eyes go wide and she turns her head to gaze right through the mirage—

Right at you—

—and grins, showing two long, narrow, and very sharp fangs . . .

And that's when you scream and—

—woke up in a lurch, a hand slapped to her chest.

"*Damn* it!" Cristina wheezed.

Darkness mottled the bedroom, but she could see the light of day leaking in from around the drapes. *That pain-in-the-butt dream again . . .* She gave herself a few moments to catch her breath. In spite of the room's coolness, she felt slopped with sweat, her pillow and sheets beneath her soaked. *Everything's going so well all of a sudden but then that damn dream keeps coming back . . .*

She was used to it now, at least. The startlement always wore off quickly, leaving her more curious about it than anything.

The nun, she thought. *With fangs . . .*

Just another weird dream—everyone had them—but why did this one plague her with such morbid features? Bowls of blood, cryptic lines of light on a dungeon wall, bizarre intonations. *Where does it comes from?* she wondered and sat up.

Same place THAT came from, she realized next when she noticed her doodle-sketch of the Noxious Nun sitting on the nightstand.

The whimsily grinning fanged nun holding the bowl of blood . . .

But the glimpse enlivened her now. She couldn't have been more excited about her next line of figurines. *I . . . can't . . . wait . . .*

Just a few days ago she felt terrified by the prospect of living in New York City, yet now, in an eyeblink, she felt the reverse. Everything came together at once—it was almost uncanny. Her relationship, the house, the neighborhood, and her creative endeavors. The only sore spot was the weird dream. *Salvador Dali CRAVED weird dreams, he even INVITED them,* she reminded herself, *because they fueled his artistic visions. I'll just have to do the same thing.*

The resolution made her feel ten times better. She was up in a moment, to drop the sheets and pillowcases in the washer, turn on the coffeepot, and then she hit the shower. *Much better,* she thought, toweling off. Her smile shined in the wall-length mirror, along with her nakedness. Then she blushed momentarily when she recalled her sexual acrobatics with Paul yesterday.

The best sex of my life . . .

She dressed quickly in jeans and a T-shirt that replicated an abstract painting by de Kooning. The Tiffany clock on the living room mantel showed her it was past nine—Paul was long gone; he generally was in the office by eight. *Now it's time for me to go to work, too.* She skipped upstairs and went directly to her studio. Her main computer she typically left on, and the first thing she did was look at the digital models for the first four characters of the *Evil Church Creepies* line. They glowed on the screen, revolving in three dimensions: first the Noxious Nun, then the Sickening Sunday School Teacher, the Corrupt Choir Boy, and the Demented Deaconess. *They're beautiful,* she praised the images. *Now if Bruno's company can only make the actual dolls look just as good . . .*

Her muse assailed her; next thing she knew two hours had passed as she'd made some initial sketches for upcoming figurines and scanned them into the 3-D program. When her eyes began to hurt, she got up and stretched, recalling her and Paul's ravening sex-play. It made her wonder about herself. *Every aspect of me is changing for the good. Why?*

It didn't matter why. That's what Britt would say. Her body and spirit were in a compatible place.

I've never really had that before, have I?

More satisfaction swept her as she gazed at the shelves on which her first two lines were displayed. But . . .

Wait a minute . . .

She was certain she put them all out yesterday after the movers had left, yet three figurines from the Cadaverettes seemed to be missing.

Gutshot Glen, Hypothermia Harriet, Leprosy Linda.

I'm SURE I put them on the shelves yesterday . . .

Or was she? There were still more boxes to unpack— perhaps the three dolls were in one. *Yeah, I guess so,* she thought and started searching. The task grew frustrating very quickly, however. She searched for a half hour but couldn't find them.

From behind a hand touched her shoulder—

Cristina nearly screamed. "Holy—"

"Scared ya, didn't I?" Britt said.

Cristina gawped. "Yes!"

"Sorry." Britt gave a light laugh. "I dropped off some papers for Jess at the office, and Paul gave me a key. He asked me to pick up some letters he forgot to mail. Said they're in the kitchen somewhere."

Cristina's pulse was just simmering down. "Don't sneak up on me like that, Britt. I thought you were a burglar."

Britt exaggerated her pose in a one-shoulder silk dress and white high heels. "Burglars don't wear Yves Saint Laurent."

"Yeah, I guess they don't!"

Britt chuckled it off, then took to examining the studio. "So this is your workroom, huh?" She frowned out the back window. "Great view—of the alley."

"The afternoon light's perfect," Cristina said, then rummaged through one more box, exasperated.

"Need help unpacking the rest?"

"No, thanks. It's mostly just supplies left. But I can't find three of my Cadaverettes."

"Well tell what's his name—Bruno—you need more. What's the big deal?"

I guess she's right. "I probably just lost them," she said, before giving up the search. *They're just plastic dolls, and it's not like anyone could've stolen them.* "I've got coffee on downstairs—Costa Rican."

"Yum. Let's go."

On their way down, Cristina asked, "Why didn't Paul just call and tell *me* to mail the letters?"

"He thought you might be working, didn't want to disturb you. I wish Jess was that considerate."

Cristina smiled over her shoulder. "What do you mean?"

"Most of the time he's like a caveman, especially when he wants sex. One time he came into my office at social services and had the gall to ask for a quickie."

"What did you say?"

"Yes, but that's beside the point."

Cristina laughed. She poured coffee, then walked to the other end of the island table. "Here are the letters Paul was talking about. Don't bother with it—I'll mail them myself."

"You sure?"

"Yeah. I'm going to go walk around town a little while, then do some more work in the studio."

Britt's high heels clipped across the floor as she browsed the kitchen and adjoining rooms. "Paul really did a terrific job with the place."

"I know," Cristina said, feeling a pang of negligence. *He did everything.* "He spent a fortune, but I'm going to pay for the refurbishments upstairs."

"That's right. You're Ms. Money Bags now."

"Not for long if the new line flops," Cristina guardedly remarked.

Britt giggled, sipping her coffee. "What is it? *Evil Church Crazies?*"

"*Creepies*," Cristina corrected. "But I'm pretty happy and so is Bruno. The first four dolls will be out in a few days, or so they tell me."

Britt fingered at an imaginary crease in her dress. "The nun—I forgot. From your dream. Have you had it again?"

A split-second's pause showed Cristina the furious, churning black, green, and red lines behind the vampiric nun. "Actually, yes. Last night. But the more I think about what my old therapist said, as well as what *you've* said, the better I feel."

"Catharsis and all that, you mean?"

"Well, yeah, and other things, too. My life in the present separates me from my life in the past."

They both meandered back upstairs. Cristina had the sudden desire to view the 3-D models again, the same way a painter might look repeatedly at a satisfactory canvas.

"I'm glad you're finally getting the gist. It can take time," Britt said, peering over Cristina's shoulder to the computer screen. "You're changing from what we call the therapeutic evolvement to a causal evolvement, and you're using your art to do it. Everybody has their own way, and this is *your* way. The resurgence of your occupational functionality."

Cristina nodded, even though Britt's use of clinical terms amid their private conversations sometimes rubbed her the wrong way. "And what's the other term you use? My therapist in Connecticut always said the same thing."

"Oh, I know. The 'impetus of positive conditioning.'"

"Yes, I think that's it. It really is true." Cristina smiled at the revolving images on-screen. "It all happened so fast, but I've never felt this good and secure in my life. I owe a lot of it to you."

"No, you don't. My job is just to put the function of therapy into relatable terms. The only person you *owe* anything to for getting you out of your shell is yourself."

"Sure, but that's pretty idealistic. I owe a lot to Paul, too."

Now Britt was looking up at the shelves containing the Botchies and the Cadaverettes. "Honestly, it can't all be from your dreams." She chuckled at the cute but morbid dolls. "I don't know how you come up with these ideas."

"It doesn't matter much, though, does it? I think that's why I've become successful. It's funny how after the Cadaverette line was finished, I couldn't come up with any ideas for the next line. Then it all fell into place over the course of a day or two."

"That fast?"

"Creative inspiration, I suppose. But then it all goes back to that impetus thing. That's why I owe so much to Paul."

"To Paul," Britt commented. "I know he's always been supportive of your work, but he was never really *into* it, was he?"

"No, it's not his taste at all—it's too 'gothy,' he says. Paul's just like Jess; he's into pop culture—Jessica Simpson, Hollywood thrillers, Jaguars, and Rolexes. My tastes are very underground."

"But still . . . You're a success."

"Yeah. There's something for everyone"—Cristina knocked on the wooden table—"which is my good luck. But I think that's why Paul and I click so well. We each have our own separate spaces that don't cross over."

"Having too much in common is worse than not having enough. Believe me, I see that in my job every day. It gives you both middle ground, some of which you share, and some of which you keep to yourselves. It's actually quite crucial for a long-term relationship." Britt's lashy eyes fluttered. "But I still don't understand how Paul influenced this Creepers line."

"Creepies," Cristina corrected. "Evil Church *Creepies*. Most of all, it was the house, and that old church right across the street. I took one look at those places and— bam—the whole thing came to me."

Britt still looked confused. "Then how do you owe your latest ideas to him?"

"It was several months ago, when he decided to buy the house. This was before the refurbishment started; we couldn't even go in 'cos it failed the city safety codes. But he told me what he wanted to do and drove me out here just to see the outside of the place. It doesn't make sense, really, but that's when all the new ideas came into my head. Don't know why, they just did. It wouldn't have happened if Paul hadn't urged me to move here with him."

"All things happen for a reason."

Cristina spun on her work seat. "And when I was thinking about what the lead-off figure should be—"

"That's when you decided to use that annoying dream of yours to your advantage."

"Exactly," Cristina agreed. It was fascinating how Britt could read her so accurately.

"You created a positive out of a negative. And we both did, in a lot of ways. That's what led me to the psychology curriculum and a career as a social services counselor."

The side note didn't bother Cristina now. She knew what Britt was talking about: the Goldfarbs and the foster house. Cristina sighed. "Yeah, I guess we're both pretty lucky."

"You can say that again." She put a hand on her sister's shoulder. "And we must never forget it."

Cristina wiped a tear from her eye, hoping Britt wouldn't see. A tear of joy, however, not one of despair. *When you go through what we went through . . . the bond lasts forever.*

Cristina only half-paid attention to the dimensional notes on her main computer. *But what am I REALLY thinking about?* She wasn't sure.

The Goldfarbs? All THAT crap?

"The best way to test the therapeutic gauge," Britt offered, "is simply by self-examining your own sex life."

Cristina wasn't sure if the comment was loaded. Was

this just a chat? Or something more, one of her older sister's ways of checking up on her?

"And since we're on *that* subject," Britt continued.

"*We?*"

"—how's yours lately?"

Yep. Checking up again. "If you want to know that truth, very recently it's been great."

"Really?" Britt seemed surprised.

"I think it's all part of that evolvement thing you were talking about," Cristina said. "I've changed more in the past few days than I think I've *ever* changed."

"Not changed. Evolved. There's a difference."

Cristina smiled, but deeper thoughts made her feel something akin to lewd. "Changed, evolved, whatever. But all for the best."

"Sex, too, huh?"

Cristina felt a blush coming on. "Especially that. I was a . . . dirty girl last night. And it was great."

"Not just great but healthy," Britt added. Now she was looking absently out the back window again, down into the sun-lit alley. "It's just more proof of our *wellness.* Reversal of the 'sexual nadir,' is how we say it in shrinkspeak. Things are great with me and Jess, too. He's a little selfish sometimes but—" She tossed a shoulder and laughed. "That's what vibrators are for. Sometimes I think my rabbits are better than men—"

"Britt!"

"Oh, don't give me that. Like you don't have one." Now Britt was looking back at the shelves of figurines. "I don't even understand how these are *made.* You don't actually sculpt them, do you?"

"No, no." Cristina was grateful for the turn of subjects. "I sketch each character from various angles, input them into the computer, then a special program turns it into a three-dimensional model. Another program assigns measurements and other attributes. Then the manufacturing contractor makes the mold that the figures are cast from. It's pretty high-tech these days." She hit some keys on the keyboard. "Here's what the first figurine in the next line will look like."

Britt's eyes bloomed at the screen. The bright cartoonish character revolved slowly, displaying itself. The angular black habit and hood, the white wimple, the blue-white pallor of the face set with the huge, fanged grin. White, black-nailed hands held the bowl of blood.

"The central image from your dream." Britt shook her head, amused. "The Notorious Nun . . ."

"Noxious," Cristina kept correcting. "Pretty vivid and cute, huh?"

"Cute's not *quite* the word that comes to mind but I guess it'll do."

"Bruno says they'll sell like hotcakes. I'm supposed to meet with him tonight for dinner. He's going to show me the new packaging." Britt errantly stroked her sister's shoulder. "That's some wacky hobby you have. I guess I'm in the wrong business."

Cristina looked up. "Say. What do *you* do for creative catharsis?"

"Have lots of orgasms."

"You're impossible!"

"I know, but it is fun." She glanced at her Lady Rolex. "I better get going. Jess wants me to get the Mercedes detailed. You sure you don't want me to mail those letters?"

"I'll take them," Cristina insisted. "There's a post office right up Broadway, near the Imax. Besides, I like to walk."

"Okay." A quick kiss on the cheek. "See ya soon. Oh, and Paul said you're having us over for a housewarming dinner soon."

"That'd be great, but I hope he also said that I'm a terrible cook."

"Shun Lee Palace *carryout*, sweetie," Britt scolded with a laugh. "We're upscale cosmopolites now, which means we *never* cook. We'll all get drunk on plum wine in your new hot tub."

"Whatever you say. 'Bye."

Cristina laughed as Britt sashayed out and down the stairs. *She's a trip, but I don't know what I'd do without her.* Eventually she went back downstairs, whistling, grabbed the letters and left the house.

Birds squawked overhead, high in the bright sky. Buildings loomed on either side of Dessorio Avenue, their windows white with sun. The skinny doorman at the condo building nodded to her. "Hello," she said back and almost laughed. The man was a cliché in his red coat and gold buttons which, these days, looked ludicrous. Next, she paused to eye the sullen church across the street, noting its gothic aura, its fine gray stone, buttresses, and stained glass.

The church looked abandoned, however. No sign out front offered service times, just a bland brass plaque: ST. AMANO'S. When she finally commenced down the street, she found her eyes flicking back several times, for a last glimpse.

Two security guards, a man and a woman, were chatting in front of the boarded-up Banana Republic, which was actually connected to the annex house. It stood like a multistoried tenement now in its disrepair. *Probably turn it into more condos*, Cristina knew. The female guard looked Polynesian with her long, shining black hair and glowing dark skin. She grinned wide-eyed at the husky male guard who whispered to her with a hand on her waist. *Hanky-panky on the job*, Cristina assumed. They broke from their intimate pose when Cristina approached. *Don't mind me.*

The mouth of the catty-cornered alley appeared, and without thinking, she entered. *I'm never in a hurry . . . so why do I always take this shortcut?* She did take a look first, to make sure the passage was clear. Just the same garbage cans and windowless metal doors cornered with rust. She walked along but then—

A sound flagged her attention from behind. When she turned to look—

What's he doing there?

A man stood bent over, yanking on the security bars that covered the ground-level basement windows of Cristina and Paul's house. She wasn't alarmed, however, because the man's appearance was plain.

A priest.

This certainly is strange. A priest/burglar? The notion was absurd. The man was portly and had a bald pate with short gray-white hair around the sides. Something seemed radiant about his black pants, shoes, and shirt in the bright sun. Cristina didn't like to talk to strangers but how could she not make an inquiry? *It is our house, after all.*

"Excuse me, sir—er, Father." She backtracked up to him and felt comfortable by the smile he immediately offered. "Can I help you with something? I happen to live in that house."

The faintest accent adorned his words. "I'm sorry. Forgive my impulse. I'm Father John Rollin. I actually used to be the custodian of this house back when it was an annex for St. Amano's."

"The church across the street?"

"Yes. I'm the pastor there as well." He shook her hand. His blue eyes seemed as bright as his smile. "And you must be Mr. Nasher's wife."

"Cristina. But we're engaged, not married." She noted the man's white Roman collar. It was so clean it seemed to dazzle. "Oh, so you know Paul?"

"Actually, no, but I'd love to meet him." A broad silver ring flashed on his finger. "The reason I'm apprised of his name is because the diocese related it to me yesterday. I'd been on a sabbatical for the past six months but I just returned. I wasn't even aware that the annex house had been put up for sale much less sold. You must've done quite a lot of work inside before moving in. For the last decade it's gotten a bit run-down."

"Paul had the building rewired and rewalled, then he refurbished the first floor," Cristina said. "Over time, we'll get the rest in order. But—" Her gaze shot down to the iron window bar. "Why were you . . ."

Father Rollin laughed. "Perhaps it's doting faith on my part, but in the past, vagabonds have been known to pry these bars out."

"Really?"

"Yes, just a few times. Even though God promises to protect the faithful, I don't know that he has time to ward off burglars as well. It was more of an old habit of mine—to check these bars every so often. Slipped my mind that the house belongs to someone else now. But I see your fiancé has replaced the old ones with a much better grade of metal."

Had he? Cristina looked closer and saw not only bars that could only be steel but also alarm system labels. "Yeah, I guess he did. I hadn't noticed. I always thought they were just the typical old iron bars you see on a lot of the buildings around here."

"Like those," the priest added. He pointed to the adjacent building, which possessed security bars that looked half-rusted-through. "I believe this building is a retirement condo—very pricey."

"Yeah, that's what Paul told me."

Father Rollin chuckled. "If they can afford condos in *this* area, you'd think they could cough up the loot for some better security bars."

The priest's callow choice of words made Cristina smile. "How long have you been the pastor across the street?"

"Decades." He glanced up the building's entire rear wall as if unconsciously. "But I don't have a congregation anymore. They all went to Blessed Sacrament and Holy Trinity now—for the air-conditioning."

"Then why . . ."

"Why am I still the pastor?" Another chuckle. "It's the diocese's way of not quite retiring me. You don't get pink slips in this business. We still use the church for ordinations, baptisms, and diocesan meetings. I guess they think I'm too old now to pound the pulpit, and maybe . . . too old-school."

"I'm sure that's an exaggeration," Cristina offered.

"I hope so! But they keep me around to look after the place. It's quite a historical building. The church needs money like anyone else, so they sell off old properties that can no longer be used for clerical purposes, like the annex house, for instance. I'm sure once I give up the goat, they'll sell St. Amano's, too. Someone'll probably turn it into a Starbucks."

Cristina couldn't help but be amused by the priest's flippancy.

"I'll be on my way now, Cristina," he said. "It's been delightful making your acquaintance."

"Nice meeting you as well, Father." *Isn't he at least going to Holy Roll me a little?* she wondered. "Stop by any evening. I'd love for you to meet Paul."

Father Rollin maintained the warm smile. "I will. Go with God," he said, then turned and walked away.

Go with God, she repeated. *I'll try . . .*

By the row of dented garbage cans, she stopped, noticing the ragged hole in the brick wall she'd seen the other day. Several magic markers lay on the stained asphalt along with an empty anchovy can. *The closed Banana Republic . . .* Could someone actually be living in there? She recalled the homeless girl who'd asked her for money.

Cristina got down on one knee and looked into the one-foot-diameter hole and then felt assured that no squatters could be within. The hole was blocked off by chunks of broken cement.

On the street she tuned out the city's noise and motion. Most of the drove of passersby looked stone-faced, preoccupied. People-watching could be fun but then there was always the chance of making accidental eye contact. As much as moving here made her feel less isolated, she still preferred to maintain a sense of tunnel vision while out in public. *I just want to have a leisurely walk . . .* She mailed the letters at the main post office off of Broadway, then headed down past Lincoln Square and Dante Park. The West End YMCA loomed, people of all classes coming and going. Several ragtag-looking women left excitedly, hyperactive as children. Their heads were wet, hair hanging in damp strings. *Poor people*, Cristina presumed. *They let them take showers there.* One girl in grubby pink sweatpants and sopping wet black hair chased out after them.

That's the girl I saw in the alley, Cristina realized.

Her cohorts all looked similar as they hustled down the steps. Old, dirty clothes, dim eyes, malnourished.

All at once, it seemed, the gaggle of broken-down women stopped.

And looked directly at Cristina.

She froze in her tracks. *Are they really looking . . . at ME?* Now two were whispering, one with large glasses, to another one with jeans and no shoes. Were they giggling?

Cristina didn't like the feeling she got. *Please tell me I'm not being mocked by a bunch of homeless women . . .* She was insecure enough; the notion was the last thing she needed. *I'm just overreacting.* There was no reason for them to be laughing at her. She felt a little better when the girl in pink sweatpants waved to her. Then they all scampered away.

Strange.

Cristina knew she was imagining it. *So what. I'm a little paranoid. All artists are.* She tried to laugh it off.

She wandered around, considered maybe lying around Sheep Meadow or Strawberry Field to brainstorm, or maybe throwing a coin for good luck into the Bethesda Fountain. *I need to think more on the next figures in the line,* she knew. *Details, to make them more unique and . . . creepier . . .* Central Park was a great place to summon her muse. She was about to head that way but ducked into a CVS first. She had some paper in her purse for notes and sketches but had forgotten a pen.

Drugstores here sure are different. She was still getting used to that. Aisles stood higher and more narrow, and there never seemed to be enough employees working the register. She shouldered around till she found the school supplies. But at the end of the aisle . . .

Them again.

The four homeless girls all congregated at the area where the pens hung. Cristina thought one of them said:

"It's her again . . ."

Four sets of eyes widened on her, and four broken-toothed grins. Then one of them grabbed something off the hooks, and they all disappeared around the end. A wave of giggles followed in their wake, which sounded childlike even though some of them might have been middle-aged for all Cristina knew.

This is ridiculous, she thought, her nerves fraying. Were they stalking her? *Of course not. Why would they do that?*

She shook it off with a frown, grabbed a Scripto fine-point roller, and went to the register.

But before she got there—

"You girls! Hey! Stop!" a man shouted.

A younger man at a register said, "Those bum girls again. Want me to call the cops?"

Cristina only had time to see the four homeless girls bang the front door open and race out of the store. An obese manager ran after them.

A woman in line sputtered, "Someone should do something about all the bums in this town."

"Ain't nothin' wrong with 'em," a hard hat said. "They

just don't wanna work. Would rather steal and beg and take drugs."

Cristina's eyes narrowed at the oddity. "What happened?" she asked no one in particular.

A young, lanky clerk said, "They ripped something off. Bums and rummies and crackheads. Stealing stuff. We get 'em all day long."

"We ought to deport all these bums and criminals and welfare trash," the hard hat not surprisingly suggested. "Just air-drop 'em all into the middle of friggin' Africa. Let 'em eat snakes and tree bark. And they sure as hell won't be shoplifting 'cos there ain't no stores!"

God, Cristina thought.

The manager came back in, huffing and red-faced. "The dirty buggers got away. Don't bother with the cops. What's the point?"

The clerk got back to ringing up customers. "Any idea what they pinched?"

"No. Didn't see."

Then a woman in line said, "It looked like one of them had several packs of magic markers in her hand . . ."

CHAPTER SIX

(I)

"Fleming, Virginia, K.," Slouch read off the printout when he walked into the morgue in the basement of the Metropolitan Hospital Center. "No Jane Doe here. Thank God for DNA profiles."

But would there be much difference? Vernon had already detached from the morbid spectacle they'd discovered behind the brewery. It usually only took a second after the initial glance; this time it took all afternoon. *I've never seen a 64 like this in my whole time as a cop . . .* His eyes scrutinized the thin, humanish form beneath the white sheet. "Fleming, Virginia, K.," he repeated. "Where'd you get it?"

"Downtown at Evidence Section. When the D.C. heard it was an *impalement*, he put a rush on."

"Good. What's her story? She *must* have a rap sheet."

"Longer than my ex-wife's divorce demands," Slouch said. He sat down and slouched, looking stark in his drab dark clothes against the room's clean white tiles. "Thirty-six years old, no registered place of residence since 1995. Pasco County, Florida. Rap sheet goes back to joovie stuff in the mid-eighties. Shoplifting, possession, accessory GTA. Since '98 she's been collared on two counts of prostitution, couple possession busts for crack and heroin. All downhill from there. Just more homeless drug flotsam. Fell off the People Radar completely three years ago."

Flotsam. Vernon felt bad that they had to think in such

terms, but there was really no other way. "Her tox screen was positive for opiates but that was no stretch." *Another one bites the dust,* he thought. "The prelim's already done. Her next stop is the autopsy suite."

"What's the cause of death?" Slouch asked with a short laugh. "I mean, besides 'Death by big motherfuckin' pole sharpened at one end and rammed from snatch to mouth?'"

Vernon huffed a sigh, then turned as the door swooshed open in dead silence. "Officers," greeted a stunningly attractive blonde in the proverbial white lab coat. "I'm Dr. Anda Burg. I'm the deputy duty M.E.—I'll be doing the post."

Vernon frowned when he noticed Slouch's eyes plastered to the medical examiner's bosom.

"And to answer your question," she continued without looking at either of them, "the official C.O.D as of now is multiple organ lacerations and dramatic perforations of viscera, trans-hemothoracic hemorrhage and pericarditis via acumenated wooden object, which entered the body at the vaginal egress and made its exit out the oral cavity. The victim weighed ninety-one pounds and was dehydrated; blood levels indicate low albumin, typical amongst the homeless. STD screen showed positive for HPV, HIV, chlamydia, and secondary syphilis. Radio-immune assay of hair root cells is consistent with that of a typified multiple drug user."

"That's what I call an answer," Slouch chuckled. "A hype and crackwhore who was already at the bottom of the barrel."

Dr. Burg rolled her eyes as she marked off boxes on a clipboard. "Any idea what this means, Doctor?" Vernon asked and pulled out a lab reading of his own. He paused a moment to wince, when he found himself, like Slouch, eyeing the attractive blonde doctor's figure. *How can a woman that good-looking cut up corpses for a living?* He cleared his throat and went on. "We found a magic marker at the crime scene—"

Dr. Burg looked up. "That's what the lab said had been used to make the lines up and down her body."

"Right. And there were some prints on it but Latent Section said they were too smeared to run. Then the O.A. lab said there was evidence of"—Vernon donned his glasses to read the sheet—"'undue accretion of sebaceous eccrine lipids via the dactyl dermal papillae.' What's that mean?"

"It means the perpetrator was dirty."

Vernon stared. "Dirty as in unwashed? Like, say, a street person?"

"Precisely. Dirty hands, in other words. That lab summation means that the print smeared due to an *excess* of body oils and amino residuum that passed through the fingerprint ridges with sebaceous perspiration. Had the hands been washed more recently, the print probably wouldn't have smeared."

"Crime doesn't pay," Slouch said, "unless you don't wash."

"That seems to be a common denominator lately," Vernon said. "Street people. Homeless addicts."

"What's that, Inspector?" Dr. Burg questioned.

Vernon shrugged but said nothing. Slouch gave him the eye.

Next, Dr. Burg uncovered the corpus like someone yanking a sheet off a piece of furniture.

"Yeah," Slouch said. "That's the bottom of the barrel. No wonder her solicitation busts stopped several years ago."

Vernon grit his teeth when he saw that one of the woman's ears was gone. "I didn't notice the missing ear earlier."

"Missing auricula, with keloid formation. It's several years old," Burg noted.

The thin corpse shined pallidly beneath the harsh overhead fluorescents. Webworks of blue veins could be seen beneath parchmentlike skin but over that remained the ghosts of the weavy lines of black, green, and red magic marker.

Burg studied the image. "My techs put her in the Kwell station for cleaning and delousing—she had a lot of lice— but the magic marker didn't come off all the way."

"When they say *permanent* marker, they mean business," Slouch remarked.

"Some kind of drug-turf thing?" Burg asked Vernon.

"I guess," he said. "We're not sure."

"Never seen anything like it before," Slouch added. "But then . . . we've never seen an *impaled* homicide victim before, either."

Pelvic bones jutted, the belly stretched tight. Vernon detected a rash of small scabs in various areas, common among long-time addicts, not to mention needle marks at the elbows and insides of the thighs. The marks looked like lines of fresh-cracked pepper. Several more track marks traced along the veins around the nipples. Vernon entertained the morbid query: *I wonder what they . . . did with the . . . pole . . .*

"This one's off to autopsy now, gentlemen," the attractive pathologist announced. "You're more than welcome to attend."

Slouch laughed. "Thanks for the invite, Doc, but we'll have to take a rain check. I was planning on a corn dog for lunch. You know, with that stick going down the middle?"

"Shut up, Slouch," Vernon griped. "Thanks for your time, Doctor."

Burg began to push the gurney away. "I'll let you know if I find anything more."

Slouch couldn't keep quiet. "You mean anything more than 'Death by big motherfuckin' pole sharpened at one end and rammed from snatch to mouth?'"

Dr. Burg made a tolerant smile. "Yes. Have a nice day, gentlemen." And then she and her dead charge disappeared through two swinging doors.

Vernon and Slouch traded cryptic glances.

"All right, How," Slouch began. "You and me? We've been giving each other that funky-look thing since five this morning, haven't we?"

Vernon nodded.

"But so far neither of us has said what's on our mind."

"No, we haven't." Vernon anxiously fingered an unlit cigarette. "So let 'er rip."

"We're both thinking the same thing, aren't we? Last winter a bunch of whacked-out homeless chicks rip off *Christmas tree stands* from a fuckin' hardware store and today we find a whacked-out homeless chick impaled on a pole mounted in a fuckin' *Christmas tree stand*—"

"Less than twenty-four hours after a bunch of whacked-out homeless chicks rip off *whittling knives* from the same hardware store," Vernon tacked on.

Slouch finished, "And the end of the pole looked *whittled* to a point. Recently. We on the same page?"

"Yeah, but I'm glad you said it first so *I* don't feel like the idiot."

Slouch laughed. "Thanks, boss!"

"It's got to all be connected, no matter how far-fetched it sounds."

"Um-hmm. No other angles to go on, so we might as well go on that one."

Vernon nodded. He rubbed his face, suddenly uneasy beneath the chilly morgue lights. "Let's get out of here. This place gives me the willies. It reminds me that one day I might be the one on the gurney going through those doors."

Slouch straggled up, jesting. "And can you believe that brick shit-house M.E.? I could look at her legs all day but . . . can you imagine being married to her?"

"I'm not following you, Slouch, but that's pretty much par for the course."

"No, serious, man. Just try to imagine being the guy who's getting it on with her and you *know* that those same hands were pulling livers out of corpses all day long."

Vernon stared. "Shut up, Slouch."

"Sure thing."

They waited for the elevator at the end of the restricted hall, but when it opened a uniformed cop walked out. "You the guys with the impalement 64?"

Vernon showed his badge and ID. "Yeah. Vernon. Twentieth Precinct."

The cop gave Vernon a manila envelope marked EVIDENCE - CLEARED BY TSD. "The lab wanted me to give this to you."

"What is it?"

"Don't know, sir. Something from the crime scene, said they found it inside the victim's clothes."

Vernon's eyes widened. "Were there any—"

"No usable latents. Sorry."

"Thanks." Vernon opened the envelope as the cop walked away.

Slouch hovered. "The mystery continues?"

From the envelope Vernon withdrew a plastic bag. Inside the bag was—

Slouch squinted. "The hell's that? A doll?"

Vernon squinted as well. It was a bizarre figurine of some kind, painted to great detail. About four inches high, plastic: a grinning cherubic little man, naked with blue-white skin and a belly that looked exploded. "Yeah, some kind of novelty doll."

"Looks pretty oddball to me," Slouch offered. "Sort of like one of those old Kewpie dolls when we were kids but with . . ."

"A shotgunned belly, I guess . . ." Vernon turned the fig-

ure over, read the tiny lettering beneath the base. CA-
DAVERETTES #7 - GUTSHOT GLEN.

(II)

"Yes, it was right after Britt left," Cristina was saying as
they sat down at a plush corner booth of Café D'Amato. A
card on the table read RESERVED. Paul seated himself after Cristina did. "I was going to mail those letters."

"The damn AmEx bill. Can't believe I forgot about it.
Lately I'm so busy at the office with Jess, I forget the simple
stuff. So, anyway, this priest was doing *what?*"

"His name's Father Rollin, and he was looking at those
security bars over the basement windows behind the
house, in the alley. Said it slipped his mind, since he did it
every day when he was the custodian. He's kind of old."

"Those window treatments are brand-new and cost a
fortune," Paul pointed out. "There wasn't anything wrong
with them, was there?"

"No, no, but that's just how I met him. It was kind of
strange. He said that when he used to look after the place,
sometimes squatters would break in through those windows, and come to think of it, lately I've been seeing this
group of homeless girls in the area."

"Welcome to New York," Paul said. "No way around
that. Just be careful walking around. Even in broad daylight. I don't care if this *is* the Upper West Side. There's
screwed-up people everywhere."

A sad refrain but Cristina knew it was true. "Anyway,
Father Rollin said he'd come by for coffee sometime. He'd
like to meet you. He even knew your name."

Paul scanned the upscale dining room, nodding to a few
people he knew. "I'll bet he does. Probably shit a brick
when they told him I'm the guy who bought the house for

a million bucks." Something about the topic seemed to bother him. He looked at his watch, distracted. "So where is this Bruno fellow?"

"Oh, he'll be here," Cristina assured. "He's a little off-the-wall but you'll like him. Oh, and thanks for getting the reservation."

"It pays to know big wheels." Paul smiled. "You look great, by the way."

Cristina almost blushed. She'd vowed to take Britt's advice and start dressing like New York but if anything she felt awkward in the veily black wrap dress and Pierre Hardy sandals. She asked for a soda water when the waitress skimmed by for their drink order.

"And you, sir?"

Paul hesitated. "Uh, just a Sprite."

He's trying, Cristina thought. He wasn't an alcoholic but sometimes he did overimbibe, which often jaded his demeanor. Cristina rarely said anything but she could tell that he knew. She appreciated his effort to cut down.

"Ah, there she is," a loudish voice boomed as a wide shadow crossed the table. Cristina rose to greet Bruno von Blanc, her toy contractor. He stood large, round, and gregarious, and had a large Burl Ives face. The deep-rust, shawl-collared jacket and yellow Ralph Lauren dress shirt was louder than his voice. "The market's top secret weapon."

"Hi, Bruno," she said after a gushing kiss on the cheek. "This is my fiancé, Paul Nasher."

The ebullient face turned as the man pumped Paul's hand. "Great to finally meet you, Paul. I hope you realize that your wife-to-be is a macabre genius."

"Oh, yeah," Paul said, trying not to raise a brow at Bruno's bad hair dye, which did nothing to disguise the fact that he was pushing sixty. The handlebar mustache and Vandyke didn't help. "I don't really know much about this novelty figurine business but after seeing Cristina's royalty statement last quarter I'd say that you guys have really got it going on."

"It's all her, Paul, all her." Bruno slid cumbersomely in next to Cristina. "Miss?" He flagged the waitress. "Grey Goose martini, please." Then he turned back to Paul. "Honestly, the diversity of Cristina's Cadaverette line turned the entire market on its ear."

"He always exaggerates," Cristina said, antsy by the compliments. *But I wonder if that's really true . . .*

"Nonsense—" Bruno paused, looking around the crowded restaurant in awe. "And how did you *ever* get a reservation on such short notice?"

"Paul has some influence here," Cristina giggled.

Paul shrugged. "My firm bailed the restaurant out of a huge sexual harassment claim. Bunch of waitresses made up a pile of BS. You've heard the story."

"Gracious. What's this world coming to?" Next, Bruno opened a small briefcase right on the linen-covered table. "And now here's what I want you both to see: the first promo fliers for *Evil Church Creepies* . . ." Bruno's hooded eyes glittered in excitement as he withdrew a stack of glossy fliers and passed one to Cristina and Paul.

"Wow," Paul said.

Cristina's voice lowered to a hush. "Bruno, it's beautiful . . ."

The flier showed half-sized color photos of the first four figurines above stylized promotional text. A small picture and bio of Cristina occupied the lower corner. The most stunning accommodation of the figures themselves were the weaving black, green, and red lines that composed the background.

"The ad department used your idea about the background," Bruno went on, "and I think it turned out great."

"The colors really make everything jump off the page," Paul said.

"Um-hmm, and that's exactly what we want." Bruno

appraised the flier with an obvious pride. "Yes, those lines really add dimension." He looked to Cristina. "Didn't you say you got the idea from a dream?"

For a split second, the dream flashed across the scape of her mind: the furious, waving lines behind the nude nun showing the fanged grin. Cristina took a breath. "That's right. And the Noxious Nun herself. It all came to me several months ago when I saw our house."

"Really?" Paul seemed surprised. "You never told me that."

"Got the entire idea in one day."

"The lightning bolt strikes!" Bruno exclaimed. He turned to flag the waitress again. "Miss? This is a special occasion. How about a bottle of Krug, Clos du Mesnil—the 1990 if you have it."

Paul's brow rose along with the waitress's. "Certainly, sir."

Cristina didn't quite know how to phrase it. "Paul and I weren't really planning to drink tonight, Bruno."

"Nonsense," the rotund man replied. "This is a celebration, my dear. You see, it's not just the fliers I've brought . . ."

"Huh?"

Bruno, if a bit too dramatically, reached back into the briefcase and slowly extracted a black, shiny cardboard box, five or six inches high with a cellophane window in front. "Hot off the molds, my dear."

Cristina's hand came to her chest. *I don't believe it . . .*

The decorative box contained the Noxious Nun.

She held it in her hand as though it were fragile as eggshells. The clarity of detail was greater than she could've ever expected: the delineated white fangs over the grin, the genuine black fabric that comprised the nun's habit and wimple, the tiny three-gemmed bowl and the way a clear scarlet resin sufficed for blood. Cristina gingerly took the figure out of the box and set it on the table.

"That is one creepy doll," Paul acknowledged.

Bruno held up a finger. "Creepy and cute—it's that juxtaposition that makes them so attractive . . . *and* marketable."

Cristina wiped a delighted tear. "I don't know what to say, Bruno. I would never have thought it could look *this* good."

"Don't thank me. The molds were made to your specifications. And I'm glad we didn't outsource this one to the Chinese. Our new manufacturer costs a bit more but the added detail makes it worth it. The first run was delivered to the warehouse this morning, ahead of schedule."

Some of the diners at surrounding tables kept eyeing the vivid curio, and when the waitress brought the champagne and ice stand, she said, "Oh, how cute! My daughter collects dolls like that."

"In that case, miss, have a flier," Bruno said and handed her one. "This one will be in the store on Friday."

"How cool! Thank you."

Bruno poured the champagne into three crystal flutes, then dispensed them. He raised his glass.

"A toast. To Cristina Nichols, and the Noxious Nun!"

"Cheers," Paul and Cristina said in unison.

Their glasses clinked.

What a wonderful night . . .

Cristina smiled in the darkness as the foyer clock struck one A.M. She sat up in bed, gazing out the window. Just a rim of moon could be seen edging over the next building. *My celebration,* she thought. The Noxious Nun sat like a goofy chess piece on the dresser.

At the restaurant they'd all gotten fairly drunk— something Cristina never did—but it was the occasion, not the champagne buzz, that left her elated and scintillant. By the time the cab had dropped her and Paul off, Cristina's newfound arousal had her in a dither; all she

could think about was getting inside and making love to
Paul. Paul tended to get cynical when he was drunk but
there was none of that tonight, and this only made him
even more attractive to her. The evening's only regrettable
defect was the misfire on Paul's part; the alcohol had
thwarted his ability to perform.

Oh, well, Cristina thought. She looked at him asleep beside her. *It was STILL a great night . . .*

She got up, still woozy. If anything the champagne
seemed to possess a delayed effect; she felt even drunker
now. She giggled as she stumbled once in the dark, then
slipped naked out of the room.

Ultimately, her happiness over the fliers and the first figure overrode the aggravation over their failed lovemaking
attempt. *So what?* She'd masturbated after Paul had dozed
off, and that seemed to take the edge off.

She padded to the kitchen where only the light over the
stove remained on. More light fell into the room when
she opened the refrigerator and found herself drinking
orange juice right from the bottle. Again, she almost stumbled, nearly dropping the bottle. *God! I really AM drunk!*
She had to concentrate on putting the bottle back inside.

She caught herself next peeking out the wooden blinds
of the front window. The church across the street stood
like a silent hulk. She wasn't certain but she thought she
saw a light on in an upper window but when she yawned it
snapped out. Perhaps it had never been on in the first place.

Drunk as she was, she felt too keyed up to sleep. She
wandered the first floor, musing over the soon-to-be-
released line. *I can't wait. The Noxious Nun looks super.* The
influence of its creation—the inexplicable dream—had
now lost all its negative power. Now it was just a novelty
toy that would be purchased mostly by goth kids and collectors. She felt tempted to go back in the bedroom to
look at it again but didn't want to risk stumbling and waking Paul.

She walked down the back hall, actually sliding against the wall to brace herself. A side door stood closed, and it occurred to her that she'd never opened that one.

The basement door . . .

She pushed it open, steadying herself. The basement, she knew, had only been structurally bolstered, not refinished. *But I've never seen it*, she realized. But why now, of all times, would she want to go down?

Pretty stupid, she told herself. *You're drunk, you could fall*, but her better judgment sidled away. When she hit the wall switch at the top of the stairs, only a single, unshaded bulb came on, and it didn't look to be more than forty watts. *Yeah, REALLY stupid . . .*

She grabbed the rail and very slowly descended.

At once an unpleasant shiver rippled her skin. The old moldy smell reminded her of the basement at the foster house, where the execrable Andre and Helga Goldfarb had regularly locked her, Britt, and their foster brother after drugging them. *Don't think about it*, she warned herself. *Remember what Britt said, the past is just junk that can't hurt me.*

The warning sufficed; when she made it to the bottom of the stairs, the basement's clutter, cobwebs, and wide brick walls made her forget about the reminiscent odor. *Pretty big,* she detected even in the wan light. She couldn't find any more switches. The only other light edging the long room came from the sodium lights in the alley, which filtered in through the low windows. The security bars drew black slats across the floor.

But there must be another light somewhere.

She waded deeper through the murk. Old rounded cobblestones formed the floor; she could feel the border of each stone on the bottoms of her feet. They felt warm, almost glossy; however—

She stopped. The rounded squares had changed to something wide and rough. *What—*

She looked down but could barely see. *Damn it. What IS that?* She could only make out a perimeter that seemed lighter than the rest of the floor and not composed of stones at all. She steadied herself again, then slowly got down on her knees, though she couldn't imagine why.

Now, however, she could discern the mysterious perimeter's dimensions just as her stomach clenched.

An *oblong* perimeter, about the same size of a coffin lid.

Don't be ridiculous. Of course, she was overreacting, and all that alcohol in her blood didn't help. *It's not a grave, for God's sake. Probably just some patchwork on the floor . . .*

She pressed her palms down and, indeed, found just a plane of rough cement. It seemed cooler than the cobblestones. *A pipe probably broke fifty years ago so they dug here to fix it*, she speculated.

But . . . why should she care?

Then she tried to rise but couldn't.

It must be the champagne, packing its final wallop, but for a stricken moment she had the oddest impression: that it was the cement patch that was drawing her down.

Stupid . . .

She attempted to rise again but this time got so dizzy, her knees thunked back down hard and she fell over on her side. *Oh, God, I can't believe I'm this crocked . . .* The dizziness distilled; she decided to lay back and rest for a little while. She took deep breaths, hoping to clear her head but then . . .

Had she been in bed, it would have been the bed that was spinning, but in this case?

It was the floor.

She seemed to be revolving, the queasiness in her belly compounding to outright nausea. With little warning from her metabolism, she quickly turned her head and vomited. She huffed, breaking out into a sweat. *I don't think I've been this sick ever.* Her vantage point continued to revolve as if she lay on a bearing'd platform; the dizziness thickened.

When she pressed her hand out to try to sit up, she felt something against her palm. A stick, maybe, or a pen. Her heart lurched a moment before she passed out, when at the furthest fringe of her vision, she thought she saw a figure standing in the corner.

"Singele lui traieste," *she hears, lying prone and nude and seemingly paralyzed. But she's not in the basement, she's in the grotto of her nightmare, the furious backdrop of black, green, and red ribbons weaving back and forth and the sound of water dripping and a dog barking and excited chatter that seems female but not in any language she's familiar with. In fact, she's not even familiar with her own name . . .*

Soft hands smooth up and down her glistening skin, drawing sensations that are as erotic as they are inexplicable.

The whispers of other voices seem to halo about her head: "Kanesae . . ."

Hands cosset her flesh more fervently. Six? Eight? A dozen hands? She senses that they're the hands of women, judging by the knowing way they touch her. Her muscles flex at the forbidden pleasure being kindled in this dark place. Several of the hands slide around between her legs now, and—

Her back arches; she sighs through gritted teeth.

—a hot, wet mouth finds each nipple.

The impossible light in the room deepens: black, green, and red. Now a desperate tongue licks up the slope of her neck, and she turns her head as the pleasure keeps mounting, and she sees . . .

What?

A man lying prone on a stone slab?

She's not sure. The cryptic mouths and hands squirm over her skin like a living gown; she's so distracted, so tempted to give in even though she knows this is all wrong.

But that's what she thinks she sees, if only for a moment, in the weird dices of light . . .

Yes.

A man lying prone on a stone slab. At the top of the slab sits . . . an object. She thinks first of a dark-glassed vase, then a wine decanter. A mongrel dog with matted fur snuffles bored about the slab . . .

When one mouth finds her sex, she shrieks and orgasms simultaneously, and then her head whips over to the other side. Her eyes go wide because, now, she sees her.

The nun.

"Kanesae, Kanesae, Kanesae," a tiny chant rises.

The nun stands naked save for her white wimple and black hood, the perfect breasts jutting as her back bows to raise the bowl. Then she looks down, and grins.

The pair of long thin fangs seems to sparkle.

Then the nun dons her black habit and retreats into the shadows.

"Oise pla'cute," one voice flutters.

Then another, "Oise pla'cute . . ."

And one more, "Oise pla'cute . . ."

"Pleasant dreams," someone else says beyond her impassioned paralysis. A round of giggles disperse above her, like bats.

And the mouths descend on her again, finding every private place. One climax after the next racks her body until she fears she might die, and then the final voice issues the disquieted words she's heard before . . .

"Singele lui traieste."

(III)

Father Rollin couldn't sleep; he tossed in his upper bed chamber, sheets entwined about his legs like a serpent. When his eyes came into focus, a shadow seemed to be splayed on the moonlit wall.

A figure? A *nun*?

He jerked up and nearly yelled as he switched on the light. *God Almighty!*

Then he shook his head at himself.

The shadow was nothing but that from a piece of cresting on the outside windowsill.

I am not in a good way tonight, the priest admitted.

He pulled on a robe, trudged to an armoire and began to withdraw a bottle of Medoc. *I shouldn't do this, but . . .* He took a long pull of the bitter red Bordeaux, then let out a stifled breath.

He switched the light back off, then lit a candle. *Back to this again,* he thought, bringing the binoculars to his eyes. The annex house stood sedate, frosted in the phosphoric street light. One of the lights continued to buzz from bright to dim. Down the street, he thought he spied several lanky figures turn into the alley.

He turned the binoculars back to the house, zooming in. A dim light shone between the slats of the kitchen louvers but that was all. Then, higher, his heart tensed a moment when he thought he saw a wan face in a second-story window, but when he zoomed even closer . . .

No. It must've been the curtain . . .

He put the binoculars down, at least in part disgusted with himself. What was he looking for anyway? And how much of this might really be geared in some deeper and more desperate channel of his psyche? *Celibate priest,* came the grim admission. *Old, atrophied, like fruit turning brown on the vine.*

Yes, the image depressed him. But the question remained, like a crow looking down from a wire. *Was I really searching for clues? Or was I hoping to see Cristina Nichols's body in the nude?*

"Give me strength . . ."

He kept it dark; he *liked* it dark. Perhaps it was because he could see less of himself, and the world and all the life in it. *Who knows?*

All he could ever think to do was answer his calling.

He considered going downstairs to the main chancel,

but more and more he felt alienated in it. *No congregation for years. I'm the house sitter for the church, too old and too eccentric for clerical duties.* It infuriated him sometimes, for he knew he could still say a spectacular Mass. *They don't WANT me anymore, so they merely KEEP me.*

It was all right by him.

He did know that *God* still wanted him, flaws and all.

He knelt at the small prayer bench in his room, beseeching the meager altar on which sat a simple crucifix given to him in Bucharest by a priest from the Holy Office. Lately, Rollin prayed here more than anywhere else, alone.

Before the crucifix's olive-wood base, he took up the chain and pendant. He kissed it as he would a Cross.

The emblem stared back at him, medieval in its scary crudity: a dead dragon strangled by its own tail, a great red cross branded on its back.

Rollin stared at the ancient totem for many minutes, while fingering the ring on his hand with the same insignia. Both read below the crest, O QUAM MAGNIFICUM, O DOMNUL.

Then he put the pendant around his neck and began to pray . . .

"*O quam magnificum, o domnul . . .*"

CHAPTER SEVEN

(I)

Sunlight from the windows cut across her eyes like a guillotine blade. *Oh my God . . .* When Cristina tried to rise from the basement floor, the flare of her life's worst headache sent her right back down on her back. She looked around in mental chaos as aching vision showed her the dank, cluttered basement. *What did I . . .*

Then she remembered, the twisted memories interlacing with her hangover. The celebration with Bruno last night, her drunkenness, then passing out down here of all places. And the dream . . .

She remained on her back, nude and shivering. *The same dream as always . . . but with new details . . .* God.

A dead man on a stone slab? A strange decanter of some kind? *And those women . . .* Not just the nun this time, but other strange, faceless women.

Cristina gulped when she remembered what the women were doing to her . . .

Jeez, what would Britt say about that? Latent lesbian tendencies carrying over from the Goldfarb house? It was just a dream—made more odd, no doubt, from all the alcohol she'd drunk.

She recalled the disturbing intonation: *Singele lui traieste.* But why should it actually disturb her? *Just meaningless gibberish from a dream.* It couldn't be another language since she didn't know any.

An alarm blared in her head. *What time is it? And . . . where's Paul?* She groaned, dragging herself up off the dust- and grit-caked floor. *He'll think I'm really out of my head if he finds out I passed out NUDE in the friggin' BASEMENT!* She was about to head up, but then the floor snagged her vision.

That patchwork, she remembered now.

She peered down. Yes, an oblong patch of new cement set into the stonework of the floor. How odd, but . . . In the better light she saw . . . something . . .

Down on one knee she examined the corner of the patch more closely. It looked like a seal of some kind pressed into the cement. She expected perhaps a date or service infor- mation from the contractor who'd done the work but instead . . .

A dragon?

Or a serpent of some kind, within a circle around which were etched the words: O QUAM MAGNIFICUM, O DOMNUL. *Latin,* she supposed. It must relate to the house's previous use by the Catholic Church. But it was the seal itself that bothered her most—the dragon. The crude artwork seemed to depict the dragon as dead, its own tail wrapped around its neck.

Then another, louder, alarm screamed in her head. As she'd been leaning to inspect the cement, her breasts edged into the peripheries of her vision.

Cristina stood up in half-shock and strode straight to the window where the most light was.

What on earth did I do to myself!

It looked as though her breasts and belly had been used as a graffiti canvas. Primitive black, green, and red lines encircled each breast, while more wavy lines of the same colors—the backdrop of her dream—streaked up and down her stomach.

Her own conclusion left her appalled. *I was so drunk last night, I DREW on myself?*

She did recall her hand landing on something that felt

like a fat pen. *This has to be magic marker* . . . She went back to the cement but couldn't find the object.

But the worst consideration slammed home. *If Paul sees me like this he'll want me to go to a shrink!* Suddenly her nudity had her feeling utterly vulnerable. And there was nothing down here she could cover herself with. She crept up the stairs, listening, then she peeked out the door when she got to the top.

Oh my God!

She could hear Paul's voice in the kitchen.

"—unfuckin' believable, Jess. Yes, yes, I know it's ten o'clock, and I know we've got to fax that arbitration rebuttal out to Massaccesi's people by noon. I haven't been this hungover in *ages*, man . . ."

What am I going to do? Cristina fretted. She glanced down in more disbelief at her streaked breasts.

"I don't even know where Cristina is," Paul was saying. "She was pretty lit last night too; I guess she went out to get orange juice or something. We had sort of a celebration party at D'Amato's with the guy who makes her dolls. Yeah, the guy named Bruno. I thought he was all hot air until he picked up the check. The fuckin' guy ordered not one but two bottles of Krug, six bills a pop, plus brandy, plus all kinds of fancy appetizers. Bet he dropped over two grand. Funny thing is, Cristina kept right up with us and, man, she *never* drinks like that. She must be one hurtin' puppy right now, wherever she is . . ."

She had no choice but to take a chance. If Paul was facing the kitchen entry she'd be all right, but if not . . .

He'll see me. He'll see his nut-job girlfriend with magic marker all over her boobs . . .

She stepped wide into the hall, turned, and zipped right into the laundry room. When she looked, Paul's back was to her.

At least a trifling relief. She pulled a robe out of the dryer and put it on, wrapping it tight. Then . . . *Here goes.*

She shuffled into the kitchen.

Paul stood in his boxers, his hair sticking up. He smiled below bloodshot eyes when he saw her.

"Oh, here she is. Anyway, sorry, Jess. My fuckup. Hold down the fort till I get there." Then he hung up. He walked over and hugged Cristina, gave her a peck on the cheek. "I hope you're not as hungover as I am," he bid.

"I'm sure I am," she said. Her head pounded with each word, along with the embarrassment of what she'd secretly done to herself. "I hurt *all over.*"

"God bless Bruno. But he must be going through the same thing so at least we're not the only ones suffering." Bewildered, Paul shook his head. "I can't believe I slept right through the alarm."

Cristina sheepishly pursed her lips. "And I can't believe I slept in the basement."

Paul almost spat out a sip of coffee. "You *what?*"

She kept the neck of the robe tightly clasped. *God, I hope he doesn't see.* "Kid you not. I was so smashed last night, I decided to go in the basement for some crazy reason. And I passed out."

"That's some shit-face," Paul laughed. "I thought you went out to the store."

"Nope. Your nutty fiancée slept off her drunk on the basement floor. I'm *never* drinking alcohol again."

"I just might second that motion. But it was a fun night, with Bruno and celebrating your new figure."

The Noxious Nun, she thought for no reason at all. "I'd cook you breakfast, honey, but I still feel so lousy—"

"Forget it. I'm over an hour late as it is." He kissed her again. "I've got to jump in the shower, dress, and get my tail to the office. Jess isn't exactly thrilled. Drink some water to rehydrate yourself and get some more sleep. But, in the bed, *not* the basement."

She stroked his cheek, then offered a pained smile. "You look hot in those boxers, you know."

"Oh, I'm sure. My eyes look like road maps—"

So do my boobs . . . "I have to go lie down. But have a good day at work. I'll have my act together when you get home, I promise."

He winked. "Good. Give me a chance to redeem myself after . . . you know . . ."

"I wasn't much in working order either, honey," she laughed and went to the bedroom. *He didn't notice. What a stroke of luck.* But she still felt asinine. *Some girlfriend* . . . She hid under the bedcovers and feigned sleep as Paul showered, dressed, and left. Then she rushed to the bathroom.

The mirror's crystalline clarity made it even worse. The colored lines encircling her breasts and streaking her stomach seemed even thicker, brighter now. *Why on earth did I do this to myself!* She jumped into the shower, head still thumping, and scrubbed hard with a washcloth and soap, then moaned aloud when she got back out and re-examined herself. The magic marker had barely faded.

Cristina was nearly in tears when she called Britt . . .

"You've *got* to be kidding!" Britt exclaimed.

Cristina reluctantly opened her robe, showing the marks. "I don't know what to do. If Paul sees this . . ."

Britt sat at the kitchen table, flabbergasted. She wore dark Seven jeans, which fit her like tights, a red faux shearling vest, and clear strap platforms. "And you say rubbing alcohol and Lava soap didn't work?"

"Didn't even come close to getting it all off."

Britt opened a paper bag she'd brought, removed a bottle of nail-polish remover. "I remember someone telling me this once. It should work."

They went to the bathroom. Cristina blushed as Britt carefully blotted the fluid on her breasts with a cloth, then rubbed.

"You're in luck. It's working."

"You're a godsend!" Cristina exclaimed.

"And *you're* a space cadet. Honestly, Cristina. It's not like you to get drunk at all, but you must've been *pie-eyed* to do this."

"I know. I can't explain it."

Britt looked up from her rubbing. "Is there something you're not telling me, little sister?"

"No, I'm not doing drugs, and I'm not hiding an alcohol problem."

Britt shook her head, reapplying more of the remover. "You better not be. Paul would've shit if he saw this. And you hassle *him* about drinking."

"Pretty hypocritical, huh?" Cristina admitted. She looked to the mirror with relief when she saw the magic marker was coming off. "And he actually wasn't bad last night. *I* was the loose screw."

"And you passed out in the basement? Did I get that right?"

Cristina nodded, ashamed. "And I had the dream again—"

"The nude nun . . ."

"Yeah, but it was a lot worse. More detail, and . . ."

Britt looked up again, reading her. "And *what?*"

"I don't know, but more and more I think the dream is some kind of flashback effect from the Goldfarbs."

Britt stopped rubbing and gave Cristina the eye. "Stop using that as an excuse. The stuff the Goldfarbs drugged us with *wasn't* hallucinatory. This has nothing to do with the Goldfarbs. It's just a bad dream, and it was made worse by your getting crocked out of your gourd!"

Cristina stared at the wall through the recollection. "But . . . there was other stuff in the dream, and it really bothered me. Other—well—people."

"Yeah?"

"It was lesbian stuff," Cristina finally said. "A bunch of women . . . touching me and . . . other stuff."

"And let me guess. It turned you on."

"Sort of."

Britt sighed, frustrated. "Cristina, every woman on earth has dreams like that sometimes. It's just subconscious mish-mash. It means nothing. And everybody gets drunk on occasion and passes out."

"Yeah, but they don't pass out and draw on themselves with indelible markers. I just don't understand any of it. It's starting to scare me."

"For God's sake," Britt said. She was finished. The marks were gone, leaving Cristina's skin pink from the rubbing. Britt looked her right in the eye. "Listen. I know what you're getting at—I'm a shrink, remember? A shrink for screwed-up women. You think you're having some kind of psychological trauma that's being triggered by the shitty stuff that happened to us in the past. What, you think you're a latent lesbian because of what god-damn Helga Goldfarb did to us, and made us do to each other? That's ridiculous; we've been through this a mil-lion times. You're overreacting, that's all—like you always do. Wasn't it yesterday you told me you felt better than you ever have and that your sex life was off the scales? But now you're acting like that pensive worrywart that you were in the old days, all because of a recurring dream."

Cristina thought about it. "I guess you're right, but—"

"No buts. I am right." Britt narrowed her eyes in some contemplation. "So where exactly did you draw on your-self? Your studio?"

"No. The basement."

Britt winced. "So you purposely brought magic markers down to the basement, in the middle of the night, to draw on yourself?"

"Uh . . . Well, no. I think the magic markers were al-ready down there. The place is full of junk. And I remem-ber touching something that felt like a pen."

Britt grabbed Cristina's hand and yanked. "Come on. Show me this ridiculous basement."

Cristina took her down. They wended around old boxes until they came to the oblong cement patchwork.

"Right there's where I passed out." Cristina pointed.

"What the hell is that? It looks newer than the rest."

"I figured a pipe broke so that's where they dug; then they patched it. I remember falling down there, and my hand landed on the pen."

Britt looked around the entire area. "No pens here now. So you picked them up this morning?"

"No."

Britt's frown deepened; she kept looking at the cement patch. "Kind of creepy. That's not . . . a *grave*, is it?"

"It can't be. Paul would've known from the deed."

"Still. It's creepy. It's no wonder you had the nightmare down here." She chuckled darkly. "A nun with fangs, a bowl full of blood."

"And this time there was a man lying on a slab, too."

Britt looked again to the oblong patch but said nothing.

"Oh, and there's an insignia down there, on the corner."

Britt stooped. "Latin, it looks like and—what is that? A turtle?"

"Looks like a dragon, or a lizard."

Britt kept shaking her head. "A dragon strangled by its own tail. The hits just keep on comin', Cristina. Let's go back up. You must've put the magic markers away and don't remember."

I don't think so, Cristina answered in thought. Back upstairs, Britt turned away from the kitchen, to the mirror-backed bar.

"It's a little early, isn't it?" Cristina asked.

"After cleaning magic marker off your boobs, then listening to your lesbian nun dream, and then seeing the creepy grave-looking thing in the basement? No. Paul won't mind if I take a nip of this Louis XIII, will he?"

"I'm sure he won't."

Britt grabbed a crystal snifter. "You want some?"

Cristina's stomach lurched. "After last night? I'll probably never drink again."

Britt shrugged and took a sip of the clear liquor.

Cristina wrapped the robe tighter, as if chilled. Something nagged at her psyche, an idea that had only just occurred to her. But how could she voice it without sounding paranoid? *I've put Britt through enough for one day . . .*

"Okay," Britt demanded. "What's wrong *now?*"

Cristina could never hide a thing from her. "I don't remember drawing on myself, Britt."

"You were sloshed."

"Yeah, but why would I do that, even that drunk? I'm starting to think that maybe I *didn't* draw on myself."

Britt's eyes snapped to Cristina's. "Come on. Paul?"

"No. He was asleep upstairs."

"Cristina, what are you saying?"

"I'm not sure." She fidgeted. "But maybe . . . someone else was in the house."

Britt slumped. "What? A burglar? Paul's got a Fort Knox–style alarm system in this place. Jess told me."

Cristina's thoughts seemed to drip. "Not necessarily a burglar, but . . . Yesterday I met the priest who used to look after this house—Father Rollin. He told me squatters would sometimes sneak into the house at night."

Britt looked as though her brandy had soured. "*Squatters?*"

"Homeless people, addicts."

"Street crazies, huh? You're nuts."

Cristina struggled to voice the rest of her fear. "I keep seeing these homeless women mulling around the area."

"They mull around *every* area in the city, Cristina."

"Yeah, I know, but there's more. Yesterday I was in a store and I saw some of them, these homeless girls. And one of them shoplifted some stuff. Guess what they shoplifted?"

Britt set the rest of her drink aside, wearied. "What?"

"Magic markers."

"I'll say it again. You're nuts—"

"Why?" Cristina whined back. "It's pretty uncanny, isn't it?"

"Homeless women break into your basement just so they can draw on you with magic markers? Listen to yourself!"

"Then how do you explain it?"

"I already have," Britt snapped. "You got loaded last night and pulled a moronic move. Alcohol does that to people, especially people who don't have much tolerance. Christ, one time in college I got so hammered on tequila at a sorority party that I threw up on a whole couch full of people—"

"Yuck . . ."

"In fact, I drank so much that I was *still* drunk the rest of the next day. You're probably suffering borderline alcohol poisoning." Britt stood up, glaring. "Now stop with all this dumb talk—it makes you sound ridiculous. I have to go."

Cristina wilted. She could tell Britt had reached her limit. *I can't do this to her; I have to be more stable than this. She's got to listen to women's problems all day long at her job—and those are women with REAL problems. An extra headache from me is the last thing she needs.* Cristina caught Britt at the door, and hugged her. "I'm sorry. You're right, I'm just overreacting."

Britt's forgiveness was plain when her frown turned to a smile. "You're a nut, Cristina, but you're *my* nut."

"I don't know what I'd do without you. Sometimes I feel so weak and scared."

"But each day you're getting stronger . . . just like me. You've probably still got a bunch of booze in your bloodstream so just sleep the rest of it off, then go for a walk and get some fresh air. You'll feel a hundred times better tomorrow and you'll be laughing at yourself. I have to go now, so . . . just do as I say, all right?"

Cristina nodded. "'Bye."

She looked out the window and saw Britt shaking her head as she got in her car. *I really am a pain in the ass.*

When Britt raced off in the white Mercedes, a movement caught Cristina's eye. It was so sudden and slight that at first she didn't even know where it came from, but then . . .

Now that Britt's car was gone, Cristina saw two homeless females sitting beneath one of the windows in the church. It looked like they were sucking the contents from ketchup packets. After a few moments, they got up and began to walk away.

One of them looked right over at the window from which Cristina peered, and smiled.

(II)

"Gemser?" Laura Eastman asked. Her Detex clock swayed like a cumbersome purse when she turned toward her departing coworker. They'd both worked for the security company that had the contract for this closed-down Banana Republic. The twelve-hour shifts were a hassle, and they only let you work three of them per week so you wouldn't qualify as full-time; that way, the company didn't have to offer a group health plan. But the work was easy and that suited Laura just fine. Rounds every hour, punch a few key stations, and fill out an hourly report was about it. She liked all the walking (the building was four floors), which kept her lissome physique even more lissome. *You got a racehorse bod,* Gemser had commented once, after which she'd ridden *him* like a horse. She knew she possessed a stunning kind of beauty, her dark complexion and part-European, part-Polynesian features gave her an exotic air and, somehow, those features coupled with the security uniform made her even more enticing. Just about every male guard in the company had put the make on her— even the married ones. Laura was the kind of girl who liked attention.

But now this.

"Yeah?" George Gemser asked bruskly. He'd been just about to go off-shift, without so much as a good-bye.

"What is wrong with you lately?" she snapped behind the security desk. "You're acting real shitty to me all of a sudden."

"Aside from you standing me up the other night, nothing's *wrong*," the large, bearded man informed.

Oh, so that's it. "For shit's sake, Gemser. Don't be such a baby. I told you, I was sick." But, lo, this was a lie. She hadn't been sick at all; she'd been detained by a last-minute offer to dinner by an ad exec who drove a Porsche.

"I don't play those games," Gemser said. "Some girls like to jerk guys around but I'm not into that."

"Oh, give me a break!"

"Hey, you do your thing, I'll do mine. All I'm in this for is to do my job, get my paycheck, and go home. I'm not into all this hot-cold, teasy grab-ass stuff, one minute you want me the next minute you don't. Not my thing. We see each other every day, we say hello, say good-bye, and that's it."

GodDAMN! Laura thought. Usually playing hard to get worked but it was backfiring here. You had to keep them humble, after all, otherwise they shit all over you. "That's pretty damn harsh, isn't it? I thought we had a little something going on, you know?"

"No," Gemser corrected. "All we had 'going on' was 'sport-fucking,' to use *your* term."

Well, it *had* been her line; meanwhile, Gemser was already heading for the front glass doors.

"Jesus, Gemser!" Laura suddenly shed a few surprise tears. "At least let's talk!"

"We'll just be friends," the sturdy guard said but his eyes were unrelenting in their lack of forgiveness. "It makes it easier 'cos we do have to work together."

Laura was beginning to do something she *never* did: yield. "Damn. I'm sorry, okay?" Her eyes fluttered. "I've always liked you."

"Fine. See ya tomorrow." He turned and walked out.

She ran out after him, ponytail flying. "Hey!"

He turned at the bus stop.

"You know, you can always come in an hour early, I mean, if you want to." She winked at him.

Gemser offered the slightest smile, then hoppd on the bus.

At least I finally got a smile out of him. Time would tell. If he showed up an hour before her shift was over, then she'd know she still had a hook in. *And I'll make it worth his while,* she vowed.

She locked the front doors behind her and officially began her shift.

Most of the first floor was the old display floor, empty save for bare metal garment racks. Much of her shift was spent locked inside, and she had Mace, a Mag-Lite, and a cell phone for emergencies, not that she'd ever had any. Four times a shift she had to make a foot patrol around the building's exterior, to check the alley out back. A couple times she'd caught some homeless girls loitering back there but they always dispersed when she whipped out her phone. The building had been a department store for decades, then the Banana Republic for several years until a developer bought it. Upper West Side meant low-key— nothing ever happened. Laura got plenty of sleep between rounds.

Upstairs were storerooms and offices; Laura had to make a door-check every hour, and at the beginning of each shift had to enter each room and check its status. Easy but monotonous. She got tired of hearing her own footfalls on the tile flooring. Downstairs, behind the display floor, were more offices and the old loading dock whose door was chained shut. One of the rooms was an employee lounge and the couch was still in it. Laura had had some on-duty fun with Gemser more than once on said couch.

I hope he comes by . . .

Boxes lined the back wall, all empty. When Laura went to the punch-key, she accidentally bumped a stack, moving them several inches from their place.

Strange . . .

She pushed the boxes away, revealing a steel door. *I've been working here all these months and never even knew this door was here.* She tried the metal knob but found it locked.

Laura peered at the door. *What the hell is behind there?*

She strode back to the security desk and retrieved the account manual, flipped back to the site map and blueprints. The map detailing each foot patrol showed no evidence of another door existing in the old lounge, but the blueprints . . .

How do you like that?

The blueprints showed another room behind that door. BOILER ROOM - INACTIVE, it read.

She noted the discovery on her shift log, then strode back to the room, keys jingling. *Must be leftover from the old department store*, she supposed.

Laura tried every key on her ring but none of them would open the door.

(III)

"It's abominable," the woman told Vernon. Her name was Ms. Lancre, a fortysomething woman in a conservative knee skirt and a blouse that seemed the tiniest bit too tight to comfortably accommodate her bosom. Brown hair back

in a bun, which added a severity to her face, or perhaps—
Vernon considered—it was the sudden upset of her discovery. This was the first time in his career that Vernon
had ever responded to a "church desecration," which he
supposed this was. Her churchly anachronism shattered
when her cell phone rang. "Excuse me, gentlemen."

"Of course," Vernon said.

Her frumpish flat-soled shoes snapped as she stepped
out the pointed doors.

"Is she a nun?" Slouch asked, eyeing her exit.

"I guess she's just a teacher, or the headmistress or whatever."

"Some rack, huh?"

"Shut up, Slouch."

Vernon turned back to the scene, officially a Signal 40
on the code sheet: vandalism. He and Slouch now stood in
the middle of the chapel supporting a Catholic girls
school called The Sisters of the Heavenly Spring—so perhaps the woman was a nun after all.

"I didn't even know this place was here," Slouch mentioned.

"Me, either. I guess that means we're apathetic cops."
He was looking at the chapel's modest altar now, whose
white cloth had been besmirched by magic marker: wavy
streaks running up and down, black, green, and red.

"This is so fucked-up it's almost funny," Slouch said of
the lines.

"We probably shouldn't cuss here, but . . . you're right."
He walked behind the altar to the tapestry that backed the
great crucifix. The perpetrators, in the same marker colors,
had crudely scrawled the words: **ME ENAMOURER AD
INFINITUM**.

"It looks Latin," Slouch observed.

"No duh." Vernon wrote the words down in his notebook. "But if our girls are what we think they are, how could
they know any Latin?"

"The bums? They all had childhoods, probably very traumatized childhoods, and some of 'em may have gone to church. Childhood impressions, you know? They say a lot of a kid's religious background leaks out later in life, once the schizophrenia sets in. Now they're crazy and they're remembering stuff."

Vernon shrugged.

"It's a solid connection, though. The magic marker jive." Slouch seemed delighted by the desecration, just as any atheist cop would be. It was a *lead*.

"Yeah, but it's still shit—"

Slouch grinned. "We probably shouldn't cuss here."

"And it doesn't matter how solid a connection we've got, Downtown will question the expense of having Technical Services come out here for a workup. So that's why we're not going to ask."

"Why not?"

Vernon whispered, "Because we'll be laughingstocks, ordering a latent crew and photographer to a minor case of vandalism. Way they see it, those costs should be doled out for the serious stuff."

"Yeah, like the murder we had yesterday, and ten to one it was the same magic markers used on the fuckin' junkie chick." Slouch bit his lip at the expletive.

"We'll do a little workup ourselves," Vernon said, "then they won't be calling us the Two Stooges at Headquarters." His eyes turned critical. "You're not very observant, are you?"

Slouch ground his teeth. "If there's hot chicks around, sure. And you know, you can say what you want but I think the headmistress or whatever she is is hot."

Vernon lifted the hem of the altar cloth up with the tip of his shoe.

"Well how do you like that?" Slouch said.

"Bag it and mark it."

Recessed there lay one green magic marker. Slouch

turned an evidence bag inside out over his hand and picked it up. "Sounds like Bouncing Betty's coming back."

Ms. Lancre's footfalls grew louder as she re-approached. Her lips seemed pursed in a manner that denoted satisfaction. "An interesting phone call, Inspector."

"Church business?" Vernon asked.

"Police business, I would think," the woman said. She crossed her arms beneath her bosom. "That was the school's secretary, letting me know that earlier today a Mr. Mills called the school to report a curious observation. You see, Mr. Mills's ten-year-old daughter, Grace, is a student here."

"Yes?" Vernon said, scribbling notes.

"Last night at shortly past nine, Mr. Mills was driving Grace home from the skating rink and their journey happened to lead them right past the school."

"Yes, yes?" Vernon tried to hurry her along.

"And they both happened to notice several homeless women loitering in front of the school."

Vernon and Slouch looked at each other.

"That could be very helpful. I'll need Mr. Mills's phone number, ma'am," Vernon said.

"The secretary will be happy to oblige," the woman said. "Mr. Mills and his daughter took note of this because it seemed uncharacteristic and a bit odd."

"Um-hmm."

"But that's not all," the woman continued as if unfolding a great puzzle. "You see, it wasn't only these homeless women they saw loitering. They said they also saw a woman who appeared to be a nun."

"A *nun?*" Vernon questioned. "So it could be someone connected with the school?"

"No, no, Inspector. For *this* nun, according to them, was dressed in the old pre-Vatican II habit and wimple, something most orders were allowed to dispense with a long time ago—since 1965 as a matter of fact. You simply don't see it much these days, not in America, at any rate. Only the most austere orders still subscribe to the old dress codes. What I mean is it's very unlikely that a nun dressed specifically in these sorts of raiments would be seen near the school, especially at such a late hour."

It's something, Vernon thought. *Now if I only knew what to do with it.* He frowned when he caught Slouch's eye cast toward the woman's bosom. "If you don't mind my asking, ma'am . . . are *you* a nun?"

Her aquamarine eyes glittered. "I'm a Bride of Christ, yes. But if you're inquiring as to *my* whereabouts at the time this other nun was seen, I was attending a blessing at the Cathedral last night—"

"No, no, that's not what I meant. I was just curious. When I was a kid, we always addressed a nun as 'Sister,' yet you introduced yourself as 'Miss.'"

"The old formalities are fading, sir," she said. "In church, I'm Sister Mabille Lancre but at school I'm Miss. It's considered less authoritarian, for the students, though I'm not sure what to think about the efficacy of such modern liberalizations. We simply do as the Holy Father bids. But I'm pleased to know that you're a Catholic, Inspector."

How'd I get into this? Vernon wondered. "Well, to be honest I was raised that way but . . ."

She gave a knowing smile. "It's easy to lose sight of God in this wicked age; however, once you start looking again, the keys to the Kingdom of Heaven will be back in your hands."

Jesus. Slouch was grinning at him over the woman's shoulder. *Get back to business . . .* "Who was the first person to discover the break-in, ma'am?"

"The janitor. If you'd like to speak with him, just ask the secretary." She looked back at the denigrated altar linens. "Regrettably, the school's chancellor, Father Bosch, has not yet been notified. He's out of town. He'll be repulsed when he hears of this offense."

Vernon tilted his head. "I'm not belittling what happened here, Ms. Lancre, but it's really not that serious. Just some light vandalism and one pried-open window."

"A crack gang would've torn the place apart," Slouch commented.

Ms. Lancre looked slapped in the face. "Not that serious? Really, Inspector, and with you raised in the Faith."

"I'm sorry, ma'am but I'm not sure what you—"

"Something much more grievous than mere vandalism has occurred here, sir."

"Really?"

She looked at him, yes, like a nun scolding him in school. "You're not very observant, are you?"

Slouch silently hee-hawed at him behind her back.

"Come here!" She led them to the other side of the altar. On the floor lay several pieces of—

"Wax paper?" Slouch guessed.

"Not quite," she said, effusing sarcasm, "but I'm sure Inspector Vernon knows, being the stalwart Catholic that he is, hmm?"

Vernon did know what the papers were; he remembered from when he was an altar boy. "The wrapping from the rolls of Communion wafers, right?"

"For the *Host*, yes," the woman explained as if sickened. "And seeing that the wraps are empty we can only come to the most repugnant conclusion . . ."

"The homeless girls ate the wafers?" Slouch assumed, confused. "Since you call that repugnant, I guess the wafers taste pretty bad, huh?"

"That's not what she means, Slouch," Vernon told him.

"Indeed not," she snapped, "and please remember that they're not merely wafers, Officer. They represent the Body of Christ."

"Transubstantiation and all that," Vernon said.

"Yes, the ultimate mystery of Faith. For the Host to be

consumed beyond the act of Holy Communion is to represent the most appalling offense. They hadn't yet been blessed, of course, but still, the very *idea*."

"Of course," Vernon tried to accommodate her, "but where there's the *Body* of Christ, isn't there also the Blood—in other words, the wine?"

"Most certainly."

"If they consumed that, too, there'll be some really good fingerprints on the bottle," Vernon informed her.

She walked to the opposite side of the altar, to a wooden cabinet mounted to the wall. "But as you can see . . ." She opened the cabinet to reveal several unopened bottles of wine. "They haven't been touched."

Fuck, Vernon profaned, then felt a little guilty when the figure of Christ aloft seemed to frown at him. He bagged the empty wrappers. *Iodine fuming*, he thought impulsively. "Ma'am? And where are the wafers *stored*?"

She walked to an identical cabinet on the other side, began to reach for it, but—

"Don't touch that," Vernon commanded. He put another evidence bag over his hand and opened the cabinet. "Nothing left," he said. "May I take this knob temporarily, Ms. Lancre?"

Slouch stepped up. "You have his stalwart Catholic promise that it'll be returned after we tape it for prints."

"By all means," she said.

Vernon unscrewed the knob inside of the bag, then inverted it. Now, however, the woman stooped over, hands on knees. She seemed to be peering at something in the back of the cabinet.

"Ms. Lancre?"

"My great Lord. *More* despicable vandalism."

Vernon took out a cheap penlight on his keys and shined it inside.

"What *is* that?" the woman asked. "It's hardly Latin, like the other writing. It looks *Slavic*."

The backing board at the rear of the cabinet was white foam-board, and on it, in the same alternating black, green, and red, the words appeared: **TARA FLAESC WALLKYA.**

"The hell is that?" Slouch asked.

Ms. Lancre stared at him, outraged.

"Sorry."

Vernon transcribed the words in his notebook. "Whatever it means, I'll find out."

"If it really means anything," Slouch amended. "Homeless schizos like to write and talk in imaginary languages sometimes."

This was true but . . . *Not this time*, Vernon felt. "I'll be in touch, Ms. Lancre," he said, his mind cluttered now. "I'll have vehicular patrols stepped up in this area for the time being."

"Thank you. Godspeed in catching these corrupted souls. I'd very much like to meet them once they're apprehended."

Vernon half-smiled. "To give them a tongue-lashing?"

"Of course not! To remind them that God forgives all."

Vernon stalled. "Right. Good-bye."

Slouch stole a last glance at the woman's bosom, then followed Vernon toward the door.

"Oh, and Inspector?" she called back.

Vernon turned back. "Yes?"

"You'll find God again, one day." She smiled very thinly. "I feel certain."

Vernon got a chill and left the chapel.

(IV)

Doke was the Man on the Scene, black and bad, and no shit for brains. He never touched his product. *Never get high on your own supply 'cos if you do, you fuckin' die.* He knew the score. And just as fast as he could bust a move, he could bust a cap in a froggy junkie's coconut. Business was business.

He was the main bagman on Broadway, from 79th to Columbus—or . . . at least he thought he was. He'd started out as a clocker at six, and had been dealing rock and black tar for five years, mostly rock. Twenty-three now, but he had the nose for the street like a player twice his age. He knew how to *work* the trash out there, he knew how to get someone to need his product, and he could always tell when someone was ready to tip.

He sold for the Kings. Z-Mob had been moving on their turf but so far, tough shit. The Kings knew how to take care of their gig; couple of times they'd caught Z-Men punks selling in the zone and these poor fuckers were found a week later in some cubed cars. *Boo-yah*, Doke thought, hitching up his baggie pants. *I'm with the right crew, not these poo-put motherfuckers.* He had $120 sneakers that blinked. Cool. Doke was a cliché and didn't even know it.

Lotta dime-dealers and assholes said working West Side was a ball-buster 'cos so many people here were rich. "Ain't no good crackheads Upper West Side, man," a fence told him once and he'd pronounced crackheads as "crackhades." "They all rich, man. They all *pill* junkies, man. Oxy, Vyky, *that* shit, man. They ain't on the *pipe* or the *needle*. Don't you know nothin'?" *Shee-it*, Doke thought, laughing. *WHO don't know nothing?* He sold to a *lot* of rich white housewives, as a matter of fact, but of course, he'd sell to anyone. Fuckers coming right out of re-hab gave Doke some quality satisfaction in employment. He was always there waiting with a free bag, get 'em right back on the Devil's Dick. Kids were fun, too, 'cos he liked the idea—he liked the *ideology*. Tip 'em with a few free rocks and next thing they knew they were ripping off cash out of their rich parents' wallets and selling shit in the house. They'd take the $80,000 Audi and sell it to a chop shop for five grand and just say some "bad man" stole it, then every penny of that five would wind up in Doke's kick. Kids tipped the quickest, see, and the earlier you got the hook in 'em, the harder it was to get out and the more it cost the *motherFUCKIN'* U.S. taxpayer in the long run. *Fuck them*, Doke thought, bopping. *What they ever do for me?* But the rich housewives were always the best. *While Hubby's busy with his job on fuckin' Wall Street, his squeeze is chipping away at the checking account, lying about the bills, selling the jewelry, and next thing you know Hubby comes home from work one day to find out Junior's college fund is bone-dry and his "high-class" wife has been a closet crackhead for the last two years.* Doke nodded as he continued down the sunny street. *Shit-yeah.*

And Doke considered himself an equal opportunity drug dealer. He did not discriminate. *Rich, poor, young, old, niggers, spics, kikes, white trash, whoever you are—I got what you need . . .*

Worst customers, however, were longer-timers on their way to what they called Rock Bottom. Get it? Mostly chicks who'd been working the street ten or twenty years but by now they looked like such shit they couldn't snag a john in a million years. Next stop? Homeless City. Lot of 'em were moving over this way 'cos—shit—try being homeless in a crack hood. You'd be dead in two minutes. They *kill* bums there, cut your throat just for the dirty clothes on your back. Doke had a couple packs of these girls who were sleeping in the closed buildings 'cos it was safer here. They were always a harder sell but if you roughed them up, sometimes you could motivate them. Then give 'em all a free toke on the pipe to remind 'em what they're missing. They'd find ways to get money. It was never much but Doke's point guy with the Kings? Dude named Archie. One time Archie told him this: "The *smart* businessman pursues all profit, large and small."

Straight up. Come on, Doke wasn't some piece-of-shit
player dealing on the street.

He was a *businessman*.

Cop gave him the eye as he was turning off 72nd, near
where some guy he never heard of named Lennon got
shot. Doke would've given him the eye back 'cept he was
carrying so he just went on his way 'cos, thank God, it was
a free country and a dude shouldn't be shook down for
walkin' the street just 'cos he *looked* like a crack-dealing
scumbag. *I'll fuckin' SUE, and win!* It happened all the
time these days. *I got my rights, motherfuckers.* Then, a couple blocks later:

Well, well, well, well, well, he thought.

Up the street two familiar faces turned into an alley, a
pair of the same homeless trash he was just thinking about.
*Haven't seen those two in a while nows that I think about it.
Thought they must've croaked by now.* If they had, that would
be fine with him, 'cos if you asked Doke, white hoes too
beat to make crack money had no right to exist. But then
he remembered what his main man Archie had said . . .

Doke picked up his pace.

"Yo! You two!" he called right after he stepped into a
side alley. "Hold up!"

The two girls turned. Big eyes in drawn faces showed
something like terror. When they turned again, Doke
shouted with authority.

"Hold UP, I said. Don't MAKE me have to run."

They stopped, leaning against the alley wall.

Yeah, those two. He remembered them. The one that
stuttered and he could never tell what color her hair was
'cos it was so dirty. Looked like she was wearing the same
jeans he last saw her in over a month ago, but now she had
a new T-shirt that said THE DAMNED on it, whatever
the fuck *that* was. Doke had slapped her up a couple of
times, not 'cos she ripped him off, 'cos . . . it was just *fun*
slapping her up. *She just LOOKS like she needs it.* Other one

was the one with pink glasses and missing a bunch of teeth. Shitty orange halter and blue jeans brown with dirt.

Doke loped up, giving them the Look. "Where you think you're goin', huh?"

"Home," Glasses said.

"Home, shit. You ain't got no home. Ain't seen you two in a *long* time. Don't you owe me for some Bits I slipped you?" he bullshitted.

"Nuh-nuh-no," the stutterer said.

Doke paused. They still looked like shit but . . . not quite as shitty as last time. *Like they gained some weight or something.* "Yeah? Well, maybe I'm thinkin' of someone *else* who ripped me off." But now the stutterer was staring at him, half in fear and half in something Doke didn't like. Like maybe . . . loathing? "What'choo eyeballin', ho?"

"Wuh-wuh-we don't smoke no more," she huffed out with a great effort.

Doke laughed. "Only way either of ya don't smoke no more is 'cos you're too skanky to turn tricks. But I can tune ya both up right now, *if* ya got cash."

The stutterer stiffened up again, "I-I-told you, we don't do crack no more-no more-no more—"

"Be quiet!" Glasses blared, little boobs swaying in all the halter's play.

"We ain't got no money neither!" the stutterer added in a testy tone.

Doke didn't like this. They were being *rude*, and *no* crackhead was rude to *him*. When he stepped right up to them, they moved back against the wall as if pressured by the distance between them.

"I'd kick both of your white-trash asses 'cept I'd get my shoes dirty." He tipped up a Nike. "And just *one* of these shoes is worth more than both of ya and all them other little dirtbags ya'll hang out with. No money, huh? Well I guess that means I gotta search ya, and I'm *keepin'* everything I find." And then he shoved the stutterer back hard against the bricks and rammed a hand down her pockets.

Fuck. "What's this shit, cunt?" The only thing he found in her pockets was a can of anchovies.

Did Glasses smile ever so slightly? She actually took a step *toward* him. "We got some money, Doke, and we'll crack it up some. We got enough for two rocks."

"Francy!" the other one exclaimed, looking appalled. "We don't do that shit no more! What would the New Mother say?"

Doke stared poker-faced. *New Mother? Fuckin' loonies . . .* "Don't know what you hoes are talkin' 'bout and I don't care. Two rocks is fifty bucks, same as always. Lay it on me."

"It's at home," Glasses said.

Doke laughed. "I'm standin' in it, ain't I?"

"We live right down here in the old clothes store. There's a hole. You have to come with us."

"Francy!" Stutterer shrieked again. "She'll kick us out of the convent-the convent-the convent, the—"

"Be quiet!" Glasses shoved the other one ahead of her, down the alley.

The convent? Doke loved the shit some of them said once their brains were gone. *Man, this is a hoot.*

He followed them down a relatively clear alley. Were they whispering? *Glasses must be talkin' the other one into it. She knows the score. Once a crackhead, always a crackhead, even when you ain't got shit left.* Their dirty flip-flops slapped ahead of him.

When they stopped, Glasses pushed a garbage can away from the brick wall of one of those fancy white clothes stores that had gone out of business. A long time ago it was a department store Doke thought his mother worked at, but he didn't really remember her much. He knew his daddy turned into a hype and always thought that maybe he killed her. Doke didn't care.

Behind the garbage can was a hole in the wall. "In here," Glasses said, and then got on her hands and knees. The stutterer had already shimmied in before her, fast as a skink.

"You fuckin' crazy? I ain't goin' in there," Doke said.

She glared back. "Fine. Then don't, then we'll have to cop from the Z-Men. Only way you're getting any money from us is by coming in here."

"Bullshit—"

"I ain't smokin' crack on the street when it's light outside!" And then before Doke could raise further shit, she shimmied into the hole.

Doke looked down. He didn't like that remark about the Z-Men. *And I'll bet they been buyin' from those motherfuckers all along* . . . And what would he have to fear by going in? It was fucked-up, sure, but there was no way they had a guy or a pimp in there. *Maybe I'll just jack both the bitches out, take their green, and kill 'em,* he considered. Doke had killed a few bums in his time. A man needed something to do when he got bored.

Fuck it. He got down on hands and knees.

He could barely get his shoulders in but after some fidgeting, he succeeded. His face seemed to constrict when he squeezed through the narrow passage. *Bum piss,* he knew. He'd smelled plenty of it in his time. As he inched through, each inhalation felt thick. But then what could he expect following two homeless crackheads into their crib? He squeezed through a larger hole, and when his hips passed the makeshift threshold, he knew he could see light.

Yeah, my time's worth a lot more than havin' to crawl into a shit hole for fifty bucks. I'm killin' these hoes . . .

He had an ice pick strapped to his ankle for such occasions.

Once inside, Doke smirked and stood up. Several candles provided the weak, urine-yellow light that flickered on the bare-block walls. This was probably a boiler room

or something a long time ago, but now only rubble, stacks
of boxes and crates, and garbage characterized its stark features. A kerosene heater sat off to the side, next to boxes
of candles and some packs of magic markers. Several ratty
sleeping bags lay on the floor.

"Over here." Glasses's voice.

But Doke remained stalled in place. In one corner a
mountain of trash sat piled, and several rats skittered like
they owned the place. "Smells like piss in here," he complained. "Shit's stingin' my eyes."

"Oh, you get used to it," came a squeaky voice he didn't
recognize but then he looked aside and saw a third girl sitting on a box. She appeared to be watching a television on
the floor but the television was off.

"You bitches told me no one else was here."

"That's Sandrine," Glasses excused. "She likes to
watch TV."

"The fuckin' TV's busted!"

Glasses giggled. "Yeah. But sometimes you can still see
stuff."

In fetid dark, the bum-chick called Sandrine enthused,
"It's true. Right now I'm watching the man on the stone
slab. It's like a show you see over and over again."

Watching the man? Doke, frowning, walked over, unconsciously ducking his head beneath low pipes. Something
crunched under his foot; then he frowned harder when he
saw what it was: an anchovy can.

"Anchovies are easier to shoplift 'cos they're smaller,"
Glasses informed.

"Now the dog's barking, too!" exclaimed Sandrine like a
little kid even though she was probably thirty.

Glasses went behind her, to smile at the television screen.

Doke looked at the screen, too. It was dead, blank. *Their
brains are garbage.* "I ain't got time to fuck around in this
piss-hole. Let's see that money or else I'll have to go ghetto
on your asses."

Glasses handed him fifty very dirty dollars.

Awright. Now what? Am I really gonna kill these kooks? Right now all Doke wanted to do was get out of this freaky place. *The smart businessman pursues all profit, large and small,* Archie's voice etched at the back of his head. *Just give 'em the crack,* Doke figured. *They'll want more tomorrow.*

He reached into his pocket . . .

"Oh," Glasses said. "We don't want any crack. We don't smoke that shit anymore. We don't do *any* drugs anymore."

Doke stared.

Sandrine looked up from the dead TV. "We've been purged. The New Mother has sanka-fried us."

"*Sanctified*," Glasses corrected.

"We only—we only told you we'd cop some crack to lure you in—you in—you in—you—"

"Be quiet!"

It was the other one, the one that talked fucked-up. Doke wasn't really nervous yet, but there was something a bit uneasy behind his rage. The stutterer had resurfaced from a back corner. She had something in her hand. Doke squinted.

A brick.

Doke blurred for a split second, and in the split second after that he had his ice pick in hand. "I'm fillin' *all* you crazy bums fulla holes—"

"*Salut*," another voice said.

Doke froze.

The voice sounded accented and . . . weird. Like someone talking through the wind.

"She's here . . ."

Black knuckles turned white as Doke's hand tightened around the pick's handle. That voice he'd heard seemed to come from every direction of the squalid room, yet something he couldn't begin to define commanded his gaze. He looked to the corner, behind the pile of garbage.

Is that . . .

A woman stood there. He could see candlelight flickering up and down her nude body, and he could also see that she wasn't any bum. She was all curves and enticing female lines. But . . .

Nude, yes, but there was something like a weird hood around her face . . .

Then the accented voice repeated what the bum-girl had said:

"Look."

As Doke's eyes widened, his vision dimmed to black, and it was in the all-pervading absence of light that he began to see things . . .

He saw his mother being pummeled by the fists of the man he presumed was his father. "Where's my skag! Where's my skag!" the man raged, arms full of needle marks, a candle burning on a table next to a spoon. The fists flew into a frenzy as his mother's face was pounded open. "Ain't worth SHIT!" Then the man collapsed her head with a rolling pin . . .

Doke hitched in a breath. "No . . ."

"Look."

Another vision: soldiers from long ago slowly proceeding into a forest, the looks on the faces in the oval chainmail hoods that of horror and revulsion. The forest seemed to extend without limit, yet between every tree stood a twenty-foot wooden pike on which a Turkish soldier with the invasion force of Mehmed II had been impaled. Some through their mouths, some through their rectums, some through their chests—there were thousands of them—and as Doke was forced to stare harder at the impossible image, he noticed that there were hundreds of women and old men impaled as well . . .

The blackness snapped away. Then—

Doke was back in the shitty room, staring at the nude

woman in the corner. Her eyes seemed alight. She was grinning.

Two very thin, inch-long teeth could be seen in the grin.

"Now, my blessed sister."

SMACK!

The stutterer brought the brick so hard against the side of Doke's head that the retinal lining of one eye detached. Half his sight winked out as he collapsed to the dirt-lined floor. The throb of pain at his head had Doke convulsing.

Shadows hovered. Doke couldn't move.

Hands pulled off his blinking shoes while greasy fingers first extracted the fifty dollars from his front pocket, then the five-hundred-dollar roll. His baggie full of crack was extracted as well, then tossed to the garbage pile. Doke could feel more than see his pants being pulled off.

He continued to mildly convulse from the preliminary effects of hematoma, yet those sociopathized brain cells continued to fire, continued to feel the pain thud like crashing waves. He thought he also felt a hand fiddle with his genitals.

The other bum-girl laughed. "It's so little . . ."

Doke was too far gone to feel emasculated, and too far gone to do essentially anything except lie there and shudder as blood and spinal fluid gently leaked from his fractured skull.

"Enough merriment, sisters." The accented voice. Did Doke sense the nude woman closer now, leaning over him? Her voice seemed to ooze along with his blood.

"Let us pay homage now, to our great and generous defender."

The girls rose and stepped away. But two of them moved up, each grabbing an ankle. They stepped apart, to spread Doke's legs.

The oozing voice smeared across Doke's mind . . .

"Singele lui traieste."

Doke's good eye blinked. He could see a fourth girl now, one with short black hair covered with bald patches, walking around.

In one hand she held a hammer, in the other a long, sharpened pole.

CHAPTER EIGHT

(I)

This is crazy, Father Rollin thought as he stood at the corner of 67th and Columbus, counting the number of hotel rooms facing the street. He counted with his finger, very intently. Several strollers stopped to peer at him. *I don't care if they think I'm out of my mind*, he asserted to himself but still felt embarrassed. He looked over his shoulder, to approximate the alignment; then he thought, *Hmm. Fourth one from the right side of the building. That looks like it . . .*

He picked up his small suitcase and entered the old brown brick Ketchum Hotel, well known for its Federal-period architecture. A quick trip up to the second floor, trying to maintain his bearing, and then he found the fire-exit map near the elevator. The fourth room from the right appeared as Room 207. *Got it. Now let's just hope I'm not wasting an awful lot of money.*

Back downstairs, he approached the check-in counter. The lobby seemed very busy, which wasn't good. *Somebody's probably already booked the room*, his cynicism told him, or perhaps it was a secret hope so that he wouldn't have to go through with this at all. He actually winced at several women in shining dresses, carrying physiques that he could only describe as . . . comely.

A lanky, narrow-faced clerk addressed him with a French accent. Rollin had always carried a trifling grudge against the French, for forcing Pope Clement V to move the papacy from Rome to Avignon in 1309. *It was all political!* he'd raged with some other priests once, after too much wine. *GOD is not political! How can the masses believe that the Church is infallible when everyone from kings to presidents can manipulate the Holy Office?* It was a silly argument, but Rollin still didn't much care for the French.

"It's a pleasure to receive you at the Ketchum, Father," said the clerk, whose brow seemed to twitch at Rollin's presence. "How may I be of assistance?"

"This is probably a fool's errand," Rollin began his lie. "I don't have a reservation, but I was wondering if Room 207 is available. Of course, seeing how busy you are today, I'm sure it isn't . . ."

The clerk's narrow face seemed to tweak at the odd request. A few taps on the keyboard, and, "You're in luck, Father. We've only three rooms unreserved today, and 207 is one of them."

"I'll take it for, say, three nights, if possible."

"Of course, Father." But then the clerk stiffened with some French-accented chuckling. "The standard rate is $279 per night—"

Rollin wilted, extracting his credit card. *God's work always costs money . . . damn it, and what is this dupe laughing about?*

"It's regrettable that I won't be able to give you the convention rate since, I feel certain, you're *not* attending the convention."

Only now did Rollin notice the looks he was getting from the flashy lobby crowd. "Convention? No, no. And the reason I've asked for Room 207 is only because I've stayed here before and love the room's view." *Priests shouldn't be able to lie so easily,* he considered. But the man had said something about a convention. "So what's the big event? Consumer trade show or something?"

Now the clerk was beside himself to stifle his amusement. His smile nearly went up to his eyes. "No, Father, I'm afraid not. It's the Adult Video Awards Convention."

Oh my God! Rollin thought. "I'll just . . . take the room, please." He collected his key-card and skirted back to the elevators. *Absolutely humiliating . . .*

More cosmetically perfected women smiled at him when he got off the elevator. "Oh, Father, I love your ring," said a platinum blonde in a body stocking. Rollin trembled when she grabbed his hand to look at it, forcing his eyes away from croquet-ball-sized breasts. "Uh, thank you. Go with God." He rushed to Room 207 and slipped in as quickly as he could. *If somebody I know sees me here . . . what on earth can I say?* But he shoved the trepidation away when he approached the wide windows and parted the drapes. The moment of truth was at hand. He took out his binoculars, stepped six feet back from the gap in the drapes, and zoomed down the alley, which cut up to Dessorio Avenue.

Well at least SOMETHING went right today, he thought when the view showed him that he'd calculated the angle with accuracy. If he stood right against the wall and hunched down, he got an almost dead-on view of the rear windows of the annex house. Rollin fixed himself some coffee, then pulled a chair to the wall to sit. *Peeping Tom time again*, he thought, amazed at his low-brow tactics. *What else can I do? Break into the place? The diocese couldn't bail me out because they don't even know!*

He tried to sever it all, along with the cosmic disappointment that a lifetime of service to God had led to this. Instead, he teased the focus ring on the glasses.

The top two floors stood drapeless and appeared empty, yet the long windows of the second level possessed raised blinds that revealed a room full of lit computers, book and media shelves, and a slant-angled table that he presumed was a drawing desk. *Must be her studio.* And below, on a balcony, one narrow window revealed a fairly wide

wedge of a very ornate bathroom, complete with a hot tub.
A floor lower, he could see the newly installed security bars
of the basement windows.

Rollin sighed. *Now what? I'm spending $279 per night of
my own money—of which I have precious little—all to afford a
view of the back of the annex house . . .*

What do I expect to see?

He supposed if he saw nothing, then his prayers would
be answered.

Movement flagged him from the studio window—*There
she is!* Rollin could see Cristina Nichols sitting at the
large computer screen dressed in a fine robe. At one point,
she got up from her work and walked to the window. She
seemed to be reveling in the sunlight, which was just beginning to pour in over the top of the higher-leveled condos behind the house.

When he coughed, the binocular's surreal clarity vi-
brated like an earthquake; for a second he glimpsed the
tops of two heads. *Who could that be?* He lowered his vantage point and saw a pair of homeless women shuffling
down the alley toward Columbus. One with glasses, and
one with scabs on her head. They jabbered silently as he
watched. Though homeless persons regularly came to the
West Side to panhandle, Rollin knew that few actually
lived there. Most of the shelters were near the lower
streets or up in the Harlem area, yet he'd seen these girls
with some frequency.

And Rollin felt certain that it was these women specifically who'd broken into the annex house a number of
times when he was its charge.

I'll have to confront them, he knew, *for all the good it'll do.
Or better yet, follow them some time.*

Rollin squinted into the eyepieces when he looked back
to the studio window. He also gulped.

Cristina Nichols now stood behind the glass with her
robe parted, her breasts bared. Rollin could hear his heart

thumping. *Don't watch. This is NOT what you're looking for, and you know it . . .*

God knows it, too.

In that last fraction of a glimpse, Cristina Nichols's face appeared blank, trancelike, and her hands were slowly caressing her breasts in the sun. The image seemed to pinpoint—on dark, swollen nipples. Then her hands slid downward . . .

What a place to do THAT—

But Rollin's heart thumped louder when he brought the binoculars back down. The two homeless girls were approaching the end of the alley. Much closer now, he could discern their unkempt details.

The one with the scabs on her head seemed to be wiping her hands off with a rag.

A white rag that came away red.

(II)

A hot fugue state was the only way she could think of it. For the second time, Cristina caught herself standing before her studio window, touching herself. She nearly shrieked when she grew cognizant of what she was doing, the recognition arriving just short of climax. *I'm turning into a nympho!* she thought when her senses returned, and she jumped back and resashed the robe.

What brought THAT on?

Her hangover had gone, replaced by *this*. She didn't like not knowing the cause of her actions, and after last night's drunken blackout, an uneasiness began to unsettle her stomach.

The nightmare, magnified this time, the drenching eroticism, the blood.

She went to shower again, to cool herself off and clear her head. What had she been doing? She turned the water from cool to cold, drawing goose bumps. *I was in the studio, working out a sketch of the next figure . . . The Vampirical Vicar . . .* It struck her as odd how the "vampire" bent had seeped its way into the *Evil Church* line: first the nun, now the vicar. She knew it was all just more influence of the nightmare. And, yes, she remembered working at her drawing table when, without invitation, remnant images had crept into her head: last night's lesbian-dream frolic, a half a dozen faceless women covering her with hands and tongues while the fanged nun looked on in proximity to the dead man on the stone slab and the queer vase sitting atop it. The unpleasant imagery should've left her desires mute yet Cristina found the opposite; she felt charged, misted with sweat, nipples tingling. *It's almost like I was in a trance,* she mused. When the dream imagery had faded, it had been replaced by something even more objectionable . . .

Britt.

Cristina felt ashamed in the recollection. She'd been sitting there suddenly remembering Britt erasing the magic marker from her skin but eventually Cristina's mind appended the memory. Next, she imagined not Britt's fingers on her skin but Britt's lips. Cristina cringed as wet lines were licked and sucked from nipples to navel, all the while Britt's fingers sliding behind to knead Cristina's rump and tease the bottom of her sex. Eventually she was urged to the bathroom floor, then Britt straddled her stomach, shouldered out of the scarlet shearling vest, and forced Cristina's hands to her breasts. Britt sighed, her face upturned. Then she leaned, propped by her arms, to slowly offer her own nipples to Cristina's mouth, a hot whisper pleading, "Suck them. Hard. Like when—"

Like when . . .

Cristina did so without reservation, in spite of the *awfulness* of the reference. Her sex moistened as if on cue, her own nipples suddenly gorged to aching.

"Yes, yes," Britt breathed through her teeth. "Just like . . . so long ago . . ."

The fantasy, however jaded, only stoked Cristina further. Her mouth continued to tend to her foster sister's areolae while her fingers fumbled frantically at the buttons of the jeans. "Take these off," she whined in a hot swivet. "Take them off right now and . . ."

The fantasy snapped and once again Cristina found herself standing open-robed before her sunny studio window—

Masturbating, she finished. *Jeez.*

After the shower, she sat at her table, ashamed. Should she tell Britt? *God, no. I've already hassled her enough. Why can't I be strong, like her?* Cristina knew she overreacted to things, perceived her insecurities with far more cruciality than they warranted. This had happened before on rare occasions, and Britt's therapeutic analyses were always dismissively similar. *Erotic latency, the forbidden made enticing by social strictures,* she would say. *It's nothing. We're not even really sisters; it's just more Goldfarb mental backwash that your mind manipulates into a false fantasy, trying to get rid of it. But sometimes it takes a while.* When Cristina reminded herself of that, she felt better.

But just a little.

It seemed that her inability to shed the past was stealing from her. *Stealing my joy, my new life here.* Again, she knew what Britt would say:

Don't let it.

Among the demented abuses of her foster parents was the forced couplings. It was the only way Cristina could think of it. While Andre Goldfarb was busy molesting Scott, their foster brother, Helga worked on Cristina and Britt. She drugged them with God knew what and then coerced them into sexual scenarios in which Helga herself would eventually join in. Scott, too, was often forced to participate . . .

Scott hadn't fared well in the aftermath, while Cristina

and Britt were able to adjust via therapy after the authorities had rescued them. *Goddamn the Goldfarbs*, she thought all too often. "They'll probably die in prison," Britt had said once. "Child molesters are anathema on any cell block. It's the worst thing to be."

I hope so . . . Cristina wasn't one for ill will but here, certainly, was an understandable exception.

Early evening approached, her studio window growing dim. *I'm still a little out of whack from last night's booze*, she reasoned. *Just like Britt said. Minor alcohol poisoning and dehydration.* She looked back at her latest precursory sketch, and found she liked it even more. The Vampirical Vicar. She smiled at the playful sketch. At first she thought of drawing a modern-day priest—like Father Rollin, perhaps—but drew this instead, a stuffy parson that appeared more English, in pompous red vestments denoting the clergy of hundreds of years ago. Large doll-like eyes were bloodshot, and like much of the line the face was more cherubic than scary. She wasn't sure if the long, straight mustache worked or not but she found she liked the image. The vicar's crooked smile showed long thin fangs, just like the Noxious Nun.

I wonder . . .

An unbeckoned thought caused her to amend the sketch. Where her Noxious Nun bore a three-jeweled bowl of blood, the Vampirical Vicar held a curious decanter—from her dream, of course—which suggested a vessel for Communion wine.

Now she liked the sketch even more.

I can't wait to show this to Bruno. Enthused, then, Cristina focused at her table, to begin a more refined draft.

(III)

"So we're here for what reason?" Vernon asked Detective Taylor in the small, computer-filled cubby loudly referred to as the Electronic Evidence Assimilation Unit at Manhattan North Borough Command. Taylor scratched his unkempt mustache and frowned. "It's what you wanted, and because you didn't tag a link on the case number from last December, I couldn't go to the Information Systems Division downtown."

Vernon's mind wandered. He was standing behind a civilian employee hunkered over a terminal. "December? Oh, the Christmas tree stand thing."

"Yeah, *that* big caper. Ain't no way it's not connected to the impalement."

"I know but it's hard to push that way."

"You're just afraid of being laughed at since making inspector."

"Tell me about it." Vernon had to agree. "Christmas tree stands, magic markers, and forty bucks' worth of whittling knives . . ."

Taylor smiled wide. "And bum-girls, speaking of which . . ." The detective pointed to the computer screen.

"There they are," Vernon said in a hush.

"When I told you the owner of the hardware store couldn't find the surveillance disk, I was wrong. They never got it back from us. It's been in the C.E.S. mainframe the whole time. Took this guy here two minutes to pull it up."

Vernon's eyes were taken by the screen, which now showed several haggardly dressed females moving in slow-motion down an aisle of the darkened hardware store. The nerdy tech at the desk would freeze the closest image of each perpetrator, hit a key, then slo-mo to the next. A printer below the desk hummed, kicking out four eight-by-ten glossies. The tech handed the photos to Vernon.

"These look great," Vernon complimented.

The tech smirked like an accountant bothered by something trivial. "You could've done it from your precinct house."

"We don't have that kind of technology at our house," Vernon told him.

The tech smirked sharper. "Inspector, it's *ten-year-old* technology."

"Like I said, we don't have that kind of technology at our house."

Taylor eyed the slick printouts. "Just like the drugstore."

Now the tech shook his head. "Where have you guys been? Nobody gets pictures developed at the drugstore anymore. Don't you have a printer and a digital camera?"

Vernon and Taylor raised their brows. "We're old-school, but thanks," Vernon said. Then he took Taylor back out to the parking lot. They studied the printouts more closely, while Taylor verbalized a description of each woman running down the aisle with several boxed Christmas tree stands:

"Ratty-looking blonde with glasses, ratty-looking brunette in pink sweatpants, *another* ratty-looking brunette in ratty-looking jeans, a ratty-looking redhead, and—"

Vernon completed the summary, "A ratty-looking woman with very short hair and patches of psoriasis—"

"And large breasts . . . not that I'd want *my* face between them. She's probably got *boob* lice."

"You sound like Slouch," Vernon complained.

"No, Slouch would *want* his face between them. You know Slouch—after a couple beers, anything goes." Taylor flipped through the photos again. "At least we know what they look like. No way to tell how old they are, but if we spot one on the street we'd probably recognize them."

"Yeah, but that's too easy," Vernon offered cynically. "That's not the way my luck runs since I turned fifty."

"Ten-year hard-luck streak, How?"

"That's *Inspector* How to you . . . Patrolman-to-be Taylor." Taylor laughed. "I'm just joshin'."

"Just what I need." Vernon threw Taylor the keys to the unmarked. "You drive. I'm too *old*."

"Yes, sir, Inspector. Where to?"

"Same area you and Slouch cruised with that twenty-five-year-old hooker who looks thirteen."

"Cinzia. Right." Taylor pulled off onto 100th, then darted into traffic on Broadway.

Vernon was thinking as he reexamined the hard copies. "The redhead was the one we busted in December, right? Where's she now, or have you been slacking?"

Taylor's dark mustache trailed down the sides of his mouth like an Italian actor from the seventies. "She's long gone. I already did the follow-up this morning."

Vernon glared. "Then how come you didn't *tell* me that this morning?"

"Because I was busting my ass trying to run down the fuckin' surveillance footage from the hardware store like you told me to do," Taylor emphasized with a raised voice, knuckling the wheel.

"Oh, right. Good job, by the way. So what happened to the redhead?"

"She was clinically fucked-up so she never stood trial." Vernon turned on the fireball-light on the dash and whooped his siren, to make an illegal turn past Cleopatra's Needle, run a red light on 92nd, and shoot a right onto Amsterdam. Other drivers leaned on their horns but Taylor didn't even hear them. "Chronic abulia and apraxia, they told me, whatever that means. And 'schizoaffective.' They let her out of the state hospital after a blue paper and ninety days of therapy; her case doctor said she was not capable of mens rea. Then the OT counselor told me she split town, took the first Greyhound out to DeSmet, South Dakota . . . Like I've heard of that. Give me some time and I'll try to run her down."

Vernon shuddered when a bus roared by. "Don't bother. The minute they're out of a therapeutic environment, they stop taking their meds and are back to square one. She was nuts and homeless here, you can bet she's nuts

and homeless in South Dakota. We'll just eyeball the
streets where the hooker said to. We've got nothing else to
do except go home."

Taylor opened his mouth but then closed it again without a word. They passed Tecumseh Playground and Verdi
Square. Post–rush hour was still heavy with vehicles. At
every corner, however, panhandlers could be seen sitting
down with their empty cups or trudging this way and that
amid the throng of the upper crust. "Who says there's no
homeless problem on the Upper West Side?" Taylor remarked.

Vernon reflected. "Like the hooker was telling us, if
they don't foot it all the way up here from the shelters
every day, they squat in recently closed buildings. It makes
sense."

"Yeah. If your career is bumming change, you're better
off doing it here than the fuckin' Bronx. Restaurants, bars,
stores, they're going under or getting bought out every day.
You shack up in one place for a week or two, then move on
to the next. I've just never really noticed so many homeless around here in the past."

"That's because this is the first time we've actually been
looking for them. And that Cinzia girl . . . Didn't she say
something about the hardware store chicks congregating
near a vendor at the corner of Dessorio?"

"Right. Slouch and I talked to the guy. He verified what
the hooker told us but—"

"Couldn't give specifics 'cos he probably sees a hundred
different homeless people every damn day," Vernon reasoned.

"Um-hmm." Taylor slowed the car, pointing. "There's
the guy now. Wanna go talk to him? Now we've got pictures he can look at."

Vernon eyed the short, stocky vendor at the corner. He
wore a New York Islanders shirt and a Mets cap, and had a

gnawed cigar between his teeth. "Naw. I told you. My luck doesn't run that way."

Taylor pursed his lips. "It's *police work*, How. You're the one who said we've got nothing better to do. Come on. And you can buy me a hot dog. I don't make enough on detective's pay."

Vernon shrugged. "All right."

Taylor pulled into a No Parking zone. The instant they both got on the sidewalk, they froze.

"I don't believe it," Vernon muttered into the flow of oncoming pedestrians.

Taylor cut a big grin. "And you said your luck never runs this way."

"Mine doesn't but evidently yours does." Vernon threw the photos back in the car and extracted his handcuffs. "Grab her."

Taylor immediately latched onto the arm of a shabby, large-breasted woman in cutoff military pants. Her very short dark hair was patched with bald spots and scabs.

"Hey!" she whined. "Take your—"

"Police," Vernon said. "You're under arrest."

"You shits! Help me, somebody! These cops are trying to rape me!" she shrieked.

Vernon chuckled. "Christmas tree stands and wood-carving knives? But relax, you don't have to tell us anything because you have the right to remain silent."

Taylor pushed her forward against the car and cuffed her.

"You can't hold me," the seedy woman proclaimed. "I can fly anything God can make! I'm gonna lock you up in a cave full of milk bottles and soup!"

Vernon rolled his eyes at Taylor. Taylor said, "Rice Krispies."

"The government put these cameras in my teeth!" She opened her mouth wide. "Now they can see you two shit-cakes!"

"Get her in the car," Vernon said, unable to refrain from smiling.

"These guys aren't cops!" she wailed. "They got fake badges that the guys who killed Kennedy gave them!"

"Those are some lines, huh?" But Taylor paused before moving her off. "Hey, How. Check it out."

Vernon stooped to peer. He was looking at the woman's very dirty hands cuffed behind her back. All of her fingernails appeared to be lined with dried blood.

CHAPTER NINE

(I)

"There he is," Paul said, looking up from his booth at Harry's Bar at the Helmsley Hotel. It was their after-work hangout, and seemed to be devoid of other attorneys but chock-full of stockbrokers, whose barside banter always proved more interesting than that of the former. Half of the brokers looked on the verge of suicide. Paul swizzled a Johnny Walker Blue on the rocks, and already had a bottle of Asahi waiting for Jess. Jess sat down as if winded, his hair perpetually disarrayed, and drained a third of the bottle.

"I take it Massacessi's people didn't dig your arbitration rebuttal," Paul suspected of his partner's more-harried-than-usual look.

"Oh, they loved it, but the traffic on Third sucks. Christ, it's past seven."

"I always cut up Eighth, then swing over on Forty-second."

"Sure, probably to stop and snag some lap dances."

"Don't need to." Paul huffed a chuckle. "Since Cristina's moved in, she's turned into a dynamo. She's wearing me out."

"There's always the Big Blue."

"Yeah. I take 'em in place of One A Days." Paul sipped his twenty-five-dollar drink. "I tweaked the highlights on

the Soledad motion and punted them. It looks good . . .
even for billing five-seventy-five an hour. So what about
Massacessi?"

"They want to renew for five years—"

"You're shitting me?" Paul said, startled. "That's great.
Hell, I ought to let you pocket the whole retainer 'cos you
did all the work."

Jess's brow shot up over his next chug of fancy beer.
"Really?"

"Fuck you . . . partner."

Both men laughed. "Don't know how you can drink
those fussy Jap dry beers, but I picked up a case for you
anyway, for this weekend."

Even Jess's spiked goatee looked sloppy. "This weekend?
Oh, yeah. Cookout at your place."

Paul smiled. "Well, *carry*out, not cookout. You haven't
seen the house since we got all the furniture in. It looks
so sumptuous I almost feel guilty living there . . . Almost."

"Once a lawyer, always a lawyer. The Catholic Church
has too much property as it is. You're like Robin Hood but
with none of that 'give to the poor' jive on the end."

Paul shrugged through another sip of scotch. "Just as
the Ten Commandments were written in stone so were
these words: 'A buyer's superior knowledge of property
value is NOT actionable.'"

"Amen."

Through the front window, they both glimpsed a minibus
waiting for the light on 3rd. Big letters along the side read:
FAMILY SERVICES FOSTER CARE OF NEW YORK.

Both men averted their eyes at once, neither speaking,
until the bus pulled off. Eventually Paul broke the silence.
"Just when you think you've forgotten about something
shitty."

"I hear ya. But I read somewhere than 90 percent of the
foster services in the U.S. are right on."

"Yeah, but we're both living with two girls who fall into that other 10 percent. It just burns me up, those Goldfarb psychos. Twenty years ain't enough."

"They'll croak in stir, watch." Jess always took the positive side.

Paul ordered another round. "Ain't good enough. Sometimes I think about paying someone on the inside to fuck them up."

Jess lost his joviality fast. He leaned over and whispered, "If you're going to make yourself liable for premeditation and conspiracy, kindly refrain from doing it in front of *me*, and think about not talking that kind of shit in a *public place*."

Paul waved it off. "You know what I mean. And don't tell me you haven't thought about it, too, 'cos if you do . . . you're a liar."

"Can't argue with ya there. Better way to look at it is Goldfarb's probably got a size-thirteen asshole by now. That's good enough for me. And you're forgetting the only good thing to come out of it."

"What's that?"

"Even after a childhood like theirs, Britt and Cristina landed on their feet and both got their shit supremely squared away."

Paul nodded but it was half-dismal. "I guess I just think too much. That was some pretty awful shit they had to go through."

"Sure. Giving barbs to little kids, and God knows what else, and molestation, I presume."

Paul looked up, puzzled. "You *presume?* Didn't Britt—"

"She told me some of it but none of the details," Jess said. "She's a strong chick, both of them are." A pause over his beer. "You mean Cristina told you everything?"

Paul reeled a bit in the posh seat. "Well, yeah, pretty much. The Goldfarbs drugged them up all the time, and had them doing everything to each other."

Jess squinted at the unpleasant revelation. "Each other? I thought it was just Andre, you know . . ."

"No, no, man," Paul corrected, smirking as though the scotch were lemon juice. "Andre and his wife were switching off between the two of them *and* the foster brother, and they made them all . . . do . . . each other. They even had their friends over. The psychos were putting those kids in orgies."

Jess looked shell-shocked. "I—I had no idea. Britt never got into that much detail."

"It was some sick shit. And the brother never made it— he's in an institution, *all* fucked-up. It was a fuckin' kiddie porn club the Goldfarbs had going. They took thousands of pictures and sold the shit to their little network of perverts. I petitioned the prosecutor's office to let me see the post-trial evidence, but I'll tell ya, I wish I never had. I actually threw up once I got back to my car. You wouldn't believe what those scumbags were doing to Britt and Cristina in those pics, and you can *tell*, even though they were just kids." Paul gulped. "You can tell by their faces that it was Cristina and Britt."

Jess just stared, his mouth sagging open.

A black aura seemed to settle over each man's head. Paul cleared his throat—"But like you said, all that matters is that they both shook it off and landed on their feet in spite of it. Most girls who go through the wringer like that don't. Neither of them are fucked-up at all . . . Well, maybe Cristina is a little sometimes—Christ, look at those dolls she designs, but the shrink she saw in Stamford said it was a constructive therapeutic outlet. And you wouldn't believe the money she made last year from those things."

"I know. Britt told me," Jess said. He was trying to shake off the shock of the bombshell that had just been dropped on him. "Britt doesn't make a whole lot of money herself but she is doing a whole lot of good. She told me that

that's *her* therapy. But I didn't know about all that other shit. I'll think twice whenever I give her a hard time about some piddly bullshit like forgetting to take my fuckin' *suits* to the cleaners. Christ."

"Yeah, and I *drink* too much," Paul said, and raised his glass. "We're both attorneys so I guess that means we're both assholes."

"Yeah, but at least we're *rich* attorneys, so that's got to count for something," Jess tried to joke. "Ultimately, there's a lot of really sick scumbags in the world, and we've got to do everything we can to protect our girls from them."

"Tell me about it. There's evil everywhere—it's a sick, sick world, all right." Paul seemed to ruminate on something. "I know this guy who does legal consultations for the cops, he's always up at the Forensic Investigations Division in Queens. I ran into him today at Joseph's Steakhouse, and you know what he told me?"

Jess looked physically pummeled by everything he'd already heard in the last few minutes. "Do I *want* to know?"

"They managed to keep it out of the papers so far but he said the cops found a woman murdered yesterday by impalement."

Jess gaped. "Impalement? What the hell is—"

"Somebody sharpened the end of a broomstick or something and pushed it up this woman's snatch till it was in her mouth. And she was *alive* when they did it." Paul clinked the ice in his glass, his eyes off-focus. "How's that for a sick world?"

(II)

Sandrine laughed, munching the macadamia nuts she'd shoplifted dirtied-handed from the bulk foods section of a Gristede's Supermarket. "It's sort of like a Christmas tree. We should get lights!"

"There's no electricity here, you dope," Francy reminded her.

"Oh. Yeah. But still, it would be cool, wouldn't it?"

She and Francy both looked with satisfaction at Doke, propped up now and quite dead on the sharpened wooden pike. He just hung there, his feet a few inches off the ground.

"He'll start to-start to-start to stink soon," Stutty commented, her wan face shifting in the candlelight.

"So what?" Francy kept looking at the corpse. Even after they'd propped him up, it had taken him a few minutes to die. She enjoyed the way he sort of *quivered* on the pike. "The New Mother said that our Prince liked the smell so much he kept impaled bodies in the room where he ate his meals."

"Gross," Sandrine offered.

"It was a different time, Sandrine."

Sandrine shuffled idly to the corner where they kept a pile of canned food and candy bars they stole. She knelt before the several dolls she'd stood up on the floor, but . . .

She'd had three. Only two stood there now.

She wiped her smudged hands off on her pink sweatpants. "Who ripped off my doll?" She examined the remaining two, one a cutesy little girl who was blue and frosted, the other a smiling girl with black bangs who looked like she was rotting. Sandrine couldn't really read but if she could she would've seen the names on the bottoms of each figurine: HYPOTHERMIA HARRIET and LEPROSY LINDA. "I had three here, but now one's missing!" she complained, glaring at her associates with suspicion. "The boy with the bloody belly is gone."

"We don't steal, except the way our Prince did," Francy reminded her. "Like the New Mother said. You only steal from those who steal from others."

"But the boy with the bloody belly was the coolest one!"

"Where-where did *you* get them?" Stutty asked with a grin.

"Well, I ripped 'em off from the lady's house, but . . . I wasn't really stealing. I was gonna take 'em back."

"That's all right," Francy bid as if forgiveness was hers to dole out. "She's not in the convent. But you know none of us stole it. We're your sisters now."

"Virginia stole it, probably-probably-probably—"

"Be quiet!"

Sandrine fumed. "It figures. She was a shitty bitch anyway—"

Francy chuckled. "And she won't be stealing *anything* now."

"Yuh-yuh-yeah!" Stutty guffawed.

Sandrine cooled off, and put the two figurines in her pocket. "I hope the New Mother comes tonight."

"She will, unless we haven't been faithful enough."

Stutty frowned at a can of anchovies. "We should-we should-we sh—"

"Be quiet!" Francy yelled.

"We should *what?*" Sandrine asked, bored now.

Stutty concentrated, her fists clenched. "We should get something good to eat tonight. I'm sick of these gross an-an-anchovies."

"We can do that," Francy approved. "We have some money now, and the New Mother says it's okay if the money comes from the faithless."

"Let's go to McDonald's and get good stuff," Sandrine enthused.

"I'd ruh-ruh-ruh—" Stutty ground her wobbly teeth. "I'd rather get a meatball sub at the Subway next to the health food store."

"We can get whatever we want," Francy told them. "Let's go now."

More than $500 comprised Doke's till; these were high times. *Thank God for the New Mother*, Francy thought with a smile full of holes. But a scrabbling caused them all to look toward the narrow entrance.

"It's probably Scab," someone said. "I haven't seen her all day."

"Oh," Francy said.

It was another homeless woman, whose name was Crazy because that's what she was.

"Not her!" Sandrine complained.

"You can't-can't-can't come here!" Stutty yelled. "This is our house."

Crazy wore a pair of plaid men's shorts she'd found in the garbage, and a black blouse with torn-off sleeves. Her black hair looked electrocuted, and one eye constantly looked to the left. She was barefoot and pallid as cream.

"Ruthie Mooseface and Blinda told me you lived here," Crazy said, scratching lice. When she started coming closer, Francy blocked her; she didn't want Crazy to see the impaled drug dealer stuck benhind the stack of boxes. *Ruthie Mooseface and Blinda, huh?* "Hi, Crazy. Yeah, we've lived here for nine months. That's how long the place has been empty, and no workmen have come yet. But don't tell anyone else we're here, okay?"

Crazy stood like someone who'd had a bad stroke, which was actually true. "The Z-Men said they'd kill me, they've been looking for me. Can I stay here a while?"

"No!" Sandrine snapped.

"Be quiet, Sandrine," Francy said more calmly. "Of course she can stay here. She can even join the convent. The New Mother said we have to help our sisters."

Crazy didn't even question the bizarre statement.

"But to join," Francy told her, "you have to die—"

CRACK!

It was Stutty who'd brought the brick down on Crazy's head from behind.

"Take her clothes off," Francy ordered the two girls. She smiled. "I'll get a stick."

(III)

Cristina awoke just as the clock struck one in the morning. She lay still, thinking. *Why am I . . . wide awake?* She should be exhausted. Paul had come home from work later than usual but he'd scarcely stepped through the front door before they'd been wrapped up in one another. Cristina could tell by his breath that he'd been drinking yet the day's rising desire melted any disfavor she might normally feel. She had his ocher-hued dress shirt off and on the foyer floor before his brain could register the act; just as fast she practically tore open his pants. Paul hadn't had to bother removing Cristina's clothes for she'd greeted him at the door nude.

She had felt desperate for the gluttonous sensations that only a man could provide—there'd be no waiting to get to the bedroom. "Here, here," she panted, her breasts pressed against his chest. Her sex seemed to *pulse* along with her heart. "Right here." And then she brought him down to the handwoven Ersari carpet. Paul was about to speak but Cristina began sucking his tongue before he got the chance. Frenzy sunk her crotch right down, taking him all the way. It didn't seem that his previous imbibing had hindered his ability, as it had the night before. Cristina's eyes rolled upward with each stroke. "Harder, my God," her voice gushed. "Do it as hard as you can—" And when he did she squealed half in shock and half in delight. She felt gored now, and pommeled, but that was how she *needed* to feel. Her lust made her blood feel thick. Paul's groin continued to bludgeon her most private place, and all she wanted was more. Each thrust only added more heat to her yearning, which now seemed primitive, more than human. She cringed as he climaxed and filled her sex with a flood of slickened heat. Cristina continued to ride him fast until he turned limp. Paul half-gasped his apology, "Aw, honey, I'm sorry I didn't last long en—"

Her mind reeled, all her thoughts a stew of lust. "It's all right, it's all right," she panted. Still straddling him, she grabbed his hands and forced them to her breasts, which now felt so full of blood and desire that they seemed alien to her, twice the size they should be. "Squeeze them, squeeze *hard*," she pleaded. When she tensed her thighs, the well of semen drained out of her. She intricately plied her sex in unison with his kneading fingers, then shrieked again and climaxed. The series of spasms first clenched every muscle in her body, then collapsed her to the floor, wracked. Her own sexual fluids had seemed to pour out of her.

"Oh, baby," he groaned when he got enough breath back to talk. "You're an *animal* . . . but of course I mean that in a good way."

She lay limp against him, one thigh draped over his stomach. "Well, this animal has been thinking about you all day long . . . even when I was still hungover. Her thigh nudged his spent genitals. "And, don't worry, I'll be taking advantage of you again before long."

Paul chuckled. "Honey, you're gonna kill me but . . . so what?"

When Cristina felt more of him trickle out of her, she suddenly lurched. "Oh my God! The carpet!"

"Probably the biggest wet spot of all time," Paul laughed, still flattened.

"It's from Uzbekistan!" she exclaimed. "You paid thousands for it." She started to jump up, to grab some carpet cleaner and rags, but Paul just pulled her back next to him.

"Cristina. I'll buy another one. Let's just . . . lie here a while . . ."

Cristina relaxed. *I wore him out, all right.* But in truth she only felt half-sated even after her own orgasm. He appeared to be drifting off to sleep right now. "Honey? Honey?" she said, gently jostling him. "You're falling asleep on the floor."

"Mmm," he replied, then blinked back some alertness.

"Since you're responsible for completely immobilizing me . . . how about some coffee?"

Cristina giggled and kissed him quick, then slipped off to the kitchen. She made coffee and puttered in the kitchen a bit, not even really mindful of the fact that she was still naked. She felt brimming in sensations, her nipples still buzzing, and the soft afterglow between her legs working its way through the rest of her. "How was work?" she called out.

Paul answered groggily. "Not as good as *after* work but not bad. Jess landed a retainer renewal worth about two-point five mil, and I just closed a deal worth about half that."

Good Lord! "You call that 'not bad'? Paul, that's fantastic . . ."

"It's all this great sex you're wearing me ragged with," he replied. "It's good luck. It's an Oriental thing: sexual harmony brings prosperity."

"I suppose you read that in a fortune cookie," Cristina joked.

"I'm just . . . very lucky," he muttered but kept glimpsing a slice of her nakedness in the kitchen. "Uh, you know it's great having a gorgeous fiancée make me coffee bucknaked but make sure those blinds are closed all the way. Wouldn't that be a riot if there was an evening service letting out of the church and they all looked over *here?*"

Good idea, she realized. The blinds *were* opened slightly but she knew no one street level could see in. "Father Rollin told me he doesn't even have a congregation anymore," she explained, darting into the bedroom to select a robe. "Said the church is mainly used for special occasions and meetings." She pulled on a caramel-brown robe but momentarily shivered when the soft silk slipped across her nipples. *I can't believe this. I'm charged up like a battery tonight.* "He said he's going to come over sometime for coffee so he can introduce himself to you."

"You can bet he was just being polite," Paul said tiredly from the living room. "I doubt that he wants to meet the shifty attorney who clipped the New York Diocese out of a couple million bucks because they didn't bother to find out how much the property was worth in the long term."

"You didn't really *clip* them, did you?" Cristina asked, but she was still distracted by the robe's silkiness.

"Technically, no," Paul chuckled. "I was just doing my job better than their guy. Rule Number One in real estate law. One man's carelessness is another man's fortune."

Cristina was grateful for a career that didn't involve such tactics. She was about to come back to the kitchen, though, when—

"*Serveste pe domnul . . .*"

Cristina froze in the short hallway. Had she really heard the bizarre utterance? It sounded foreign and . . . muffled.

Then she heard a creak of some sort. She stood right beside the door to the basement. Cristina opened the door and looked down . . .

"Honey?" Movement in the other room, and hushed footsteps. "Where'd you go?"

Cristina looked over, concerned. Paul came forward, pants back on but belt buckle and shirt still undone. "I could've sworn I heard a voice, and—I'm not sure—but I think it came from down here." At once the obscure fear she'd expressed to Britt slammed back: that someone else was in the house.

Paul rolled his eyes. "I heard the same thing the other night, only upstairs. It's the people in the condos next door. They're all retired and hard of hearing; they turn their TVs up." His arm touched her shoulder. "Relax. It's nothing."

Cristina remained poised, eyes wide on the open doorway.

"Just to set your mind at ease," Paul said and snapped on the light switch, "I'll go look."

"Oh, please," she mumbled. "It was just so strange. It sounded foreign."

"So, they watch foreign *shows* next door. A lot of those old people are immigrants who made a lot of money starting businesses in the fifties." But Paul descended the basement stairs just the same.

What if, Cristina fretted, *someone really is down there?*

What would she do? And what if she really were right in what Britt dismissed as paranoia and overreaction, that last night in her stupor *someone else* had scrawled on her breasts and stomach?

For a moment, all the invisible blonde hairs on her arms stood straight up like filings under a magnet.

"Nothin' there, baby," Paul said, trudging back up.

"It just sounded so—"

He put a finger to her lips. "Don't worry your little heart about something that's impossible anyway. Every single exterior door and window in this house has not one but two alarm triggers." He snapped off the light and closed the door. "Come on." He put his arm around her and returned to the kitchen. "Now where's that coffee?"

Cristina poured him a cup, sluffing the incident off. "Sorry I'm such a nut today." She couldn't even begin to tell him everything else. "It's late. Have you even had dinner yet? Let me fix you something."

"Actually, with all the excitement at the office today, I'm not the least bit hungry, and besides"—Paul yawned— "I'm exhausted now, thanks to you. I'll have something delivered for you. Grace's delivers."

"I'm not hungry either." Now that her hasty fears had been allayed, she felt oversensitized again. "I'm never hungry after great sex . . . except for *more* great sex."

Paul laughed with a shake of the head. "Let's give the Captain a little time to get back to shipshape."

Shortly thereafter Paul had gone in to take a shower but

evidently Cristina's voracity had taken a bigger toll than he'd let on. She'd lounged on the couch for a while, reading through a book on Max Ernst and the "irrationalism" art movement, but when she peeked in the bedroom she found Paul already asleep. Her more greedy side felt let down but then she admitted, *He is forty, for God's sake, and his job's a pressure cooker,* so she resigned to bed herself, presuming to awake fresh in the morning, but—

Here she lay now—hours later—wide awake. She pressured her mind to recover anything she might have dreamt that would waken her so abruptly but found to her relief that there was nothing, just a pleasant *blankness* chaperoning her slumber. Suddenly that aggravated confusion permuted to satisfaction. She smiled in the dark. *No nightmare this time. No evil nun, no bowl full of blood in a dungeon with a man on a slab.* Paul lay sound asleep beside her; she touched his shoulder as the dirtiest inkling suggested itself: that she should excite him in his sleep and let him wake to find her atop him—she was certainly aroused enough—but then she elected not to. *I practically raped him tonight.* She traced her fingers across her sex and winced at the gust of pleasure. *Sex maniac,* she scolded herself and gently edged off the bed, slipped on her robe, and left the room. The clock ticking followed her to the kitchen, and it somehow amplified the rest of the house's silence. Even from outside—no sounds at all.

She lemoned some ice water as she reflected on the day. She'd gotten quite a bit of work done once her hangover had ebbed out; that and her ludicrous mishap with the magic markers. *Jeez, what a ditz,* she thought. It was funny now. *Sometimes I'm so on edge,* she realized, while other times not at all. *Maybe everyone's that way but I just don't see it.* She wandered the living room, sipping her water. A lewd smile came to her lips when she spied the expensive carpet that she and Paul had sullied; then she found herself turning out all but the light above the stove and peeking out through the wooden blinds. The church's upper windows were dark, though she couldn't imagine why she'd even be looking.

But of course: the priest. Father Rollin struck her as a very nice man, but his spirit seemed *crimped* by something, like a nerve pinched. But she'd only thought of him in the first place via the abstraction; she'd just begun on a *priest*, of sorts, for the second set of figures in her *Evil Church* line. At once her artist's inclinations sparked, and she was heading upstairs for her studio to tweak her day's work. Her feet took her quickly up the plush crimson carpet to the bare hall that led her to her studio.

She snapped on all the bright white overhead fluorescents, then turned on her computers. Several preliminary sketches, old and new, lay arranged on the drafting table. She eyed the most recent one—the Vampirical Vicar—then eyed the configured drawing model on the computer screen. *No, no, no,* she realized at once. It was the "tone" of the figure's dress that was off. *Too English,* she realized. She wanted antiquated and Gothic but more European. Even the name now—vicar—struck an out-of-tune chord. *Too obscure.* She got to sketching again, keeping the figure's dark eyes, prominent nose, and thick, straight-across mustache, but appareled him in religious raiments more reminiscent of early-Renaissance Eastern Europe. Her excitement surged. *It's so much more on the mark!* she exclaimed to herself and kept sketching. *No more Vampirical "Vicar,"* she resolved. Her thoughts ticked. *Kids today don't even know what a vicar is, but . . .* A quick glance to the first figure in the line—the Noxious Nun—and she thought, *Every nun needs an abbot, right? So . . .*

She wrote the words on the pad to see how they looked lettered out: THE ABOMINABLE ABBOT.

Yes. Much better . . .

Was this why she suddenly couldn't sleep? Her muse

stirring her to make this change forged in her subconscious? It didn't matter. The image and the name was much more interesting.

She tinkered another half hour, growing more and more satisfied as her conception of the character grew more and more complete. An hour later she felt as mentally exhausted as a ditchdigger must feel physically. She spun in her chair, lounging back. Her feet reeled off the floor and she knew that one of her moods was returning—a *sexual* mood. Suddenly she felt pressed in by her needs, thinking back to her spontaneous escapades with Paul right on the floor. When she glimpsed his picture on a bookshelf, she bristled with more pent-up excitement.

I can't believe I'm doing this, she told herself. She felt childlike, about to raid the cookie jar, but in this case they were very *adult* cookies. *I know it's here somewhere*, she thought, rummaging through several boxes of supplies she hadn't yet unpacked. *Ahhh . . .* She didn't pack it with her clothes for fear of Paul finding it; instead she'd secreted it in this box of power strips and extension cords . . .

Her vibrator.

It had been the instrument's style that essentially caused her to buy it—a stout plastic handle that tapered to a rubberized wand not much wider than a cigarette. She distilled her thoughts of Paul's body after she retook her seat and let the device's tip buzz over the pinpoints of her nipples. The sensation defied effective description, save to say that it seemed to stimulate nerves she didn't know she had and in ways that no other such device—or man—could effect. *You naughty girl*, she thought, cringing as she removed the buzzing tip from her nipples and stroked the shape of each breast entirely with the wand's curve. She imagined Paul's mouth on her sex as she continued, eventually sweeping the wand slowly across her belly and up and down the insides of her thighs, but—

She had to be honest with herself.

It wasn't so much Paul she was thinking about but instead the lustier aspects of last night's dream: the queue of women stroking her body with their hands and mouths alike. She tensed more in the soft chair, her belly sucking in and out as she now brought the maniacal tip closer and closer to the hood of her clitoris. *If Paul walked in right now . . . what could I ever say in a million years?* But the rankling thought was too weak to banish the fantasy. The images thickened in her head, and at last she let the tip find its target. She breathed through clenched teeth as the lesbian fancy summoned all those rising sensations at once and set them off like a bombshell. One orgasmic wave after another claimed her, leaving her helpless to spasm off in the chair, all the while those forbidden images in her head seeming more and more real as though she were *genuinely* being cocooned by several women.

Her body went slack in the chair; that *rawness* of postclimax would not allow her to leave the vibrator in place. It fell from her hand, buzzing inertly on the floor as she simply lay there in the chair as if floating.

When her breath returned she felt assailed by guilt. Sneaking upstairs to masturbate along with fantasies that didn't include the man she loved seemed like psychic cheating. Nevertheless, she couldn't deny the potency of the vibrator's prowess. She reached down, turned it off, and stuck it in a drawer.

What am I going to do with myself? She sputtered and pushed her tousled hair off her brow.

Then her eyes shot wide.

In a split second, Cristina went rigid as if from a bolt of fear. She spun in her chair without volition but found herself staring in dread at the back windows. She knew the source of the sudden dread; it was the impression that she was being watched.

She rushed to the windows. But it would be impossible for anyone in the alley to see her all the way over at her desk. *Why do I feel like someone was watching me?* She gazed between the slats of the newly installed blinds. *And who COULD?* Across the alley only a few balconied condos could be seen a street back, and Cristina knew likewise that the sheer angle from those lofts wouldn't allow for a voyeur's prying eye. But when she inspected the windows more closely she found that when she looked to the right there was a vantage point she'd been previously unaware off: half of the alley's opening could be viewed, and through it a wedge of the main road and some hotels and other buildings.

She frowned and shook her head, sputtering again. The notion was folly; even if someone that far away *could* see in here, what would compel them to? *They'd need binoculars or a telescope, for God's sake.*

Enough of this. *Back to bed.* Downstairs, however, she paused at the door to the basement. *Why am I . . .* She looked at the door, touched the knob. Then she laughed to herself. Between passing out down there last night, and then her insistence of hearing strange voices several hours ago, she knew she had something to prove to herself. *A test . . . to prove there's nothing down there.*

Unafraid, she opened the door, switched on the lone bulb, and went down. Masses of dust-skinned clutter seemed congealed in the dark. Boxes, mostly. *None of it's our stuff,* she knew. *The church must've abandoned it all once Paul bought the house.* She peered into several of the boxes and found everything from old toasters and electric can openers to books decades old. One box was filled entirely with *The Book of Common Prayer* and another, *Catholic Prayers for the Dead*, but years of humidity left them bulged with rot. *We'll have to clean this place up eventually,* she thought but found her eyes skimming along the floor. Would she find the magic marker she was sure she'd touched last night? Or perhaps she wasn't even looking. The boxes formed wide aisles and now she meandered through them, toward the sodium light pouring in through the street-level windows. She looked out and saw only the alley street and the bricks of the buildings beyond. Without thinking, she tried the windows to make sure they remained intact and locked. She found herself trying to focus but didn't know on what. No foreign "voices" were in evidence down here, nothing amiss. *See?* she challenged herself. But she never noticed the erratic footprints on the dusty floor toward the rear.

She had to squint in the weak light, half-feeling her way back toward the steps. Then she peered down . . .

That oblong patchwork of cement.

"The same exact spot I passed out on," she told herself aloud.

The coolness of the cement reached up through her feet but strangely transformed into heat. She felt every square inch of skin beneath the robe glaze with a light sweat, while that maddening oversensitivity returned twofold. The silk robe was again charging her skin; at once she was anxious nearly to the point of audibly whining. Her nipples erected, and her sex began to prickle through some heady frisson. *I'm insatiable*, she realized. Even after the powerful sexual release just minutes ago, she cringed again in the same wantonness.

She kept staring down. *Not again* . . . She cupped her breasts outside the robe, then within, as she encircled the patch's small emblem with her toe, the crude design that looked like a strangled dragon . . .

Her eyes widened, then squeezed shut, and in that black interim, images from the nightmare splashed into her mind like paint thrown against a wall: the fanged nun, the three-gemmed blood-filled bowl, the weird voices and the man on the slab and the bizarre decanter and the many sets of feminine hands cosseting her body . . .

And, indeed, when Cristina winked out of the mental jag, she caught herself openly caressing herself, right where she stood. *This is crazy!* she thought. She didn't like this place. What had caused her to even come down here? She sashed her robe—frowning at not only herself but this new and seemingly limitless sexual angst—and started back toward the stairs.

A figure, obscure as soot, blocked the way.

Cristina's heart gave a jolt.

"Cristina!" Paul exclaimed. "What are you doing down here?"

"Jesus, Paul, you scared me half to death!" Cristina wilted in the aftershock. But . . . how would she answer his question? "I—I'm not sure why . . ."

When Paul took several steps, the basement's single bulb surfaced him from the blots of darkness. "When I woke up, you weren't in bed," he said, looking around with disapproval at all the excess clutter. "Then I thought I heard voices. Were you . . . talking to yourself down here?"

Had she been? She knew she did that sometimes. "I guess I could have been," she admitted. Suddenly she became overly aware of her erected nipples pushing bumps in the sheer robe. Would he notice? And, worse, had he seen her caressing herself. *My God, I hope not.*

"Well, I talk to myself sometimes, too," he said. The stacks of stained boxes seemed to annoy him. "Christ, I didn't realize how much *junk* the diocese left. I'll have to hire some refuse people to take it to the dump."

Cristina's head filled with a mild drone. She felt woozy by the sight of him meandering closer; her desires were hijacking her. *I can't help it,* she thought hopelessly. *I . . .* "Paul?" she whispered and let her robe come undone. "I need you again."

Had the light dimmed by some fluke in the current? Suddenly he was just an obscure shadow again.

"*Oise plac'ute,*" flowed the weird accent-tinted words and that's when Cristina felt electrocuted by the shock of discovering that this figure in the dark was *not* Paul, it was a curvaceous woman, nude save for a nun's wimple and hood, her flesh seeming half-composed by the darkness itself but flesh nonetheless for when her hands reached out to touch Cristina's breasts they were warm and very, very real, and then the woman grinned, showing two long thin fangs ringed by wet lips. Cristina couldn't budge as the lips moved closer, sealed over her own, and then the hot, phantom tongue slid between the fangs and plunged brassily right into Cristina's mouth, all the while the nun's hands kneading her breasts and twisting her inflamed nipples. Cristina had the impression of other figures scurrying around her from behind and sneaking up the stairs, but her horror quashed the observation. Meanwhile, the nun's hot mouth sucked all the air from her lungs, and then Cristina quailed, rose up on her tiptoes, and fainted dead away.

(IV)

Paul shuddered out of sleep just as the clock in the hall struck two. His arms raked the bed's left side where he expected to feel Cristina but she wasn't there. As his grogginess wore off, he discerned the hiss of the shower, could see the thin thread of light under the door.

Paul rubbed his eyes. He felt some odd sensation that he couldn't name but then forgot about it when he thought back to his and Cristina's frizzly lovemaking earlier. *What more could I ask?* he thought, chuckling. Just as he was drifting off again, he heard the shower hiss stop. A pause for a minute or two; he could hear her now, drying off. Then a wedge of light hit his eyes as the door partly opened. Just as Cristina would step out, the light snapped off, leaving Paul blind. He could hear but not see her approach the bed, felt the mild jostle when she sat on the mattress-edge near his knees.

"Couldn't sleep?" he asked.

Her hand ran down his stomach. "Uh-uh."

I'll bet I could go again, he realized, but when he touched her bare shoulder and attempted to slide his hand to her breast, she straddled him, gently grabbed his wrists, and placed them above his head. Then her own hands came back to his groin.

Oh, yeah . . . Paul still couldn't see a thing. Cristina's fingers wasted no time exciting him, but they also distracted him. "Aw, baby," he said. He'd hardened already, and then his teeth clicked together at the meticulous way she was handling him, unlike anything she'd done before. He reached down, then, and touched her leg—

"Honey, that feels so—"

"Shhh!" she demanded and quickly returned his hands back up over his head, feigning bondage, he supposed.

"Oh, kinky, huh?"

Again, "Shhh . . ." And then her mouth immediately lowered to his genitals. Paul tensed up at once. Her mouth worked frenetically, fingers working in unison. She was performing the intimate act with a fast, slick intricacy that astonished him. It was noisy and wild. Paul's head reeled at the feeling. *She's never done it this good before,* he realized in a lusty stupor. *She must be watching pornos or something . . .*

Her mouth continued to *work* him. She was simply doing it and demanding nothing in return. In spite of being so thoroughly drained on the living room floor, Paul's climax was breaking before he knew it, her mouth never abating. He tensed for many moments as his lust emptied, then went slack on the bed. Her lips remained tight as they eventually slipped off. He heard her swallow.

I guess it wouldn't exactly be romantic to tell her that that was the best blow job of my life, he wondered. "Oh, damn, baby, that was just so—"

She errantly gave his spent genitals a caress, then the bed creaked as she got up. Was she walking around the bed? He still had no night vision thanks to the momentary shock of light when she'd come out of the bathroom. "Where are you . . ."

The bedroom door clicked open, but there was so little light in the hall that he could barely detect her form stepping out of the room and heading for the kitchen.

"Honey? Would you get me a can of Sprite?" he asked.

"Um-hmm." And then her shadow disappeared.

Wow. That was something. I'll bet Jess doesn't get action like that . . .

Paul remained lying back, sated. He kept drifting in and out, but when he focused his thoughts and looked at the LED clock, he saw that ten minutes had passed and Cristina hadn't come back to bed. It didn't matter, he had to go to the bathroom anyway. He turned on the lamp by the bedside, glanced over, then did a double take at Cristina's airy, walk-in closet. The door hung open and he noticed several dresses on the floor. They must've fallen from their hangers but it was odd. Cristina was a neat freak. *Not like her to overlook something like that.* Then he went into the bathroom, still steamy from her shower, but noticed water on the floor, the towel lying there, and the shampoo sitting on its side. *What a mess.* And again, it was odd to observe. Cristina always picked up after herself.

He finished, put on his robe, and went out to the kitchen. Another raised brow, then, when he noted more minor disarray: the refrigerator door an inch ajar, several cabinets hanging open, a bag of plantain chips busted open and sitting on the counter, along with crumbs. He chuckled at her sudden slovenliness.

But where was she?

Several chips crunched underfoot when he walked to the stairs. A glance up showed him her studio lights on. *I guess tooting my horn gave her some creative inspiration,* he joked. But she often would work spontaneously, sometimes jumping up from bed just to jot down some notes or pen a quick sketch. Artistic people were like that.

He thought of going up to talk but decided not to. *Don't interrupt her. Besides, my jones is taken care of for a while*. But when he turned he noticed yet another oddity.

A pair of shoddy old blue jeans and an orange tube-top lay in the hall. Had she just dropped them there? *Why not put them in the laundry room ten fucking feet away?* he wondered, now a bit testy at her carelessness. *I paid a lot of money for this joint and all of a sudden she's treating it like a trailer*. After a few seconds, though, he thought back to the outstanding sex and reconsidered. *On second thought . . . she can mess the place up all she wants. I'll hire a damn maid*.

Next, he squinted at the clothes. *Must be old stuff she wears when she works*, he reasoned. He couldn't even recall ever seeing her in the tube-top. *I'll just go back to bed*, he decided, but after a glance into the cove at the foyer's end, he amended, *Or maybe I'll have a drink first*. One couldn't hurt, right? *I work damn hard*. Quietly as he could, he went to the glass-and-mirror bar, poured two fingers of Dewar's eighteen-year-old, and snuck back to the darkened kitchen for some ice. It only bothered him a little to sneak around like this; he knew more often than not her objections to his drinking were overreactive. Nevertheless, he went back to the bathroom to sip his drink, in case Cristina came back down unexpectedly.

The expensive scotch filled him with that inexplicable warm buzz, which blossomed in the belly, then crept to the brain. *That's even better than a cigarette after sex*. He'd quit several years ago; these days, smoking only tarnished the upscale image he needed to accommodate his success. A Cuban Monte Cristo on the other hand was another story, but Paul only lit one up on special occasions. He kept an ear tuned for the bedroom door in case he had to dump the drink in haste, but all remained nice and very quiet.

As he drank, however, his thoughts had no choice but to drag back . . . to *her*. She was so beautiful and, now, so voracious. *This house and this city really does suit her*. She

still had her sullen moods sometimes but what woman
didn't? *Probably true for me, too.* He repictured the lascivi-
ous scene from the handwoven carpet, the sight of her
creamy thighs splayed over his hips, her back arched, forcing her desire-gorged breasts out. *Damn,* he thought next.
Just *picturing* her body had him half-aroused again. He finished his drink. *Can't hurt to try. As kinky as she's been
lately?*

He brushed and gargled, then popped three mints in his
mouth and headed back to the stairs.

In the hall, he stopped short.

The jeans and halter that had lain crumpled there minutes ago were gone. *I didn't even hear her come down.* Frowning, he shrugged, then hiked up the stairs to the studio.

What the hell is going on?

The overhead lights blared but Cristina was nowhere
to be seen. Paul scratched his head, duped. "Cristina?" he
called down the dark hall. Then to the stairs, upward:
"Cristina? Jesus! Where are you?" He thought he heard a
creak but knew it was only the house frame. A bellow this
time, "CrisTINA!" But only a sterile echo bounced back.
There's no reason for her to go past the second floor, he realized. Nothing there but empty rooms, no fixtures, no lights.

Then he heard—or *thought* he heard—a voice.

Downstairs.

What is this bullshit? he thought, and thumped down.
"Cristina?"

First thing he noticed back downstairs was the basement door in the back of the short hall. It stood open a
crack, and he could see an outline of light from the basement's only bulb. Paul pushed the door right open and
proceeded down. "Cristina, why on earth are you—"

The air smelled moldy. He didn't even have to go
halfway down before he could see her lying limp on the
cobbled floor. *Jesus!* He raced down. She lay crumpled, as
if she'd collapsed. Her robe was tied shut but strangely

parted over her chest to reveal her breasts, and V'd below the sash to reveal her pubic area. She must've simply fallen that way. The syrupy dread that poured over his mind dissipated when he felt a strong pulse. "Cristina?" He touched her face, jostled her slightly, until she began to moan a little.

Paul picked her up and carried her back upstairs.

CHAPTER TEN

(I)

Slouch had just brought her in from the unit's temporary lockup. "The lady says she doesn't want an attorney."

"That's all right," Vernon replied from his desk. "We're not going to be asking her anything anyway."

The woman had been cleaned up and dressed in a blue cotton smock and drawstring pants. Slouch sat her down, her wrists cuffed in her lap. Vernon gulped at the condition of her scalp.

"Says her name is Scab," Slouch said. "Won't tell us her real name."

"Fine." Vernon studied her. The woman sat in silent adamance. "Scab's fine. She must know that her prints and DNA aren't on file." He made eye contact. "Scab? You're going to be transported to the jail wing of the hospital in a little while, for an evaluation, a thing called the blue paper. We're not going to ask you any questions but we will tell you some things just so you understand what's going on. Is that all right with you?"

She pursed her lips. "That's a question."

"What?"

"You just said you wouldn't ask me questions but you asked one."

"Sharp lady," Slouch said.

"Doesn't look crazy to me," Taylor said from the other

corner. He was pouring coffee that looked like blackstrap molasses.

"You're absolutely right, Scab," Vernon said.

"But you can ask me anything you want, I still won't tell you anything. I don't have to. I'm saved."

"That's cool." Vernon tried to sound hip. "Religious girl."

"No, I'm no Holy Roller—shit, I *hate* them. One tried to rape me once," she babbled, looking around. "I've been saved by the New Mother. I'm in her convent. She saved us from drugs. We're *all* in the convent."

Vernon nodded. "Right. The girls you ripped off the hardware store with a few nights ago and last December. We know all about them. By the way, we have photographic evidence against you on the December job, and an eyewitness when you stole those whittling knives."

The woman rolled her eyes, muttering. "That ho who looks like a little girl, the shit."

Vernon smiled. Taylor said from across the room, "Scab, the reason Inspector Vernon is talking to you right now is because he wants you to understand the *seriousness* of these crimes."

Scab's large, sloppy bosom rocked when she laughed. "Christmas tree stands. Yeah, that's real serious."

"No, but murder is," Vernon remarked. "One of those stands was used in a murder. You know . . . Virginia Fleming. And her body was written on in black, red, and green magic markers, just like the ones we found in your pocket when we brought you in yesterday."

Scab fidgeted in her seat.

Vernon continued, "And just so you know, we haven't found Ambrose Alston."

"Who?" Scab asked, fuddled.

"Nickname's Doke, a petty drug dealer. We did this thing called a Five-Probe Match from the blood on your hands. The blood belonged to him."

"But we'll find him," Taylor assured. "We won't ask you where he is."

Scab shrugged. "I have to pee."

"She already went to the bathroom, How," Slouch said. "Before she left the lockup."

"You'll have ample chance soon," Vernon told her. "It's funny, though. A minute ago you mentioned being saved. Another eyewitness saw you and your friends at the Sisters of the Heavenly Spring Catholic school—when you and your friends vandalized the chapel there with—wouldn't you know it?—black, red, and green magic markers."

"Don't forget taking care of their munchies with the Communion wafers," Slouch added.

"And a bunch of bizarre words," Vernon tacked on. "Interesting. It must be hard squatting, though, in this part of town."

Scab was rocking in her seat, barely listening. "I'm not gonna tell you where we live but we used to live in the shelters down where all the numbered streets end. They're no good, though, 'cos you can get raped in those places sometimes. We're sick of guys raping us. We used to squat in the old buildings in the Meatpacking District, and we stayed for three months in one place that used to be a sex club but got closed down. It's no good there now because there's workmen everywhere. And we used to hop around the Upper West Side whenever a place would get sold—the flower shop on Seventy-second, and the Irish bar—but you could usually never stay more than a couple of weeks because workmen came and turned it into something else." She looked to the window, clasping her hands. "We just take the subway a lot now, from other places. It's worth the trouble 'cos the panhandling's great here."

"Um-hmm." Vernon stewed on her words. *She's probably not lying but . . . why do I think that she is?* Her body language and eye movement had changed rapidly when she'd mentioned the subway.

"It don't matter. I'm saved," she said. "I could die right now and I'd be saved."

"Oh, right. You'd be saved by the nun who was with you when you broke into the school."

Her eyes snapped right to Vernon's.

Yes. Very interesting.

"I told you, I gotta pee."

"In a minute, Scab." Vernon tapped an eraser against his blotter. "It must be hard being homeless, though—"

Scab laughed.

"That'a girl!" Taylor exclaimed.

"No, it's peachy," she came back. "I hope you get to do it yourself someday."

"Honey?" Slouch said, "if the inspector doesn't solve this case, he *will*, and we'll be right there with him. We might even be panhandling with your friends by the hot dog vendor."

Scab's eyes narrowed.

Slouch clapped. "We'll all be one big happy family."

"You guys are assholes," Scab muttered.

"You got that right, lady!"

"Slouch," Vernon said. "Shut up." He turned back to the woman, who wasn't sounding terribly incompetent right now. "I could never hack being homeless in the city. The winters? No way. That's got to be the worst part."

"No," she groaned. "The worst part is never having food and watching so many rich stuck-up assholes walking into restaurants where steaks cost fifty dollars and they won't even give you a fuckin' quarter."

"Where's Marx when you need him?" Slouch asked.

"But the cold wasn't bad this winter," she went on, " 'cos we found one of those kerosene heaters last fall in a Dumpster near that Greek restaurant that closed. We'd go there a lot to dive."

"Dive?" Taylor asked.

"Dumpster dive. The guys working the kitchen would

never give us a hard time. But anyway, just before they closed, we found the heater and it still works."

Proximity, Vernon thought. *Maybe she jived me about taking the subway so I'd think she wasn't cooping in our neck of the woods.* He made a mental note. *Greek restaurant, closed last fall . . .* "Scab. I'm going to break my promise just a little, and ask you one question."

The woman stared at him.

"Nothing you might say will likely be admissible anyway, so what's the harm, right?"

Slouch hooted. "Now *that's* what I call conscientious police work!"

Vernon nodded through a frown. "You don't have to answer it, but I'll ask just the same. So level with me? What's with this nun?"

Suddenly the woman looked uncomfortable.

"You said something about a *convent.* This nun is from a convent? Is she the *New Mother* you mentioned? Explain it to me."

"It doesn't matter, except she saved us." She gazed off. "Ask me something else. I can't talk about her."

I love this job, Vernon thought with a rising sourness. "Okay. What can you tell me . . . about this?" And then he placed the small figurine on the desk. "It's some kind of novelty toy, I suppose." The cherubic doll smiled through its morgue-blue pallor, the exploded stomach gaping red. "We found it in Virginia's pocket—you know. The girl you impaled on the wooden rod mounted in the Christmas tree stand."

Scab seemed to vaguely recognize the toy figure. "Oh, Virginia must've stole it—she was a shit anyway." Her hollow eyes flicked to Vernon. "I didn't kill her, if that's what you're trying to worm out of me. But we just do what the New Mother says." She looked again to the macabre figure. "Virginia stole it from Sandrine, 'cos I think it was Sandrine's. She had a couple of 'em."

At least he was getting something. *Mental Note Number Two*, Vernon registered. *Sandrine must be the name of one of the other girls on the video.* "So it was Sandrine who killed Virginia," he stated rather than asked. "We know you were *all* there, though. The magic markers."

Scab made her eyes go cockeyed at Vernon. "The fish people are coming to get you—they told me so on the TV that doesn't work. You can smell them when they get close—they smell like the Fulton Market. Oh, the government put cameras in my fillings." And she snapped her mouth open.

"That's priceless!" Slouch exclaimed, his feet up on his desk. "Pretending to be crazy again, huh?" Vernon nodded. *So what if there's no criminal conviction? Even an NGRI solves the case.*

But not *all* of the case.

"Scab?"

She scowled. "I told you, I have to pee!" She spread her legs in the chair. "It's your floor."

I just want to retire, Vernon thought. *Florida, maybe. Or Texas.* "Slouch, get a female officer to take our friend to the head."

"Right away, boss."

Scab's knees were knocking. Maybe she really *did* have to go. Slouch returned with a tall blonde sergeant in uniform. "Honey, Sergeant Perschy here is going to take you to the tinkler." He winked to the poker-faced blonde. "Keep an eye out for the fish people."

Vernon turned the recorder off when Scab and her escort left. "It's all a bunch of Ganser BS, if you ask me," Taylor said.

"Probably," Vernon said, thinking. "They'll find out at her eval, and so what if the P.D. says we coerced information from her?"

"What's this *we* shit, Lone Ranger?" Slouch said in a mock Indian voice.

"Either way, she goes up for a long time," Taylor noted, smirking at another sip off coffee. "There's got to be a ringleader, though, and she ain't it."

"I agree," Vernon said. Now he absently fingered the plastic doll. "A woman named Sandrine, and a Greek restaurant that closed sometime after last fall. That part didn't sound like bullshit."

"It's something we can go on," Slouch observed.

Vernon smiled. "What's this *we* shit, Tonto? You need to shag ass out of here and pound some street. Go ask some restaurant managers about the Greek place. I'd love to know how close it is to the crime scenes."

Slouch shuffled to the door, pointing to Vernon but looking at Taylor. "Got a man here, doesn't like the Red Sox."

"I'm punishing you, traitor," Vernon said. "And bring back some doughnuts before you go off-shift. We're police. We have clichés to maintain."

"Got it covered."

The door shut.

"This is some case," Taylor proposed with a smirk. "Homeless bum-girls."

"We're just bums with pensions and salaries." Vernon mused, *It's all the same, in a way.* The case seemed alien to him. "How long's it take her to pee?"

"She's a woman in custody," Taylor reminded, "who's acting nuts. It'll probably take her all day."

Vernon felt stifled and bored at the same time. *If she doesn't come back soon, I'll fall asleep at my desk.* But he had a feeling that something would be livening him up rather soon.

As the homeless woman did her business in the stall, Sergeant Perschy groaned to herself. *Damn ulcers.* She paced the sterile bathroom, keeping an ear to the stall for any funny business. *What a shitty job, in a city full of shitty people . . . and half of those shitty people I've dated.* But at last she caught herself smiling in the long mirrors over the sinks. No one had ever wanted to marry her—and now that she was forty, she was all right with that—but at least she'd finally found a decent man who she could come home to every night. Tony was a narc detective in Midtown South. Five years younger than her and still pretty virile. He made her feel like a woman again, and she could tell he wasn't the cheating type. *God knows I've had enough of them.*

She frowned when the lights fizzed out.

"Hey!" the prisoner exclaimed in the stall. "What's—"

"Brownout, maybe," Perschy said. "It happens sometimes in the summer." Suddenly the foggy wired glass over the bathroom's only window barely offered any light at all. "Hurry it up in there. You're due for transport soon."

"Gimme a minute! Jesus!" the whiny voice echoed.

Sergeant Perschy continued to pace the darkened room. *Tap!*

She turned, startled, reflexes sending her gun hand to her holster.

"What was that noise?" asked the girl in the stall.

"I don't know. It—"

It hadn't come from the stalls but from another door near the exit. JANITOR, a sign read. Perschy opened the door and leapt back when a broom fell out and clattered on the floor.

"Hey! What are you doing out there?"

"It's just a broom," Perschy laughed. "Now hurry it up." But when the sergeant proceeded to pick up the broom and replace it in the closet . . .

She stalled, staring.

Next to the large sink, more brooms and mops stood in the closet, but something else stood there as well:

A figure.

A shadow that only looked half-formed. *"Salut,"* it said in a faraway voice.

Sergeant Perschy felt woozy, yet she drew her service pistol and aimed. "This is a restricted—"

"No, no," whispered the voice in a gentle accent. "To really see what you need to know . . . you must *look*."

Perschy gulped, gun hand wavering. Something forced her to stare at the figure's eyes, which were merely darker holes in the shadowed patchwork that gave it shape. It was the shape of a woman.

"So . . . Look," it said.

When Perschy looked, her own eyes closed, and it was then that she began to see.

"Alas, poor love . . ."

Perschy saw two men in shabby clothes. One sat at a dirty table, counting pieces of crack cocaine from a considerable heap. The other man was raping an unconscious woman on a linoleum floor scarred by cigarette burns. The scene ensued in a queer silence. When the man on the floor was finished, he stood up with a confident smile, rebuckling dirty jeans. Clipped to his belt was an NYPD detective's shield. "To hell with health and dental. Now that's what I call a great employment benefit."

The man at the table laughed. "Where else can we get paid, get laid, and walk with crack money all at the same time?" *He scooped the pile of crack into a plastic bag.* "Shit, the Kings will lay five or six hundred bucks on us for this." *And then he grinned up.*

It was Tony.

"Good deal." *The other man nudged the unconscious girl with his foot. Her pasty breasts wobbled.* "Say, you still dating that sweat-hog blonde?"

Tony chuckled. "Shit, I'm living with her, man, at her place. The slob is so in love with me she pays all the bills and all I've gotta do is pop her a few times a week and whisper sweet nothings."

"Classy guy."

"I save a big kick with her paying the rent. In this city? What I save there, plus what I make reselling the dope we rip off these

*fly-by-nights, I've got some big, big money sitting in a num-
bered account. Offshore, man. No names. My retirement'll be
set. You have a numbered account?"*

"Naw."

"Look into it. You get interest instead of letting your haul sit
in a shoe box. Trust me, every cop needs a numbered account."

"You mean every crooked cop," the other detective laughed.

"Well . . . yeah!"

Tony stood up. The other guy pointed to the girl on the floor.
"You want another piece before we split?"

"No, I'm set." Tony got a quarter from his pocket, and flipped.
"Call it."

"Tails," the other guy said.

The coin landed tails.

"Damn," Tony bellyached. "That's three in a row you've
won."

"Tough luck, my man. But look at it this way. You're really
making the city a better place. Have fun."

Tony tore the cord out of a shabby lamp and wrapped it
around the girl's neck. He tightened it hard, kneeing her chest
while she flipped and flopped. Her face turned bright red. He
waited a few more minutes until he was confident she was dead.

"Ready when you are."

"Hey," Tony said. "Since I offed the hose-bag, you drive."

"You got a deal. What do you say we go Mexican?—"

—and then Sergeant Perschy's eyes snapped back open,
full of tears. Her lower lip quivered. Her hands shook.

Now the shadow seemed bolder, details of a strong but
pretty face showing through her murk. Dark-rose nipples
and creamy white rings of breasts showed now, as though
edging out from a pool of petroleum. The eyes, though,
were just blacker holes, and as she spoke, twin white
needlelike teeth augmented her grin.

"For when you look, you see the truth," the accented
voice fluttered like finch wings. "The truth you've always
known . . ."

Sergeant Perschy put her service weapon to her head.

"No, no, not yet, my soiled sister," fluttered the voice. "Very few receive the honor of what you are about to witness."

Perschy's gun hand lowered. When she reached into her pocket, she blinked, and in the space of that blink saw a stone room with glassless windows, a gorgeous forest beyond. In the room sat a sturdy man at a heavy wood table. He was dunking bread into a bowl of blood, then eating the bread with gusto, muttering prayers. Though the prayers were in another language, Perschy understood that the words were prayers not to God, but to the Devil. The man wore shining chain mail augmented by jeweled leather. When the bread was gone, he drank from the bowl.

Perschy's mind seemed to glitter the darkest radiance. From her pocket she withdrew her key ring.

Scab came out of the stall. She offered her cuffed wrists and let Perschy unlock them. Then she calmly removed her transport garments and approached the closet.

Vernon and Taylor scrambled when they heard the single shot. They both had their guns out when they hit the door and stepped into the consternation of the hallway. "Watch for exits!" someone shouted. "Watch the doors!"

"Good thing we're wearing our vests, huh?" Taylor forced the scary point. Neither of them were. "Anybody see a perp?"

Probably some Al-Qaeda wannabe, Vernon thought. *Got fired from his mailman job so now he's going to kill infidels.* But then his guts sank when someone else shouted, "One of the bathrooms it sounded like!"

"Men's room's clear!"

Five cops three-pointed into the women's room. First, silence. Then three walked out, guns lowered, faces blanched.

Please, no, Vernon thought and entered as if stepping into a morgue.

The image of all that blood struck him like a sudden bellow. A veritable scarlet pool shined over a great portion of the tile floor. In the pool's farthest perimeter lay Sergeant Perschy, looking up at the ceiling with wide, dead eyes. She appeared to have been shot directly in the Adam's apple at a hard upward angle, for a plume of cranial matter that grimly reminded Vernon of lasagna flared behind her head. Her service weapon lay to her left. Later forensic analysis would determine that she'd committed suicide.

Vernon's eyes followed the rest of the blood to its alternate source: the homeless arrestee known as Scab. It took Vernon's powers of cogitation several moments to even conceive what had happened to her, but when he did so, he realized it was a treatment of something he'd seen before.

Scab sat in a grotesque squat, pallidly naked, head craned upward and mouth strained open. She sat impaled on a broomstick whose end had been hastily sharpened. Vernon could only guess how she'd achieved this exotic act of self-termination. *She must've sharpened the handle, climbed up on the top of the stall, and then lowered herself down. Her body weight did the rest . . .*

The broomstick entered her body at the vagina, and exited out her mouth.

Everyone simply stared.

"No way they didn't do a body-cavity search at the lockup," one of the cops said. "How'd she sharpen the broomstick?"

Vernon felt wobbly on his feet, but inadvertently noticed a key ring lying in the pool of darkening blood. "Right there," he said.

"Perschy's keys," another cop said. There was a penknife connected to the ring, the blade opened.

"And God knows what this crazy shit is," one cop said as he opened the door to the stall that Scab had probably been using to relieve herself. Fingered in blood were these words: **TARA ROMANEASCA, TARA FLAESC RO-MANAE. TARA FLAESC WALLKYA.** "The fuck's that?"

"Look here, Inspector," observed the other uniform. "Perschy must've died before the girl."

Vernon nodded, just now noticing some bare footprints in blood skirting most of the pool. "I guess Sergeant Perschy killed herself, then the prisoner walked over to get her key ring."

"Yeah," Taylor said, "but how do you explain this?"

Taylor pointed to more footprints closer to the impalement, where Scab's prints logically ended.

Another set of bare footprints had tracked back through Scab's blood and led into the custodial closet, where they disappeared.

"That's just great," Vernon intoned. His voice echoed. "Two different sets of bare footprints in the room, but only one person with no shoes on. Yeah. That's just fuckin' great . . ."

(II)

"Cristina?" A smiling face: youthful, handsome, short dark hair and insightful eyes focused through the haze. "I'm Dr. Stein. Paul called me over to have a look at you."

"Hi, honey." Paul's voice, just beyond. Cristina felt her hand squeezed. Only seconds transpired between her waking and her recollection of what happened last night. At once, her heart raced.

"My, God. Paul. A woman was in the house last night." Now her vision had cleared. She trembled. "She attacked me in the basement."

Paul and the doctor fell silent, just as Cristina noticed that Jess and Britt were there, too. They all stood around

Cristina's bed, faces drawn by concern. Sunlight poured in through the plush, parted drapes. She could see the clock; it was past noon.

"There was no one in the house, Cristina," Britt said. "It's like what we were talking about yesterday."

"But there was!" Cristina exclaimed and leaned up.

Dr. Stein was putting away a blood-pressure cuff. "Just calm down, and take it easy today. You're in perfect health, Cristina. There's nothing to worry about. You simply suffered from an hysteria-related shock."

Cristina wouldn't be deterred. *I know what I saw.* "Doctor, if there wasn't someone else in this house last night, then I'm *not* in perfect health. It means I'm hallucinating—"

"Um-hmm," Dr. Stein agreed.

Britt and Jess cast Stein an alarmed look.

"Honey," Paul said softly. "Let Dr. Stein explain. See, you *were* hallucinating last night, and I may have been, too."

Britt cut in, "Paul, what are you talking about? Hallucinosis is serious."

"A temporary symptom. I've seen it before," Dr. Stein told them.

"It's all about the basement, Cristina," Paul added.

Cristina's mind swam. She remembered full well what had happened down there. She'd originally dismissed the voices she'd heard, and maybe they had, indeed, been from the condos. But . . .

The woman, she thought. "I think my mind . . . added things, the power of suggestion and all that. Some of it, sure—I can agree it was imagined." She recalled Paul coming forward in the basement but after a blink he'd changed—into a nude woman. More imagination from the stress of her dreams and her work stress had added a nun's wimple to the intruder . . . and fangs. "But I didn't imagine *all* of it. I know I didn't. There was a woman. In the basement last night, and she—" But she couldn't say the rest, probably not even to Britt if alone with her. This woman had molested her sexually, and the worst part was several fibers of her being, which lay low beneath her terror, had *enjoyed* it. "I'm just . . . certain there was someone there," she finished.

But the doctor seemed perfectly content. "Cristina, when Paul showed where he'd found you last night, I noticed it right away. Your basement is full of mold—water molds, slime molds, New York City has hundreds of cases per year of persons being stricken by symptoms of mold toxicity. Do you know how many wet, dark basements there are in this city? It happens all the time, especially to contractors."

Cristina contemplated the words. "Mold toxicity."

"Yes," the doctor asserted. "Sporadic exposure rarely causes serious long-term symptoms, but the temporary symptoms can be quite profound, especially in poorly vented areas."

"Such as every friggin' basement in Manhattan," Jess commented. "Hell, when I first moved to the city, I had to drop some large coin getting the mold cleaned out of my damn *closets* in the Village."

"Symptoms can cause mild fever, respiratory irritation, and varying degrees of hallucinosis," the doctor went on. "In particular, myxomycetes molds produce airborne spores that in many cases lead to hallucinatory effects as well as paranoia. I'm not a mycologist but the blackish molds I noticed growing in your basement look like the same strain."

Paranoia, too? Cristina couldn't deny it. "All of a sudden your explanation sounds very reasonable."

"I even felt woozy when I was bringing you up from there last night," Paul told her. "It explains everything, honey, and like the doctor said, it's not that serious."

Jess was pinching his goatee. "Hey, Paul, remember Jack

Molina we went to school with? He represented a landlord against a multiple-tenant class-action suit put up by
Gogh and Michaels. The landlord was renting moldy basement apartments, and most of the tenants were getting
sick as dogs and started seeing things."

"Right," Paul recalled. "But it turns out the landlord
fudged the city health codes so he wouldn't have to pay
the cleaning fees. Molina lost his ass."

"Well, Molina didn't, but his client sure as hell did.
Molina still snagged four-fifty per billing hour anyway."

Jess and Paul erupted in laughter.

"Lawyers," Britt complained. "What a jolly bunch."

Dr. Stein wrote several prescriptions. "So that's it in a
nutshell, Cristina. You'll be fine. But don't go in the basement again until you get a bonded contractor to get rid of
that mold. For the next few days, take this mild antibiotic;
it'll help clear any spores that might still be lodged in your
upper respiratory tract. And also a mild sedative in case
you have trouble sleeping." He turned to Paul. "If
headache or fever persist beyond forty-eight hours, have
her in to see me."

"Will do, Doctor."

Stein bade his farewell, leaving Cristina feeling quite
relieved but also foolish now as she lay in bed past noon
surrounded by the people closest to her.

"Well there you have it," Jess said.

"Mold spores," Britt said. "It can give you a pretty good
trip, I guess."

"You wouldn't believe it," Cristina admitted. "Not only
was I convinced that a woman had broken into the house
but . . ."

"But what?" Paul asked.

"I can't say it because you'd think I was loony."

"Come on," Britt egged.

Cristina smiled at her own embarrassment. "The woman
was a vampire."

Everybody laughed. "You're loony," Paul said, "but I still love you."

"Thanks."

"That's a riot," Britt said. "Last night you thought the Noxious Nun was in your basement!"

"It seems so. Blame my subconscious mind."

"Just so long as you're all right," Paul said. "But until further notice, the basement's off-limits."

"Oh, don't worry. I don't need any more experiences like that."

"Just the same," Britt asked, "how are you feeling?"

"Like an ass, but aside from that and being a little tired, I feel all right."

"Come on, everybody, let's clear out of here so she can get dressed," Britt ordered.

"Jess and I have to get back to the office anyway," Paul said. "But if you need anything, call."

"Thanks, honey," Cristina bid and kissed him.

As Britt herded them out, she said, "I'll hang around a while. We can go get lunch."

"Great. I'm starved."

The door didn't quite close all the way. As Cristina dressed she could hear everyone talking in the foyer.

"Mystery of the day solved," Jess joked. "Mold in the basement. Say, Paul. You ought to sue the diocese for selling you contaminated property!"

Paul and Jess roared laughter.

Cristina shook her head, and continued to spruce herself up. In the closet, though, some of her dresses seemed to be disarranged, as if they'd been rehung in haste. One hanger was empty. Was something missing? *Stop imagining things,* she ordered herself. Next, in the bathroom, she was brushing her hair when something unconscious caught her eye.

What . . .

There, in the mirror's reflection. Cristina turned very

slowly and saw that the Noxious Nun figure Bruno had given her was sitting on a vanity shelf behind her. The figure's fanged smile seemed to harass her, the toy-sized bowl of blood held as if it were being offered to her.

Cristina was certain she'd taken the figure upstairs a day or so ago, to display it with her other figurines.

She had absolutely no recollection of bringing it back down here.

CHAPTER ELEVEN

(I)

What to do, what to do? Rollin fretted. He sat in the chancel of his own empty church, not praying so much as worrying. Last night, from his window at the Ketchum Hotel, he'd seen enough to spark an escalating dread. Through his voyeur's binoculars, not only had he witnessed Cristina Nichols masturbating unabashed—twice—he'd seen at least one other woman in the house, and—

I'm pretty sure I've seen that woman before . . .

One of those homeless girls who'd always seemed to gravitate toward the house. Another thing he'd noted over time was this: it had been going on for almost a year, as though the house might be preparing them for something, coaching them. *Like the house has recruited its own attendants*, he abstracted.

Rollin only knew what he had been warned.

If it's true . . . what in God's name can I do about it, especially if I don't even have access to the house anymore?

The priest errantly touched his ring. After Cristina Nichols had left, Rollin identified the woman he had seen in the studio window as one he often saw scrounging the streets, a dilapidated urchin still carrying around a ghost of a long-faded prettiness. *Pink, bulky glasses, blondish hair, an orange halter top lately*, he thought. *Who is she? And those other ones she runs about with?* At least they appeared better nourished than when he first began to notice them. He could only imagine who might be manipulating them . . .

Rollin walked to the end of the narthex of the church; he opened the massive front doors and peeked out. The annex house stood bright in sunlight, its windows shining. How many times had he peeped in those windows? Two well-dressed men laughed as they came down the steps—a broad-shouldered, dark-haired man, and the other goateed, with longer hair—and got into an expensive sports car. *I wonder which one was Paul Nasher?* As the car drove away, a stunning woman with shoulder-length and almost-black hair waved good-bye from the annex house's threshold. *A friend of Cristina's, I guess . . .* For a fraction of a second the woman made eye contact with Rollin. *Damn!* He smiled feebly, stepped back, and closed the door.

He hadn't seen Cristina since her masturbatory bout last night in the studio. Rollin decided he'd keep the expensive room at the Ketchum for a few more nights. Surveillance was important but so far it had yielded little.

Echoes of footsteps clattered as he walked back down the darkened nave. He crossed himself at the altar, though his mind wasn't particularly close to God at the time. *The homeless woman with the glasses,* he reflected. He knew that he'd seen her in the house, and if she'd found a way in, so must have the others. *But how?* he wondered. *How are they getting in? And from where?* These were the questions that vexed him.

Perhaps today he'd stroll the streets and keep an eye out. But his stomach ached with the next thought: the certainty that he'd have to find a way to enter the house and find out how they were getting in.

Even if it means breaking into the place myself . . .

(II)

Vernon felt dissolute, actually wobbly as he came down the steps of police headquarters on Madison. The yelling still echoed in his ears. Behind him he frowned at the infamous One Police Plaza as it loomed in its grandiosity, while the actual HQ building he'd just left looked more like him: old and weathered. Slouch picked him up in the unmarked in the small half-court out front.

"I probably won't be able to sit down," Vernon said when he opened the door.

"What?"

"The commissioner just gnawed my ass so hard, I don't think I have one anymore."

Slouch laughed. "He was probably on the rag. I heard he gets that way. But it couldn't have been that bad."

Vernon slid in and sighed. "I thought he was gonna have a stroke he was yelling so loud. There were veins sticking out at his temples. All I know is I've got a sergeant in good standing killing herself twenty feet from my office and a suspect in custody dead by *impalement*—a *homeless* woman—two days after *another* homeless woman was found dead by impalement. And I've got evidence of a third person in the room at the same time but when the PC asks me who the third person was, I don't have an answer. 'What are your leads?' he asks, and the only thing I can say is a quartet of still more homeless women who stole some Christmas tree stands and whittling knives from a fuckin' hardware store. I've never felt so inept in my life. I'm supposed to be on the ball but right now I'm *under* it. I wouldn't blame him if he transferred me to the impound lot."

"Come on." Slouch tried to sound positive. He whipped into traffic, passed Foley Square, and turned up Centre Street. "It's a fucked-up case. Everybody gets 'em."

"A fucked-up case?" Vernon grimaced like someone with gas. "The PC calls it an 'unacceptable deficiency of protocol and professional foresight.' All I know is we have to find those other girls on the video or I might as well turn in my papers."

"Can't help you now, How," Slouch said. "I've got court." He pulled into the criminal court complex. "You wanna take the car?"

"No. Drop me. I'll take the subway back to the precinct."

Vernon got out and allowed the walk to Varick Street to clear his head. He walked as if with blinders, distraction leaving him scarcely aware of where he was. He took the One Line and got out at the Lincoln Center stop. When he ascended up from the platform, a row of homeless sat against the first building, some squawking crazily, others just sitting there with halos of flies circling their heads. One of them, a woman, looked up with eyes whose whites had turned to the color of cigarette ash. "Can you spare a couple bucks, Officer?" she asked.

Vernon pretended not to hear, and high-stepped away. *I must be wearing a sign.* Brazen graffiti besmirched the polished stone below a bank's front windows. One scrawl read **Z-MEN RULE** but was X'd out, while another read **BUY ROCK FROM THE KINGS.** *Hang them all,* Vernon thought bitterly, but then he chuckled. *Or better yet, impale them. No one would sell drugs if we impaled the dealers in public.* His distraction focused down without conscious effort as he neared 69th and Columbus but when he spied the hot dog vendor, his awareness engaged. He was scanning alleys and passersby. *Where are they?* he thought. He took out copies of the prints, studying them as he walked. The most prominent of the three remaining thieves was the girl with glasses. Even in the grainy print, they looked like pink horn rims, like a child might wear. *Probably found them in the garbage and they worked.* He could tell the woman was missing teeth, for she was grinning in the freeze-frame, boxes of several unassembled Christmas tree stands under her arm. *The nuttiest case of my career . . .*

An upcoming throng nearly overwhelmed him; it made Vernon realize he no longer functioned at the same rapid pace as most New Yorkers. He waited for the moving crowd to divide around him, then found himself standing in front of the vendor. Today he wore a New York Giants hat and a Jets jersey. "Hot dog, Officer?" he asked, cigar stub jittering. "On the house."

Vernon wilted. *Made again.* "How did you know?"

The stocky vendor laughed. "I saw you yesterday busting that bum-chick, you and your buddy who needs a haircut."

Bum-chick, Vernon thought. *I guess that's what we reduce them to.* "I'll take a dog, thanks. With kraut, please. Oh, but first—" He thrust forward the hard copies. "You've seen these women around?"

The vendor barely looked at the pictures. "Yeah, yeah, your guys have already shown those to me. I see 'em every now and then, every other day, maybe." But the man's amusement was plain. "With all the crime in this city? Why waste time with a few bum-chicks?"

"They impaled a woman on a wooden pole," Vernon said automatically, then regretted it.

The man laughed. "Jesus! Can't have that!"

Probably thinks I'm bullshitting . . . and I wish I was. "You seen any of these girls today?"

"Naw, don't think so. But you know, I see a lot of peo-ple. During a rush I ain't gonna notice."

"Sure." Vernon gave him his card. "Next time you see them, call that cell number. I'll give you a hundred bucks right out of my wallet."

"No shit?"

"No shit."

The vendor eyed the card, nodding. "Awright."

Vernon took the piled-high hot dog wrapped in foil. "Thanks."

"That's Sabrett's. I ain't like some of these other guys who say they're Sabrett's but they ain't."

"I believe it." Vernon pointed to the card. "Call that number. I'm serious about the hundred."

"You must want these bum-chicks bad."

Vernon stared as if at a bombed building. "More than anything you can imagine," he said and walked away.

The first bite told him the hot dog was not Sabrett's. *Tastes more like one of those generic chicken dogs.* But he wasn't about to complain. Suddenly a figure startled him, a raddled woman who smelled bad.

"Hey, mister. If you don't eat all of that, can I have the rest?"

Vernon's eyes locked. *Not one of mine,* he knew instantly. The woman stood short and squat, oddly wearing a wool scarf. Rotten tennis shoes were wrapped up in sheets. A baggy pea-green shirt looked streaked with old vomit. He thought of showing her the pictures but, *If she knows them, she might tip them off.* For some reason, being so close to the woman made him nervous. He gave her the rest of the hot dog and a five-dollar bill, then strode off.

The street was so crowded he had to walk along the buildings to stay out of the way. He wasn't quite sure what snagged his attention, though, when he stopped in front of one store. SPIKE'S COMIC EMPORIUM, the glass read. Then he stared at the glass and caught the small colorful mini-poster behind it. IN STOCK! CADAV-ERETTES! Vernon stooped, squinted. It was a promotional poster, showing several cute but morbid figurines all in a row. Then, *Cadaverettes,* he remembered. The word had been imprinted on the bottom of the doll they'd found in Virginia Fleming's pocket . . .

He flinched at the bell that clanged when he pushed through the front door. Shelves of comics occupied the front, while toys and shirts were in back. "Where are these Cadaverette things?" he asked the man at the checkout who looked to be Vernon's age but had spiked blond hair and a leather vest.

"Aisle Four," he said without even looking at Vernon. "The new shipment just came in, and we also got a few Plastic Surgery Botchies back."

Vernon felt duped. He shouldered through high, labyrinthine aisles, sniffling at the store's mustiness. Rows and rows of action figures, dolls, and figurines—some quite elaborate—clogged the shelves. He dragged his vision along. "Gurl-Goyles, Fantasmic Fishies, Living Dead Dolls, Verotik World," he recited. Then, "Ah. Here they are."

Boxes five inches high and three thick sat on end, each with cellophane windows displaying dolls that smiled in spite of grievous wounds. CADAVERETTE #2, read one box, Y-SECTIONED WANDA, and inside stood a cutesy figurine of a grinning nude girl whose pallid thorax was marked by stout black stitches—presumably surgical staples—in the fashion of the autopsist's Y-incision. Vernon couldn't guess what market appeal might exist for such novelties; some of the dolls were actually scary, but all at least unsettling in their amalgamation of grotesqueness and whimsy. A row of larger boxes contained four figures in each: Headless Helen, Hypothermia Harriet, Gutshot Glenn, and Floater Frank. *That's the one Virginia Fleming had*, Vernon recognized of Gutshot Glenn. The very idea puzzled him. *I guess I'm just an out-of-it old fuck*, he thought. *Somebody MUST be buying these things—there're shelves and shelves of them . . .* Another section with a similar style boasted PLASTIC SURGERY BOTCHIES. More of the same but a different theme. Tummy-Tucked Tina sported a horrendously mishandled abdominal augmentation; the lower half of Botox Bonnie's face was all inflated lips. *Jeeeeeesus*, Vernon thought. Then: *Why am I looking at this stuff?* It was only coincidence that one such figurine was found in a decedent's pocket.

"You must be into the Nichols stuff," said the spiked proprietor. He flapped Vernon a large, shiny card.

"Nichols?"

The clerk seemed half-offended that Vernon had questioned the name. "Cristina Nichols. Right now she's the hottest name in novelty figurines, created the Cadaverettes that you asked about." He gestured to the card. "We'll be getting the first four figures in her *Evil Church* line in a few days, but if you want any, you better preorder. They're almost gone."

Vernon didn't know what the *hell* this guy was talking about. He looked at the card . . .

Suddenly his blood felt like ice water.

It had to be coincidence. Of course. Nevertheless, the first thing he noticed on the card were wavy black, green, and red lines, ribbonlike, floating behind four figurines of a similar style as the Cadaverettes he'd just been appraising. CRISTINA NICHOLS PRESENTS: EVIL CHURCH CREEPIES! read the top of the glossy card. Four grotesque dolls were shown, all portraying some sort of Gothic church motif.

The first figure was a nun.

Vernon had to drag his sentience back, while still eyeing the nun and the wavy lines. "This some kind of promotional thing?"

"Right," said Spiked Hair. "It's Nichols's brand-new line, and it's making serious waves. If you want any of the first run, like I said, you better preorder." Then the guy went back to the register.

Coincidence, yes, but almost too uncanny. *Black, green, and red,* Vernon thought in a drone, *just like the markers at the crime scenes . . .*

And a nun.

THE NOXIOUS NUN! read the title beneath the figure. She grinned with whory red lips, brandishing fangs, as she seemingly held a bowl of blood. The front of the bowl sported three spots to denote jewels: one black, one green, one red.

What am I thinking? he wondered. He couldn't imagine. On the back was distributor information and shipping dates, plus a tiny picture and biographical data about this person named Cristina Nichols. There was also some manufacturer information and a website.

Vernon walked in a daze to the register. The clerk looked suspicious. "If you don't mind my saying so, you don't really look like someone who's into novelty figurines. You look more like a cop."

I do mind you saying so, Sawhead. "Uh, they're for my . . . niece." Vernon had no idea why he was doing what he was about to do. "I'd like to preorder," he said.

"Smart move. But you have to pay in advance. They're $12.95 each, or all four for forty."

For fuckin' dolls! Vernon gave him his credit card. "Just the nun, please. This promo thing, though. It says that Cristina Nichols lives in Connecticut. Any idea what town?" But why on earth would he even ask? What purpose could there be in contacting her? "My niece . . . collects autographs of her favorite . . . doll designers."

The clerk didn't bat an eye at the howling lie. "Actually, that bio's dated. She recently moved to New York."

"Not Manhattan," Vernon could only assume.

"The distro rep came in here the other day and believe it or not Nichols lives right around here someplace. Just a few blocks. I'm trying to get her in here for a signing but I guess she's kind of reclusive. We'll see. Just check the window every week for an announcement." The clerk gave Vernon his credit card back. "We'll call you when the order's in. What's your number?"

Vernon gave him a precinct card and smiled. "Thanks very much. My . . . niece will be delighted."

The clerk arched his brow at the card. "Sure."

Vernon walked out, befuddled. *I just spent thirteen bucks for a nun doll and I don't know why.* The coincidence? The black, green, and red lines? *And Scab mentioned a nun*, he knew. *And on the night of the chapel vandalism . . . a nun was seen with several homeless women . . .*

Vernon walked all the way back to the precinct house, thinking that it might be a good idea to turn in his retirement papers.

(III)

Rollin stared listlessly into the infinity-shaped field of his binoculars. He couldn't help but feel self-conscious, not just from the technical fact of what he was doing, but also what he sat in the midst of. *Behind closed doors,* he thought. For the price, these motel rooms should be better soundproofed; the adult-video convention was in full swing now, and evidently some of the participants took many respites in their own rooms. Rollin could hear wanton moans, climactic shrieks, and bedsprings creaking for the entire time he was there.

By now, eyestrain was getting the best of him. He kept the glasses trained on Cristina Nichols's studio window, not sure what he was hoping to see. She simply sat at her desk, tapping on her computer or turning on her stool to sketch something. Rollin only wished his vantage point was better angled; he couldn't see at least half of the studio. Once every so often, he raised the glasses to the windows of the upper two floors but discerned only bare walls and unmoving shadows.

No interlopers.

But they'd have to be crazy to sneak into the house in broad daylight while the woman was home, he reasoned, then caught himself in the gaff. *Have to be crazy?*

They probably ARE crazy . . .

He sat there until his voyeurism became paralyzing. The day was dimming, and so was his energy. He began to nod off but snapped awake when movement hailed him. Two women were shuffling down the alley.

Is it them?

He couldn't be sure.

Enough for today. Maybe he would see something tomorrow. *Or the day after that, or the day after that . . .* Frustrated and still partially ashamed, he closed the drapes and left the hotel room.

Grins floating above fleshy cleavage and plenteous bosoms mocked his Roman collar when he exited the lobby. *Seven P.M.*, he saw on his watch. *Maybe . . . Paul Nasher's home from work now . . .*

He walked straight down Dessorio and moments later was knocking on the opulent front doors of the annex house.

"Oh, hi, Father," Cristina cheerily greeted when the door opened to a gap.

"Hi, Ms. Nichols. Hope I'm not disturbing you," he said, "and if not, I thought I'd take you up on your offer for a cup of coffee. I'd love to meet your fiancé."

"He's working late tonight, but come on in anyway." Her hand took his arm and showed him into the living room. "I was just about to make some anyway. I hope you like Costa Rican. It's the best. We get it at Barney's."

Rollin felt stifled once inside. "Uh, yes, please. Costa Rican will do quite nicely," But Rollin mostly drank whatever he could afford on his stipend. It was the sight of the room that waylaid him; the binoculars hadn't done the place justice. Italian marble, velour wallpaper, custom-made furnishings. "It's amazing what you've done here," he finally said.

"Oh, yeah. Paul went all-out fixing the place up."

The priest chuckled. "Quite a bit different from what it used to be when I was the charge of this house."

Cristina smiled, her blonde hair slightly mussed. "I would imagine, but I guess as a priest you might not approve of what we've done here. The house must strike you as the peak of materialistic sin."

"There are far worse sins," he assured.

"Good. Come and see the kitchen," she invited.

Rollin followed, eyes wandering to every corner. The kitchen was more of the same, the best of everything. The aroma of coffee almost intoxicated him; Rollin felt desensitized to everything else. Even Cristina's honest prettiness, made more provocative by tight jeans and an obvious bralessness beneath her blouse, assured him that at least lust was one sin he would not have to account for today. The woman simply seemed perfect in her genuineness. She tinkered at the coffeemaker while engaging in small talk, regretting that Paul wasn't home yet. She handed him a cup. "I never did quite understand how the house came to be sold," she said.

Rollin fumed at himself. *It was sold for a song because I happened to be on a six-month sabbatical and the bunglers at the diocese thought they were making a killing.* Instead, he said, "In truth the Catholic Church owns too much land and—after all—money is money. Not all church property is tax-exempt, you know."

"Really?"

"Oh, no. The church must justify each exemption, and if a property is deemed to no longer be serving an active purpose *for* the church, then Big Brother wants his tax. It's actually quite fair; otherwise the church could buy up foreclosures all over the place and not have to pay a penny in property tax, then reap huge profits when values take off." He chuckled again. "The Catholics really aren't the greedbarons we're made out to be. The truth of the matter is, the diocese had no reason to continue owning this house, so they sold it."

"How interesting. About the taxes, I mean." Just then, a phone rang in a distant room. "That's probably my boss calling, so I may be a little while. But feel free to look around."

"Thank you."

He watched her skirt energetically into a small den of some sort. "Oh, hi, Bruno. Yeah, sure we can do that now . . ."

It seemed that she'd be talking at some length. Rollin stood there, thinking. *I suppose if I had some actual courage I could . . .* The contemplation heckled him. Walking softly, he left the foyer and entered the short hall next to the stairs. The basement door seemed to challenge his being there, saying, *I dare you.*

Rollin opened the door and went down.

Half of his conscience focused on the opportunity, the other half feebled over a suitable lie should he be caught down here. The basement looked no different. *Still the same cluttered old place. All of this junk is actually ours,* he knew. *But we'll let Mr. Millionaire Paul Nasher get rid of it at his own expense.* Boxes of books—church books—formed walkways. Cobwebs festooned the corners. He walked quickly to the windows in back and checked them for signs of tampering. *I know they're getting in here somehow,* he thought. *And the more time that passes, the worse it will get.* But as far as Rollin could tell, the windows were secure. He couldn't imagine how they'd been sneaking in here.

Then he thought, *The vault . . .*

He walked around another outcropping of boxes and assorted stuff, and there it was: the patch of cement bearing the seal. Unconsciously, he first touched his ring, then slipped his own pendant out from under his shirt, rubbing his fingers over the embossment as he looked down.

My God, he thought.

The seal in the concrete was intact, but the concrete surface itself was cracked. Between two boxes, he noticed a small sledgehammer and a chisel . . .

A click. Rapid footsteps. Rollin's heart sped up.

"Father Rollin!" Cristina exclaimed. She'd come halfway down the steps but seemed to hesitate there. "You mustn't come down here!"

Rollin grabbed a book out of one of the myriad boxes, then came around to the steps. "Oh, I'm terribly sorry. I should've asked first. The diocese left a lot of stuff down here, and I was simply retrieving something, this Thomas Merton book. It was one of my favorites." He held the book up, to validate the bald-faced lie. "I apologize, Ms. Nichols. I'll put it back if you like. Technically, I suppose it *is* yours."

"No, no, keep the book, of course, but come up from there right now!" she seemed frantic. "It's dangerous down there."

Rollin hastened up the steps and turned as she closed the door. "Dangerous?"

Cristina seemed relieved he was out of there. "Of course, you wouldn't know. But we found out this morning that the basement has toxic mold in it."

Rollin was nearly speechless. "How . . . odd. I suppose it is a bit moldy, as basements can often be. But *toxic?*"

"That's what the doctor told us this morning," she informed, leading him back to the kitchen. "I actually had a spell down there."

Rollin looked at her. "A . . . spell?"

"Yes." She seemed intrigued. "I actually passed out from the spores. Believe it or not, the mold made me see things."

"You don't say?" But Rollin only wished he could relate his true thoughts: *I hate to tell you this, Ms. Nichols, but it wasn't MOLD that made you see things . . .*

CHAPTER TWELVE

(I)

Cristina surged as she straddled him—she knew she was *using* him for his body yet again tonight, yet she couldn't deny her desires. It was like a drug—her lust.

"Jeez, hon," Paul muttered beneath her. "I don't think I *can* again . . ."

"Try, try," she moaned, rocking on him in the darkness. "Please . . ." *Don't lose it,* she begged him in thought. She knew she was asking a lot of him, but her desires were demanding much of her as well. Cristina's blood felt like oil heating up on a stove top. Paul was gasping with every thrust. The shadows seemed to push her face down toward him. She began to slowly suck down the side of his neck, and when her tongue laved over his jugular vein, she could feel his pulse beating like a hummingbird's. Next, their tongues were playing around in the other's mouth with more fervor than she could ever recall. Paul's hand slipped between them, his fingers hunting for nipples to tweeze in time with his thrusts, and when he began to pinch, she panted, "Harder, harder," into his mouth. "Please, honey, as hard as you can." She squealed and orgasmed when her plea was answered, and a moment later, Paul spent himself as well.

Good, good, she thought.

She collapsed atop him and sighed. She felt like butter now, melting into still-warm bread. The words in her head arrived like a zombie's drone: *I just couldn't get enough tonight. Just like last night, and the night before* . . . "Paul? That was wonderful . . . Paul?"

But he was already asleep beneath her. *I'm surprised I didn't kill him*, she thought. *Lately I've been riding him like a mechanical bull.* Even in her exhaustion, though, she felt beaming, her nerves energetic in the revel of life. She slipped off the bed's silk sheets, nipples constricting as the air-conditioning dried her glaze of perspiration. She traipsed about the room, sated in its darkness and silence. Only the moon leaked in through the louvers. In the big mirror over the dresser, the silverish light on her face surrealized her features, leaving lines and wedges black but luminescing the rest.

Her thoughts strayed when she decided to wander the house. *What a relief*, she regarded of Dr. Stein's diagnosis. *For a while there, I thought I was going crazy.* Hearing things, seeing things? *All because of mold in the basement.* Tomorrow a contractor was coming to give them an estimate for the cleanup. She'd been surprised, though, by the look on Father Rollin's face when she'd mentioned it earlier. *He was in and out of this house for years,* she knew. But he'd probably spent very little time in the basement. Through the dining room blinds, she peeked quickly outside.

Hmmm . . .

At first she'd thought she'd seen the tiniest glint in one of the church's dark windows but, *Just the streetlight, or the moon*, she dismissed.

It was past one in the morning now. The stillness of the house lulled her. It scarcely registered that she'd been wandering around in the nude—something she'd rarely done in the past—but now that she thought of it, she smiled. Her fingers stroked her hips without forethought. *I like being nude*, she thought. *I like being naked in the house, at night, in the dark and the silence.* The observation surprised her, as did the recognition that just this instant, she couldn't imagine being happier. It was a joyous complacency, rooted in so many things, she supposed: her youth and health, her success in hand with Paul's, this new environment and the love she felt pouring over her. If such a thing as an aura existed, she knew that hers must be blazing white.

She slipped back into the bedroom and got into bed. Sleep welcomed her—*After all that sex?* she thought naughtily—but her mind still tinkered with some thoughts. What could really explain her mood changes? One day shy and sheepish, the next day voracious? *It's everything*, she knew.

It was all part of her now—the *real* her. Yes, she knew she was changing, and she knew it was all good.

Cristina fell asleep with an arm and leg hooked over Paul's strong body. Hence, she was not awake to see the curvaceous, shadow-formed figure ooze into the room, grin down at her, and run a single finger up the side of her throat.

Nor was she awake to hear what it whispered in a voice like smoke: "*Tara Romaneasca, tara flaesc Romanae . . .*"

Cristina wakened at seven, to the sound of the shower. *My God, I'm sore*, she thought when she leaned up. Her muscles ached but a smile touched her lips when she realized why. It must be from their frenetic lovemaking. *We tried some pretty off-the-wall positions*, she recalled. She pulled on her robe and went out to make coffee, which was ready the same minute Paul rushed out of the bedroom, adjusting his tie. "Oh, you're a gem," he said, kissed her quick, and grabbed his insulated traveling cup. "Thanks."

"You're up real early," Cristina noted. "I thought lawyers didn't work till ten."

"Not today, baby." He finally knotted his tie. "Jess and I have a *big* client coming in at eight-thirty. Primo important."

"Primo, huh? Too primo to skip out without breakfast? I could make you something."

"No, thanks. Ann's bringing in some of those egg-muffin things—"

"Ann?" Cristina grinned. "Should I be jealous?"

"You know, Ann, our secretary."

"Is she pretty?"

"She's very pretty. And very lesbian." He paused to look at her. "Not nearly as pretty as you, anyway."

Cristina gave him a hug. "Have a good day—"

"You, too—" He was pulling away, jingling his keys. "Oh, and try to find that menu for Shun Lee's; we're getting the carryout there when Jess and Britt come over. I know it's around here somewhere."

"Okay—"

"Oh, and don't forget about the guy coming at nine."

"The mold guy."

"Right. The sooner we get that mold out of there, the better I'll feel."

"Me too."

"Gotta run, love you." He gave her another peck and was out the door. Cristina smiled after him.

Later, a contractor arrived—a tall young man with an eye patch. *I hope it wasn't mold that caused that,* Cristina thought. "That's quite a job title," she said when he assured her he was "an IAQ-certified mold inspector" and "a full member of the National Board of Mold Remediators." He put on a mask like a painter and descended the basement steps with what he described as an "infrared swatch scope." *I didn't know mold was so technical,* Cristina thought. He returned in about a half hour, mask off and jotting on a clipboard. "Pretty bad down there, huh?" Cristina assumed the worst, but his reply was surprising. "No, ma'am. When your fiancé called, he said he had a *toxic* mold problem, but there's nothing toxic down there. It's just a simple black Mycota mold."

"Really? Our doctor said it was the kind that could make you sick and even see things."

"Probably just covering his bases," the man said without ever looking at her with his one good eye. He kept scribbling as he talked. "The molds we get around here look a lot like some of the protostelids that sometimes cause hallucinations. I've given you multiple estimates for whatever kind of work you might want: basic remediation, aqueous Ph-control and sequestrant-based sealing, or full reconditioning. If you want to know the truth, all you need is the basic unless you want to turn the basement into an apartment."

Cristina brushed her hair out of her eyes, flummoxed. "Nothing harmful down there?"

"No, ma'am. The mold you've got down there wouldn't make a parakeet sick." He scribbled some more, and gave Cristina the top sheet. "And we can also fix that crack in the cement, if you want."

He left as abruptly as he arrived. *Well . . . he was young,* she realized. *We better get a second analysis.* And what had he said about cracked cement? *I never noticed any cracks,* she told herself. She started to go down herself to look, but then paused at the door. *No. I better not. If that kid's wrong about the mold, I don't want to be passing out and God knows what else.*

As she was mounting the steps to her studio, she grimaced. The aches in her back and shoulders had trebled, which only confounded her. *Why am I so damn sore all of a sudden?*

Cristina's muscles throbbed as if she'd been doing some heavy manual labor. *Forget working today,* she resolved and turned back down. *I'm going to go take a nice, warm bubble bath . . .*

(II)

The room buzzed.

And it stank now worse than ever. "How do I look?"

Francy asked, striking a flapperlike pose amid the glowing candles. "Do I look *maaaaav*-alous?"

Stutty looked awed and even jealous of the diaphanous red dress. The label read Dolce & Gabbana, but she'd never heard of him. "I wish I could wear it-wear it-wear it," she lamented. She was whittling points onto some more broomsticks.

"You don't have the right curves, Stutty. *I* do."

"Gimme a break!"

"Big deal," Sandrine muttered. She fiddled with her Hypothermia Harriet doll. "It's a rich-person dress, and I say *shit* on rich people. We don't even really know if you're ever going to need it."

Francy fell silent, glaring at her sullen companion. "The New Mother said I would, Sandrine."

Sandrine shrugged.

"You don't believe the New Mother?" Francy took an authoritative step on two dirty feet. "After all she's done for us? The New Mother can see the future. Don't you believe that?"

"I . . ."

"'Cos if you don't believe that, you can't be in the convent!" Francy half-yelled. "She's known the future since our Prince lay down on the stone table! Since the time of the Infidels! Since when the time the Darkness came to the land and blessed them!"

"I believe the New Mother," Stutty offered. "She said we'd be off crack and now we are. She said that guy and the woman would move into the church-house, and they did. And-and-and she told us what was there, and we've seen it. She said she would come to us, and she has, has-has-has-has-hasn't she?"

"Yes," Sandrine dolefully agreed.

Candlelight flickered over the dress to make it look alive. "So how can you not believe?" Francy questioned.

Then Stutty, enthused before the dead television said,

"As the Time gets closer, the New Mother becomes more real, just like she said. We even *felt* her last night, right?"

"Well . . . yeah," Sandrine said.

"She's always been real, Stutty," Francy corrected. "Just less here, and more somewhere else, since the time of the Prince. But now that's reversing."

"Okay!" Sandrine rebelled. "But so what? What do we get out of it?"

Francy leaned close, lowering her voice. "We get to live forever."

"Forever?" Sandrine winced, offering her hands to the reeking, garbage-strewn room. "Here? Like this?"

"No, Sandrine. Like *her*. And anyone who doesn't believe it can't be in the convent." She eyed the moldering corpse of Doke in the corner. It was a warning.

Sandrine, in her depression, continued to object. "So why can't we go to the house and get the thing ourselves?"

"Because that's not what's in the future," Francy reminded. "That's not what the New Mother said. It has to be the woman. The New Mother already knows what's going to happen. It was all planned a long time ago. The woman has to touch it first."

Sandrine fidgeted, prone to clinical depression. "I don't know what's wrong with me. But I do believe . . ."

"Good," Francy stated.

"She's just fucked-fucked-fucked-up," Stutty diagnosed. " 'Cos of drug-drug-drug-drugs."

"Oh, right," Sandrine exclaimed. "*I'm* fucked-up."

"We're *all* fucked-up!" Francy celebrated. Then all of them, even Sandrine, laughed.

"You should take the dress off for now," Sandrine said. "If you don't, it'll be all dirty by the time you need it."

"Yuh-yeah," Stutty added. "You'll stink it all up!"

"Kiss my ass!" Francy cracked back. "I took a shower last night, in the house."

"You did?"

Francy's eyes widened. "Yeah. And you should'a seen the bathroom. I'll bet Donald Trump doesn't have a bathroom like theirs."

"Who's Donald Thump?" Sandrine asked.

Francy smirked. "Never mind. But it was the best bathroom."

Stutty grinned. "Yuh-yuh-yeah? But what else *did* you do?"

"Shut up!"

They all laughed again.

Francy continued to strike poses. "The New Mother's coming out earlier and earlier now, and pretty soon she'll be as real as us. But we have to believe. We all *must* believe." Suddenly her posing stopped and she got serious again. " 'Cos anyone who doesn't . . ."

She pointed to Doke. Then she pointed past more boxes, to Crazy, and impaled next to her was Ruthie Mooseface and Blinda, whom they'd impaled early this morning.

The room buzzed.

(III)

Vernon found it inconceivable that the vast campus of Columbia University existed entirely in the middle of Morningside Heights. From the end near the Teacher's College it looked endless. He'd walked so much his feet began to hurt . . . *Big fancy Ivy League place like this and they don't even have a campus directory.* He hoofed past Fairchild Hall, squinting for building numbers. He felt invisible amid the throng of youthful students . . . and depressed when he realized, *Jesus, I'm almost old enough to be their grandfather* . . . Statues of Hamilton and Jefferson seemed to eye him with suspicion as he trudged on through beating heat. A crude xerox flapped on a lamppost: SAVE DARFUR, NOT IRAQ! it suggested. Vernon shrugged.

Why save either? Both countries hate our guts. Next, it was *The Thinker* giving him the eye, as if to say *What's a busted, over-the-hill cop doing Here?*

Good question, Vernon admitted. *Probably another wild-goose chase.*

Finally he found a map and directory board, which showed him that the building he sought sat at the other end of the campus. A small billboard next to the directory had this message: STUDENTS PARTICIPATING IN "SARAN WRAP" PARTIES WILL BE EXPELLED.

Vernon didn't even want to guess.

The building was back near the Teacher's College, where he'd first entered; the cool air sucked him in. The first door he came to read, DR. CARL AURED - LINGUISTICS, which stood open a few inches. Vernon stuck his head in. "Dr. Aured?"

A graying man who was bald on top looked up from his desk as if annoyed. "I can't be bothered now—I have an appointment with a police officer."

"I'm the police officer, sir. Inspector Howard Vernon."

"Forgive me! You don't look at all like the police."

Vernon smiled gratefully. *Well, that's a change.* "I appreciate you making the time to see me on such short notice."

He held his hands up and pffft'd, like a Jewish patriarch. "The summer sessions? Not very busy. Please, have a seat."

Vernon sat down, having noticed enough of the cramped office to tell it was sterile and lackluster, which probably paralleled this man's job.

"On the phone you mentioned 'strange' writing at some crime scenes," Dr. Aured recalled. "It sounds intriguing. May I ask what crimes were committed?"

"Murder and vandalism," was all Vernon said. He slipped the man the notes he'd taken. "Pardon my handwriting. But the words look to be from several languages. One, I suppose, is Latin, and the rest . . . Well, that's why I'm here."

Dr. Aured appeared thrilled as he focused on the notes. "Mmmm," he muttered several times, and, "Um-hmm." After only a few moments, his gaze snapped back up. "It's all Latin, in a sense—Latin-rooted, I mean—because it's all founded in Vulgar Latin; a Romance language, in other words. This line here, for instance . . ." Aured touched the tip of his pen to what Vernon had transcribed from the closet in the precinct women's room:

TARA ROMANEASCA, TARA FLAESC ROMANAE and TARA FLAESC WALLKYA.

"It's a bit of a hodgepodge," the linguist said. "Latin mixed with Saxon and Old English, and quite a bit of Finno-Ugris—the language of the Magyars of Hungary. Before the Turks overwhelmed the Slavias in the mid-1400s, the crusader princes of Romania and Bulgaria—all under the supervision of the Polish and Hungarian kings—frequently spoke in a meld of these languages so that Turk spies and non-Christians would be less likely to understand them. But these quotes are very strange . . ."

"But what does it mean?"

"Oh! Sorry! Of course, the reason you're here," the elderly man exclaimed. "It means something akin to 'This land of Romania, this flesh of Romania.' And 'Tara flaesc Wallkya' roughly translates to 'This flesh of Wallachia.'"

"Wallachia?" Vernon questioned. "What's that?"

"Southern Romania, referred to, of course, in the first quote."

The next line was: ME ENAMOURER AD INFINITUM.

From the chapel. Vernon tried to keep things sorted.

"This is more bastardized Latin, just *less* bastardized. 'My true love forever.'"

Vernon didn't know which was stranger, the first quote or the second. *Why on earth would bum-girls write something like that?* But then he realized the folly of the question. *How could they come to write ANY of it?*

Unless someone was teaching them . . .

Dr. Aured chuckled. "But this next quote, is by far more interesting."

Vernon looked at the notes again and saw: SINGELE LUI TRAIESTE, the words written in magic marker on the impaled body of Virginia Fleming.

"Yes, much more interesting, indeed. It seems to be an unaccented attempt at modern Romanian or Româna. You see, Inspector, the modern Romanian language is derived from Aromanian and Megleno-Romanian, seven vowels, twenty consonants, and twenty-eight letters. To ease some of the confusion, we have this system today known as the IPA—"

Why do I have a feeling that doesn't stand for India Pale Ale? Vernon thought.

"—the International Phonetic Alphabet, which in some cases standardizes the different accents, diphthongs, triphthongs, etc., that exist throughout the world. But your criminals aren't regarding the IPA at all, almost as if they're trying to write by ear, and aren't particularly educated."

"You nailed that one," Vernon told him.

Did Aured smile ever so slightly? He looked at Vernon and said, " '*Singele lui traieste*' means 'His blood is alive.' "

Vernon squinted at him.

"You have some very unique criminals here, Inspector. Ultimately, they're fudging phonotypic Cyrillic with Old Church Slavonic. No diphthongs, no triphthongs, no accents."

"You're already way over my head, sir."

"Just the fact that the words are Romanian, I mean. It's almost funny—not that murder can ever be funny, of course." The linguist was digressing in his overkill of knowledge, apparently amused by something Vernon couldn't comprehend. "Then the reference to Wallkya—Wallachia, in tandem with the line, 'His blood is alive.' "

"You're *still* over my head."

Now the old academician smiled outright. "I'm afraid that's all I have for you, Inspector." He chuckled loudly. "Unless your murder victim happened to be *impaled*."

Vernon nearly fell out of his chair. "Was that . . . in today's paper? Nobody told me."

Aured's smile turned blank. "Well, no. I just made it up, based on the only inference I could assume. You don't mean that your murder victim actually *was* impaled?"

Vernon felt as though someone had smacked him in the head. "We actually have *two* victims who were impaled, Doctor. How could you know that? I know for a fact that it's *not* in the papers yet."

"Oh, dear." Aured's eyes thinned in perplexity. "Just . . . from the words, Inspector. I was making a joke but now it seems . . ." He cleared his throat. "Wallachia is the province of Romania that was once overruled together with two more provinces, Moldava, and Transylvania, and in the mid-1400s, the warlord of these provinces was Vlad the Impaler—the historical Dracula."

CHAPTER THIRTEEN

(I)

"Yeah, I'm sorry but this was last-minute," Paul's voice re-layed over the phone. "Jess and I have to grab a commuter flight to Boston in two hours. Big accreditation conference in the morning, and there's no way out of it. We won't be back till tomorrow after six."

"That's okay," Cristina told him. "If you have to go, you have to go."

"It's this license-renewal stuff that we have to have be-cause of a lot of our clients. But it's only one night."

Cristina winced to herself when the implication finally set. *I'll have to spend the night here by myself*, she thought. But just as quickly Paul added, "Britt's coming over, though, so you won't be by yourself."

"Oh, okay. That's great," she said in a repressed relief.

"And, remember, we're still on for tomorrow night with Jess and Britt, but don't worry about anything. We'll pick the carryout up on our way back from the airport. But grab some plum wine at the store, okay? And a couple six-packs of this beer called Tsing Tao. It's really good with Chinese food."

She didn't balk at his mention of alcohol. *He only gets over the top when he's drinking liquor.* And, besides, it was a very busy day he'd be winding down from. "Sure, honey. Have a safe trip, and call me when you get in." Then she half-joked, "And don't be letting Jess drag you to any of those strip-joint places. Promise?"

Paul chuckled over the line. "Of course, I promise. What do I need to go to a strip joint for when I've got a hot number like you waiting for me?"

Cristina blushed at the crude flattery. "Good answer, so the minute you get home, I'll give you a lap dance you'll never forget," she assured, and then they exchanged their "I love you"s and hung up.

Cristina gritted her teeth when she flexed her shoulders back. Every muscle in her body continued to ache. She popped two Advils just as the knocks sounded at the door.

"Hi!" Britt greeted at the threshold. "Your overnight guest has arrived, and—" Thunder rumbled overhead. A light drizzle had just accelerated to heavy rain.

"Come in!" Cristina urged and stepped back. "I hadn't even noticed that a storm was coming." When Britt rushed in, Cristina peered down the street and watched late afternoon grow darker in fast increments. She began to close the door but paused when she thought she noticed a curtain flutter in a sidelight window across the street. *The church*, she thought. Then her eyes darted right; wet footsteps slapped down the sidewalk as two unkempt women ran, giggling, to escape the rain. Cristina watched after them but they disappeared quickly amid the torrential sheets. *I wonder if it was those girls I saw.* She came off her heels an inch when a crack of lightning roared. Cristina slammed the door and locked it.

"You don't hear that a whole lot," Britt called. "Jeez, like a bomb going off." She'd set down her small overnight bag, plus a grocery bag, and was already in the bathroom drying her hair off.

Cristina meandered back. "No, you don't." She stopped at the spacious kitchen counter, looking at the bag. "I just don't like the idea of Paul and Jess flying somewhere when there's bad weather."

"Little sister, a flight from here to Boston is so fast the stewardesses barely have time to get the complimentary drinks out before they're landing. And if there's lightning, they'll delay the flight a little while till it's gone. Relax. They're big boys."

Cristina nodded to herself, peeking into the grocery bag.

"And we'll have fun!" Britt continued. "We can watch movies and get smashed!"

"I'm still a little wobbly from all that booze the other night with Bruno." Cristina pulled some things out of the bag, including a bottle of teriyaki marinade. "What did you bring?"

"Dinner. You ever have skate filets? There's delicious with teriyaki, taste just like sea scallops. Plus some fresh soybeans. The Japanese say that skate is a *big* aphrodisiac." Britt laughed. "Too bad the boys are away, huh?"

"Great," Cristina said. "You're cooking this stuff, right? I can't cook."

"Leave it to me. You stick with weirdo art, I'll do the cooking. And I can't *wait* till tomorrow night. That'll be even more fun."

Cristina guessed she was right. The thunder rumbling kept her off-track. Britt bounced back out, having changed into shorts and a tank top. "And I don't know about you, but I'm starving so let's give this to-die-for kitchen of yours a workout. You do the soybeans, I'll do the skate, okay?"

"Sure," Cristina said. She cumbersomely began popping the small beans out of their pods while Britt flopped two big triangles of pale fish into a bowl and added the marinade.

Skate, Cristina thought with some doubt. *I didn't even know people ate it.*

Britt grabbed a large fry pan off the rack. "So how have you been since the big Mold Mystery was solved?"

"Fine," Cristina said but winced again at the nagging aches in her arms and back. "But a contractor came out and said the mold wasn't the toxic kind."

"You're kidding me?" Britt shrugged. "Forget about it. Whether it is or isn't, let Paul get the basement pressure-washed anyway. It can't hurt. Besides, I'd trust the doctor's opinion over some punk contractor."

Good point, Cristina surmised. "I just basically took it easy today."

"Good. Rich doll designers have that luxury." Now Britt prepared some cooking oil and spices. "And speaking of luxury, I'm off till Monday so how about getting me a drink? A rum and Coke would do quite nicely, and do me a favor and pour yourself one."

"How is *me* drinking doing you a favor?"

"Then I won't feel like a lush!"

Cristina smiled and walked around to the bar. "I'm not in the mood myself. Maybe later." At the bar, though, she noticed the basement door opened a crack. *I'm sure that was closed earlier*, she thought but stalled. *At least I think it was.* She closed it and got Britt's drink.

"What's on your mind?" Britt asked after a sip of her drink. "You don't seem yourself."

Snap out of it! I always do this! I bring other people down with my moods! "No, no," she half-lied and got right back to the soybeans. "I'm fine, and I'm really excited about the new line."

"The first four figures are in stores when?"

"Maybe tomorrow."

"That's great. All the more reason to celebrate. Actually we'll celebrate twice. Tonight *and* tomorrow night. I haven't had Shun Lee carryout in ages. Tell Paul to be sure and get an order of the ostrich."

"Ostrich?" Cristina exclaimed. "Skate, ostrich, cuttlefish—you're really into some off-the-wall food."

"Not just food," she giggled but didn't comment further.

As Cristina popped more soybeans out, she noticed that even her fingers were inexplicably sore. "I've had these outrageous muscle aches all day," she said.

"Too much sex," Britt laughed. "But I wish I had muscle aches for the same reason."

Cristina frowned. "It could be, considering how much we've been doing lately. I feel like I've been digging ditches all day."

"I love it! Sex equates to digging ditches!"

"That's not what I meant. I just . . . *ache*."

"Trust me. It's from sex, and that's a *good* thing." Britt grinned wolfishly. "Come on. How often do you and Paul do it?"

A pang of embarrassment flared. "Two or three times a night, I guess. Sometimes more."

Britt squealed.

"And I guess it's more me than him," Cristina admitted next. "I'm just . . . insatiable sometimes, and Paul's always ready to accommodate me."

"I'm so *jealous*, girl!" Britt had the pan heated up now, and was sliding in the skate. "Jess only gets that way on weekends so during the week I give him his treat at bedtime and just let him go to sleep. *Then* I let Mr. Rabbit out of his hutch."

She's something, Cristina thought and smiled.

The bizarre dinner turned out to be excellent, and over the course of the evening, Cristina did indeed begin to unwind. Paul called briefly to let her know they'd arrived safely at their hotel, after which Cristina felt awash with relief. At ten she fixed herself a drink while preparing Britt her fourth. They lolled on the wraparound couch watching old movies and found themselves mainly laughing at antiquated hair- and dress-styles.

Within an hour, Cristina was huddling close to Britt, as if for solace from the storm. Sheets and sheets of rain teemed against the house; that and the lightning flashes seemed hypnotic. All the while, the alcohol lulled her further. She nodded in and out, and at one point when she roused, she found Britt fast asleep beside her. The TV was still on but the sound turned down silent, the house still all around. The rain had stopped; lightning continued to flash in the windows but noiselessly now. *We should go to bed now,* Cristina thought groggily but before she could drag Britt or herself up, she fell fast asleep herself—

—only to be dropped right into the middle of her recurring dream and all its accoutrements . . .

Moisture trickles over the damp stone dappled by candlelight as she squirms in the clenching pleasure. She's so familiar now with these cryptic surroundings that she feels at home in them while the warm hands and bodies incite her nerves. A haze sweeps across the scape of her vision, like looking through a veil, and she sees the other faces moving this way and that—faces that are smiling with the same lust that's making her cringe on the warm stone floor. She feels blanketed by moving hands that explore every inch of her body. Two wet-lipped mouths descend through the dark haze to lick her neck, tongues circling in corkscrew shapes until they find their way to her nipples. Another mouth toys with her navel, then licks up and down her sweating belly, the wet tip inching ever so slowly down . . .

Now her lust is as much a haze as her vision. She knows that something else is occurring around her but the crush of sensations prevents her from concentrating. She's seen all this before but now she senses she hasn't seen it all. She tries to focus but then her attendants press down. The blanket of hands and mouths has now become a blanket of hot, squirming bodies, and the firelight changes into the furious illumined lines of black, green, and red shifting snakelike on the stone walls. She cranes her neck even as her phantom lovers take her, and she glimpses the stone slab beyond and the angled shadow that grows more resolute with her stare: the nun.

"Kanesae . . . ," the voice—a man's voice—croaks, and that's when she notices the man on the slab in heavy leather, boots, and chain mail. He's quivering on the slab, a deep gash at the side of his throat. To his side sits the decanter you remember

from before, and you sense that it's full of blood but when you glance at the nun again, she shows you the fangs amid her grin and lowers the bowl she's just filled. "Singele lui traieste," *she whispers, and then she grabs the man's wrists and with little effort pulls him off the slab and begins to drag him up crude stone steps.*

The colors churn. A dog barks. Her body goes tense and she releases one echoic shriek after the next as her climaxes break and her lovers titter and giggle and grin down at her, all showing needlelike fangs. . . .

Cristina felt in a trance as cognizance returned. Her mouth pressed forward while smooth thighs vised her cheeks. *What am I . . .* Her thoughts began to trickle through. She felt fingers ranging through her hair. *What am I doing?* Another thought told her it must still be that nasty dream but eventually, as her lips continued in their task, she knew this was too real to be a dream.

I have no idea where I am or what I'm doing . . .

Her mouth inched back—

"Cristina!" a voice complained. The fingers in her hair urged her face back down. "You can't just *stop!*"

But Cristina did stop. Only her confusion felt sharper than the sudden acknowledgment that something was wrong. She struggled back, rose up on her knees and looked down.

It was Britt who lay splayed and naked beneath her.

"Oh, my God! What—"

"What are you stopping for?" Britt snapped but then as she looked around herself, she appeared just as confused as Cristina. They were both naked, yes, and there could be no denying what they'd been doing. No dream. Reality. And they weren't in the bedroom nor on the couch.

They were both on the brick floor of the basement.

Britt jumped up to her feet, covering herself. She was only partly visible in the feeble sunlight from the back windows. "Jesus Christ! How did we get down here? I thought we were in the bedroom!"

Cristina had no response. Her heart fluttered. "Let's get out of here!" And she, too, jumped up. They both stampeded up the stairs.

Neither of them spoke as they clamored to pull on robes in the bedroom. Cristina looked appalled at the nightstand clock: it was 8:30 in the morning.

"All right," Britt said after composing herself. "What just happened?"

Cristina sat on the bed, hands in her lap. She shook her head.

"What were we doing down there?" Britt asked. "I mean, besides getting it on?"

"I don't remember going down there," Cristina's voice ground. "And I can't imagine why we would anyway. And . . . I don't remember . . . how the other stuff happened."

"Well, I remember the 'other stuff,' Cristina." Britt sat down next to her. She seemed more annoyed than bewildered now. "Let's not hedge the issue. We were *having sex*, for God's sake. And I don't even remember who started it."

Cristina gulped, memory struggling. "I guess . . . I did. And I've got no idea why." She put her face in her hands. "I'm sorry, Britt! I don't know what to say . . ."

Britt fumbled for a cigarette, squinting. "Don't worry about it, Cristina. I guess it was just one of those things that happen sometimes. I guess we were drunk but . . ." Britt kept shaking her head. "But we weren't that drunk, were we? I had three or four drinks but, Christ, that's not enough to make me black out."

"I only had one," Cristina added. "I don't think we were drunk. And there was no reason for us to go into the basement."

Britt paused through more thoughts, spewing smoke. "This is really fucked-up."

Cristina looked at her. "And I had the dream again, with—you know—the lesbian stuff like I told you the other day. Maybe when I woke up . . . I thought it was still the dream, so I . . ."

"It doesn't matter," Britt sputtered to herself. "Let's try to take this apart. You had a blackout the other day, and woke up in the basement. And what happens tonight? We *both* have a blackout—"

"In the basement."

"Right, so we don't have to be Sherlock Fucking Holmes to see the common denominator, huh? The damn basement." Britt stood up abruptly but winced. "Damn. My arms and legs ache, and—" She looked at her hands. They had some small scuffs and cuts on them. Then she pointed to her knees, which were scuffed as well. "What the *hell?*"

Cristina showed similar scrapes on her own hands and knees.

"Come on!" Britt ordered and stomped out of the room.

At the basement door Cristina stalled. "Britt, wait. Maybe we shouldn't go down there. Maybe it *is* toxic mold."

Britt wouldn't hear of it. "The doctor says it's toxic, the contractor says it isn't—Jesus, Cristina. I don't give a shit. I've been in the basement before and nothing happened to *me*. We're not *hallucinating* now, are we?"

"No, but—" Cristina looked at the door. "I don't want to go."

Britt grabbed her hand. "It's just a basement. Come on!"

Cristina followed her down.

"What are all these damn boxes?" Britt complained. She began shoving some out of the way.

"Stuff the church left," Cristina peeped.

Britt strode to the back and opened the windows. "Whether we remember it or not, we came down here for a reason." She began visually combing the aisles between the clutter. Cristina stood aside, rubbing her arms. She didn't have a clue what to do.

"Look at this," Britt said.

Cristina came around to peer at that cement patch with the odd symbol imprinted in it but now the patch was webbed with cracks.

"It's all broken up," Britt said. "It wasn't like that a few days ago."

"I know. The contractor only mentioned one crack."

Britt looked at her scuffed hands again. "It's not too hard to put two and two together, little sister. *We* did this."

"But with what? We don't have any tools to break cement."

Britt pushed two stacks of boxes apart. She pointed. "Oh, yeah?"

In the gap lay two small sledgehammers and some chisels.

Britt gave a sarcastic chuckle. "Yeah, I guess we *must've* been drunk last night."

Cristina contemplated the remark but just couldn't believe it. "It doesn't make any sense."

"Neither does us coming down here in the middle of a friggin' thunderstorm to get it on, but we did anyway. Something must've prompted us to do this, and if we were drunk it was probably pretty stupid. Shit, we probably thought there was treasure buried under there or something."

Cristina frowned. "Britt, I really don't think we were that—"

"It doesn't matter." Britt began to think logically. "We did it for a reason but as we can both see, we didn't finish the job. Maybe we'll *remember* the reason if we *do* finish the job."

"Britt, that's absurd. You don't mean—"

Britt grabbed Cristina's hand again, urged her toward the steps. "Come on. We have to get dressed and go."

"Go *where?*"

"To the nearest store that sells work gloves and shovels," Britt told her.

(II)

What a sucker I am, George Gemser berated himself. *I always fall for it, don't I?* He nearly collapsed when he withdrew and let Laura unwrap her coltish legs from around his back. *She'll start shitting on me all over again now. Guaranteed.* From where Laura lay on the couch, she grinned up like a cat that had just fed, her pants off, her security blouse open.

"Now *that's* how I like to end a twelve-hour shift," she said, and she just lay there, not moving—deliberately, Gemser felt sure—just to let the image of her svelte body dig deeper into his brain.

"And that's how I like to start them . . ." He got up and began to get dressed, feigning so much. *Act like it's no big deal, just another notch on the gun*, he pleaded with himself, but he knew he was failing. For George Gemser, this girl *was* a big deal, even after all the smugness and cold shoulders, after all the hard-to-get cat-and-mouse games she liked to play—even after all the times she'd have sex with him one day and stand him up the next. He knew she lived on those head games, but Gemser also knew that he secretly lived for her. Every time he tried to break it off and retain some self-respect, she was right back in his face with that unfathomable body and *Mona Lisa* smile. *Hauls my ashes and thinks she's got me wrapped around her finger again. And she's right*, he thought.

Again, he pleaded with himself. *Don't be a wuss. Be a man.* He strapped on his belt. "I gotta clock in and get on my rounds. See ya."

"See ya?" she questioned and was on her feet in a blink. "Oh, so you're gonna be Mr. Asshole now?"

He looked back at her. *My God, I love you, you-you-you bitch.* "Ain't no big deal, right? Sport-fucking? You're the one who wants it that way."

She remained pants-less, blouse still open to reveal pert lemon-sized breasts and stomach as flat as the floor. "How do you know I don't want it the *other* way?"

George's resolve was bending. "Hey, I tried it the other way, remember, and got shit on."

She traipsed over on the balls of her feet, to maximize the tone of her legs. She smacked a crude, wet kiss and pressed against him. "Forget about anything that happened in the past. Things change, you know? Maybe I have, too."

George was wilting. He could melt in her arms right like this. The heat from her perfect body seeped right through his uniform to his heart. Then she broke away, and began to get dressed.

"You want to know something, Gemser?" she asked in a neutral voice. "And I don't even care if you believe it."

"What?"

"The only guy in the world I want to date, and the only guy in the world I want to *fuck* . . . is you." She collected her things and shrugged. "Don't believe me? Then there's nothing I can do about it. I guess if you call me, then I'll know it's still on with us, and if you don't . . ."

All that shining, long black hair billowed when she walked out the door of the old employees' lounge.

Gemser stood there, shaking. *She's leading you on again! Don't believe her! And DON'T run after her like a pussy!*

Gemser blinked . . . and ran after her.

"Hey! I'll call you!"

She paused at the glass front doors. Turned. Smiled. "That'll make me very happy . . ."

Gemser gulped.

"Have a good shift," she said, and pushed open the doors. "Oh, and see if you can find the keys to that door behind the boxes. It's in my log. The blueprints say it's an inactive boiler room but it's not on the site map."

"Uh—yeah, I will—"

Then she was gone.

Jesus, please us, he thought.

The smell of her hair and perfume was all over him as he made his first round of the building. It proved a maddening distraction. Gemser knew she'd set the hook again. *Or maybe—maybe—she's for real now* . . . He punched his clock in every empty room, checked every window and every door, thinking about *her* every step of the way. He wouldn't see her again for twelve more hours, and knowing this would make the shift seem twice as long. But after tomorrow they both had two days off in a row. *Then we'll be able to go on a real date—like regular people*, he realized, suddenly giddy.

But he'd caught the entry on her log sheet, about the door not on the site map. A door no one had ever noticed, not even the developers who'd bought the place. They'd never noticed it in the lounge due to the boxes. Gemser went back in and looked at it. Steel frame, metal door face, but what looked like an older lock. *An old disk tumbler*, he recognized. Gemser knew locks; ten years in private security had taught him much. *I'll bet that lock's been on there for forty years. And I'll bet I could open it in forty seconds* . . . Gemser reached in his pocket, fingered his set of HPC lock picks, then withdrew his hand. *Better not. What do I care? It's in the log. If the boss wants to see what's behind it, he can get the keys from the property owner.* Why risk getting in hot water when he didn't have to?

Still, he thought he better check for an alternate entry. Gemser didn't like assuming security responsibilities while not having access to every door. *Could be paint back there, or faulty wiring. A firetrap.* He made some notes about it in his own shift log, then made a foot patrol outside.

He cut through the side alley and walked down. The

alley stood relatively clean—a surprise for this city. Several old garbage cans lined part of the building's back wall. The old loading dock's bay door was chained and locked shut, and when he checked it for tampering he found no signs. An exit door which they *did* have keys to remained secure as well. But there was nothing else.

At the end of the building, he thought he heard . . .

What the hell's that?

He followed his ear, noticing the muffled yet distinct sound of metal clinking metal, but . . .

His ear led on, past the actual boundary of the Banana Republic building. Now he was standing behind the building next to it, like an old brownstone but without the same style. Mark Funari, their boss, had told them the place used to be an annex house for the church across the street, but now some people lived in it. The place obviously had a basement because as he walked farther he saw several street-level windows complete with decorative security bars. Now the clinking sound was louder. *The owners must have some construction going on in the basement, that's all*, he realized. Then he left the alley.

Back inside, he returned to the employees' lounge and kicked back on the couch. The Detex clock told him he had thirty more minutes before his next round, and in spite of his post-lovemaking excitement he found his eyelids drooping. *Laura*, he thought in a semi-dream, and the tighter he closed his eyes the more vividly he saw her: the sweep of shining black hair, the dark eyes aglitter, the seductive slopes of her body. The dream beckoned him deeper, and here they were again, naked and pressed together, ravening each other's senses. "Suck these now," she panted, sliding upward to let her breasts blare in his face. Her nipples felt like hot coins beneath Gemser's tongue, which he was soon sucking in adoration. They swelled in his mouth. Then he licked her cleavage and could feel the hot blood vessels in each breast beating as the rest of her lissome body squirmed against him. Gemser's eyes bulged in the crush of sensations.

Now it was her turn; her mouth trailed all the way down his chest and stomach, and when it drifted even lower, he groaned and turned his head aside. It was a daydream, yes, a fantasy—this he knew, so why would this ecstatic muse place him in such an odd location?

A dank room of stone bricks that looked like a dungeon.

Gemser didn't care; it wasn't real, it only *felt* real. Were those figures he spotted half-formed in the shadows? One of them a *nun*? He heard water trickling, and ticking as of a dog's nails pacing the stone-block floor . . .

Laura's mouth worked fervently, causing Gemser's body to tense as the sensations continued to point and encroach his groin. He was about to—

"Not just yet," she giggled and slid back up to him. "We've got forever."

Gemser didn't get it, and he didn't understand why the muse heightened its weirdness by showing him the other end of the dripping room and an elevated stone slab.

Was there *blood* on the slab?

Gemser blinked. *This is just a dream,* but when he tried to open his eyes, he couldn't. He could only continue to see behind them as Laura angled up with lust in her eyes and drool on her lips, and then her mouth opened wide to show glistening fangs, which tore into his throat and began to suck—

Holy shit! Gemser jerked himself back to full wakefulness, caught his breath, then laughed. *I guess my subconscious doesn't like Laura,* he reckoned. The fantasy had taken its own course to merge her voluptuousness with a symbol of predation.

Get off your ass, he commanded himself and got up. *With my luck, Funari would waltz in here and fire me for loafing.* Still, the edges of the daydream nipped at him. He slung the Detex clock back over his shoulder but before he could exit the lounge he heard:

scritch-scritch-scritch-scritch

The sound came so faintly he couldn't even be sure he'd heard it. *Scratching or something.* Very slowly, he looked to the other door.

Rats. I'll bet that's what it is. But before he put it on his log sheet he wanted to be absolutely sure. He slipped out his lock picks, isolated a "double-ball" as well as the tiny tension wrench. He got to work.

All he had to do was tease the pick along the top, then the bottom of the keyway while exerting the most minimal rightward pressure against the wrench, and—

click.

—the cylinder turned.

Gemser opened the door to almost be shoved backward by the stench of urine, garbage, and something he couldn't really have known was decomposing human flesh. The *scritching* sound stopped; then he swore he heard someone say, "It's the guard."

Gemser got past the gagging and commanded in a stout voice, "Who's in there? I'm calling the cops. This is private property." *Probably a bunch of bums living in there all this time and no one knew,* he realized, sliding out his aluminum flashlight and stepping into the doorway.

A woman's voice said the strangest word: "Salut . . ." And just as Gemser proceeded and before he could turn his flashlight on, many hands grabbed him and hauled him into the darkness. Then the door slammed shut.

CHAPTER FOURTEEN

(I)

"Nothin' like good old *Baston* to wear a lawyer out," Jess commented as he parked the car, but Paul didn't hear him; he was looking up at the house with a smile in his eye. *I've only been away one night but I miss her so much it's like a year.*

Jess had an idea by looking at his friend. "Come on, lover boy. Let's go in. The weekend has officially begun. I need to eat, drink, and get laid."

"I second that." Paul snapped out of it. "Grab the last bag."

The smell of all that gourmet Chinese food drove them nuts on the drive back. They carried three big carryout bags toward the front steps. Paul was about to go up when—

"Excuse me. Would one of you be Mr. Nasher?"

"Yeah, that's me," Paul said. It was the doorman from the condo building next door. He looked kind of slinky and stooped over in the stock getup.

"I'm terribly sorry to interrupt, sir, but the management of my building asked me to speak with you."

Paul looked puzzled at the tall condo building, then back to the doorman. "Is there a problem?"

"Oh, just a tiny one. Some of our residents have complained about the noise that seems to be coming from your basement."

"Noise?" Paul frowned. "We had a contractor in there, I

think, but just for an appraisal. I can't imagine what *noise* you mean."

"Perhaps it's an exaggeration then, sir, but I was asked to mention it. You see, many of our residents are retired and getting on in years. They go to bed early. Quite a few on the first floor claim to hear noises like hammering in the wee hours—er, more of a *clinking* sound."

"A clinking sound?"

"Yes, sir, over the past several nights, not to mention for an hour or so this afternoon. The sound was described by residents as something like hammers to chisels. I knocked on your front door earlier but there was no answer and, I'm very sorry to trouble you with this. But if you could look into it?"

"I, uh, I will," Paul faltered.

"Good day to you, sir."

The doorman returned to his post.

"Clinking sound? What the hell was that all about?" Jess asked, one arm wrapped around a carryout bag.

"I don't know and I don't care." Paul mounted the steps. "All I want to do now is scarf down my char-grilled lemongrass pheasant satay and ball Cristina's brains out . . . and *not* necessarily in that order."

"You dog, you!"

Paul paused to grin at the door. "I'm telling you, man. Cristina's never been so good. She makes me feel twenty again. All of a sudden she just so, so, so . . ."

"Horny as a mutt in heat?"

"I was thinking more along the lines of voracious but, yeah, that'll do."

"Come on."

"We're here!" Paul announced when he and Jess barged through the front door. They stalked to the kitchen to set the bags down.

"Damn, that smells good," Jess remarked, putting his face to a bag. "Hey, where are the girls?"

"Here we are," Britt said. They must've been in the bedroom. She and Cristina simultaneously embraced their men. "Oh, baby, I really missed you," Paul said, breathing in the scent of Cristina's hair.

She gave him a half-lewd kiss. "How was your trip?"

"A pain in the ass but now it's over."

"Amen to that," Jess said, arm around Britt.

Cristina got four beers from the fridge. "Here's the Chinese beer you wanted."

"We're ready," Jess said.

Britt looked in the bags. "I hope you got the Hunan-style ostrich steak."

"Two orders," Paul said. "Plus pheasant satay, crab rangoon made with Cousie crab, prawns in XO sauce, drunken chicken—oh—and sweetbreads with black mushroom."

"What exactly are sweetbreads?" Cristina asked.

"I don't know, lamb brains or something. Thymus glands."

"I know what I *won't* be eating . . ."

They all grabbed a beer, but Paul and Jess looked at each other as if by premonition. Something didn't seem quite right. *The girls*, he thought. They both looked wearied in some way, their blouses smudged, their jeans dusty. It was as though they were trying to smile to cover up their fatigue.

"Everything all right?" Paul asked.

"Yeah, you girls look like you've been hanging Sheetrock," Jess said, halfway done with his beer already.

Now it was Cristina and Britt who traded glances. But neither spoke.

"Come on. What's up?" Paul prodded, and then the thought struck him. "You girls weren't doing anything in the basement, were you?"

Britt's eyes widened. "Why . . . do you ask?"

Paul was just shy of getting ticked. "The doorman at the place next to us said some of the old folks were complaining about *noises* coming from the house." He eyed Cristina in particular. "From the *basement*. But how could that be? The basement's off-limits."

"The funky mold," Jess added.

"Well," Cristina began but then faltered and looked to Britt.

"All right, we *were* in the basement," Britt spoke up.

Paul's anger flared. "Britt, you were *here* when the doctor said—"

"Forget about what the doctor said," she came back. "He was wrong. The contractor told Cristina the mold was typical and harmless. It's not important. And we were down there all day and we didn't get sick, we didn't hallucinate."

"We found something down there, Paul," Cristina said.

"Look, I'm totally confused now—" Paul shook his head, aggravated. "What are you talking about? You *found* something?"

"Let's show them," Britt said, and then she and Cristina headed for the basement steps.

"Women are *kooky*," Jess said.

They followed them down.

Paul didn't like it even before he hit the steps. "I don't know about this," he muttered.

"Yeah," Jess added. "I think we should do what the doc said and stay out of here until it's clean."

Britt frowned over her shoulder. "Oh, Jess, *forget* about the fucking mold! You've got to see this."

A lot of the boxes had now been stacked aside, widening the aisle. A few more yards down, Paul spied some shovels, a small sledgehammer and a chisel.

"I thought the freaky doorman was high," Jess said. "Guess that explains the *clinking* sound."

When Paul saw most of the cement patchwork broken up and piled to the side he almost had a fit. "Cristina! Why the *hell* would you do this?" There was also some dirt piled to the side. "You've been digging? For what?"

"I—I wasn't sure," Cristina said. "But the patch was already cracked."

"*What?*"

"Paul, calm down," Britt said. "Just . . . look." And then she pointed down.

After they'd broken out the cement, they'd dug several feet down. "We couldn't get it out," Britt told them.

Cristina looked down, too. "It's too heavy."

"So we figured you two he-men could lift it out of there."

In the hole sat a single barrel of some sort that seemed to be covered in rust.

"What is that? A metal drum?" Paul asked and got down on his knees.

Jess knelt as well. "Maybe it's a keg of wine, like, three hundred years old or something."

"Or maybe buried treasure," Paul fantasized.

Britt tapped her foot impatiently. "We won't know *what* it is unless you guys can get it out."

The men hesitated. Then they shrugged and got to work.

"Lever it up," Paul said, his feet in the hole and pulling the strange drum backward. Jess got the shovel's edge beneath the cannister's base. Paul then pulled it over on its side with a huff.

"Jesus, the damn thing's heavier than a floor safe . . ."

Jess lifted up on the rim, then shot a frown at Britt. "We're lawyers, not forklifts!"

"Quit whining," Britt egged on, laughing. "Would you rather Cristina and I mess up our beautiful nails?"

Paul and Jess failed at the first two attempts to lift the small barrel, but on the third—

"Up, up!" Paul grunted.

"Fuckin'-A!"

"Be careful," Cristina fretted.

They hoisted it out on its side, then after a few more grunts got it set upright.

"Now what?" Jess asked, sitting exhausted against some boxes. "I'll bet that thing's made of cast iron."

"And look at the lid," Paul observed. "It's crimped under the lip."

"Try this," Cristina said, offering the hammer and chisel.

Paul got to work, gradually hammering, then bending the iron lip up around the rim. The noise was nerve-racking. "I think I'm getting it . . ." Eventually—

"Bingo," Britt said.

When Paul pried the lid open, Jess lifted it away and—

clang!

—heaved it aside.

Britt dropped to her knees and shouldered between the two men, reaching in. The smell that eddied up was nothing unpleasant but surely a fetor that suggested antiquity: old metal, old wood, and the scent of fabric that should be rotting but for some reason wasn't. Paul froze, and Cristina and Jess stared when Britt lifted some unknown object swathed in old, burlaplike cloth.

"Well, I can tell already it's not jewels or gold coins," she said, setting it on the floor. She began to carefully unwrap the cloth, then gagged.

Everyone else gagged as well.

"That's just great!" Jess said, repelled.

Paul muttered, "You've *got* to be kidding me."

Within the emaciated cloth lay a yellowed animal's skull.

"It looks like a dog's skull," Cristina said, a hand to her stomach.

"What the *fuck* is a dog skull doing buried in our basement?" Paul remarked.

"But there's something else." And Britt was reaching in again, lifting out another object padded by the ancient, crumbling fabric. "It feels like some sort of a—"

What she held up was a crude bowl—about the size of a

cereal bowl—that seemed to be made of fired clay. A disturbed look touched her face even before she turned it around.

"What's that there on the side?" Jess asked with some excitement.

"Maybe they *are* jewels," Paul hoped.

Britt said nothing when she showed the feature to Cristina, who croaked, "Oh, my God," and then fainted immediately.

Into the front of the bowl had been set three circular polished stones: one black, one green, and one red.

(II)

"O quam magnificum, o domnul . . ."

Father Rollin sat dejected in his heavily curtained study, nervously thumbing his pendant under which had been etched the same words he'd just muttered to himself. And then he looked at his ring, and saw the same words etched again. Paul Nasher and the other man had returned a while earlier, Rollin had seen through his window. With his binoculars, then, he watched the four of them mingle in the kitchen for a few moments; then they disappeared.

Where are they? the priest wondered, his stomach strangely tight. They hadn't gone upstairs because he'd kept the glasses trained regularly on the steps.

Why do I have this feeling they're in the basement?

The light was draining out of late afternoon. Rollin couldn't guess where his surveillance might be best posted tonight: here, or his room at the Ketchum. He dreaded returning to the hotel tonight, for the bawdy convention was going strong. *Just don't have it in me tonight.* But he couldn't believe what he was doing next: leaving his church on the pretense of going for a walk.

A walk around the alley.

Those homeless girls kept weighing on his mind. *They're all prostitutes, or were in their better days*, he felt sure. *And Canessa herself was a prostitute.* Was he seeing too much into it?

He didn't know. Sometimes he felt like he didn't know anything.

How hackneyed. He was whistling as he walked down Dessorio Avenue—Bach's *Passacaglia.* of all things—to seem inconspicuous. An old man walking his dog nodded to him; then a woman in a business dress walked briskly by without even noticing. *I'm invisible to everyone but the old*, he joked, but liked the idea. *I wish I could BE invisible, so I could walk right into the annex house and see what they're up to.*

Ludicrous.

The old Banana Republic stood dark, which was strange for he knew there were guards there round the clock. Just before he cut into the alley, a patter of footfalls startled him. Had he heard giggling, too? He jerked around and glared back down the street but there was nothing.

A dark alley is no place for a priest at sundown, he caught himself worrying, yet he felt fairly sure that God would protect him from muggers. *Fairly* sure. *Do I even deserve his protection?* Perhaps not. Now he felt inane. He turned left down the alley, pretending to meander, until he was directly behind his old annex house. One high sodium lamp provided the only useful illumination. *Don't let your shadow be seen*, he warned himself. Then he'd *really* have some explaining to do. *If they ARE in the basement, they might see me . . .*

He hunkered down quickly and peered in the street-level windows.

Did he hear voices? *Just my imagination?* he wondered, but for a moment he thought he'd heard agitated conversation. Then: *No*, he thought. The basement stood completely lightless, all that looked back at him were solid panes of black.

Rollin walked back toward the alley exit in long strides, and when he passed the Banana Republic he shivered for no apparent reason.

Back at the church, he found the door unlocked. *I couldn't possibly have*, he felt sure. Nevertheless, it was. "Absentmindedness is a symptom of men my age," he muttered next. He'd done it before, and he always reasoned that there was little to steal in a barely used church. He pushed into the murky nave entrance and turned on a few dim lights, and then locked the doors.

I don't know what I'm going to do now but of course . . . I NEVER know what I'm going to do.

He had no appetite so he skipped making himself dinner, and instead elected to go back upstairs to watch some more with his field glasses. Now the front study's murk was double what it had been before he left; he left the door open but didn't turn on a light. Only a slant of illumination leaked in from one of the few lights in the long hall. He approached his chair and the slight part in the drapes, was about to pick up the binoculars again when—

His heart surged at a pattering of sound.

Footsteps in the hall?

Damn it. Someone DID come in. "Who's there? There's nothing to steal so you may as well just be on your way."

His call was only answered by what he thought must be giggling, yet he didn't step forward nor even turn on the light. Instead, he stood frozen, staring.

The shadow of a figure now faced him from just aside the door.

Rollin gulped.

"Who are you?"

The reply seemed to build first with a sound like blowing

leaves. "You already know," came the feminine words, lilting and accented. "You've been awaiting me for some time, as have your pitiful ancestors—traitors to your country's true heart."

Rollin couldn't have moved even if at gunpoint. His teeth actually chattered but he managed to command: "Get out! This is hallowed ground!"

A raspy chuckle flitted about every corner of the room. "Servitor, how dull, this God of yours. As pitiful as your corroded spirit."

"You can't be here! This is a sanctified place, a house of God!"

More rustling, the sound like leaves, yet the angled figure didn't budge. "Power is like faith, servitor. It fades away. It grows palsied and it dies. Like virility, and like empires."

Rollin's eyes couldn't blink.

"Like you . . ."

The priest tore away from his stance and turned on the nearest lamp. The shadow was gone. Perhaps it had never been there at all, for now he saw that it may have merely been a queer shadow cast by the coat stand.

Christ, give me strength . . .

From another room, something of glass fell and broke. Rollin trotted down the hall, switching on lights as he went. His heart chugged in his old chest, then surged again and he actually shrieked.

Just as he prepared to enter his bedroom, the door burst open and out ran two dirty women with disheveled hair. A stream of giggles poured from their mouths. Rollin's initial jolt backed him against the paneled wall and as the second interloper passed, she brazenly grabbed his crotch and squeezed. As she headed toward the stairs, the priest noticed that she was nude from the waist down, and carrying a pair of dirty jeans with her. She wore a T-shirt that read

THE DAMNED, and the other one had pink sweatpants on. Their bare feet thunked down the stairs with more giggles.

Rollin knew he was too old and heart-diseased to give chase. Feebly, he shouted, "You little buggers! I'll have the police after you!" But the warning was only answered by more mocking laughter.

One of the girls' voices echoed from downstairs, "Sleep good in your bed tonight, asshole!"

Rollin caught his breath and entered the bedroom. What had fallen was a framed picture of the Nave of Snagov Monastery, in southern Romania. Glass glittered on the old carpet like wet rock salt. He groaned when he noticed the wavy streaks of black, green, and red besmirching the white walls. His cross above the bed had been taken down and placed on his pillow. "Goddamn them," he profaned when he picked it up.

It was wet, and the pillow and sheets were drenched. The odor he was only noticing now told him it was urine.

He heard a door slam deep downstairs, which he knew must be the back kitchen door. *Those homeless bitches are long gone now,* more unpriestly profanation occurred to him. He'd never felt so useless, so impotent.

He swore no further once down in the chancel. *What could I expect?* Blank-faced, he discovered similar desecration. The same scrawls of magic marker streaked the white altar linens. These weedy vagabonds had brought stout bladders, for another great wash of urine tinted not only the linens but the front carpet. The Communion decanter had been gulped dry, the packets of the Host torn open, their contents wolfed down. Evidently one of the wretches had forced herself to vomit, for that was what now filled the Holy Chalice.

Rollin calmly dragged the fouled linens off the altar and carried them to the laundry room.

(III)

"It's impossible," Cristina droned after having come to on the couch. Her eyes held wide on the ceiling.

"Honey, it's a coincidence," Paul countered. "Sure, a little weird, but it's still coincidence. You're overreacting again, right, Britt?"

They all sat close around the couch, save for Britt, who stood, smoking. Was she nervous? "Yes, it's—"

"Bullshit, Britt!" Cristina railed. "How can it be *coincidence?*"

Jess held the odd three-gemmed bowl in one hand, and Cristina's Noxious Nun doll up in the other. "That is pretty wild, the gems, I mean. Even the order of the colors are the same."

"Yeah, but that's the only thing," Britt insisted. "There's a logical explanation, Cristina—we're just not seeing it yet. You're freaked out because you've been dreaming about a nun holding a three-gemmed bowl, and today that's what we find buried in the basement."

"And you think *that's* coincidence?" Cristina said.

"Yes. The two bowls don't even look alike; in fact that thing from the basement doesn't even *look* like a bowl, does it? It's kind of warped." She took it from Jess and placed it on the coffee table, rim-side down. "It's probably some kind of old centerpiece. It's not a *bowl.*"

"What difference does it make!" Cristina almost yelled.

Paul put his arm around her. "Calm down, honey. Britt's right. There's a logical explanation. Do you really believe you're *psychic?* That's the only other explanation."

Cristina sighed, sitting back. "I don't know. I just can't believe I'm the only one who thinks this is really nutty."

Paul spoke softly. "Honey, didn't you say that you've talked to the priest several times, the guy from across the street?"

Cristina looked oddly at him. "Yes. Twice. Yesterday I invited him in for coffee. What's that got to do with it?"

Paul swept a quick glance to the others. "He used to look after this house; the church has owned it for decades."

"What are you getting at?"

Britt stepped closer. "Isn't it possible that the priest told you that thing was buried in the basement? And maybe even described the color of the stones set in it?"

Cristina tensed again. "No, it's not possible, Britt, and you know that. I've been dreaming about that bowl for a long time, and I didn't meet the priest till *several days* ago."

"Sure, honey," Paul kept on, "but maybe you met him that first day I brought you by the house right after I bought it. Maybe you met him back then . . . and maybe he told you about that bowl. Back then."

Now Cristina looked infuriated. "What? So I'm *lying?* I'm making it up to be dramatic?"

Paul hugged her and chuckled. "No, no, that's not what I'm saying at all. But, look, your memory's not exactly the greatest—"

"And you are a little absentminded at times," Britt added.

"—and you *have* had a blackout, right?"

Paul continued, "So I'm just suggesting that maybe it was something like that. The priest told you about the bowl and you simply don't remember. I forget stuff all the time, we all do."

"Yeah," Jess piped in, "like last month when I worked my ass off on the titles for the Manera deal and *you* forgot to overnight them."

"And Jess forgets to put the toilet seat down *every damn day*," Britt said.

Paul nodded through a smile. "We all forget stuff, honey, and I'm sure that's what happened here. You're getting way, way too worked up over this."

Cristina slouched against him. "I guess you're right."

"Objectively speaking, what happened? We found this funky thing in the basement and it happens to look a little bit like the bowl your nun doll is holding. Big deal."

Now it was Jess's turn to add some levity. "And, Cristina? If you really *are* psychic . . . the lotto's up to twenty-two million, so if there are any numbers floating around your head, how about laying them on us?"

Even Cristina smiled, now that the incident had softened. "All right, so I'm a nut job." She rose from the couch. "Let me heat up the Chinese food."

"I'm *dying* for some of the Hunan-style ostrich steak." Britt went to the kitchen with her. "Let's get this party started." Paul and Jess followed them, to get more beers.

"But what do you think that thing really is?" Britt posed.

"Like you said, probably just some old church relic, a centerpiece of some kind, and the dog skull? Probably some bishop's pet from a hundred years ago," Paul answered.

Cristina withdrew some plates from the cupboard. "Whatever it is, I guess it's not really even ours. We should give it back to the priest."

Paul and Jess looked at each other, brows raised.

"There they go doing their *lawyer look* again." Britt asked, "It must still belong to the church, right?"

"Not in this state," Jess said. "It's considered abandoned property."

"Anything the church left in the house," Paul added, "whether by accident or intentionally, becomes the property of the buyer after thirty days."

Jess swigged his beer. "And I'm sure we're all wondering . . . what are those stones? Could be a black diamond, an emerald, and a ruby."

"Can't hurt to get it appraised," Britt said.

"Ann, our secretary, sometimes dates a woman who's a jewelry importer," Jess said. "I have to go into the office for a few hours in the morning, and Ann'll be there. I'll show it to her."

"She dates a *woman?*" Britt asked.

"*Women*," Paul corrected, "and, yeah, I do remember her saying that. Maybe she can get it appraised for us. Wouldn't it be funny if those stones turned out to be worth a lot of money?"

"It wouldn't be funny to the monsignor!" Jess railed. "Ouch! Ripped off again!"

He and Paul laughed hard.

The previous mishap forgotten now, the four of them resumed their get-together, though none of them were aware that the basement door stood ajar, and if any of them had looked at that precise moment, they would've seen an ear in the gap . . .

All but Cristina had imbibed enough to get tipsy, and the Chinese food, even reheated via microwave, had been delicious. When they all turned in at about one A.M., the entire situation made Cristina think of her college dorm days—or nights, actually—when the muffled sounds of sexual frolic could be heard through the walls. She and Paul got started even before the bedroom door could be closed, though it was more Cristina's initiation than his. Her spontaneous urges overwhelmed her, as it had been so much of late. *I just can't help it*, she thought, kissing him and feeling his body through his clothes at the same time. Paul was hard in his pants at once, which delighted her; even half-drunk, it seemed, she could always rouse him. Still fully clothed, she sat him down in the chair and whispered, "That's right, I promised you a lap dance." And that's what she presumed to do even though she wasn't really sure what that was. First she straddled him, and didn't even remove her blouse when she braced his face in her cleavage, all the while her jeaned hips squirming over his. She could feel him through the denim, his flesh beating. He kept trying to open her blouse, disrobe himself and her, but she wouldn't let him yet. She wanted him titillated first. She held his head and urged him to suck her unbra'd nipples through her blouse, a notion that seemed kinky in some way, a forced restraint that would only make him crave her body more. "Like that, like that," she breathed as he sucked wet circles into her blouse. Her fingers fiddled up his crotch but only in snatches. The teasing made him hold her tighter, suck her nipples harder as she let herself, too, be titillated but not relieved.

"Baby, I can't stand it anymore," he panted, covered in sweat. He suddenly tore her blouse open and began to crudely lick the orbs of her breasts. "You're teasing the hell out of me tonight."

She let but one finger dawdle at his groin. "If you want me . . . you have to *take* me." And with that he rose, hoisted her over his shoulder, and turned to the luxuriant black-sheeted bed. She squealed like a child on a carnival ride when he flung her on the mattress.

She didn't help him; she simply lay there with the cat-like grin. Evidently, Britt and Jess were in their own throes of pleasure, for Cristina could easily hear them through the walls, and for some reason that only stoked her desires further. Paul roughly rolled her jeans off her legs, then one fist yanked off her panties to leave them dangling off a foot. The other foot teased his crotch to deliberately interfere with his hasty effort to unbuckle his belt but when his pants were finally down, he shoved her knees to her shoulders and lay right into her.

Cristina had asked to be taken, and that's what she next received, waves of pleasure spiraling upward with each primitive thrust. The bedposts knocked against the high-priced wallpaper, but she didn't care. All Cristina cared about was that he lasted long enough to satisfy her own lust.

He throttled her more, as Cristina's pants turned to something close to shrieks, and she let every lewd image spill into her head. Both were racked by climaxes nearly at the same time, and then he collapsed on her as the wet heat he'd put inside her began to trickle. *It just keeps getting better,* she thought. Her fingers toyed in his hair. Soon he fell asleep, so she slipped out from under him and turned off the light.

She snuck out of the room to the dark kitchen, wearing nothing more than the ripped blouse, and then opened the fridge.

"Raiding the leftovers, huh?" Britt surprised her from behind. She came through the darkened kitchen in just bra and panties. "You read my mind. Any of the ostrich left?"

"I think so." Cristina found the proper white carryout box and passed it to her.

Britt sniffed the aromas from the box. "Just the way this stuff *smells* drives me nuts. I love classy Asian cuisine."

"Me, too. This is just what I need after . . ."

Britt grinned in the white refrigerator light. "After mongo sex? Oh, we heard you in there."

Cristina blushed. "Yeah, well you and Jess weren't exactly low-key either."

"It was great," she said with a mouthful of ostrich. "He definitely got the job done."

Cristina's eyes drifted to Britt's bare stomach and legs but she dragged them off after a moment. Britt obviously noticed but didn't say anything. Suddenly Cristina broke away and loped for the living room. "I want to look at it again . . ."

"Look at *what?*" Britt came after here.

"You know. The thing. The bowl."

"Centerpiece," Britt said. "Bowls aren't lopsided, little sister, but—"

At once Cristina was frantic. The coffee table was empty save for several beer bottles. "Britt! It's gone! I know I left it here!"

"Calm down, you nut!" Britt almost raised her voice. "Jesus, you're always such a live wire!"

"It's gone!"

Britt sighed. "Jess put it in the trunk so he doesn't forget it tomorrow. You heard him, he has to go to the office for a little while."

"Oh, that's right." Cristina slumped. *Overreacting again.* "So the secretary can show it to her jeweler friend."

"You're always on pins and needles, Cristina." She padded back to the kitchen for more tidbits. "You'd think that after getting laid, you'd have simmered down."

She's right . . . as always. Again she caught her gaze lingering over Britt's well-toned body. "But it is weird, isn't it? Sure, maybe I did meet the priest briefly months ago, but why would I dream about that bowl to the extent that I'd incorporate it into my next figurine?"

"Because it's all subconscious imagery," Britt nearly snapped. She was obviously getting tired of her foster sister's obsessions. "Everybody has fucked-up dreams."

"And the dog skull? Come on. Lately there's been a dog in the nightmare."

"So *what!* Stop with all this! You're going to drive everybody nuts. A fucking animal skull in a hole in the ground. Who knows why it's there and who cares?" Britt looked at Cristina with some scrutiny. "You know, a little Prozac would do you a world of good. Stop obsessing."

Cristina gave a sheepish nod. "And what was the design? On the cement patch? What do you think that is?"

"How the fuck do *I* know?" Britt flared.

"Maybe I should ask the priest."

"Well then do that. Nobody gives a shit, Cristina. It's just some stamp in the cement with some Latin on it. It's some church seal."

"Well . . ." Cristina fidgeted. *Why can't I let it go?* "Isn't there something that neither of us told Paul and Jess?"

Britt's eyes narrowed as she tried to rein her anger. She whispered, "What, that we both got a wild hair last night and made out? We can *never* tell them that. Are you crazy?"

"That's not what I meant. I meant last night. It was you and I who broke that cement up, and we didn't even remember it. I'm not the only one who had a blackout. You did, too. Last night."

Britt grabbed her shoulder and shot a fierce whisper in her ear. "I know that, Cristina. And it probably *is* some flashback shit from the Goldfarb days, but we agreed to ignore that. If we don't, it'll screw both of us up in the head. The past is past. It doesn't matter! After what we went through, we can't *let* it matter, otherwise we'll never have our own lives. We've been through this and through this. So just stop!"

"I'm sorry," Cristina offered, a tear in her eye now. "It just . . . bothers me."

"Don't let it. And we can never tell the guys about last night. It's none of their business anyway."

Cristina fidgeted some more. "Let's go down in the basement, just to look around. Maybe there's more stuff in that hole."

Britt glared. "Cristina, if you go back in that *fucking* basement, I'll kick your butt. I'm not kidding. I don't care if Davy Jones's Locker is in that hole. We're not going down there. The place is bad luck." She squeezed Cristina's shoulder. Hard. "You hear me?"

Cristina nodded.

"Good. We're going to have *fun* this weekend. No more of this bullshit. And don't be talking to that priest, whoever the hell he is. With all the shit you read about priests these days, who knows what kind of weirdo he might be. Let's go back to bed now."

Cristina knew it was the best idea but, still, she hesitated.

"Look, Jess is going to the office tomorrow." Britt put the leftovers away. "What's Paul doing?"

"I think he's playing golf."

"Good. Tomorrow, let's you and I get dressed up and go to lunch at the Four Seasons, or maybe D'Amato's, okay?"

"I'd like that."

"I brought some killer dresses with me, and you can wear that red dress I gave you last Christmas. We'll *turn* some heads, girl!"

Cristina smiled, knowing that Britt had probably only suggested it to get her mind off these other things. Britt's arm slipped around Cristina's back; she urged her toward her and Paul's bedroom.

"Sorry I'm such a pain in the ass," Cristina peeped.

"Forget it. Now go to bed."

In the dark, then, they joined in a "sisterly" peck on the cheek but after a moment . . .

Was it Cristina who refused to let go?

Cristina's mouth drew to Britt's, and she pressed her breasts forward. She had no awareness of her intent yet she found herself doing it anyway. Their tongue tips touched; Britt paused breathless, but when Cristina sought to kiss her more deeply, it was Britt who nudged away.

"We can't. It's not right."

Cristina kept her hands on Britt's hips.

"What happened last night was just a fun accident," Britt whispered almost inaudibly. "But I love you. You know that, right?"

Cristina nodded in the dark.

"Go to bed." Britt smiled, let her fingers trail down Cristina's arm. "See you in the morning." Then she returned to the guest room where Jess could be heard snoring.

Cristina remained in the dark hall a moment. Did she shiver? She thought of the basement again, but cringed. *I have to try to be better.* She went back to bed and fell into what would be a very welcome *dreamless* sleep, and she was happy by her final resolve. She had never burdened Britt with her final worry: that maybe the house was haunted.

CHAPTER FIFTEEN

(I)

Mark Funari was the security account and personnel manager, a bristly man with dull dark eyes and steel-wool hair, short in height and temper. He didn't like site calls unless it was an emergency. But this?

Laura Eastman stood sleek at the front glass doors, tapping her foot. "Finally," she said when Funari debarked from his company car.

"Did you knock?"

Lines creased Laura's pretty face when she frowned. "No, I yodeled. Of course I knocked. I've been knocking for a half hour." She pointed through the glass to the security desk. "His stuff's not on the desk, and neither is the Detex clock."

"He probably fell asleep!" Funari barked, grimacing at the desk. "Did you call his—"

"Cell phone? Of course," she sputtered. "Just voice mail. I think he split."

"Split as in quit, you mean." Funari had never liked her; she was too snooty like so many women with the right looks. He liked her even less after she'd twice had sex with him in return for a buck-an-hour raise. *They're all whores, all of them.* "What about his car, brainchild? Is his car here?"

She shot him a look that could kill. "Mark, Gemser doesn't have a car, for the same reason I don't and damn near everyone else who works for you. You don't pay enough."

"Watch that."

"Anyway, I knocked for a half hour; then I called you," she said, and the way she stood, at a slight angle, allowed the nipple of one perfect breast to be half-seen in the loop between two buttons of her security shirt.

Bitch is doing it on purpose. Funari was so mad he could barely get the keys in the door, but eventually they opened and after a quick search of all the desk drawers, he realized that Gemser probably did quit without telling anyone. His knapsack was gone, along with his bag lunch and thermos. The site keys were gone as well but at least Funari had duplicates.

"Gemser's got his shit together too much to quit," Funari asserted. "He's worked for me ten years."

"And . . . *how* many raises?" Laura made the snide remark.

Funari leveled his gaze. "You better watch it, sweetheart. Your company record ain't exactly setting the world on fire. You need this job."

Laura laughed and sat down sloppily behind the desk. She put her feet up. "You're gonna fire me for making honest comments? Go ahead. I'd sue you for sexual harassment, and you know I'd win. I'm a minority, a downtrodden woman in a man's world, forced to subject myself to sexual debasement to keep from starving."

Funari felt like he was broiling.

Laura grinned. "And if you want another go, for another dollar an hour . . ." She parted her legs on the desk and winked.

"Get your smart ass out of that chair. We have to search the building. My bet is you cock-teased him one too many times and he just got sick of it so he walked out—"

"I think Gemser's too *big* of a man to do something like that." She winked again.

Funari got the innuendo. *Don't take the bait.* "I'm too busy to let you piss me off, but one thing I'm sure of,

Gemser's at least enough of a class act that if he quit, he'd leave the keys and leave a message. You take the first and second floors, I'll take three and four."

Funari strode off, heel snapping. Laura laughed and casually got to the task.

An hour later, they were done, and there was no sign of Gemser.

"Fuck this. That mother*fucker!*" Funari growled back at the desk. "I have to find a substitute fast. You'll have to work a sixteen-hour shift."

"You know me, Mark. I'll do anything for triple-time."

"Bullshit. Time and a half."

"Have a good day." Laura grabbed her bag and headed for the door.

"All right, triple-time!" *Bitch, bitch, BITCH!* Funari tossed her the keys and now *he* headed for the front doors. He didn't look at her when he said, "And if that scumbag shows up here tonight with his dick in his hand, have him call me."

Laura offered a light, spiccato chuckle. "He'd need *both* hands, Mark. Unlike, well . . ."

Funari banged out the doors and stalked to his car. He reminded Laura of a toddler about to have a tantrum.

"What a loser," she muttered. She locked up after him. But now that her pathetic boss was gone, the empty building seemed immense, and she was alone in it. She began her first round, wondering where the *hell* Gemser could be.

(II)

Gemser wasn't quite dead yet, proof of the resilience of the human body. He'd been stripped and erected on the sharpened pole and now hung there as if mounted, and in truth, he'd never even gotten a good look at the people who'd done this to him. Only a few candles lit the stench-filled room, and he could see their shadows squatting aside as they seemed to divide his lunch among the three of them—egg salad sandwich, chips, and a tangerine—chug his coffee and riffle through his wallet. He could feel his heart thumping hard and slow as the pain coursed through him like dull electricity. In deeper shadows, he saw several other figures who'd suffered the same fate. They were all macabre mannequins now.

"Suh-suh-suh . . . someone'll come," one of the figures said.

Another. "The New Mother will protect us. She protected us from *him*, didn't she?"

"Yeah." A third female voice. "But it'll all be over soon anyway."

"That's right!"

More eating sounds, then:

"Francy, when will you have to leave?"

"Soon. The guy with the goatee has to go to his office in a little while, but I'll already be there. I'll take the subway."

"I-I-I wish I could go instead-instead-instead—"

"Be quiet! And how could you go anyway, Stutty? You don't talk right—he wouldn't believe you."

"Yuh-yeah? How do you know he'll buh-buh-buh—believe you?"

"Because the New Mother said he would! We must have faith! We have to *believe!*"

"Shut up, Francy. We do. You're too bossy."

"I am n—"

"Huh-hey! This guy has four hundred bucks in his wallet."

"That's great. We'll put it with what's left of Doke's money. Is there any sandwich left?"

"No."

"Shit." A chuckle. "It's funny, though. He made it but we ate it!"

Crazy, Gemser's half-firing brain managed to think.

"Wuh-wuh-we should agorn him now."

"*Adorn*, Stutty!"

"That's what I said!"

Gemser felt like he'd been shuddering for hours. When would he die? His body seemed to minutely toss around the stake each time his heart beat. Feet scuffled, and now his eyes could dimly detect the three shapes crowding around him. Gemser tried to scream but all that came out was a rough, wet rattle.

"He's still alive!"

"The New Mother said that sometimes the Prince's enemies would live for days on the pikes."

"Wuh-wow!"

Madness, Gemser thought.

A sharp, familiar smell reached his nostrils, and though his nervous system was growing less and less responsive, he could feel something, too. *Magic marker*, came the insane thought. They were drawing lines up and down his body with magic marker.

"I think it's cool he's still alive."

"Hey, I wonder if . . ."

Now Gemser felt a hand plying his terror- and pain-shriveled genitals.

"Sandrine, you weirdo! He's almost dead! He can't—"

"I . . . just wanna see if . . ." And next Gemser felt a mouth down there. Gemser blinked.

"Told you, Sandrine, you perv."

The shadows all cackled.

I'm . . . in hell, was the last thought to drift through George Gemser's mind before he died.

(III)

Jess was used to hangovers; it scarcely impeded him from getting up at eight, showering, and dressing. As he knotted his tie he paused to stare at Britt who lay asleep and belly-down on the tousled bed. The sheets were mostly off, and what Jess was musing over was her nearly bare body just lying there for him to view, the sweep of her back, the sleek legs, and her buttocks barely covered by the tissue-thin panties. *Nope*, Jess thought. *I ain't gonna do better in a million years.*

"You're up early," he commented when he came out to the kitchen. Cristina puttered at the coffee machine, wrapped in a robe. She seemed perturbed.

"I got a coffee craving," she said. "I didn't sleep much but I slept great."

"Then how come you look pissed off?"

Cristina reflected. "I guess because I sort of am. Britt and I are going to lunch later, and I wanted to wear that red Dolce and Gabbana dress she got me. But I can't find it anywhere."

"It'll turn up," Jess small-talked. He grabbed his briefcase. "Has Paul left for the golf course yet?"

"He's in the shower."

"Tell him I'll try to meet him for the back nine, will ya? I have a little paperwork to do."

"Sure," she said, distracted. "Why don't you and Britt stay tonight, too? We're not doing anything."

"We'll probably take you up on that." Jess chuckled. "Paul and I'll bring back a couple fifty-dollar pizzas from Barbetta's."

"That would be great. Oh, and don't forget to show that bowl-thing to your secretary."

"Are you kidding? I'm dying to know what the stones are." *Probably paste*, he figured, but the lawyer in him couldn't resist. "See ya tonight."

" 'Bye."

Jess rushed out, jumped in the car, and twenty minutes later was at the office. His eyes gave a sexist bulge when he entered the office and saw Ann already at her desk. He could see her runway model legs beneath the glass-topped desk, black leather skirt hiked up high enough to just barely betray the fact that she rarely wore panties. *Jesus. These Lipstick Lesbians LOVE to rile up middle-aged straight guys.* At least she was good at her job, too. "Here's the rest of those lease reports you wanted," she said. She frowned within a banged frame of blonde hair. "I've been at it since six."

"What a gal." He thumbed through the papers. "You sure it's all here?"

"Of course."

"Good, then you can go—"

"Serious?"

"It's Saturday, Ann. No sense both of us being here if we don't have to be."

"What a guy!"

"But could you do me a favor?" He pulled the three-gemmed bowl from his briefcase. "That chick you know who has a jewelry business? Could you give her a call and get me an appraisal appointment?"

"Sure . . ." She dialed, then peered at the bowl. "Looks old. Where you'd get it?"

"It was buried in Paul's basement, believe it or not. We just want to know what the stones are."

Ann eyed the object further, then began talking on the phone. When she was done, she said, "She'll have someone here within an hour to take a look."

"Thanks, Ann. Now you get out of here and have some fun."

"Oh, I'll definitely do that," she said, batting big lashes. She got up but paused to take one more glance at the bowl. "Yeah, it looks old, all right. *And* . . . creepy."

Jess reglanced at it through narrowed eyes. A vertigo seemed to shift his vision, the three stones flashing. "Yeah," he murmured.

Ann bade her grateful farewell, while Jess chose to sit at

her desk to go over the paperwork. But only minutes later, there was a tap at the open door.

Jess looked up, slightly taken aback by a wan woman with medium blonde hair that looked poorly combed, late thirties, probably, and kind of pallid. Red lipstick looked overly applied, but she wore a stunning scarlet dress that must've cost a bundle. *That's what I call worn around the edges,* he thought. The dress clashed with the rest of her, and only a smidgen of prettiness seemed to struggle beneath the weathered veneer, and to top it all off, she wore uncomely pink glasses. "Oh, hi," he said. "You must be Ann's friend, the jewelry appraiser."

"Um-hmm, right. I'm Francy." Her eyes seemed to spark when she noticed the bowl atop the glass desk. "Is that it?"

She looks more beat than a rented drum, Jess thought, *but she sure got here fast.* "Yes, and come in. I'm Jess Franklin."

The woman seemed to walk sheepishly, as if unused to the classy high heels. With each step, her eyes grew wider on the bowl. "Wow," she said, coming right around to where Jess sat and leaning over. Her bare arm rubbed his shoulder at once. *This is . . . weird,* he thought, just the immediacy with which she brushed against him. He felt vaguely uncomfortable.

As she leaned, she picked up the bowl. The three rounded stones gleamed in their mounts. "It's . . . interesting," she said, though her voice sounded as worn as she looked. "Looks like an old cistern . . . Eastern Orthodox . . . maybe, about five hundred years old."

Another thing bothered him: the way she stalled before each group of words, almost as if reciting something. She pronounced each word slowly. Her arm rubbed him more overtly as she continued to look, half-spellbound. "We see these every now and then. They're worth about three or four hundred dollars to collectors."

Damn, he thought, his greed stifled. He glanced aside, was about to speak, but noticed the woman's small breasts almost fully visible due to the angle she leaned in. *Yeah, she's beat, all right. Rode hard and put away wet.* Her broken teeth looked stained as well. *But she's got to be for real if Ann's friend sent her . . .*

"So the stones aren't valuable?" he finally asked.

"Not on their own . . ."

Now Jess's discomfort merged with something else when she absently put her left arm around him and pointed to each stone with her right index finger. He noticed the nails were shabby and bitten down. *Ann's friend sure sent me a piece of work. I think she's putting the make on me . . .*

"See. Obsidian, green garnet, and red garnet," she said, then squeezed his shoulder. "Don't take them out, then the bowl would be worthless."

In the leaning gap of her dress top, Jess saw that her nipples looked raggy, as if chewed. He felt half-repulsed by her, but then something primal in him stirred. He offered a fake chuckle. "And we were thinking black diamond, emerald, and ruby . . ."

She laughed in a high titter, and squeezed his shoulder again. "Oh, no. The stones by themselfs are worthless."

ThemSELFS? he thought. *This woman's something.*

"But I can give you four hundred dollars for it." And now her right hand had a wad of cash in it.

Jess winced. *This is fucked-up.* "It's not even mine, I just wanted it appraised." He blinked. "So . . . you're really a friend of *Ann's?*"

"Oh, yeah." She giggled. "We make out all the time—"

Jess's breath caught in his chest. "Uh, yeah, well—"

"You . . . sure you don't want to sell it?" Now her words, however stilted, came out as a hot gush, and her right hand slipped below the desk, traced up his thigh, and landed on his crotch.

"Hey, what is this?" Jess objected. "Is this a con?"

She rubbed, brushing right against him. "Hmm?"

Jess wanted to rise and throw her out of the office . . .

but didn't. He seemed to melt, remaining there, and she continued. *This is FUCKED-UP.* Some crude lust fogged his senses but eventually a thread of reason pushed through.

"You're just trying to work me over for the damn bowl, aren't you?"

"Uh-uh." She rubbed some more, started to slide her fingers under his belt.

He was about to grab her hand just as it slid beneath his shorts. "I—" A thought flashed. "I get it. She put you up to this. Right?"

"Um-hmm. Anna."

Jess frowned. "You mean Ann."

"Right, Ann." The odd woman noticed the front office door open. "Come on, back here. We don't want anyone to see." She urged him out of the seat and back into Jess's office.

He didn't stop her. *What am I doing?* "Listen. I'm *not* selling you the bowl—"

"That's okay. But if you change your mind . . . let . . . Ann know, and I'll buy it." She pushed Jess's office door closed, walked right back up to him, and sat him down.

"Look. Just . . . stop—"

She smiled. "Let me. I want to. I like it . . ."

Jess didn't move. He supposed it was the crudity of it all, and the abruptness, that pushed his resistence over the edge, the way she knelt before him and yanked his pants and shorts right down to his ankles in one pull.

"Look," he objected yet again but before he could say more, he tensed right up when—as abruptly as everything else—she began to fellate him.

Holy shit, what am I—

"Mmmm," she murmured through the act.

The sensation was riveting, and judging by her technique, she'd had some considerable experience. *Shit, that's the best . . .* A dizzy glance down at the back of her head, and he half-noticed the label on her dress—Dolce & Gabbana—but the coincidence was lost by the fastidious, wet rhythm and excruciating pleasure. Another minute and he spent himself in her mouth.

"Mmmm," she kept murmuring through the earthy denouement. His release left him tingling and lax.

The woman stood up and grinned at him. She didn't expectorate anywhere. "If you change your mind about selling the cistern, have . . . Ann call me."

Jess stared. The bizarre woman waved and left the office.

He snapped out of it a few moments later, jumped up and hauled up his pants. *What the hell was that shit all about?* A tinge of guilt seemed to fleck his spirit. *Did I just cheat on Britt?*

No. Not really.

He stepped into the restroom, got himself back to rights. *Some girl who looks like a bum in a nice dress just blew me in my office,* came the bald realization. A worse realization occurred moments later, when he errantly reached into his back pocket.

That ho! That thieving bitch!

Jess's wallet was gone.

Anger mapped his face with lines. He couldn't even think straight when he heard tapping. Someone knocking on the office door.

Furious, he barged out to the front area—

"Mr. Franklin?" asked a mousy-looking woman in jeans and a pink blouse. "I'm Daniela Agren, from Doria Jewelers. Ann said you needed an appraisal."

Jess stood mute. He jerked a gaze to the front desk and saw that the bowl was gone.

CHAPTER SIXTEEN

(I)

The same man with the absurd blond mohawk and leather vest greeted him from behind the counter. He'd called Vernon an hour previously. "One Noxious Nun coming up. You were smart to preorder." He turned his hand toward the shelves. "We sold out the same day of their release."

Charming. "Thanks for calling," Vernon said. He still couldn't figure why he'd ordered the thing. He looked at it in its box. The actual figure looked more unsettling than the ad pictures: a cute little toy nun holding a bowl of blood.

"Pretty impressive detail," bragged the proprietor.

Vernon said nothing, just stared at the thing. He thought of a hypnotist's totem. The tiny eyes beamed, the tiny white fangs in the tiny mouth seemed to shimmer. When Vernon blinked, he could have sworn the hardened scarlet resin in the tiny bowl rippled as if liquid. *This thing really is bizarre.* What unsettled him more than the rest, though, were the weaving black, green, and red lines that decorated the box.

Vernon gulped.

"Your niece'll *love* it," said the shopkeeper.

"My niece?" Vernon looked at him. "Oh, yes, I'm sure she will—"

"—and she'll definitely want the rest of the line. I can give you a 5 percent police discount—"

"Really?" Vernon felt flattered.

"—if you preorder the next ten figures."

Vernon winced. "Let me give it some thought," he said. *I hate the hard sell.* He thanked the man and left.

Saturday morning traffic wasn't bad. He cruised down 69th, subconsciously eyeing the street for signs of his "bum-chicks." Still nothing more to go on, but at least there'd been no more impalements. When he pulled onto Amsterdam, he rechecked the address on his notepad, then parked illegally. *Here it is.*

One of the city's many grand old rent-controlled apartment buildings hulked before him. He went up narrow stairs, huffing when he reached the third floor, and found the number. His hand paused before knocking, for the oddest of door knockers caught his eye.

It had been mounted on the drab door's center stile, an oval of tarnished bronze depicting a morose half-formed face. Just two eyes, no mouth, no other features.

In the strangest notion, Vernon imagined that for a split second, the knocker had grown a mouth—a grin—which showed tiny fangs.

Why do I feel haunted today? He shook it off, knocked, and was welcomed by a stoop-shouldered man who had to be eighty.

"You must be Inspector Vernon," the voice cragged. "Do come in. I'm Professor Fredrick."

"Thanks for agreeing to see me, sir." Vernon stepped in, his briefcase tugging his arm. At once he stood surrounded by what he might expect of an archaeologist's abode: walls lined floor to ceiling with books and assorted statues, busts, and old stone nicknacks. *Smells like a museum*, he thought.

Fredrick walked with difficulty, requiring a cane. Vernon frowned when he noted that the cane's brass head looked identical to the half-formed face of the door knocker. Its tip snapped along the bare wood floor.

"I thank God," the old man chuckled, "the man below me is deaf. Have a seat."

"Thanks." Vernon sat in an armchair angled before a cluttered desk backed by huge computer screens filled with text. "I can see you're busy, sir. I hope this isn't too much of an inconvenience. When Dr. Aured recommended you, he mentioned you were working on a book."

When Fredrick sat down, either his chair or his bones creaked. "Not busy enough. I'm too old to teach during the summer sessions anyway. We all must pursue our immortality, eh?" He lit up a sweet-smelling pipe. "This book on Daco-Roman Romania is one I've meant to write for thirty years but, lo, other things kept popping up."

Romania, Vernon thought. He got out his notes, and suddenly felt foolish. *Home of Vlad the Impaler.* "Romania, yes, sir. Dr. Aured said you were an expert on Romanian history."

Fredrick, in spite of his age, had a full head of black hair that didn't look dyed. "Oh, I'm an expert, all right. I almost died thanks to that blasted country. Earthquake. Southern Romania lies on a fault line. They get serious earthquakes every fifty years or so. The worst one occurred in 1977, and I was unlucky enough to be there at that precise time. A rectory wall collapsed during the tremor, and crushed my leg." He absently raised his cane. "It took years to heal."

"I'm sorry to hear that," Vernon said for lack of anything else.

Fredrick smiled aloofly, puffing the pipe. "I suppose I was lucky. My teaching assistant was killed instantly." He pointed to an old framed picture of a chubby young woman in boots and field dress, with a burgeoning bosom. "Her name was Janice, a lovely girl. At least she died in the midst of her dream."

"Her dream?"

"It had been her lifelong goal to see Snagov Monastery, a most unique place in the annals of fifteenth-century European history." Now the old man's smiled turned sardonic. "It was also the final resting place of the man we've come to know as the historical Dracula."

Vernon looked back at him; he suddenly felt hollow. He cleared his throat, then showed the old man his notes and began to explain his dilemma . . .

(II)

"Sure, we'd love to," Britt said in the cab. "It's the weekend, and your house is a lot better suited for a get-together than ours. We'll pick up where we left off last night."

Before I screwed it all up by overreacting about that damn bowl or centerpiece or whatever it is, Cristina thought. This would be a chance to make it up to them by having them spend the night again.

Britt whispered, mindful of the cabdriver. "And there's something about your house that lights a fire under Jess's butt. You know. Sexually."

Cristina smiled. "Good. And thanks for lunch. I'd never been to Four Seasons before. I just wish I could remember where I put that gorgeous dress you gave me." Cristina had given up looking for it, and worn a nice Gianni summer dress. "I could've sworn I unpacked it and put it in the closet."

"You'll find it." Britt looked forward, to the street signs. "I actually have to go home for a few hours, though. I want to call the office and do some e-mails. But what time tonight?"

"Just come over when you feel like it. Jess and Paul are bringing pizza when they're done golfing."

"Which means they probably won't be back till seven or

eight. Those guys spend more time in the 'nineteenth hole' than on the course."

A sudden distraction infused itself in Cristina as the cab drove on. A bright, hot day passed before her, the city bustling with life. A high billboard showed three beautiful women on a beach, an ad for Victoria's Secret bikinis, yet the colors of the beachwear were black, green, and red. It reminded her unpleasantly of the night she'd scrawled the same colors on her own body while blacked out. *What would compel me to do something so bizarre?* she stressed to herself. When she briefly closed her eyes, she saw the three women but now they stood not on a beach but in a dark stone room, naked, their flawless bodies streaked with the same colors. At the corner, then, she glimpsed a black-clad figure in some kind of hood.

A nun?

Cristina squinted forward but saw that it was merely an old woman in a cloak.

"What's with you?" Britt asked. "You in the twilight zone?"

Cristina flinched out of it, smiling as if all were normal. "No, I was just thinking."

"Not about that damn centerpiece, I hope."

"No, no . . ."

"Did you have the dream again?"

"Miraculously, no. Don't remember dreaming anything last night, which is surprising 'cos I guess I was really worked up when we found that thing."

"All that means is you're getting accustomed to the new house, and your new life here."

Yes, Cristina felt sure.

They exchanged farewells when the cabbie dropped Britt off at her townhome, then continued on with Cristina. "Just drop me here, please. I'd like to walk," she said when the cabbie stopped at a traffic light. He seemed about to thank her for an ample tip but was sidetracked when his gaze raked across her bosom in the low-cut dress. *Jeez. Drool, why don't you?* But more male heads turned when she proceeded down the street. *I guess it's just a sexist world,* she thought, and then noticed more high billboards sporting attractive women with sexual glints in their eyes. *Everything's sex these days.*

Why was her mood being mauled? *Maybe I SHOULD take Prozac,* she considered. She should be looking forward to tonight instead of wilting from the glances of others. *It only means I'm attractive, so I guess I should be grateful.*

"A beautiful woman for a beautiful day," cracked a voice, and suddenly a hot dog was thrust before her.

"Thank you," she muttered, halfheartedly, "but I just had lunch." It was the vendor she saw so often now, who always had a cigar stump crimped between his teeth.

"Have a wonderful day," he offered, "because it's a wonderful world, isn't it?"

"Yes, it is," she replied and hustled away. *Maybe it's me,* she considered next. Maladapted—that was a word Britt used sometimes to characterize most of her cases at social services. *Maybe I'M the maladapted one. That vendor was just wishing me well, but I immediately think it's just lust.*

The bleak self-analyses collapsed when she spotted a big poster in the comic shop window. *Now THERE'S something to be happy about!* The poster bragged of the release of the first four *Evil Church Creepies*, while a piece of tape informed: SOLD OUT! MORE ON ORDER. Suddenly her day felt reborn. *I'm pretty successful for someone so . . . maladapted!* A brisker pace took her down the street, and just as her happiness grew to full awareness, she slowed at the corner and—

Is that Father Rollin?

Another figure in black caught her eye, though not a woman and not becloaked. A priest with the same looks and build as Father Rollin approached the elegant front doors of the Ketchum Hotel. She stared after him as pedestrians swept by on either side. When the crowd cleared, the priest was already inside.

Why is he going in there when he lives right across the street?

A giggling sound, almost like chirping, caused her to spin around. Another throng of pedestrians were crossing the street but between the intermittent gaps, Cristina thought she saw two girls peeking at her from an alley entrance. *Those homeless girls?* she wondered. She stood on tiptoes, glared between heads, but then the crowd cleared and no one remained in the entrance.

This day keeps tipping up and down. She took off her high heels and power-walked back to the house.

Once inside, she felt yet another distraction: the house's silence seemed all-consuming, a great dead space, and in spite of the air-conditioning, her skin prickled with heat. She stepped out of her dress right there in the foyer, then glimpsed herself in the bar mirror near the hall. She looked back at herself, noticing with a slight shock that she was naked. *I never leave the house without panties on!* Yet she couldn't remember making the decision not to wear them. Sweat glistened on her face, breasts, and stomach. *I must be under the weather,* she concluded; now she felt burning up. When she checked the answering machine, she didn't even smile at Bruno's enthusiastic messages declaring that the first four figures in the *Evil Church* line were out of stock via preorders, and even after only a day or two reorders were pouring in, especially for the Noxious Nun.

Cristina walked listless to the bedroom, closed all the drapes to make it as dark as possible, and collapsed on the bed.

(III)

Laura "cooped" in the middle of her shift. Cooping was security-guard parlance for sleeping on the job. But why not? Her rounds were all made. *Just a nap*, she told herself, stretching out on the couch in the old employees' lounge. Half-drowsing, she smiled at the knowledge that not only had she gotten a lot of shut-eye on this couch, but she'd made love with a number of men. *All on the clock*. Each time she nodded off, however, some dream-snippet would shove her back to wakefulness, along with a jolt in her heart.

Was it a naked woman she saw in the flash, with fangs? *Jesus . . .*

And in the next drowse—

Shit!

—she bolted wide awake because she thought she heard a voice.

Just more dream shit, she concluded. The words had sounded foreign and accented, whispered by a woman.

Get a catnap. I'm working a sixteen-friggin'-hour shift . . .

Her eyes slowly closed again; she felt fogged in darkness, then saw a great white wash of blood behind her eyes and—

"Singele lui traieste . . ."

"Damn it!" She sat upright, her attempts to "coop" ruined. *What the hell is this?* Had she heard the words in her head, or for real?

She looked immediately at the old boiler room door . . . *Sounded like it . . . came from there.*

When she pushed herself off the couch, her hand accidently slipped between two cushions, and touched something metallic. *Couldn't be*, she challenged herself when she flipped the cushion up.

There, amid nameless food crumbs, petrified french fries, and an old porno novel that looked thirty years old, lay a metal ring full of keys.

No way, she felt convinced; then her jaw dropped when she saw one key marked BOILER ROOM.

"I do not believe this," she said aloud when she turned the key and heard the bolt release.

She pushed the door open and almost gagged at the sour stench that drifted out. *Probably dead rats.* She'd smelled that on many different job sites. She flicked the wall switch but nothing happened, then checked the circuit breaker near the couch. *How do you like that?* All of the circuits for the building were on, save for one slot—BOILER ROOM—whose breaker had been removed. Laura grabbed her flashlight out of her bag, snapped it on, and stepped into the black doorway.

Were her batteries weak? It seemed that with each step, the surrounding darkness sucked away at the flashlight's beam. The smell was revolting. She saw boxes filled with garbage and stubby candles burned down. *Hypes,* she guessed. Heroin addicts would sneak into closed buildings just to heat up their works and shoot up. But if so, how would they get in here? *There's no exterior door.*

She turned the corner, then, and the door slammed behind her.

Laura held her ground, even as the flashlight beam grew undeniably deficient. *Keep cool. Don't freak out.* Now the light's intensity seemed to pitch up and down. She grabbed her Mace with her other hand. *Get out of the room, there might be someone in here,* was her first thought.

Her second thought, less than wisely, was to proceed.

She took several more steps, then turned a cinderblock corner.

Laura was a gutsy girl, but not *this* gutsy. When the meager thread of the flashlight beam crawled upward—

"Singele lui traieste . . ."

—she screamed, staring right into the face of the woman whose image had marauded her sleep. The woman stood gloriously naked, full breasts thrust forward. Her hands, first, bid the rest of the filthy room, then extended toward Laura.

Oh my God oh my God oh my God! her thoughts shrieked as she swept the flashlight to turn but saw slivers of more faces: pallid women grinning like the nude woman, then the faces of corpses somehow mounted in the darkness.

One of the faces was George Gemser's, besmirched with streaks of black, green, and red . . .

A piece of rebar knocked Laura's Mace away, and then the atrocious room's darkness exploded with a cackling as dirty hands shot forward, grabbed her, and dragged her down.

Accented words fluttered: "*Me enamourer . . . for infinitum.*"

Laura was being mauled, bitten, beaten about the head with the rebar. Her struggles didn't last long. Just before her consciousness would be knocked out of her, she saw the nude woman's face closer this time, her grin wider and sporting long, thin fangs.

CHAPTER SEVENTEEN

(I)

"Man, Paul, I'm sorry," Jess babbled at the golf course. "I fucked up, I *really* fucked up."

Paul smiled cockily. "What are you talking about? Those lease arbitrations?"

"No, no, man." They walked into the bar at the nineteenth hole, Jess having arrived too late to play at all. "The bowl."

"The—oh, the centerpiece our nutty girlfriends saw fit to dig out of the basement?" Paul laughed and ordered drinks at the bar. "What, you dropped it?"

"No, man." Jess worriedly pushed his hair off his brow. "It . . . got ripped off." And then he explained the bizarre encounter with the woman who'd masqueraded as the jewelry appraiser. "The cunning bitch even stole my wallet."

Paul sipped his drink. "I've heard screwy things before, Jess, but not that screwy. How would this woman even know you'd called for an appraisal? She would've had to know in advance since she arrived *before* the real appraiser."

"You got me." Jess downed his beer in two slugs, then ordered another. "I figure she was either standing right outside my office when Ann called, or maybe she overheard the information from the jeweler's office."

Paul frowned at him. "That's ridiculous, Jess."

"Don't you think I know that? But I can't think of any other way she could've known about it."

Paul chuckled. "So, what, you were sitting there and this 'woman who looked like a bum but in a fancy dress' picked up the bowl and walked out with it? *And* your wallet? With you sitting there?"

"Not . . . exactly." Jess shook his head. "She kind of . . . tried to seduce me, I guess 'cos I refused to sell it to her."

"And?"

"And, well, she took me back in my office—the bowl was on Ann's desk—and, well, you know, she, uh—"

Paul stared incomprehending.

"She blew me," Jess whispered.

Paul almost spat out his drink.

"Then, uh," Jess continued, "she left. I went to the bathroom, and—"

"She ripped off the bowl while you were getting your Johnson back in your slacks," Paul finished.

"Yeah."

"After hearing that, I need another drink." Paul gave Jess the eye. "If I didn't know you better I'd say you sold the bowl for a bundle, and are bullshitting me about the rest."

"Hey, I'm a lawyer, not a thief."

"Meaning?"

"I'd never steal from a *close* friend."

Paul just laughed out loud and shook his head.

Jess looked dismayed. "Man, I thought you'd be pissed at me."

"About *that* dumb-ass thing? I'm glad it got ripped off."

"Glad?"

"Sure. There was a bad vibe about it—*whatever* it was. Cristina's off-balance enough as it is, that thing just made her worse—I don't need something *else* twisting her out of shape. For a while I think she believed she'd *dreamed* about the fucking bowl before she actually saw it for real."

"Women," Jess muttered.

"Like they say, can't live with 'em . . ."

"I'll drink to that," Jess said. "But what should I say when they ask about the appraisal?"

"I'll bet you the pizza tab they're both at the house now half-plastered on mimosas. They'll forget all about it."

(II)

"Well," Vernon said after explaining the case and augmenting it with Dr. Aured's less-than-serious insinuations. "You're not frowning, you're not laughing, and you haven't thrown me out yet."

"It's . . . interesting," Professor Fredrick remarked. He had the habit of sometimes making comments with his eyes closed and face raised, as if in a muse. "Fascinating, actually."

"Come on, Dr. Aured said the same thing, but he *did* laugh at me. Vlad the Impaler?"

"It's not that uncommon, is it, or have I watched too many murder movies? Copycats. That's what you call them, right?"

"Over the past few days, I've been forced to think along the same lines, sir," Vernon chuckled. "I feel a little bit more assured now."

"Why?"

"Because, like I said, you haven't thrown me out and dismissed me as a nut."

"There's nothing 'nutty' about the historical figure known as Vlad Tepes," Fredrick intoned, serious and also at odds with something. "And part of his name really was Dracula; he actually signed his name as such. Vladislaus Dracula is the phonetic equivalent. As for your copycat murderers, however, I'm a little mystified. Homeless women, you say? Inspector, it would take someone who's quite adept at historical research to perpetrate these crimes to such detail. Not the impalements themselves—everybody knows that Vlad engaged in this atrocity quite without restraint. But the colors—your average 'Dracula fanatic' would have to dig deep for that accuracy, not just the colors but the order of the colors. And then the words themselves—they're even more disturbing." He looked back at Vernon's notes, toking his pipe. "I'm sure the good Dr. Aured informed you that these sentences seem to be Vulgar Latin peppered with Saxon, Old English, Finno-Ugris, and others." And then the professor paused. *"Tara flaesc Wallkya,"* he uttered under his breath. He seemed coerced by a studied enthusiasm. "Molested aspects of Latin."

"Dr. Aured used the word *bastardized,*" Vernon volunteered, "but I get it. Someone writing things without much actual knowledge of the languages."

"Um-hmm. And the attempts at Romanian. I'd be interested in knowing Aured's reaction to *that.*"

"Along the same lines. Words not quite right but right enough. Sentences not accented—something about an International Phonetic Alphabet."

Fredrick nodded, eyes closed.

"As if these homeless girls, or whoever really is doing it—"

"Are half-faking it," Fredrick finished. "Doing the best that they can with the available information source." He looked at the next line and smiled. "'*Singele lui traieste . . .*' And if the impalements weren't alarming enough, that line, 'His blood is alive,' most certainly smells of Vlad Tepes and his subsequent occult legend. Nor can we ignore the colors of the markings left at the scenes. Add all these elements together and you simply must have some sort of . . ." His words trailed off along with pipe smoke.

He doesn't want to say it, Vernon presumed. "A gang of homicidal Dracula fanatics. A *cult.* It sounds too far-fetched until you look at the possibility more-more—"

"Concretely. Throughout history there have been many

cults that kill in the name of what they believe in, devil worshippers and the like. Mostly just as a systematic rebellion against an oppressive church order. Today, on the other hand, it's almost become a cliché: disgruntled youth with no direction in life, and defected by antisocial environments, drugs, and what have you—sacrifice animals and sometimes even people to the so-called devil. They're delusional, of course. That boy in Oklahoma, and that group in New Hampshire, for example. And more clichés abound, the 'Goth' movement, an obsession with dark clothes, gloominess, pale skin, and last but not least, vampirism. It's very true that there are vampire clubs and cults and social coteries that exist today and always have existed. There are people who *believe* not only that vampires exist but that they are vampires themselves. Where some men get together on Friday nights and play cards, and some women have their Tupperware parties, *these* people have gatherings where they drink each other's blood. But of course . . ." Fredrick smiled.

"They're all whackjobs." Vernon got the gist. He'd read of such things many times.

"So why couldn't such a group take the next logical—and psychopathic—step? In this day and age, it's not at all outlandish that sick individuals obsessed with this topic could become killers, thinking of their murder as an offering that will bestow upon them good fortune in some dark afterlife." Now Fredrick looked back at Vernon. "All these quotes, the details of the desecrations, and then the impalements themselves are, for lack of a better term, *Draculian*."

Vernon let the strange word slip around his head. "I don't quite follow you about the colors, though. You mentioned a specific detail that would require some historical research."

The old man's brows rose and fell; then he looked again at the morgue photos of Virginia Fleming and the black, green, and red lines streaking up and down her pallid body. "Well, in the vampire legend, Dracula wore a black cape but the *real* Dracula wore three capes: black over green over red. They're specifically the colors of an order of knights—the Order of the Dragon—which is well known. But these colors? Not so well known. Red stands for the blood of Christ, green the color of the Holy Roman Empire, and black over it all to actually *hide* the first two colors: these knights were to operate incognito, so as not to solicit the sin of pride."

"Now I see what you mean," Vernon admitted. A haphazard glance to the shelf made him flinch, when he spotted a small bronze statue of a woman with multiple arms. Vernon shuddered once. "Vagabonds wouldn't know that."

"Unless somebody else told them, I suppose," the professor added. "Cults of this nature often have a ringleader, so to speak, don't they? 'Jonestown,' for instance, from the seventies, the Echols tragedy in Arkansas, that multiple-murder group in San Diego not so long ago. It's mostly sheep who follow such leaders."

Sheep. The figure of speech jolted him. *Homeless women who are mentally unstable . . . following a leader . . .*

The nun?

Vernon felt inept for not having thought of it so concisely. "That suggestion is very helpful, sir. 'Sheep' following a homicidal leader who is clinically obsessed with all this Vlad stuff."

"It's a thought," the old man remarked. He retamped his pipe.

"And these women were seen once . . . with a nun."

Fredrick's eyes leveled in an inexplicable way. "You don't say?"

"There's also this odd coincidence," Vernon continued, "that I really can't explain but can't help but think *isn't* a coincidence."

Fredrick smiled. "The fabled gut-feeling of the veteran investigator?"

Vernon laughed. "Sure. You'd be surprised how often they ring true in this business." Again, he felt foolish. "Take a look at this," he offered and reached into his briefcase.

He placed the boxed Noxious Nun on the scholar's desk.

"This *is* a bit odd," the old man admitted, noticing at once the weavy black, green, and red lines decorating the package. "The lines are quite like those found at some of the crime scenes."

"Yes, sir. I still don't know what the connection might be, but it does make me think. A nun witnessed with vagabond girls just before a desecration that involved black, green, and red lines drawn up and down on an altar cloth, similar lines on an impaled body, and now this novelty toy of a *nun*." Vernon smiled. "Sounds like I'm reaching for—"

"Shit?" The professor smiled. "Maybe, maybe not. Why couldn't the lines be the coterie's emblem, the same way the Zodiac Killer left his own emblem?" Fredrick creaked back in his seat. "No, Inspector, it's not that which rubs me the wrong way. It's the nun." He picked up the box for closer scrutiny. "This *vampiric* nun."

Vernon was duped now by the expression on the man's face. He seemed *bristled* by something.

"Dracula's membership in the Order of the Dragon was inherited from his father," the professor began. "Much has been written of this—*too* much, in fact. But just to give you some background, Vlad initially participated in the Order not so much for religious reasons but to potentially benefit his dedication to fighting the Turks and driving them out of Romania. Keep in mind, the Order was sanctioned by the pope and the Holy Roman Emperor, neither of whom Vlad was keen on since they were Catholics and Vlad was Eastern Orthodox. Nevertheless, Vlad converted to Catholicism, more than anything to support his own agenda."

"I don't understand," Vernon said.

"There are a number of explanations behind the Vlad *legend*; in other words, his vampiric curse. And one involves a nun . . ."

(III)

Father Rollin's heart seemed to drop into his guts when he watched Cristina enter her studio. *Good Lord. She's found the cask. It's all happening . . .* He'd kept the hotel window's drapes parted only wide enough for one binocular lens, and just as he'd been focusing on the rear studio window, his entire soul seemed to rust.

She was naked and glassy-eyed. She'd placed two objects down on one of the desks, one just out of view but the other all too visible.

The dog's skull.

The identity of the other object he'd missed just as he was focusing in. Rollin knew now beyond a doubt that Cristina—as he'd feared—was growing more and more subject to the black, paramental will that had targeted her. *She's doing its bidding, just as was written.* And of course she'd be naked, and highly sexualized, to mimic the blasphemer herself.

But . . . what was the other object?

It must be the cistern, and if she's found that she may also have found—

Another woman entered the room, pausing in a mild shock before Cristina's dull gaze and brazen nudity. *The dark-haired one again, the friend,* he knew. Now she was yelling at Cristina, shaking her bare shoulders to snap her out of the hold that seized her.

It's all happening. It's all for real. And then the priest lowered the binoculars and fell to his knees to pray.

(IV)

Britt emotionally exploded when she stepped into the studio and found Cristina sitting naked in her work chair, staring at the wall. *Is she catatonic?* she feared at first but then, thank God, the eyes blinked and recognized her. Britt nearly shrieked when she saw what her foster sister had brought up from the basement: that yellowed dog skull, which she'd placed on a shelf right next to the Noxious Nun figure.

"Cristina! What the HELL is going on?" She grabbed Cristina's shoulders and shook her till her head wobbled. "Are you drunk? Are you on drugs? What IS it?"

Cristina drooled, then blinked several times. Next, Britt slapped her in the face.

"Cristina!"

Cristina rubbed her face, took a deep breath. "Jeez . . ."

"Yeah! Jeez! You're all fucked-up!" Britt shoved a blouse at her. "Put that on! The guys could be home any minute!"

Cristina roused as if from anesthesia, but eventually complied.

"It's either booze or drugs, so just tell me. And no bull-shitting!"

Cristina frowned. "Stop yelling. I don't take drugs and I didn't have anything to drink."

"Then explain. You looked like you were in a vegetative state when I walked in here. Now I want an explanation, and it better be good 'cos if it's not, I'm checking you in for a psych evaluation right away."

The threat braced Cristina. "I'm all right. I just—"

"Just *what?*" Britt's temper continued to boil. "You

obviously went into the basement"—she pointed to the detestable skull—"and brought that thing up here! Why?"

Cristina sat up straight, buttoning her blouse. "I don't know, it just occurred to me—"

"It *occurred* to you? It occurred to you to go back down into that goddamn basement—*nude*—and bring that gross skull up here? Cristina, do you know how crazy that sounds?"

"Stop yelling!" she whimpered. "I'm not sure what happened exactly."

"Did you black out again?"

"No, no, this time—well, I remember feeling weird, after the cab dropped me off. And I was hot, so I took off my clothes and took a nap. Then I remember going down into the basement, and-and . . . it was because I just felt *impelled* to. I can't explain it beyond that, Britt. It's like something *told* me something else was down there."

Britt sat down, still fuming. "Jesus Christ, that damn basement's got you delusional. Something else down there? Cristina, you already knew that dog skull was down there. We all found it together, remember?"

Cristina thought through a stasis. "Not the dog skull. Something else. I found something else, and . . . you probably won't believe it."

Britt sighed. "Cristina, go ahead and try me. After all this, I think I can handle anything. So you found something else? Where? In the hole?"

"In the iron barrel. Something didn't seem right about the depth so I looked at it closer and found a false bottom."

Britt stared at her.

"Go look if you don't believe me. There was a false bottom in it, to hide *this*." Then Cristina reached into her desk and withdrew a foot-high object that looked like an old stoppered decanter.

Britt fell silent. She wasn't quite sure how to assess this, or her friend. At her job she saw unstable women gradually become delusional all the time, but this?

"Didn't you tell me a couple days ago that recently your recurring dream has taken on new details?"

Cristina nodded. "Yes, first it was just the nun with the bowl, and the colored lines. But then I'd notice other things in the dream that weren't there before: a man on a stone slab, a"—she glanced to the skull—"a barking dog, and . . . some sort of a flask or decanter. Like this one."

Impossible, Britt thought without saying it. *But then so was the bowl. She either knew those things were down there in advance, or she has a psychic sensitivity.* She decided to deliberate on that later. Instead, she picked up the decanter. It felt heavy. *Full,* she thought at once. *But full of what?* "Show me this false bottom," she ordered. "Then I *might* believe you."

Without a word, Cristina took Britt back down into the basement. The hole remained as they'd left it when the men had pulled the barrel out. Britt knelt and studied it, and saw a circular plate of rusted metal lain aside. She hefted it up, placed it in the barrel, and saw that it did not go all the way to the bottom. It left a good six-inch gap.

She's not lying, Britt thought, uneasy now. "All right. I believe you. But Paul and Jess won't. They're going to think you knew about this in advance. They're going to think you made it up to bring attention to yourself."

Cristina looked down solemnly. "Do you believe that?"

"No."

Britt didn't know what to think now. Her eyes tracked along the floor without any forethought but stopped.

Most of the cement patchwork now lay in pieces; one piece, however, retained that odd imprint: the dragon strangled by its own tale, a warped cross branded on its back, and the words, O QUAM MAGNIFICUM, O DOMNUL.

Britt flinched from a chill, then rose and grabbed Cristina's hand. "Come on. The guys would go ape-shit if they caught us down here." *What am I going to do with her?* she worried. *And what the HELL is going on here?* Back on the first floor, she urged Cristina toward her room. "Get dressed, sis. They could be home any minute."

Cristina nodded meekly and disappeared into the bedroom.

Britt let out a long sigh, then poured herself a drink. *That's great. She's nuts and I'm a drunk. Thank God for positive environments.* But the alcohol softened her cynicism with the first sip. She strode back upstairs and looked quizzically at the decanter. *Did she REALLY dream about this before she found it?* Britt was well versed with liars but . . . *Cristina's never been a liar. What, then?*

The decanter felt creepy with its dull clay surface, which felt similar to the clay that covered the bowl. Worse, though, was the decanter's *fullness.* Was it wine? Old holy water? She squinted, then, and noticed tiny scratchlike writing around the decanter's base.

KANESAE, ENAMOURER OF WLAD, CNIHT OF DRWGLYA

An inexplicable queasiness came to her stomach. *Drwglya,* she thought, and felt even sicker when she realized what that resembled. She gulped, put the decanter in a desk drawer along with the animal skull, and went back downstairs.

Cristina had dressed in jeans and a different blouse, and now sat quietly in the kitchen.

"I don't know what to make of any of this," Britt broke the silence.

Cristina couldn't have looked more forlorn. "You said Paul and Jess would think I'm lying if we told them about this . . ."

Britt patted Cristina's shoulder, then sat down. "They probably would. They're *men,* Cristina, and they're lawyers. That usually means they're stubborn, intractable, and very close-minded. They only think inside their own box."

A hopeful glint showed in Cristina's half-teary eyes. "Then . . . let's just *not* tell them."

Britt nodded. "Maybe we will one day, but not any time soon. It wouldn't do anybody any good. I put the decanter and that creepy skull in your desk. We won't tell them anything."

Cristina seemed relieved.

"When they get home, they'll probably be half in the bag already, and that'll work to our favor. We just have to act like everything's normal, okay?"

Cristina nodded.

"You see, Cristina. Guys like Jess and Paul live in a black-and-white world. They can never see the gray . . ."

Some kind of cognizance came to Cristina's face. "What *is* the gray? That's really what we're talking about, isn't it?"

Britt sipped her drink and nodded, but didn't look at Cristina.

"Britt? There's something in this house, isn't there?"

"I think . . . maybe. Yes," Britt admitted her deepest thoughts. "And *that*, honey, is what we're really talking about. It's affected me several times, not to mention that it's put *you* through a wringer. Let's just not worry about it for now." She gave Cristina a morose look. "Let's treat it like we treat our childhood. Pretend it never happened, and who knows? Maybe we'll figure it out some day." Next, she uttered a humorless chuckle. "Yeah, it just might be that this dream house of yours is haunted."

CHAPTER EIGHTEEN

(I)

"A nun, huh?" Vernon questioned.

Did Professor Fredrick smile? "Oh, yes, but to understand her role, you must understand Vlad's conception of the Order of the Dragon. The only reason he wore the Order's colors was to appease the Holy Roman Emperor, who—after Vlad's repeated victories over the Turks—promised additional troops to reinforce Vlad's depleting ranks. But it was a *false* promise. No reinforcements were ever dispatched, and Vlad suffered a catastrophic defeat just south of Bucharest. His army was all but wiped out."

The ultimate screwjob, Vernon thought.

"Hence," Fredrick continued, eyes closed again, "Vlad felt so betrayed by the emperor and the pope that he maintained the pretense that he was still a knight of the Order while secretly *despising* what the Order stood for."

"Catholic doctrine?" Vernon guessed.

"Exactly. Like the late Templars who continued to wear the cross but engaged in atrocity, sexual abandon, and—some say—Satanism. Now here's where history becomes besmirched by myth. Vlad had two legal wives, though he had little to do with them—his true love was a concubine and prostitute named Kanesae, who was *quite* diabolical in her own way. Vlad was so incensed by the emperor's betrayal that he supposedly cursed God so vehemently that God condemned him. This is where Kanesae comes in; not only did she urge Vlad to become a heretic, she would assist him. Vlad would have her masquerade as a nun and actually commit sacrifices in the devil's name. She would recruit other prostitutes to help her, and they would impale Christian women of childbearing age. There were rumors of rituals as well."

"When does the vampire angle come in?" Vernon was curious.

"At the same time, toward the end of Vlad's life. The favorite legend is that Vlad became a vampire by being bitten by one, but one of the older explanations from codices of Orthodox Romania claim nothing of the sort. It implies that on the night Vlad cursed God, he was visited by the subcarnate spirit of the succubus, who came bearing the blood of Lucifer himself. Vlad consumed the blood and then became the prince of the undead. The codices also bear out that the succubus was Kanesae. She was actually *sent* to Vlad, to do the devil's bidding."

"A succubus masquerading as a nun." Vernon tried to get it straight.

"Whose duty was to assist Vlad in becoming one of the most evil men in history." Fredrick picked up the boxed figurine again. "Which brings me to *this*."

"A vampire *nun*," Vernon said.

"Um-hmm. Quite like Kanesae, especially when you consider the object in her hands."

"Oh, the bowl with the three gems in it," Vernon remarked.

Fredrick grimly appraised Vernon. "That's *not* a mere bowl . . ."

.

(II)

Cristina didn't ask the men about the bowl. *Britt's right. Don't bring it up, and don't mention the decanter.* It made sense but she *was* curious. She wondered if they'd gotten the gemmed bowl appraised yet.

She could hear the others downstairs, laughing, digging into the fancy pizzas. Cristina had said she'd join them after doing a little more studio work but this was a lie. *I need to get my head straight,* she told herself at her desk. It was the decanter that bothered her most of all . . .

There's no way I knew about it before it appeared in the dream—Another message appeared on her answering machine: Bruno again, but not to rave about preorders this time. His voice sounded strange. "Cristina, dear. I just received a peculiar call—regarding you. Call me as soon as you can." But Cristina only sighed. *I'll call him tomorrow. Don't feel like dealing with it now.*

She opened the drawer, wincing right off at the macabre dog skull. *Why would anyone do that?* Then she reached past it and withdrew the decanter.

Dusk seemed to slip into the room as she looked at the odd object. Was it really wine? She held it up to the light, to discern some writing on it.

KANESAE, ENAMOURER OF WLAD, CNIHT OF DRWGLYA

Drwglya, she tried to pronounce the word in her head. *Sounds like Dracula* . . . The first word, though, disturbed her more.

Kanesae. Did I hear that word in a dream, too?

She turned quickly at the sound of a hiss. Was it just the air-conditioning blowing against the drapes? She revolved on her chair, then found herself staring into an open closet.

Her mouth slowly drooped as the darkness within seemed to form an outline—a figure.

An angled shape like a woman in a nun's habit.

"Cristina!" Paul called out. "You better get down here before the pizza's gone!"

The closet, of course, was empty. *Just my screwed up imagination again,* she knew. "Coming!"

She checked the closet more closely, then put the decanter away and headed downstairs.

(III)

"If it's not a bowl, then what is it?" Vernon asked.

"It's a relic, very rare, and only referred to in the codices I previously mentioned," Fredrick said. Now he seemed puzzled and intrigued simultaneously. "Which is the oddest part of all. Very little has ever been written of this particular angle of the legend. It's all the Bram Stoker stuff these days, which were just hearsay exaggerations from Romanian monks who'd fled to England during one of Vlad's religious scourges. But the myth I'm referring to? It's never even been translated into English."

I'm losing him again, Vernon realized. "You mean this Kanesae woman, and this thing that looks like a bowl?"

"Yes, yes."

"Then how do *you* know about it?"

"Because I read the actual codices myself, after I'd recovered from my injuries during the earthquake. My point is, their contents is hardly common knowledge, Inspector. They're archived in a convent in the town of Dobruja."

"In other words, it's not like these texts are available at the public library," Vernon speculated.

"Heavens no," Fredrick replied. He kept eyeing the sinister figurine. "That's why this is so surprising."

Vernon tried to contain a rising aggravation. "I don't understand, sir. The *bowl* is what's so surprising?"

"Yes, yes, but not a bowl—it's a chalice, or I should say the representation of a very evil relic mentioned all too rarely in the Romanian registries. It's supposed to be the chalice that Vlad drank Lucifer's blood from—a perversion of Christ's Communion to the Apostles. Just as Christ gave his blood to the faithful, so did the Devil. The bowl was said to be the skullcap of Adam, set into clay from the Tigris River; hence, its talismanic power. And it was Kanesae—the subcarnate—who came to Vlad bearing the chalice."

"Subcarnate?" Vernon queried.

"A demonic incarnation only half-flesh—only able to become palpable at night, and it was this entity, Kanesae, who then brought Adam's skull as a mock chalice, filled to the brim with the blood of Lucifer himself. Just as God had abandoned Vlad on the battlefield, Vlad would abandon God in his heart . . . and he drank the blood. He sold his soul to become undead." Now a partial grin came to the old man's lips. "At least that's how *this* version of the legend goes. Now, of course, you're wondering how so many relative similarities can be not only found on your crime scenes, but who exactly is the person who designed this doll? How did he become privy to such obscure legend?"

"Not he, she," Vernon said. "One of my investigators is trying to locate her through the manufacturer's data on the box."

Fredrick steepled his old fingers. "Would this woman be Romanian?"

Vernon shrugged. "I have no idea, sir. But a toy dealer did tell me she lived nearby."

The old man paused. "This just gets stranger and stranger, doesn't it? Ultimately, then, what do we have as far as you're concerned? We have homicide evidence as well as an unrelated *doll*, which both reflect details of this myth."

"A myth that almost no one knows about," Vernon added. "But I wouldn't even say the doll is 'unrelated.' I found another doll by the same designer at the first impalement."

Fredrick sat through a timely pause. "It seems that your perpetrators are pulling an exceedingly well-researched series of copycat killings, and at the same time this bizarre doll seems equally well researched. They're creating symbols that the boyar registries say will signal the resurrection of Vlad Dracula."

Vernon felt thrown for a loop. "Pardon me?"

Fredrick eyed him, then winked. "Here's how it works, if you believe the legend, and I'll reiterate for clarity. Since 1476, Kanesae, as a subcarnate vampire, has been prowling the earth, protecting Vlad's secret. What's the secret? No one knows exactly, but we do know bits and pieces. It is said that upon the thirteenth lifetime of Vlad, Kanesae will initiate a series of sacrifices—your murder victims, for example. This will prime the rite of resurrection that Vlad orchestrated on the day of his death, and when this has fully occurred, Kanesae will bestow Vlad's blood—secreted so long ago in a clay flagon—"

"A *what?*" Vernon frowned.

"A flagon—it's like a flask, a decanter. A vessel for liquid. And Kanesae will bestow the blood upon a worthy successor. This blood—partly the Devil's blood, remember—will revive Vlad's spirit in the body of the heir. Then Vlad will walk the earth again in a new body, with Kanesae at his side, to resume his reign of vampirism and atrocity upon mankind." Fredrick chuckled minutely. "That's—like I said—if you believe the legend. . . ."

Vernon winced. "How did his blood get in this flagon?"

Fredrick labored to rise, got a book off one of his shelves, and photocopied a single page. "For your interest, here's a xerox of the only portrait ever produced of Kanesae, the mistress of Dracula."

Vernon looked captivated at the reproduction of a crude wood-block print. One corner read NURNBORG 1498, the other: KANESAE, ENAMOURER OF WLAD, CNIHT OF DRWGLYA. *I'm not liking this,* Vernon thought. In the print's center stood a fanged nun suspiciously similar to Cristina Nichols's figurine. The likeness proffered a bowl with three small circles on it.

Not a bowl, Vernon reminded himself. *A chalice.*

A headless man lay on a stone slab in the background and at its base rested what appeared to be the severed head of a dog. Further off a crude castle could be seen, but surrounding the entire scene were dozens of impalement victims.

"What's with the dog's head?"

The old man sat back down. "Vlad's body was said to be decapitated when it was discovered by a monk near Snagov Monastery but when the grave was dug up the bones of a headless dog were found instead. Vlad's *actual* body was probably cremated nearby or dumped in Lake Snagov." The professor pointed to the print. "And you'll note the flagon containing Vlad's blood."

Vernon caught the detail: the modest carafelike vessel sitting beside the slab. "And the guy on the slab is Vlad?"

"Yes. His head was probably traded by the monks to Turkish soldiers in exchange for protection. The sultan of the Ottoman Empire—Mehmed II—had quite a bounty on that head. He needed to prove to his people that the dreaded Vlad the Impaler was dead."

"So the monks who found the body cut off his head?"

"More than likely, and the reports that Vlad had been assassinated or killed in battle were invention."

More confusion. "So the monks really killed him?"

"No, no. Vlad was already dead when the body was found. According to the legend, it was Kanesae who killed him. She bled him to death on the slab. She cut his throat."

"So *she* put his blood in the flagon." Vernon finally got it.

Fredrick nodded. "But to make things even *more* complicated, Vlad whispered a secret to Kanesae, with his last breath."

Terrific. The block-print made Vernon's eyes hurt. "Earlier, you said the legend tells of an orchestration, some su-

pernatural strategy that would resurrect Vlad's spirit after
his thirteenth lifetime."

"That's right."

"When is that?"

Fredrick leaned back again, obviously fatigued. "Well,
since you asked . . . It's right about now."

(IV)

Please, no, *she pleads but she knows that most of her means
yes. The phantom faceless women stroke her glistening body as
the all-but-nude nun holds the gemmed bowl.* "Tara flaesc
Wallkya." *The words crawl around the stone-lined undercroft.
The colors, like vertical snakes of light, squirm and churn, and
their movement seems to escalate as her passions rise.*

"Serveste pe domnul!" *The words fly batlike out of the
dark while hot hands and mouths press more closely. A sound
echoes amid the chamber: a barking dog . . .*

*She convulses as her orgasm quakes. Delighted squeals rise.
Through slit eyes she sees the nun's grin, the pink tongue tip between narrow fangs, and behind the churning light, she sees the
stone slab and the decanter but this time no sign of the man in
leather boots and strange armor. A streak of blood stains the
stone where the neck would be.*

"It's time, it's time!" *voices chatter.*

"Look!" *And a finger points.*

*She rises, not knowing why, and suddenly she's somewhere
else. When she turns to look back at the nun and her wanton
suitors, she only sees tiny white fangs—four sets of them—
dissolve away in the dark.*

*Now she's standing in a dense forest. It seems that between
every tree is a tall wooden pole on which someone has been impaled, some through their hearts, some through their groins,
some upside-down through their mouths. Some of the bodies are*

rotten, yet others still twitch with life, and the sound of moans fills the forest like the wind.

She walks naked between trees and pikes, moonlight shivering through the branches. Then she hears—

thwack! thwack! thwack!

—and in the moonlit drear she sees a monk wielding a sword, cutting the head off of a prone body. He grabs the head by its mane of dark hair—a man's head, with a great black mustache—and he hands it to some men in turbans and long-handled axes. The men walk off in the other direction, steely-eyed, solemn-faced.

The monk looks up, looks directly at her.

She wants to scream but then realizes that the cloaked man doesn't see her. He stoops and begins to drag the headless corpse toward the edge of a vast lake beyond which looms a walled monastery, and then she blinks—

—and—

"Kanesae!"

—she's back in the dank undercroft, hypnotized by the churning black, green, and red light, and three wan faces hover above her as her body spasms and their grins fill with fangs, and then the faces plummet with glee and she can feel those long, narrow needle teeth sink into her neck, and the nun, now in her black habit and white wimple, says, "Blessed one, the wonder is nearly upon us but before you rejoice, you must take that accursed seal and break it to pieces," and the words grow dimmer and dimmer as her blood is sucked and sucked and she prays, It's a dream, it's a dream, it's just a dream!

Cristina stood tensed, on tiptoes, as if about to fall from a highwire. *Just a dream, just a—*Her hands felt desperately at her throat where she was sure she could feel a raging, raw pain.

But there was nothing. No wounds. No blood.

Just a dream, came the allaying thought. *Just that damn nightmare again.*

She expected to find herself in the bedroom, but—

Oh my God . . .

She was in the basement. She crept up the steps, peeked around. Stillness. Dark. The mantel clock read just past midnight. *Everyone must be asleep . . .* Just to make sure, she put one eye to the gap in the bedroom door and saw Paul fast asleep. An ear to the guest room door revealed Britt and Jess moaning in unison. *Good. No one'll know.*

Her nightgown felt drenched, strings of her blonde hair slicked to her face by sweat. *I'm losing it,* she thought. *Britt'll want to check me into a hospital . . . and I guess that's what I should do.*

Only then did she realize that she had something rough in her hand . . .

Several flat chunks of cement. She put them on the kitchen table, like puzzle pieces. *What did I do?*

It didn't take long to recompose the strange seal that had been imprinted in the cement patch downstairs. She'd obviously fractured it with a hammer. Reassembled, she could barely make out the dragon strangled by its own tail, and the words O QUAM MAGNIFICUM, O DOMNUL.

Cristina dropped the pieces in the garbage . . .

(V)

"And you said Vlad was forty-five when he died?" Vernon asked.

"That's right," Fredrick affirmed.

"And this . . . reincarnation is supposed to occur after this thirteenth lifetime?"

The professor smiled. "Noting an irregularity, hmm? You must be a math whiz."

Vernon had been, but that was a long time ago. He took out his cell phone and turned on the calculator function, fumbling with the tiny keys. "I knew that sounded a bit off.

Thirteen times forty-five is two thousand sixty-six, Professor. That's a ways off." Vernon looked at him. *Is this old guy pulling my chain?* "Why did you tell me the time was now?"

Fredrick smiled like a wise grandfather. "You're correct, thirteen times forty-five is indeed two thousand sixty-six . . . but not on the Diocletian calendar."

"Huh?"

"That was the calendar used in Orthodox Romania back then. They'd always rejected the Julian calendar, and they didn't accept the Gregorian calendar either, because of Pope Gregory's use of mathematics by the astronomer Charles Rommes. Rommes was not just an astronomer but also, allegedly, an astrologer, which was considered sorcery by the Orthodox. Hence, many Eastern European states used their own pre-Gregorian calendar based on Diocletian—the first Roman emperor to ease persecution of Christians and also because he conquered Persia in the 300's. Remember, Turkey—part of what was known as Persia—was Christianity's greatest enemy eleven hundred years later in Vlad's time."

"Jesus," Vernon muttered. "The *Diocletian* calendar. I knew you'd have an answer."

Fredrick nodded. "So, based on *that* calendar, the thirteenth lifetime of Vlad is right around now. It seems your ritual murderers are apprised of this, and that's why these crimes have occurred."

"Because they *think* that Vlad's spirit will be reborn," Vernon said, more to himself. A pause. "You don't believe it, do you?"

"Inspector? Do you mind if I have a glass of wine?"

Vernon laughed. "Of course not, sir. It's *your* home."

"And please join me. You can't still be on duty at this hour . . ."

Holy shit, Vernon thought when he looked at his watch. *It's past midnight. I've blown this old guy's entire day.* "I'm terribly sorry, sir. Time got away from me."

"Oh, believe me, Inspector. Your indulgence is my pleasure." Fredrick awkwardly brought two glasses to the desk. "I seldom get a chance to talk about these things."

Vernon looked at the dark wine. *I never drink before ten o'clock, and . . . it's past ten o'clock.* "Thanks very much."

"Did you know that Romania is the ninth largest wine producer in the world? This one's from the Tarnave vineyards . . . in Transylvania."

Vernon paused before taking a sip, then thought, *Fuck the French. That's damn good.* "I just have a few more questions, if that's okay."

Now the old man seemed lulled. "Please . . ."

"It helps me to *know* what our killers actually believe. But I'm still not clear on Vlad's death."

"Understandable, since there are so many versions. Vlad's vampirism and heretical atrocities were reported to the pope and the emperor. Vlad knew it was only a matter of time before he'd be assassinated by them, or by contractors hired by the Turks. So he circumvented it all by planning his own death, allowing Kanesae to bleed him to death. Think of this as the very beginning of a chain of events, the last of which—your killers think—are taking place now. But, remember, Vlad's last words on earth were the words he whispered to Kanesae as his blood was drained into the flagon—the secret."

"What was the secret!" Vernon raised his voice.

"Well, that's subject to interpretation. Monks who had remained loyal to the true Order of the Dragon seized Vlad and cut off his head, to end his reign of evil. They were dumbfounded, though, when Vlad's body didn't bleed upon decapitation. They presumed that this was a symptom of his vampirism . . . but they were wrong."

"I *still* don't get it."

"They never knew that Vlad had already set an occult rite into motion. The monks buried the flagon, along with the chalice, in the monastery's stream, which served as the property's water supply. Since this was consecrated ground, the stream ran with *holy* water, and this would prevent any malign entity—such as Kanesae—from absconding with it."

Vernon frowned. "So this stuff is *still* beneath this stream in Romania?"

Fredrick shook his head, a grimness now in his eyes. "The flagon and chalice had been secured in an iron keg, but this keg was upheaved during the 1977 earthquake. Some men ran off with it, and I know this to be fact because I saw it with my own eyes."

That's right. His leg was crushed during the same quake, Vernon recalled. "Who were the men?"

"I'll never know for sure but they may have been descendants of the original Order of the Dragon, since the rumor abounds that the Order never dissolved. Keep in mind, when I saw this I thought I was going to die; it could've been a near-death hallucination or something."

Vernon thought things over. *Impalements. Desecration involving the colors of the Order. And homeless women who believe in the spirit of a vampire nun . . .* "You said that Kanesae recruited *prostitutes?*"

"To be her acolytes, yes. To assist her."

Virginia Fleming and Scab both had rap sheets for prostitution, Vernon reminded himself.

Fredrick continued, "Allegiance in return for reward—an age-old symptom, Inspector. They believed that they would be granted immortality, as vampires. Supposedly, as Kanesae's power peaks, and as she becomes more and more flesh and less and less spirit, her acolytes would become vampires as well." The old man sipped more wine, relaxing. "Over the years, I've researched every angle of the legend, more by default than anything."

"Sir?"

"Before the earthquake I had no professional interest

whatsoever in fifteenth-century Romanian history. But after an experience like that?"

Of course. He was almost killed at the same place all this supposedly happened, Vernon realized.

"And so not to fully avoid your question of a while ago," the professor began and smiled. He fired up his pipe again. "No, I don't believe the legend myself."

Sure, but somebody does. And that's my biggest lead. They both jumped a little when Vernon's phone rang. It was Slouch.

"Oh, good, I was beginning to think you'd been impaled."

"What are you talking about, Slouch?" Vernon frowned.

"Well, you never signed off-shift, and nobody's heard from you for about twelve hours."

"I'm in the middle of a consultation with an expert on . . ." Vernon stalled. *Forget it.* "But I'm leaving soon."

"So I can go home now?"

"Yes, yes! Did you get that—"

"—current address for Cristina Nichols? What do you think I am, a slouch? Of course I got it. Finally reached the company owner, a guy named Bruno von Blanc. He wasn't too keen on giving up the info but then I sweet-talked him, you know?"

"Yeah, like you sweet-talked me for your last promotion," Vernon said.

"She lives with a hotshot lawyer named Paul Nasher."

"Yeah, but *where* does she live? That's what I need to know."

Slouch paused for effect. "Are you ready for this one?"

"Yeah."

"No, I mean are you really ready?"

"I'm ready to transfer you to motor-pool duty. How's that?"

Slouch laughed. "Cristina Nichols lives four doors down from the corner where all our bum-chicks have been seen."

Vernon stared.

"You there, How?"

"That's a bit odd, isn't it?"

"That's a big hell yeah, boss."

"Give me Nichols's address."

Slouch did so, then Vernon recited the information as he jotted it down: "1387 Dessorio Avenue . . . Jesus. That's right down the street from that hot dog vendor."

"Um-hmm. Strange, huh? But you're not going there now, are you? It's past midnight."

"No, but I might drive by just to see the place, and see if any of these homeless women are out."

"Okay, boss. But watch out for sharp sticks."

Vernon hung up, intrigued. Another link, however inexplicable.

Fredrick had overheard. "So this Nichols woman is—"

"A novelty toy designer," Vernon said. He held up the plastic nun again. "The creator of *this*."

CHAPTER NINETEEN

(I)

All the pieces are coming together, Rollin thought miserably. He trudged home from the hotel, eyes wide open in a dreadful contemplation. He pulled the pendant out from his shirt and touched its surface, then touched the silver ring.

I'll have to enter the house myself, with a gun if need be . . .

His surveillance of the annex house had amounted to nothing tonight. Through the binoculars, he'd seen Cristina Nichols come in and out of her studio several times later, but that was all. Were those two friends of hers staying the night again? Rollin had only seen the dark-haired woman once. *I'm spying on the place from two directions*, he thought, *and what good has it done me?*

Again, he faced the fact: he'd have to enter the house himself, and without the owner's knowledge. *I don't suppose priests fare well in jail*, he chuckled to himself.

The hotel behind him now, full dark stretched down Dessorio Avenue. Traffic and pedestrians seemed strangely scant. When he passed the alley, though, he thought he heard the faintest voice, then a scuffling.

One of the homeless girls?

He squinted in the grainy sodium light. Two wan figures stood by some garbage cans, then—to his disbelief—one of them seemed to disappear. He could tell they were women. *Where did she go?*

Rollin walked along the edge of the alley, using the

shadows to conceal himself. *Yes!* he thought. He could see the second woman now: greasy-haired, and a T-shirt that read THE DAMNED. *It's them* . . . He froze in the dark and watched, fascinated. Now she was lying on her belly. After a moment she, too, seemed to disappear between the garbage cans.

So that's where they've been hiding the whole time . . .

He quickened his pace. When he arrived, he could see that the garbage can had been dragged back. *From inside the building?* It must be. Very carefully he moved the can back and saw the hole in the brick wall, about a foot in diameter.

Rollin was delighted that he'd finally found their hiding place, but . . .

What now?

He looked at the hole without much confidence. *I'm probably too fat to squeeze in there.*

Calling the police made the most sense but then that would only bring undue attention in proximity to the house. *A lifetime of service to God may well be boiling down to this moment,* he considered.

He whispered a brief prayer, then got down on his belly and began to crawl into the hole . . .

(II)

Vernon didn't know what induced him to glance down the alley at that precise moment, but when he did he saw what appeared to be a portly figure in black fidgeting on the pavement. *Oh, for God's sake, I guess I better* . . .

He pulled the unmarked into the alley, just one turn before the road that Cristina Nichols lived on. He didn't know why but he wanted to look at the place, figured he'd stop by and question her tomorrow. But now this . . .

It is my job, he reminded himself. He parked in the alley and got out. *Probably some wino having the D.T.'s, but then* he looked close and saw that this person was wearing decent black shoes and slacks. A man, obviously. Vernon shook his head.

He's crawling into a hole in the wall . . .

Vernon nudged the man's leg with his shoe. "Police," he announced. "Crawl back out of there or I'll pull you out."

Amid grunts and scuffs, the portly figure shimmied back out and stood up, clearly embarrassed.

Vernon slumped. It was a priest.

"Uh, uh, good evening, Officer," the man bumbled in a slight accent that sounded European. "I'm Father John Rollin, of St. Amano's Church on Dessorio. I can imagine how this appears."

"Why is a priest crawling into a hole in the wall of an abandoned building at twelve thirty at night?" Vernon tapped his foot. He didn't smell alcohol, at least.

The priest seemed to ruminate, obviously nervous. "My church was vandalized recently, by several homeless women—"

Suddenly Vernon was all ears.

"—and I just spotted two of them, right here, crawling inside the building."

Vernon suddenly felt overenergized. He all but grabbed the priest and dragged him to the car. "Really, Officer, I—"

"Bear with me, Father." Vernon grabbed his flashlight from the car, along with an envelope. "Have you ever seen *these* homeless women?" He shined the light while the priest examined the photos.

Rollin looked right into Vernon's face, deadpan. "This is uncanny, Officer. Two of the women in these photos are the same two I just saw crawl into this building. I'm 100 percent certain."

Vernon suddenly felt weak-kneed.

"And this third woman here"—the priest pointed at the next security picture—"the one with the pink glasses. I've seen her in this area many times as well."

I may have just solved the fucking case, Vernon thought, incredulous. *The killers have been using this old Banana Republic as a place to squat . . . and two of them are in there right now . . .*

"Pardon me, Officer, but is there some reason that you look overjoyed right now?"

Vernon gaped at him. "You wouldn't understand, Father." He took out his gun. "Excuse me." He stepped past the priest and got down on his belly.

"You're . . . going in?"

"You were going in, weren't you?"

"Well, yes . . ."

"Look," Vernon said over his shoulder, "if I'm not back in ten minutes, call the Twentieth Precinct, will ya?"

"I'd like to follow you in, if you don't mind," Rollin asked uncomfortably.

"Fine, fine. Come on."

Vernon's slender build didn't impede him. He slipped through the hole into a maw of malodorous darkness. Another hole could be seen only a few feet ahead. He plowed the flashlight beam forward, saw distant clutter, then shouted, "Police! Identify yourselves and come out of there!"

There was no sound in response. He waited a moment and listened some more.

Nothing.

This is really stupid, he thought, then crawled through the next hole.

Good God! he thought, gagging. The stench was overpowering. *Something dead in here,* he knew. The flashlight beam seemed dimmer for some reason. He turned it back to the wall and saw the priest laboriously squeezing his way through.

"What an awful stench . . ."

"Tell me about it," Vernon said. *Looks like an old boiler room,* he noted. A pile of trash filled one corner, while boxes of more trash seemed to partition the room. Smaller boxes and milk crates sat arranged on the floor around a broken television, and there were unlit candle stubs everywhere. Vernon took a step forward and—

Shit!

—almost fell flat on his face. He'd stepped on something that had rolled. *Pay dirt,* he thought when he shined the light down.

What he'd slipped on was a red magic marker.

"There's no one here," the priest said.

"We don't know that. They could be hiding in the boxes, so be careful." Vernon slowly nosed around, gun forward.

"I really don't think there's anyone here, Officer." The priest was looking around behind him. "And if they're not *here*—"

"Where did they go?" Vernon's gut clenched when he looked behind several more boxes and saw several broom handles whose ends had been whittled to sharp points. A few whittling knives lay beside them.

"There must be some other access, which makes sense," the priest said.

"What?"

"Just because . . ." Rollin's next words faded as he began to pad around the wall.

But Vernon was already staring. What he'd noticed first were two plastic figurines sitting on the floor. *More of Nichols's dolls . . .* He picked them up without thinking, tainting any fingerprints, and read their bases. *Hypothermia Harriet, Leprosy Linda . . .*

Then he turned into another area sectioned off with more boxes. The stench trebled, and when he shined his light toward the wall he felt his heart stop a moment.

"Officer? Could you bring your light over here?" Father Rollin requested.

"No," Vernon croaked. "I need you to look at this."

Careful footsteps scuffed.

"God Almighty . . ."

The flashlight beam hovered across six corpses impaled on broomsticks: two men, four women. Pools of blood congealed at each base, the telltale Christmas tree stands. Two had been impaled upside-down, and all were nude. Most of them had been scrawled on with black, green, and red markers.

Vernon and the priest backed out of the cubby, hacking. Rollin muttered prayers in Latin, in spite of being half in shock, while Vernon reached into his pocket and swore.

"Father, I left my cell phone in the car. I need yours."

Rollin blinked out of daze. "I—I've never owned one."

"Let's get out of here so I can call this in."

"Yes, but . . . Look at this first." The priest guided Vernon around more clutter to the wall. "They must've left through here." Vernon held the light while the priest showed him an area low on the wall where two cinderblocks had been prized and pulled out.

"They're in the house next door," Rollin said. "Cristina Nichols's house."

Vernon's eyes widened. "You know her?"

"Oh, yes, and I also know that these homeless women have been sneaking in and out of her house for some time now. They've been . . . preparing for something."

Vernon out of impulse grabbed Rollin's black shirt. "Is there a *nun* with them?"

Rollin stalled. "She's not really a nun. She merely poses as one. Her name is Kanesae."

Vernon leaned against the wall, to think. "Listen. I have to go in there. I want you to crawl back outside, get my cell phone, and call 911."

Rollin sighed. "I'm afraid I'll have to insist on coming with you, Officer. Your 911 won't help you, believe me."

Vernon was about to shove him back outside but his eyes flicked to something around the man's neck. There was a cross on a chain; behind it, though, was pendant, a small disk showing a dragon strangled by its own tail, and the words:

O QUAM MAGNIFICUM, O DOMNUL

Rollin absently touched a ring on his finger, with the same emblem and words. "Let's go now, both of us. You don't know what's happening here." He crossed himself. "I do."

(III)

Did Britt hear a voice?

"Singele lui traieste . . ."

It was more like a dream-sound behind something else: the wind rustling through a dense forest.

And a dog barking . . .

Britt tried to open her eyes but the dream kept her pinned behind its caul of sheer black. At the same time, though, the lewdest sensations began to crest. What was happening? Her back arched, her hands came desperately to her breasts, and then a ravenous orgasm broke as what could only be a mouth tended to her most private place. Still, there was only utter darkness, and for a moment she received the ghastly impression that she'd just had her orgasm in a closed coffin.

When her hands reached down to run her fingers through Jess's hair, her eyes finally opened. It took a moment to remember where she was: *Cristina's guest room. That's right, we spent the night again.* She looked down and smiled, still playing with Jess's hair. "Oh, Jess, honey, that was lovely. You know how much I like it when you surprise me like that . . ."

"My name's not Jess, it's Sandrine," came a sharp female voice.

Britt sucked in a long deep breath to scream when she

saw the dirty face rising from between her legs, some vagabond girl with crusty hair.

When the girl grinned, two narrow fangs flashed.

A hand slapped across Britt's mouth, stifling the scream. Suddenly two more unkempt, naked women were on her, both grinning with similar fangs.

"You can join the convent, too," said the one with her hand over Britt's mouth. Dirty blonde hair, clunky glasses.

A third giggled, "It's the Nuh-Nuh-New Mother's time. She's almost fluh-fluh-fluh-fluh-*flesh!*"

"Look now," said the one with the glasses, and she shoved Britt's head to the right, where Jess lay asleep.

But he was more than asleep, she saw. His skin was pale bluish white, and he lay drained, fang marks pocking both sides of his throat.

"We have the power now," said the one between her legs, "just like she promised."

"We-we-we-sucked him dry!"

"Just like we're gonna do to you," whispered Glasses, and then all three of them converged, their fanged mouths gnawing Britt's throat like a dog chewie. She convulsed as she felt her blood being sucked straight into their bellies, and as her vision dimmed, she noticed the figure standing in the doorway.

A nun. A grinning nun.

(IV)

Paul woke in a lurch. Had there been a noise? He sat upright a full minute before his eyes could acclimate. *Jesus . . .* His heart was hammering, but . . . why? *Must've had a nightmare.* Moonlight leaking through the blinds showed him that Cristina wasn't in bed.

She was acting weird again tonight. With my luck she's going off the deep end. All that crap from her childhood? Who knew what effect that could have on someone years later? He pulled on his robe and went out to the kitchen.

"Cristina?"

He'd half-expected to find her out here with Britt, doing their girl-talk. But the kitchen stood dark save for the light over the stove. *Something's not right*, he thought without knowing why the notion came to him. He padded to the guest room, where the door stood open. *Jess snores like a polar bear*, he realized, but the hall was dead silent. Paul stuck his head in . . .

He stared for a while at the motionless shapes atop the bed. *They're sleeping*, he told himself. *Right?* But something seemed to drag him in. He felt colder with each step toward the bed, until he was staring down, mouth agape.

"Jess? Britt?"

He nudged Britt's shoulder in the near-pitch dark, then turned on the light.

What he saw there shoved him out of the room where he collapsed in the hall, but the image followed him: Jess and Britt both naked and pale, their eyes and mouths locked open. Both of their throats had been gnawed deep.

Instinct more than reason shot him back to the kitchen. "Cristina!" he yelled. "Get out of the house!" He picked up the phone to call the police but—

"Shit!"

No dial tone.

The next series of minutes proceeded as a mad blur. His cell phone wasn't to be found, and neither was Cristina's. *Get out*, came the next impulse. *Whoever killed them could still be here* . . . But as he raced for the front door, he stopped in his tracks.

I can't leave without Cristina . . .

"Where are you?" he bellowed. His mind was a tumult; he couldn't fix on a single thought. Next, he was staring up the stairs.

A light was on.

The studio . . . Had she fallen asleep, or had another blackout?

Is she even still alive?

He ran up the stairs, however terrified, and bolted into the room.

Cristina stood in front of the windows, nude. She didn't move.

"Cristina! Come on! Someone broke into the house and killed Jess and Britt!"

Lying on the floor were several broom handles whose ends had been sharpened to points.

"What the hell is that? Cristina?"

She remained standing utterly still. She didn't seem to hear him. Paul simply stared as she turned and walked toward her work desks. Her eyes looked glazed.

"What's wrong with you!"

Paul's stare was drawn deeper when Cristina opened a drawer. She pulled out a yellowed dog's skull, kissed it, and set it down.

What on earth . . .

Her blonde hair dangled when she leaned over again, this time removing a strange stoppered bottle that looked old. She clutched it to her bare bosom, then walked slowly out of the room, never once noticing Paul.

I don't know what the hell's happening but . . .

He had to get out.

Then his eyes widened more. Had it been Cristina who'd killed Britt and Jess? *A psychotic episode or something. A schizophrenic break* . . . He went out to the dark hall, and saw Cristina's white body moving slowly up the stairs, to the unfinished rooms.

Paul screamed when he turned, almost fell over.

Britt and Jess stood before him, both smiling with drawn, white faces. They looked skinny now, sapped. Their gnawed throats had clotted up, and both of them had been scrawled on: wavy lines of black, green, and red trailing up and down their nude bodies.

"She's getting ready, Paul," Jess said. "You don't understand."

Britt stepped forward. "We didn't either, until we were brought over by the New Mother."

Paul's mouth fell open.

"It's going to happen tonight . . ." Britt's nipples and lips were blue. "But it's something that was planned a long time ago. All we needed were the chalice and the flagon, and we've got them both now." And finally she grinned openly, showing two long white fangs.

Jess bared fangs as well. "It's the flagon, Paul, don't you see? It contains the blood of the Prince, and when Cristina drinks it, the Prince will live again, in her body . . ."

"It's miraculous, and we all get to be a part." Britt's eyes seemed to burn. "You do, too . . . sort of."

Britt and Jess stepped closer.

Britt lifted something off the floor and passed it to Jess. "Submit willingly, and you'll be held in a higher favor."

The object she'd given Jess was a sharpened broom handle.

Paul backpedaled, then fell down again. Britt lunged on him, her hands pinning him to the floor; he couldn't budge against her impossible strength. "Let us take your blood first, then we'll mount you as a homage to the Prince."

"You'll get to live forever, Paul, with us. We'll all live forever in hell . . ."

Britt's mouth opened so wide it seemed as though her jaw came unhinged.

"It only hurts for a minute," Jess promised.

Paul pushed up, squeezing Britt's throat as hard as he could, his legs kicking wildly. All the while, though, Britt's mouth continued to lower. He tried to squirm out from under her, but to no avail. A desperate glance behind him showed him a figure standing in the darkness, as if watching in approval.

The figure looked like a nun . . .

The tips of two fangs touched Paul's throat—

"Save some for me," Jess chuckled.

A voice boomed up the stairs: "*O quam magnificum, o domnul . . .*"

Britt hissed, her pale dead face suddenly stamped with disgust. She rolled off Paul and looked up. Jess dropped the broom handle, gagging.

Another hiss sounded from the dark end of the hall.

A thin guy in slacks and a tacky sports jacket came first up the steps, holding a pistol. Behind him came a gray-haired priest.

"*Strigoi,*" said the priest. "Get thee hence."

Jess and Britt looked sickened, and when the priest raised a circular pendant of some kind, they both vomited blood, then scurried into the studio. The priest hung the pendant on the inside doorknob, then closed the door.

Paul didn't know which end was up. "Who are . . . you?"

"Never mind," snapped the guy with the gun. "I'm a cop. Where's Cristina Nichols?"

"I—Upstairs . . ."

"What did those two tell you?" the priest asked in a faint accent. He pointed to the studio door.

Paul shook the terror out of his head and got up. "Something about . . . a chalice and—"

"Where is it? It doesn't look like a regular chalice—it's just a bowl, a clay bowl."

The recollection bloomed. "We found it in the basement, then—"

"Then what?" the priest snapped.

"Some woman stole it."

The cop looked bewildered while the priest looked grim.

"They also said something about a flagon," Paul added.

"They said it had blood in it that they wanted Cristina to drink."

"Where is it?"

"She took an old bottle upstairs a few minutes ago."

"That's it." The cop looked up the stairs. "Come on, let's go."

"Wait," the priest advised. Were his hands shaking? "We have to . . . think about this."

The cop raised his gun. "Let *me* do the thinking."

"That will do you little good, Officer."

"I'll believe that when I see it . . ."

"Listen to me," the priest insisted. "We can't let Cristina consume the contents of that flagon. Otherwise . . ."

"Otherwise what?" Paul asked.

"We'll have no choice but to kill her."

"Why!"

"Because it won't be Cristina anymore." The priest stared off. "It'll be someone else."

And that's when they heard a voice calling them from downstairs . . .

(V)

Cristina felt jubilant, eyes wide open as the dark colors swirled. Black. Green. Red. She'd set the flagon down in the first empty room. The figure waited for her.

Kanesae.

"I must show you now. You must see your glorious destiny . . ."

She was standing in the dream as it whirled around, a dark yet radiant maelstrom. The shimmering lines of black, green, and red churning against the bare walls and her bare skin. When the nun kissed her, Cristina sunk deeper into the evil muse . . .

"Look. And see . . ."

Again she's in the dripping, rock-walled chamber. The man is no longer on the stone slab, and then she remembers that he'd already been dragged out, yet Kanesae remains, bloody-mouthed and enraptured as she carefully pours the blood from the crude chalice into the flagon.

"His blood is alive," Kanesae whispers.

(VI)

Vernon couldn't possibly calculate all that he'd seen in the last few minutes, so he gave up trying. *We have to find Cristina,* he realized, and Cristina was upstairs. But now someone had just called out, from *downstairs.*

"I should've known there'd be detractors in wait," Rollin muttered and fingered his cross.

"What do we do?" Paul asked without much confidence.

"We go down there," Vernon said. He thrust his gun forward. "Follow me."

They crept down the steps, eyes peeled. Most of the lights had been turned out, leaving the foyer and living room plunged in darkness, and from that darkness a thin figure stepped forward after she'd said, "Come down here. I want to make a deal with you . . ."

One of the homeless girls, Vernon recognized.

Dirty shoulder-length hair looked like black noodles on her head. The farther Vernon proceeded down the stairs, the more details he could make out. She was emaciated and naked, her skin streaked by the multicolored magic markers. In her hand she held a sharpened pole.

"Listen to me," she said. "You can leave now, just leave. We won't follow you, we won't kill you."

"I've got the gun, honey," Vernon pointed out.

When the woman's barely visible face smiled, the fangs glittered. "Shoot me, and you'll see."

To hell with it. Vernon squeezed the trigger—

BAM!

—and watched a bloodless hole appear between the woman's sagging breasts.

Then he fired five more shots into a tight group over her heart.

"So just leave. Right now," she said, and took another step forward. "Don't interfere. You might even be rewarded someday."

"In hell, you mean," Rollin voiced and stepped ahead of Vernon. "We're not interested." Then he raised his cross.

The woman only smiled wider. "What I can't see can't offend me." And now she was close enough that Vernon could discern the crucial detail: she'd dug her own eyes out.

"The New Mother says that the most powerful force that exists is faith. Watch me." The fangs shined in the blinded face. "I'll show you my faith, but if you go upstairs, this will be done to you." And then she held the sharpened pole above her head, opened her mouth, and began to slide it slowly down her throat.

"God in Heaven . . ."

Vernon closed his eyes but could still hear it. The woman stood with her feet apart, and continued to shove the pole down in increments. When it exited her crotch, she continued to shove, until the point hit the floor.

She stood for a moment, in perfect stillness, then fell over.

Fuck this, Vernon thought, reloading his gun.

"She was distracting us," Rollin said. "Time's running out if it hasn't already. We have to go upstairs and prevent Cristina from consuming the contents of the flagon."

Vernon gulped, looking at the impaled woman. "Uh, well . . ."

"We have to go upstairs," the priest said. "We *must*."

When Vernon turned back around, he stopped short. The landing was empty.

"Where the hell did Paul Nasher go?" Vernon asked.

(VII)

Was it his lawyer's morality . . . or something in the house?
Paul thought he understood what was going on here.
Power, for one thing. A power timeless and everlasting.
Why should I let someone else get it? came his reasoning.

When the priest and the cop had gone downstairs, Paul
had slipped up to the third floor. The air felt thicker up
here for some reason, as if it were alive with something.
Moonlight tinted the dark corners of the hallway and unfinished rooms. *Got to find her,* he thought. *Can't let her
drink the blood . . .*

He froze in the next doorway.

There she was—Cristina—kneeling naked in the middle of the vacant room. Was she muttering under her
breath?

Or praying?

Paul stepped back to conceal himself, and watched.

There was a soft grating sound when Cristina twisted
the stopper out of the flagon. Instantly, the moonlight in
the room seemed to darken; Paul wasn't sure, but he
thought he could also see churning lines of light in the
back of his mind, lines that were black, green, and red. After what he'd seen Jess and Britt become, Paul could believe anything now, even the prospect of immortality. As a
lawyer, he'd always gone for the gold and had gotten it
every time, via brains, bravado, and ruthlessness. *Survival
of the fittest. That's how it's always been, since men were
apes . . .*

Now Cristina was slowly pouring the contents of the
flagon into the clay bowl they'd found in the basement. The
blood inside was black now—*The Prince's blood,* Paul reminded himself—and it dripped as slowly as old motor oil.

Cristina gazed at the filled bowl as though it were a crystal ball. What did she see in it?

Paul bounded into the room.

"What are you doing here?" Cristina screamed, her eyes feral. She reached for the bowl—

THWACK!

—but Paul kicked her in the head.

"Change of plans, Cristina," he said.

She leaned up, groggy. "Get out! You'll ruin everything!"

"Depends on your point of view, honey." And then, as she lunged for the bowl again, Paul easily grabbed her hair and yanked her to the corner. She kicked and shrieked. "Guess we all have a bad side," he added. "Now you get to see mine."

Still holding her hair, he hauled her up and began to bang the back of her head against the wall. Five thuds. Ten. When he was done, the wall showed dents. Cristina collapsed to the floor. He hoped she wasn't dead. *She'll be the first one I feed on . . .*

Paul turned and stared at the bowl. Very slowly, then, he leaned over and picked it up . . .

(VIII)

On the next landing, Vernon put his gun away and picked up the sharpened broom handle that Britt had dropped outside the studio. *This is fucked-up,* he thought, when he realized exactly what he was doing. Behind the studio door, he heard a hissing and a gurgling.

"Up the next flight," Rollin urged. "I'll go first."

Whatever you say, Vernon thought.

Only moonlight lit the third floor from the unshaded windows. A noise from the first room signaled him.

"She must be in there," Rollin whispered. "Remember, if she's consumed the blood, you must kill her—" He looked at the pole. "With that."

Vernon nodded.

The priest stepped ahead of him and entered the room.

But it wasn't Cristina who stood there. It was Paul.

"Stop!" Rollin shouted. "You don't know what you're doing! You don't know what you're bringing back!"

Paul stood poised, with the bowl inches from his lips. "You're wrong about that, priest. I *do* know what I'm bringing back. That's why I'm doing it."

Paul gulped down the contents of the bowl, and when he tossed the bowl aside, it shattered on the floor, revealing that the clay had been merely a surface, covering what appeared to be a human skullcap.

"Now!" Rollin yelled to Vernon.

Just as Vernon would charge into the room, a thin figure grabbed him from behind. "Yuh-yuh-yuh-you can't!" exclaimed the emaciated woman suddenly on his back. She, too, was nude and scrawled with the black, green, and red lines. Dirty nails clawed at his face; the pole fell from his hands. "Yuh-you don't belong here-belong here-belong here!" Vernon yelled when the fanged mouth began to snap open and closed an inch from his face. "I could use some fuckin' help here, Father!" he bellowed, but the priest was absent. Had he fled? Ninety pounds or not, the pallid woman fought like a gang member. Vernon thrashed on the bare floor; it was all he could do to keep the woman's snapping mouth off his throat.

"Gonna suck you-suck you-suck you dry . . ."

Vernon's strength began to falter; her foaming mouth drew so close he could feel the sour breath gusting on his throat.

He wasn't thinking when he fired four shots up into the woman's chest. It hadn't worked before, so why had he done it now? The woman paused to chuckle, then leaned harder toward his throat.

One more shot: BAM!

"You can't hurt me with that-with that-with—"

BAM!

The sixth shot blew the woman clean off of Vernon like

a catapult. She lay lopsided against the baseboard, convulsing.

"Fuh-fuh-fucker . . ." And then she fell dead.

Vernon had fired four shots in a straight line down her chest, then a fifth to the right, and the sixth to the left, the bullet holes forming the configuration of the cross.

He dragged his gaze to the middle of the room.

Father Rollin was on his knees, exhausted, while Paul Nasher twitched on the floor, the sharpened pole rammed fully through his chest, puncturing his heart.

Vernon glared at the priest. "Is it Miller Time yet?"

"I killed him before the transference could take place," Rollin wheezed. He pointed to Cristina who lay in the opposite corner. "See if—"

Vernon rushed to her, felt for vitals.

"Is she—"

"She's got a pulse. We've got to get her to the hospital. Looks like Nasher damn near beat her to death." Vernon groaned when he put her over his shoulder. Rollin was already in the hall but something stopped him in his tracks.

"What now!" Vernon yelled.

"Is it my imagination . . . or do I smell smoke?"

Vernon labored to the stairwell, looked down. The crackling was undeniable, and so was the roaring light. "Somebody set the fuckin' house on fire!"

"Hurry!"

They rushed to the second-floor landing as smoke began to pour up in volume. The living room was engulfed in flames. *We'll have to jump from a window,* Vernon thought, but then the priest bulled down the stairs.

"Are you nuts!"

"Come on, we can beat it!"

Vernon followed, Cristina getting heavier on his shoulder. The front door of the house was already behind a wall of flame. "Now what?"

"Here!" Rollin shouted. "The way we came in!"

That's right. The basement . . .

He thunked down more steps into the basement, wondering how long it would take before the floor collapsed on them, bringing down rafters of fire.

"Hurry!"

No, YOU hurry, Vernon thought. *I'm the one carrying someone . . .*

Now the house was shaking from the conflagration. Rollin was already on the floor, backing into the narrow hole. "I'll pull, you push!" he yelled.

Makes sense. Vernon knelt as he fed Cristina's limp body into the hole. Rollin could be heard grunting his exertion; Cristina disappeared in increments. "Any time now!" Vernon exclaimed, hearing the fire upstairs roar.

Vernon pushed on the unconscious woman's legs until she was all the way in. Would the fire spread to the next building before they could get out? He could hear fire alarms going on at the adjacent condo. Vernon began to crawl into the hole, to fully exit the house.

When he was halfway in, two hands grabbed his ankles and pulled him back.

Vernon yelled the whole way.

"What happened?" Rollin shouted from the other side.

"Just get her out! The fire's spreading!" He reached for his gun but realized he was out of ammunition. When he rolled over in the darkened basement, he saw a figure high above him.

The third and final homeless woman. *The one with the glasses,* he recalled from the pictures.

She sat naked atop a stack of high boxes, her pallid skin streaked with the familiar lines of homage.

The moonlight lit her face and her fanged grin.

"You should stay here with me," she said, her feet rowing back and forth.

"Why?"

"Then we can go to hell together. We'll live forever, just like the New Mother promised."

"The nun," Vernon croaked. "Kanesae. Where is she?"

"Nowhere, and everywhere. Like all evil. Come with me and all your questions will be answered."

Fat chance. But then Vernon remembered what Professor Fredrick had mentioned. "The thirteenth lifetime is over. You blew it. But . . . what was the secret that Vlad whispered to her as she was draining his blood?"

The woman grinned. "If I told you . . . then it wouldn't be a secret anymore."

From the first floor, he heard the stairs collapse. The fire's roar now sounded like a blast furnace. *I have to get out of here. Now.*

"Let me impale you," she said. "An offering to the Prince. You'll be smiled upon in hell."

"I'll pass," Vernon said.

The woman shrugged her bony shoulders. "Suit yourself. I guess someone should live to tell the tale."

Vernon stared as the temperature vaulted.

"*Singele lui traieste*," the woman whispered. She hitched forward on her perch. Only then did Vernon notice that she'd positioned a sharpened pole mounted on a Christmas tree stand just below. She hopped off the box, bringing her crotch right down on the point. She wriggled and fidgeted, then, as her body slowly slid down. She still showed the fanged grin when the point halted at the roof of her mouth.

Vernon dove back in the hole and crawled out just as the ceiling collapsed amid an avalanche of flame.

CHAPTER TWENTY

(I)

"I"m realizing just now that I'm way too old for this," Rollin said in the passenger seat. Sweat beaded his adrenaline-pinkened face.

"You and me both, Father." Vernon floored it to the nearest emergency room: Mt. Sinai, his suction-cup cherry ball pumping red and blue light into the city's labyrinthine darkness.

Who's gonna believe this? he thought, but then realized it didn't matter. He would tell no one. "Check her, will you?" He glanced into the backseat, where Cristina lay. Her head had been lacerated pretty significantly. *God, I hope she doesn't die . . .*

Rollin labored to lean into the back. "Her pulse feels strong. Breathing looks regular . . ."

Vernon squealed wheels around a corner. "So . . . what exactly happened? Kanesae had—"

"Kanesae had been growing stronger and stronger," explained the exhausted priest, "as tonight got closer. With her strength came not only her ability to corporate—or become flesh—but her ability to influence her target: Cristina. Once Kanesae's strength had peaked, she was able to fully overcome Cristina's will, and I'm sure she'd been gradually doing that all along. It was Kanesae's goal to manipulate Cristina into drinking the blood in the flagon, but—"

"Paul got to it first, and damn near killed Cristina getting it."

The priest nodded wearily. "Once Paul had pilfered the flagon and consumed its contents, Vlad's spiritual agency came into Paul."

"And then you killed him with the pole."

"Yes, and not a second too soon."

"So what happens now?"

Rollin stared out the window, into the throbbing dark. "I don't know. Kanesae has discorporated. Since the vessel for Vlad's spirit is gone, I suppose she'll have no choice but to go to hell—and stay there."

Vernon let the words sink in. *Jesus. What a night.* He'd 911'd the fire department as he'd sped from the scene and at least saw that the adjoining condo seemed to be evacuating safely.

He skidded to a halt at the ER entrance. "Meet me inside," Vernon ordered and jumped out. "And don't talk to anyone."

Rollin nodded, rubbing his eyes.

Yeah, I'm too old for this, all right, Vernon agreed as he huffed Cristina's unconscious form through the sliding doors. Just as two male nurses got her on a gurney, Cristina's eyes fluttered open.

"Hey. I'm Howard Vernon, I'm a cop." He squeezed her hand.

Confusion filled her eyes, and she tried to speak but couldn't.

"Don't worry," Vernon said. "You're going to be okay."

Finally she uttered, "I . . . can't remember." Then her face paled. "That woman . . . that nun . . ."

"She's gone now. We'll talk later—"

A nurse shouldered Vernon out of the way. "Step back. We have to get her to x-ray right now."

"I want to go," Vernon interjected.

"No way—"

Vernon flashed his badge. "Come on, man."

The nurses agreed and pushed off, Vernon hustling to keep up. In the elevator, Cristina looked at him again.

"Who did you say you were?"

"I'm a friend of Father Rollin. Do you know who I mean?"

Concentration; then she nodded.

"We brought you here." But Vernon didn't want any more talk for now. *I don't think she's quite ready to learn that her boyfriend's dead, her friends are dead, and her house is on fire.* "Just relax for now."

"Okay."

One nurse pushed the gurney through double doors, but Vernon grabbed the other nurse. "Is she going to be all right?"

"How do I know?" the man snapped. "She could have a concussion, a cerebral hemorrhage, a skull fracture."

"Sure, but—"

"Her vitals are good and so's her dilation, and that's all a good sign." He turned toward the door. "This is as far as you go. Ask reception for updates."

The doors swung closed in Vernon's face.

Only now did the totality of his exhaustion fully hit him. *Holy shit.* In the elevator down, two more nurses peered at him, sniffing.

I must smell like a backyard grill, he realized.

He didn't see Father Rollin in the waiting room. *Old bastard probably fell asleep in the car,* Vernon guessed. He got two coffees in the vending room, was about to go outside with them when some heated talk was heard from the reception cove, then—

"Everybody out of the way!" a voice barked. Suddenly lights flashed outside, tires screeched and sirens drew close. A half a dozen uniformed cops rushed through the sliding doors, and raced for the elevators.

What the hell?

Vernon flashed his badge as another cop entered. "What's going on?"

"Multiple assaults reported from the second floor, sir," the officer answered without stopping. "X-ray."

Vernon's mind blanked. He followed but missed the elevator so he trotted up the fire stairs.

An odd silence filled the hall. No cops were in evidence, but both doors to the x-ray lab were now propped open. Two cops walked out, hands to foreheads.

Vernon rushed in.

Holy Mother of God . . .

The two male nurses he'd seen earlier lay twisted on the floor. Both of their throats had been gnawed open, torn veins and arteries showing. Their faces looked wizened, a pale whitish blue. The ends of two snapped-off broomsticks had been rammed through their chests, yet almost no blood had leaked from any of their wounds.

"Where's Cristina Nichols?" Vernon demanded.

"Who?"

"These two guys brought her in here a few minutes ago for x-rays!" Vernon's eyes darted around desperately. "Where is she?"

No one answered, but then Vernon noticed two more cops looking perplexed out a nearby window. The window had been smashed from the inside out.

Vernon turned and ran. *Rollin . . .* He almost tripped going down the stairs. More cops were pouring in when Vernon bulled out through the ER doors into the driveway.

No, no, no, he thought.

An intern whispered to a nurse, "Must be a full moon or something. I just heard there were two murders upstairs . . . and now this right at the same time."

Vernon walked in a daze to the scene. Before his car, several doctors were rising from their knees. An EMT was carrying away a portable defibrillator.

Father Rollin lay stretched out on the pavement, unmoving. Another EMT put a sheet over his face.

A physician's assistant leaned against the car, writing on a clipboard.

"What happened?" Vernon droned.

"Multiple heart attacks, big ones. We did everything we could." The P.A.'s eyes flicked up. "Is your name Vernon?"

"Yes," Vernon croaked.

"Before he lost consciousness he asked me to relay a message to you. I wrote it down." And then he took out a small notepad. "But keep in mind, he was delusional at the time, it doesn't make sense."

"What . . . did he say?"

The P.A. squinted at the pad. "'The flagon was fake. She fooled us.'"

Vernon chewed his lip. "That's it?"

"That's it. But you knew the man?"

"Yes . . ."

"Do you know the nun, too? We'd like to talk to her."

Vernon suddenly felt as though he were standing on a 100th-floor ledge. "What did you say? A—"

"A nun," the P.A. repeated without a lot of interest. "Couple people said they saw a nun talking to him just before he collapsed, but"—he glanced around—"I don't see any nun."

Vernon stared.

"Oh, almost forgot. The priest asked me to give this to you." The P.A. pulled something out of his pocket and dropped it into Vernon's hand.

It was Father Rollin's cross and a ring with the crest: a dragon strangled by its own tail, and the words, O QUAM MAGNIFICUM, O DOMNUL.

EPILOGUE

"Do you remember your name?" her accented voice echoes.

You pause. "Cristina Nichols . . ."

The brick walls drip, the torchlight flickers. You stand half in and half out of this final vision as the luminous black, green, and red lines churn over the dungeon's rough-hewn bricks.

Kanesae is *showing* you, and now you understand that this is what she's been doing all along . . .

She's never looked more real, more *flesh*, than at this moment. She's dressed fully in her black habit now, her face aglow in the white wimple, her fangs shiny as diamonds.

"Do you remember back at the house?"

You slowly shake your head.

"The ruse worked," Kanesae informs. "Thanks to self-ishness and greed—the hallmarks of humanity."

You see now, the upper room. Paul drinking the flagon's precious blood himself.

"It was not the blood of the Prince in the flagon. *That* was the secret."

Your eyes widen, and you *see* . . . the past.

You see Kanesae in this chamber so long ago. On the stone slab she is cutting the head off of a dog, and draining *its* blood into the flagon.

"Then . . . where did you hide the Prince's blood?" you ask.

Kanesae grins. "In *me*, and that's where it's been, for thirteen lifetimes. Until now."

You look down at your belly, which feels full and hot inside. The two men at the hospital were but tidbits, while your *first* meal proved the most paramount.

More of the vision pours into your mind. You see Kanesae so long ago gashing the throat of the man on the slab, letting his blood flow into the chalice, then gulping it down. Then she shows you what you did at the house: Kanesae cutting her own wrist and filling the chalice with what gushed out.

And handing the chalice to you.

"The diversion succeeded," she says, "just as the Prince whispered it would so many centuries ago . . ."

You stare at her.

"The past is done."

The weaving colors fade—

"All that awaits is the future, its darkness like ripe fruit set out for us . . . For *you*."

—and then the vision dissolves and you're back on the streets of this monolithic city in the middle of a hot, star-filled night.

You can hear every heart beat.

Kanesae leads you through alleys and byways, through black streets and across rooftops, and then . . . up a stairwell.

She pauses at the landing and smiles. Is there a tear in the nun's eye? "*Me enamourer ad infinitum . . .*"

You look back at her. You suddenly feel strong, audacious, and without fear.

"Do you remember your name, my love?"

"Drwglya," you breathe.

"Let us begin . . ."

You turn to face the door in the hallway that reads FREDRICK, and you raise your hand to knock.

Summer and the City

A CARRIE DIARIES NOVEL

CANDACE BUSHNELL

Summer and the City

A CARRIE DIARIES NOVEL

BALZER + BRAY

An Imprint of HarperCollinsPublishers

Balzer + Bray is an imprint of HarperCollins Publishers.

Summer and the City: A Carrie Diaries Novel

Library of Congress Cataloging-in-Publication Data
Bushnell, Candace.
    Summer and the city : a Carrie diaries novel/ Candace Bushnell.
— 1st ed.
        p.   cm.
    Sequel to: The carrie diaries.
    ISBN 978-0-06-219368-1
    [1. Young women—Fiction. 2. Female friendship—Fiction.
3. Manhattan (New York, N.Y.)—Fiction.] I. Title.
PS3552.U8229 S86   2011   2011009325
[Fic]—dc22   CIP
                                                      AC

Typography by Sarah Hoy
12 13 14 15 16   OPM   10 9 8 7 6 5 4 3 2 1
◆
First paperback edition, 2012

For Alyssa and Deirdre

PART ONE

Beginner's Luck

CHAPTER ONE

First Samantha asks me to find her shoe. When I locate it in the sink, she asks me to a party.

"You might as well come, seeing as you don't have anyplace else to go and I don't feel like baby-sitting."

"I'm hardly a baby."

"Okay. You're a sparrow. Either way," she says, adjusting her silk bra as she wriggles into a green Lycra shift, "you've already been mugged. If you're kidnapped by a pimp, I don't want it on my hands."

She spins around and eyes my outfit—a navy blue gabardine jacket with matching culottes that I'd actually considered chic a few hours ago. "Is that all you've got?"

"I have a black cocktail dress from the 1960s."

"Wear that. And put these on." She tosses me a pair of gold aviator sunglasses. "They'll make you look normal."

I don't ask what normal is as I follow behind her, clattering down the five flights of stairs to the street.

"Rule number one," she declares, stepping into traffic. "Always look like you know where you're going, even if you don't."

She holds up her hand, causing a car to screech to a halt. "Move fast." She bangs on the hood of the car and gives the driver the finger. "And always wear shoes you can run in."

I skittle behind her through the obstacle course of Seventh Avenue and arrive on the other side like a castaway discovering land.

"And for God's sake, those wedge sandals. Out," Samantha decries, giving my feet a disparaging glance.

"Did you know that the first wedge sandal was invented by Ferragamo for the young Judy Garland?"

"How on earth do you know that?"

"I'm a font of useless information."

"Then you should do just fine at this party."

"Whose party is it again?" I shout, trying to

be heard over the traffic.

"David Ross. The Broadway director."

"Why is he having a party at four o'clock on a Sunday afternoon?" I dodge a hot dog cart, a supermarket basket filled with blankets, and a child attached to a leash.

"It's a tea dance."

"Will they be serving tea?" I can't tell if she's serious.

She laughs. "What do *you* think?"

The party is in a dusky pink house at the end of a cobblestoned street. I can see the river through a crack between the buildings, turgid and brown under glints of sunlight.

"David's very eccentric," Samantha warns, as if eccentricity might be an unwelcome trait to a new arrival from the provinces. "Someone brought a miniature horse to his last party and it crapped all over the Aubusson carpet."

I pretend to know what an Aubusson carpet is in favor of learning more about the horse. "How'd they get it there?"

"Taxi," Samantha says. "It was a very small horse."

I hesitate. "Will your friend David mind? Your bringing me?"

"If he doesn't mind a miniature horse, I can't imagine he'll mind you. Unless you're a drag or a bore."

"I might be a bore but I'm never a drag."

"And the stuff about coming from a small town? Nix it," she says. "In New York, you need a shtick."

"A shtick?"

"Who you are, but better. Embellish," she says with a flourish as we pause in front of the house. It's four stories high and the blue door is flung open in welcome, revealing a colorful throng, twirling and weaving like a chorus in a musical show. My insides throb with excitement. That door is my entrance to another world.

We're about to cross the threshold when a shiny black marble of a man comes rolling out, a bottle of champagne in one hand and a lit cigarette in the other. "Samantha!" he screams.

"Davide," Samantha shouts, giving the name a French twist.

"And who are you?" he asks, peering at me with friendly curiosity.

"Carrie Bradshaw, sir." I hold out my hand.

"How divine," he squeals. "I haven't been called 'sir' since I was in short pants. Not that I ever was in short pants. Where have you been hiding this delightful young person?"

"I found her on my doorstep."

"Did you arrive in a basket like Moses?" he asks.

"Train," I reply.

"And what brings you to the Emerald City?"

"Oh." I smile. And taking Samantha's advice to heart, I quickly blurt out, "I'm going to become a famous writer."

"Like Kenton!" he exclaims.

"Kenton James?" I ask breathlessly.

"Is there any other? He should be here somewhere. If you trip across a very small man with a voice like a miniature poodle, you'll know you've found him."

In the next second, David Ross is halfway across the room and Samantha is sitting on a strange man's lap.

"Over here." She waves from the couch.

I push past a woman in a white jumpsuit. "I think I just saw my first Halston!"

"Is Halston here?" Samantha asks.

If I'm at the same party with Halston and Kenton James, I'm going to die. "I meant the jumpsuit."

"Oh, the jumpsuit," she says with exaggerated interest to the man beneath her. From what I can see of him, he's tan and sporty, sleeves rolled up over his forearms.

"You're killing me," he says.

"This is Carrie Bradshaw. She's going to be a famous writer," Samantha says, taking up my moniker as if it's suddenly fact.

"Hello, famous writer." He holds out his hand, the fingers narrow and burnished like bronze.

"This is Bernard. The idiot I didn't sleep with last year," she jokes.

"Didn't want to be another notch in your belt," Bernard drawls.

"I'm not notching anymore. Don't you know?" She holds out her left hand for inspection. An enormous diamond glitters from her ring finger. "I'm engaged."

She kisses the top of Bernard's dark head and looks around the room. "Who do I have to spank to get a drink around here?"

"I'll go," Bernard volunteers. He stands up and for one inexplicable moment, it's like watching my future unfold.

"C'mon, famous writer. Better come with me. I'm the only sane person here." He puts his hands on my shoulders and steers me through the crowd.

I look back at Samantha, but she only smiles and waves, that giant sparkler catching the last rays of sunlight. How did I not notice that ring before?

Guess I was too busy noticing everything else.

Like Bernard. He's tall and has straight dark

hair. A large, crooked nose. Hazel-green eyes and a face that changes from mournful to delighted every other second, as if he has two personalities pulling him in opposite directions.

I can't fathom why he's paying me so much attention, but I'm mesmerized. People keep coming up and congratulating him, while snippets of conversation waft around my head like dandelion fluff.

"You never give up, do you—"

"Crispin knows him and he's terrified—"

"I said, 'Why don't you try diagramming a sentence—'"

"Dreadful. Even her diamonds looked dirty—"

Bernard gives me a wink. And suddenly his full name comes back to me from some old copy of *Time* magazine or *Newsweek*. Bernard Singer? *The playwright?*

He can't be, I panic, knowing instinctively he is.

How the hell did this happen? I've been in New York for exactly two hours, and already I'm with the beautiful people?

"What's your name again?" he asks.

"Carrie Bradshaw." The name of his play, the one that won the Pulitzer Prize, enters my brain like a shard of glass: *Cutting Water.*

"I'd better get you back to Samantha before I

take you home myself," he purrs.

"I wouldn't go," I say tartly. Blood pounds in my ears. My glass of champagne is sweating.

"Where do you live?" He squeezes my shoulder.

"I don't know."

This makes him roar with laughter. "You're an orphan. Are you Annie?"

"I'd rather be Candide." We're edged up against a wall near French doors that lead to a garden. He slides down so we're eye-level.

"Where did you come from?"

I remind myself of what Samantha told me. "Does it matter? I'm here."

"Cheeky devil," he declares. And suddenly, I'm glad I was robbed. The thief took my bag and my money, but he also took my identity. Which means for the next few hours, I can be anyone I want.

Bernard grabs my hand and leads me to the garden. A variety of people—men, women, old, young, beautiful, ugly—are seated around a marble table, shrieking with laughter and indignation as if heated conversation is the fuel that keeps them going. He wriggles us in between a tiny woman with short hair and a distinguished man in a seersucker jacket.

"Bernard," the woman says in a feathery voice. "We're coming to see your play in September."

Bernard's response is drowned out, however, by a sudden yelp of recognition from the man seated across the table.

He's enveloped in black, a voluminous coat that resembles a nun's habit. Brown-shaded sunglasses hide his eyes and a felt hat is pressed over his forehead. The skin on his face is gently folded, as if wrapped in soft white fabric.

"Bernard!" he exclaims. "Bernardo. Darling. Love of my life. Do get me a drink?" He spots me, and points a trembling finger. "You've brought a child!"

His voice is shrill, eerily pitched, almost inhuman. Every cell in my body contracts.

Kenton James.

My throat closes. I grab for my glass of champagne, and drain the last drop, feeling a nudge from the man in the seersucker jacket. He nods at Kenton James. "Pay no attention to the man behind the curtain," he says, in a voice that's pure patrician New England, low and assured. "It's the grain alcohol. Years of it. Destroys the brain. In other words, he's a hopeless drunk."

I giggle in appreciation, like I know exactly what he's talking about. "Isn't everyone?"

"Now that you mention it, yes."

"Bernardo, *please*," Kenton pleads. "It's only practical. You're the one who's closest to the bar.

You can't expect me to enter that filthy sweating mass of humanity—"

"Guilty!" shouts the man in the seersucker.

"And what are you wearing under that dishabille?" booms Bernard.

"I've been waiting to hear those words from your lips for ten years," Kenton yips.

"I'll go," I say, standing up.

Kenton James breaks into applause. "Wonderful. Please take note, everyone—this is exactly what children should do. Fetch and carry. You must bring children to parties more often, Bernie."

I tear myself away, wanting to hear more, wanting to know more, not wanting to leave Bernard. Or Kenton James. The most famous writer in the world. His name chugs in my head, picking up speed like The Little Engine That Could.

A hand reaches out and grabs my arm. Samantha. Her eyes are as glittery as her diamond. There's a fine sheen of moisture on her upper lip. "Are you okay? You disappeared. I was worried about you."

"I just met Kenton James. He wants me to bring him alcohol."

"Don't leave without letting me know first, okay?"

"I won't. I never want to leave."

"Good." She beams, and goes back to her conversation.

The atmosphere is revved up to maximum wattage. The music blares. Bodies writhe, a couple is making out on the couch. A woman crawls through the room with a saddle on her back. Two bartenders are being sprayed with champagne by a gigantic woman wearing a corset. I grab a bottle of vodka and dance my way through the crowd.

Like I always go to parties like this. Like I belong.

When I get back to the table, a young woman dressed entirely in Chanel has taken my place. The man in the seersucker jacket is pantomiming an elephant attack, and Kenton James has pulled his hat down over his ears. He greets my appearance with delight. "Make way for alcohol," he cries, clearing a tiny space next to him. And addressing the table, declares, "Someday, this child will rule the city!"

I squeeze in next to him.

"No fair," Bernard shouts. "Keep your hands off my date!"

"I'm not anyone's date," I say.

"But you will be, my dear," Kenton says, blinking one bleary eye in warning. "And then you'll *see*." He pats my hand with his own small, soft paw.

CHAPTER TWO

Help!

I'm suffocating, drowning in taffeta. I'm trapped in a coffin. I'm . . . dead?

I sit up and wrench free, staring at the pile of black silk in my lap.

It's my dress. I must have taken it off sometime during the night and put it over my head. Or did someone take it off for me? I look around the half darkness of Samantha's living room, crisscrossed by eerie yellow beams of light that highlight the ordinary objects of her existence: a grouping of photographs on the side table, a pile of magazines on the floor, a row of candles on the sill.

My head throbs as I vaguely recall a taxi ride packed with people. Peeling blue vinyl and a sticky mat. I was hiding on the floor of the taxi against the protests of the driver, who kept saying, "No more than four." We were actually six but Samantha kept insisting we weren't. There was hysterical laughter. Then a crawl up the five flights of steps and more music and phone calls and a guy wearing Samantha's makeup, and sometime after that I must have collapsed on the futon couch and fallen asleep.

I tiptoe to Samantha's room, avoiding the open boxes. Samantha is moving out, and the apartment is a mess. The door to the tiny bedroom is open, the bed unmade but empty, the floor littered with shoes and articles of clothing as if someone tried on everything in her closet and cast each piece away in a rush. I make my way to the bathroom, and weaving through a forest of bras and panties, step over the edge of the ancient tub and turn on the shower.

Plan for the day: find out where I'm supposed to live, without calling my father.

My father. The rancid aftertaste of guilt fills my throat.

I didn't call him yesterday. I didn't have a chance. He's probably worried to death by now. What if he called George? What if he called my landlady? Maybe the police are looking for me, another girl who mysteriously disappears into the maw of New York City.

I shampoo my hair. I can't do anything about it now.

Or maybe I don't want to.

I get out of the tub and lean across the sink, staring at my reflection as the mist from the shower slowly evaporates and my face is revealed.

I don't look any different. But I sure as hell feel different.

It's my first morning in New York!

I rush to the open window, taking in the cool, damp breeze. The sound of traffic is like the whoosh of waves gently lapping the shore. I kneel on the sill, looking down at the street with my palms on the glass—a child peering into an enormous snow globe.

I crouch there forever, watching the day come to life. First come the trucks, lumbering down the avenue like dinosaurs, creaky and hollow, raising their flaps to receive garbage or sweeping the street with their whiskery bristles. Then the traffic begins: a lone taxi, followed by a silvery Cadillac, and then the smaller trucks, bearing the logos of fish and bread and flowers, and the rusty vans, and a parade of pushcarts. A boy in a white coat pumps the pedals of a bicycle with two crates of oranges attached to the fender. The sky turns from gray to a lazy white. A jogger trips by, then another; a man wearing blue scrubs frantically hails a taxi.

Three small dogs attached to a single leash drag an elderly lady down the sidewalk, while merchants heave open the groaning metal gates on the storefronts. The streaky sunlight illuminates the corners of buildings, and then a mass of humanity swarms from the steps beneath the sidewalk. The streets swell with the noise of people, cars, music, drilling; dogs bark, sirens scream; it's eight a.m.

Time to get moving.

I search the area around the futon for my belongings. Tucked behind the cushion is a heavy piece of drafting paper, the edge slightly greasy and crumpled, as if I'd lain clutching it to my chest. I study Bernard's phone number, the numerals neat and workmanlike. At the party, he made a great show of writing out his number and handing it to me with the statement, "Just in case." He pointedly didn't ask for my number, as if we both knew that seeing each other again would have to be my decision.

I carefully place the paper in my suitcase, and that's when I find the note, anchored under an empty bottle of champagne. It reads:

Dear Carrie,
Your friend George called. Tried to wake you but
couldn't. Left you a twenty. Pay me back when
you can.
Samantha

And underneath that, an address. For the apartment I was supposed to go to yesterday but didn't. Apparently I called George last night after all.

I hold up the note, looking for clues. Samantha's writing is strangely girlish, as if the penmanship part of her brain never progressed beyond seventh grade. I reluctantly put on my gabardine suit, pick up the phone, and call George.

Ten minutes later, I'm bumping my suitcase down the stairs. I push open the door and step outside.

My stomach growls as if ravenously hungry. Not just for food, but for everything: the noise, the excitement, the crazy buzz of energy that throbs beneath my feet.

I hail a taxi, yank open the door and heave my suitcase onto the backseat.

"Where to?" the driver asks.

"East Forty-seventh Street," I shout.

"You got it!" the driver says, steering his taxi into the melee of traffic.

We hit a pothole and I'm momentarily launched from my seat.

"It's those damn New Jersey drivers." The cabbie shakes his fist out the window while I follow suit. And that's when it hits me: It's like I've always been here. Sprung from the head of Zeus—a person with no family, no background, no *history*.

A person who is completely new.

As the taxi weaves dangerously through traffic, I study the faces of the passersby. Here is humanity in every size, shape, and hue, and yet I'm convinced that on each face I divine a kinship that transcends all boundaries, as if linked by the secret knowledge that this is the center of the universe.

Then I clutch my suitcase in fear.

What I said to Samantha was true: I don't ever want to leave. And now I have only sixty days to figure out how to stay.

The sight of George Carter brings me back to earth with a thump. He's sitting dutifully at the counter of the coffee shop on Forty-seventh Street and Second Avenue, where we agreed to meet before he trots off to his summer job at *The New York Times*. I can tell by the set of his mouth that he's exasperated—I've been in New York for less than twenty-four hours and already I'm off course. I haven't even managed to make it to the apartment where I'm supposed to be staying. I tap him on the shoulder, and he turns around, his expression both relieved and irritated.

"What happened to you?" he demands.

I set down my suitcase and take the stool next to him. "My purse got stolen. I didn't have any money. So I called this girl, the cousin of someone

I know from Castlebury. She took me to a party and—"

George sighs. "You shouldn't be hanging around people like that."

"Why not?"

"You don't know them."

"So what?" Now I'm annoyed. This is the problem with George. He always acts like he thinks he's my father or something.

"I need you to promise you'll be more careful in the future."

I make a face.

"Carrie, I'm serious. If you get into another jam, I'm not going to be around to help you out."

"Are you abandoning me?" I ask jokingly. George has had a crush on me for nearly a year. And he's one of my dearest friends. If it weren't for George, I might not be in New York at all.

"Actually, I am," he says, sliding three crisp twenty-dollar bills in my direction. "This should tide you over. You can pay me back when you get to Brown."

I look from the bills to his face. He's not kidding.

"The *Times* is sending me to DC for the summer. I'll get to do some actual reporting, so I agreed."

I'm stunned. I don't know whether to

congratulate him or chastise him for deserting me.

The impact of his defection hits me, and the floor drops out from below my feet. George is the only person I really know in New York. I was counting on him to show me the ropes. How am I going to get by without him?

As if reading my thoughts, he says, "You'll be fine. Just stick to the basics. Go to class and do your work. And try not to get mixed up with any crazy people, okay?"

"Sure," I say. This wouldn't be a problem but for the fact I'm a little crazy myself.

George picks up my suitcase and we stroll around the corner to a white brick apartment building. A tattered green awning with the words WINDSOR ARMS shields the entrance. "This isn't so bad," George remarks. "Perfectly respectable."

Inside the glass door is a row of buttons. I press the one marked 15E.

"Yes?" a shrill voice shrieks from the intercom.

"It's Carrie Bradshaw."

"Well," says the voice, in a tone that could curdle cream. "It's about time."

George kisses me on the cheek as a buzzer sounds and the second door clicks open. "Good luck," he says, and pauses to give me one last piece of advice: "Will you *please* call your father? I'm sure he's worried about you."

CHAPTER THREE

"Is this Carrie Bradshaw?" The voice is girlish but demanding, as if the caller is slightly annoyed.

"Y-e-e-e-e-s," I say cautiously, wondering who it could be. It's my second morning in New York and we haven't had our first class yet.

"I have your bag," the girl announces.

"What!" I nearly drop the phone.

"Well, don't get too excited. I found it in the garbage. Someone dumped nail polish all over it. I was thinking about leaving it in the garbage, but then I thought: What would *I* want someone to do if I lost my purse? So I called."

"How'd you find me?"

"Your address book. It was still in the bag. I'll be in front of Saks from ten o'clock on if you want to pick it up," she says. "You can't miss me. I have red hair. I dyed it the same color red as the Campbell's soup can. In honor of Valerie Solanas." She pauses. "The *SCUM Manifesto*? Andy Warhol?"

"Oh, sure." I have absolutely no idea what's she talking about. But I'm not about to admit my ignorance. Plus, this girl sounds kind of . . . bizarre.

"Good. I'll see you in front of Saks." She hangs up before I can get her name.

Yippee! *I knew it.* The whole time my Carrie bag was gone, I had a strange premonition I'd get it back. Like something out of one of those books on mind control: visualize what you want and it will come to you.

"A-hem!"

I look up from my cot and into the scrubbed pink face of my landlady, Peggy Meyers. She's squeezed into a gray rubber suit that fits like sausage casing. The suit, combined with her shining round face, gives her an uncanny resemblance to the Michelin Man.

"Was that an outgoing call?"

"No," I say, slightly offended. "*They* called *me*."

Her sigh is a precise combination of annoyance and disappointment. "Didn't we go over the rules?"

I nod, eyes wide, pantomiming fear.

"All phone calls are to take place in the living room. And no calls are to last more than five minutes. No one needs longer than five minutes to communicate. And all outgoing calls must be duly listed in the notebook."

Duly, I think. That's a good word.

"Do you have any questions?" she asks.

"Nope." I shake my head.

"I'm going for a run. Then I have auditions. If you decide to go out, make sure you have your keys."

"I will. I promise."

She stops, takes in my cotton pajamas, and frowns. "I hope you're not planning to go back to sleep."

"I'm going to Saks."

Peggy purses her lips in disapproval, as if only the indolent go to Saks. "By the way, your father called."

"Thanks."

"And remember, all long-distance calls are collect." She lumbers out like a mummy. If she can barely walk in that rubber suit, how can she possibly run in it?

I've only known Peggy for twenty-four hours, but already, we don't get along. You could call it hate at first sight.

When I arrived yesterday morning, disheveled and slightly disoriented, her first comment was: "Glad you decided to show up. I was about to give your room to someone else."

I looked at Peggy, whom I suspected had once been attractive but was now like a flower gone to seed, and half wished she *had* given the room away.

"I've got a waiting list a mile long," she continued. "You kids from out of town have no idea—*no idea*—how impossible it is to find a decent place in New York."

Then she sat me down on the green love seat and apprised me of "the rules":

No visitors, especially males.

No overnight guests, especially males, even if she is away for the weekend.

No consumption of her food.

No telephone calls over five minutes—she needs the phone line free in case she gets a call about an audition.

No coming home past midnight—we might wake her up and she needs every minute of sleep.

And most of all, no cooking. She doesn't want to have to clean up our mess.

Jeez. Even a gerbil has more freedom than I do.

I wait until I hear the front door bang behind her, then knock hard on the plywood wall next to my bed. "Ding-dong, the witch is dead," I call out.

L'il Waters, a tiny butterfly of a girl, slips through the plywood door that connects our cells. "Someone found my bag!" I exclaim.

"Oh, honey, that's wonderful. Like one of those magical New York coincidences." She hops onto the end of the cot, nearly tipping it over. Nothing in this apartment is real, including the partitions, doors, and beds. Our "rooms" are built into part of the living room, forming two tiny six-by-ten spaces with just enough room for a camp bed, a small folding table and chair, a tiny dresser with two drawers, and a reading light. The apartment is located right off Second Avenue, so I've taken to calling L'il and me *The Prisoners of Second Avenue* after the Neil Simon movie.

"But what about Peggy? I heard her yelling at you. I told you not to use the phone in your room." L'il sighs.

"I thought she was asleep."

L'il shakes her head. She's in my program at The New School, but arrived a week earlier to get acclimated, which also means she got the slightly better room. She has to walk through my space to get to hers, so I have even less privacy than she does. "Peggy always gets up early to go jogging. She says she has to lose twenty pounds—"

"In that rubber suit?" I ask, astounded.

"She says it sweats the fat out."

I look at L'il in appreciation. She's two years older than I am, but looks about five years younger. With her birdlike stature, she's one of those girls who will probably look like she's twelve for most of her life. But L'il is not to be underestimated.

When we first met yesterday, I joked about how "L'il" would look on the cover of a book, but she only shrugged and said, "My writing name is E. R. Waters. For Elizabeth Reynolds Waters. It helps to get published if people don't know you're a girl." Then she showed me two poems she'd had published in *The New Yorker*.

I nearly fell over.

Then I told her how I'd met Kenton James and Bernard Singer. I knew meeting famous writers wasn't the same as being published yourself, but I figured it was better than nothing. I even showed her the paper where Bernard Singer had written his phone number.

"You have to call him," she said.

"I don't know." I didn't want to make too big a deal of it.

Thinking of Bernard made me all jellyish until Peggy came in and told us to be quiet.

Now I give L'il a wicked smile. "Peggy," I say. "She really goes to auditions in that rubber suit?

Can you imagine the smell?"

L'il grins. "She belongs to a gym. Lucille Roberts. She says she takes a shower there before. That's why she's always so crazy. She's sweating and showering all over town."

This cracks us up, and we fall onto my bed in giggles.

The red-haired girl is right: I have no problem finding her.

Indeed, she's impossible to miss, planted on the sidewalk in front of Saks, holding a huge sign that reads, DOWN WITH PORNOGRAPHY on one side, and PORNOGRAPHY EXPLOITS WOMEN on the other. Behind her is a small table covered with graphic images from porno magazines. "Women, wake up! Say no to pornography!" she shouts.

She waves me over with her placard. "Do you want to sign a petition against pornography?"

I'm about to explain who I am, when a stranger cuts me off.

"Oh, puhleeze," the woman mutters, stepping around us. "You'd think some people would have better things to do than worrying about other people's sex lives."

"Hey," the red-haired girl shouts. "I heard that, you know? And I don't exactly appreciate it."

The woman spins around. "And?"

"What do you know about my sex life?" she demands. Her hair is cut short like a boy's and, as promised, dyed a bright tomato red. She's wearing construction boots and overalls, and underneath, a ragged purple T-shirt.

"Honey, it's pretty clear you don't have one," the woman responds with a smirk.

"Is that so? Maybe I don't have as much sex as you do, but you're a victim of the system. You've been brainwashed by the patriarchy."

"Sex sells," the woman says.

"At the expense of women."

"That's ridiculous. Have you ever considered the fact that some women actually *like* sex?"

"And?" The girl glares as I take advantage of the momentary lull to quickly introduce myself.

"I'm Carrie Bradshaw. You called me. You have my bag?"

"*You're* Carrie Bradshaw?" She seems disappointed. "What are you doing with her?" She jerks her thumb in the woman's direction.

"I don't even know her. If I could just get my bag—"

"Take it," the redheaded girl says, as if she's had enough. She picks up her knapsack, removes my Carrie bag, and hands it to me.

"Thank you," I say gratefully. "If there's anything I can ever do—"

"Don't worry about it," she replies proudly. She picks up her placard and accosts an elderly woman in pearls. "Do you want to sign a petition against pornography?"

The old woman smiles. "No thank you, dear. After all, what's the point?"

The red-haired girl looks momentarily crestfallen.

"Hey," I say. "I'll sign your petition."

"Thanks," she says, handing me a pen.

I scribble my name and skip off down Fifth Avenue. I dodge through the crowds, wondering what my mother would have thought about me being in New York. Maybe she's watching over me, making sure the funny red-haired girl found my bag. My mother was a feminist, too. At the very least, she'd be proud I signed the petition.

"There you are!" L'il calls out. "I was afraid you were going to be late."

"Nope," I say, panting, as I join her on the sidewalk in front of The New School. The trek downtown was a lot farther than I expected, and my feet are killing me. But I saw all kinds of interesting things along the way: the skating rink at Rockefeller Center. The New York Public Library. Lord & Taylor. Something called the Toy Building. "I got my bag," I say, holding it up.

"Carrie was robbed her very first hour in New York," L'il crows to a cute guy with bright blue eyes and wavy black hair.

He shrugs. "That's nothing. My car was broken into the second night I was here. They smashed the window and stole the radio."

"You have a car?" I ask in surprise. Peggy told us no one had cars in New York. Everyone is supposed to walk or take the bus or ride the subway.

"Ryan's from Massachusetts," L'il says as if this explains it. "He's in our class too."

I hold out my hand. "Carrie Bradshaw."

"Ryan McCann." He's got a goofy, sweet smile, but his eyes bore into me as if summing up the competition. "What do you think about our professor, Viktor Greene?"

"I think he's extraordinary," L'il jumps in. "He's what I consider a serious artist."

"He may be an artist, but he's definitely a creep," Ryan replies, goading her.

"You hardly know him," L'il says, incensed.

"Wait a minute. You guys have *met* him?" I ask.

"Last week," Ryan says casually. "We had our conferences. Didn't you?"

"I didn't know we were supposed to have a conference," I falter. How did this happen? Am I already behind?

L'il gives Ryan a look. "Not everyone had a conference. It was only if you were going to be in New York early. It doesn't matter."

"Hey, you kids want to go to a party?"

We turn around. A guy with a Cheshire cat grin holds up some postcards. "It's at The Puck Building. Wednesday night. Free admission if you get there before ten o'clock."

"Thanks," Ryan says eagerly as the guy hands us each a postcard and strolls away.

"Do you know him?" L'il asks.

"Never seen him before in my life. But that's cool, isn't it?" Ryan says. "Where else would some stranger walk up to you and invite you to a party?"

"Along with a thousand other strangers," L'il adds.

"Only in New York, kids," Ryan says.

We head inside as I examine the postcard. On the front is an image of a smiling stone cupid. Underneath are the words, LOVE. SEX. FASHION. I fold the postcard and stick it into my bag.

CHAPTER FOUR

Ryan wasn't kidding. Viktor Greene *is* strange.

For one thing, he droops. It's like someone dropped him out of the sky and he never quite got his sea legs here on earth. Then there's his mustache. It's thick and glossy across his upper lip, but curls forlornly around each side of his mouth like two sad smiles. He keeps stroking that mustache like it's some kind of pet.

"Carrie Bradshaw?" he asks, consulting a list.

I raise my hand. "That's me."

"It is *I*," he corrects. "One of the things you'll learn in this seminar is proper grammar. You'll find it improves your manner of speaking as well."

I redden. Five minutes into my first real writing class and I've made a bad impression.

Ryan catches my eye and winks as if to say, "I told you so."

"Ah, and here's L'il." Viktor Greene nods as he gives his mustache a few more comforting pats. "Does everyone know Ms. Elizabeth Waters? She's one of our most promising writers. I'm sure we'll be hearing a lot from her."

If Viktor Greene had said something like that about me, I'd be worried everyone in the class was going to hate me. But not L'il. She takes Viktor's praise in stride, as if she's used to being regaled for her talent.

For a moment, I'm jealous. I try to reassure myself that everyone in the class is talented. Otherwise they wouldn't be here, right? Including myself. Maybe Viktor Greene just doesn't know how talented I am—yet?

"Here's how this seminar works." Viktor Greene shuffles around as if he's lost something and can't remember what it is. "The theme for the summer is home and family. In the next eight weeks, you'll write four short stories or a novella or six poems exploring these themes. Each week, I'll choose three or four works to be read aloud. Then we'll discuss them. Any questions?"

A hand shoots up belonging to a slim guy with glasses and a mane of blond hair. Despite his resemblance to a pelican, he nevertheless manages to give off the impression that he thinks he's better than everyone else. "How long are the short stories supposed to be?"

Viktor Greene taps his mustache. "As long as it takes to tell the story."

"So that could mean two pages?" demands a girl with an angular face and tawny eyes. A baseball cap is perched backward over her luxurious crop of dark hair and she's wearing a pile of beaded necklaces slung around her neck.

"If you can tell a whole story in five hundred words, be my guest," Viktor Greene says mournfully.

The girl nods, a triumphant expression on her beautiful face. "It's just that my father is an artist. And he says—"

Viktor sighs. "We all know who your father is, Rainbow."

Wait a minute. *Rainbow?* What kind of name is that? And who is this artist father of hers?

I sit back and fold my arms. The guy with the long nose and blond hair catches Rainbow's eye and nods, edging his chair a little closer to hers, as if they're already friends.

"I have a question." Ryan raises his hand. "Can you guarantee that after taking this course, we'll all become writers?"

This causes Viktor Greene to droop even

more. I actually wonder if he's going to disappear into the floor.

He frantically pats down his mustache with both hands. "Good question. And the answer is no. Chances are ninety-nine point nine percent of you won't make it as writers at all."

The class groans.

"If I'm not going to make it as a writer, I'll have to demand my money back," Ryan says jokingly.

Everyone laughs, except Viktor Greene. "If that's the way you feel, you should contact the bursar's office."

He twirls the ends of his mustache between his fingers.

That mustache is going to drive me insane. I wonder if Viktor Greene is married and what his wife thinks of all his mustache stroking. Living with that mustache must be like having an extra person in the house. Does it have its own name and eat its own food as well?

And suddenly, I'm burning with passion. I don't care what Viktor Greene says: I'm going to make it. I'm going to become a real writer if it kills me.

I look around the room at my fellow students. Now I'm the one judging the competition.

❖ ✳ C~B~ ✳ ❖

"All right," I say, plopping onto L'il's bed. "Who is Rainbow's father?"

"Barry Jessen," she says with a sigh.

"Who the hell is Barry Jessen? I know he's an artist and all, but—"

"He's not just any artist. He's one of the most important artists in New York right now. He's the leader of some new art movement. They live in abandoned buildings in SoHo—"

"Rainbow lives in an abandoned building?" I ask, perplexed. "Do they have running water? Heat? She doesn't look like she's homeless."

"She's not," L'il says in exasperation. "They only *used* to be abandoned buildings. Garment and print factories. But then all these artists moved in and started fixing them up. And now they have parties in their lofts and take drugs and people buy their art and write about them in *The New York Times* and *New York Magazine*."

"And Rainbow?"

"Well, her father is Barry Jessen. And her mother is Pican—"

"The *model*?"

"That's why she's so beautiful and will get anything she wants. Which includes becoming a writer. Does that answer your question?"

"So she's a million times cooler than us."

"Than 'we are,'" L'il corrects. "And, yes, she is.

Her parents know a ton of people, and if Rainbow wants to get a book published, all she has to do is snap her fingers and her father will find someone to publish it for her. And then he'll get a bunch of journalists to write about it and critics to give her good reviews."

"Damn," I say, impressed.

"Meanwhile, if the rest of us want to be successful, we have to do it the old-fashioned way. We have to write something great."

"What a bore," I say sarcastically.

L'il laughs while I pick at an imaginary thread. "And what about that guy with the blond hair and the attitude? He acts like he knows her."

"Capote Duncan?" she says in surprise. "I'm sure he does. Capote's the type who knows everyone."

"Why?"

"Oh, he just is. He's from the South," she says, as if this explains it. "He's kind of dreamy, isn't he?"

"No. But he is kind of an asshole."

"He's older. He and Ryan are seniors in college. They're friends. Apparently the two of them are quite the ladies' men."

"You're kidding."

"I'm not." She pauses, and in a slightly formal

tone of voice, adds, "If you don't mind—"

"I know, I know," I say, jumping off the bed. "We're supposed to be writing."

L'il doesn't seem to share my overweening interest in other people. Perhaps she's so confident in her own talents, she feels like she doesn't need to. I, on the other hand, could easily spend the entire day engaged in gossip, which I prefer to call "character analysis." Unfortunately, you can't engage in character analysis by yourself. I go back into my cubbyhole, sit down at my desk, roll a piece of paper into my typewriter, and sit there.

Ten minutes later, I'm still sitting there, staring at the wall. There's only one window in our area, and it's in L'il's room. Feeling like I'm suffocating, I get up, go into the living room, and look out the window there.

Peggy's apartment is in the back of the building, facing the back of another nearly identical building on the next street. Maybe I could get a telescope and spy on the apartments across the way. I could write a story about the residents. Unfortunately, the denizens of that building appear to be as dull as we are. I spot the flickering blue screen of a television set, a woman washing the dishes, and a sleeping cat.

I sigh, feeling thwarted. There's a whole

world out there and I'm stuck in Peggy's apartment. I'm missing everything. And now I only have fifty-nine days left.

I've got to make something happen.

I race to my cubby, grab Bernard's number, and pick up the phone.

I hesitate, considering what I'm about to do, and put it down.

"L'il?" I call out.

"Yes?"

"Should I call Bernard Singer?"

L'il comes to the door. "What do you think?"

"What if he doesn't remember me?"

"He gave you his number, didn't he?"

"But what if he didn't mean it? What if he was only being polite? What if—"

"Do you want to call him?" she asks.

"Yes."

"Then do." L'il is very decisive. It's a quality I hope to develop in myself someday.

And before I can change my mind, I dial.

"Y-ello," he says, after the third ring.

"Bernard?" I say, in a voice that's way too high. "It's Carrie Bradshaw."

"Aha. Had a feeling it might be you."

"You did?" I curl the phone cord around my finger.

"I'm a bit psychic."

"Do you have visions?" I ask, not knowing what else to say.

"Feelings," he murmurs sexily. "I'm very in touch with my feelings. What about you?"

"I guess I am too. I mean, I never seem to be able to get rid of them. My feelings."

He laughs. "What are you doing right now?"

"Me?" I squeak. "Well, I'm just kind of sitting here trying to write—"

"Want to come over?" he asks suddenly.

I'm not sure what I was expecting, but it isn't this. I suppose I had a vague yet hopeful idea that he would invite me to dinner. Take me out on a proper date. But asking me to come to his apartment? Yikes. He probably thinks I'm going to have sex with him.

I pause.

"Where are you?" he asks.

"On Forty-seventh Street?"

"You're less than ten blocks away."

"Okay," I cautiously agree. As usual, my curiosity trumps my better judgment. A very bad trait, and one I hope to amend. Someday.

But maybe dating is different in New York. For all I know, inviting a strange girl to your apartment is just the way they do things around here. And if Bernard tries anything funny, I can always kick him.

On my way out, I run into Peggy coming in. She's got her hands full trying to maneuver three old shopping bags onto the love seat. She looks me up and down and sighs. "Going out?"

I deliberate, wondering how much I need to tell her. But my excitement gets the better of me. "I'm going to see my friend. Bernard Singer?"

The name has its desired effect. Peggy inhales, nostrils flaring. The fact that I know Bernard Singer has to be killing her. He's the most famous playwright in all of New York and she's still a struggling actress. She's probably dreamed of meeting him for years, and yet here I am, only three days in the city, and already I know him.

"Some people have quite the life, don't they?" She grumbles as she goes to the refrigerator and extracts one of her many cans of Tab—which are also off-limits for L'il and me.

For a moment, I feel victorious, until I take in Peggy's despondent expression. She jerks the ring from the top of the can and drinks thirstily, like the solutions to all her problems lie in that can of Tab. She drains it, absentmindedly rubbing the metal ring against her thumb.

"Peggy, I—"

"Damn!" She drops the can and sticks her thumb in her mouth, sucking the blood from the cut where the ring has sliced the skin. She closes her eyes as if holding back tears.

"Are you all right?" I ask quickly.

"Of course." She looks up, furious that I've witnessed this moment of weakness. "You're still here?"

She brushes past me on her way to her room. "Tonight's my night off and I intend to make it an early one. So don't be home late."

She closes the door. For a second, I stand there, wondering what just happened. Maybe it's not me Peggy hates. Maybe it's her *life*.

"Okay," I say to no one in particular.

CHAPTER FIVE

Bernard lives in Sutton Place. It's only a few blocks away, but it might as well be in another city. Gone are the noise, the grime, and the vagrant types that populate the rest of Manhattan. Instead, there are buildings constructed of soft-colored stone with turrets and green copper mansards. Uniformed doormen wearing white gloves stand under quiet awnings; a limousine idles at the curb. I pause, breathing in the atmosphere of luxury as a nanny passes me wheeling a baby carriage, behind which prances a small fluffy dog.

Bernard must be rich.

Rich, famous, and attractive. What am I getting myself into?

I scan the street, looking for number 52. It's on the east side facing the river. Swanky, I think, hurrying toward the building. I step inside, where I'm immediately halted by a low growl from a stern-faced doorman. "Can I help you?"

"Going to see a friend," I mutter, attempting to snake my way around him. And that's when I make my first mistake: never, ever try to get around a doorman in a white-glove building.

"You can't just walk in here." He holds up one gloved mitt, as if the mere sight of his hand is enough to ward off the unwashed.

Unfortunately, something about that glove sets me off. There's nothing I hate more than some old guy telling me what to do. "How did you expect me to enter? By horseback?"

"Miss!" he exclaims, taking a step back in displeasure. "Please state your business. And if you cannot state your business, I suggest you take your business elsewhere."

Aha. He thinks I'm some kind of hooker. He must be half blind. I'm hardly even wearing makeup. "I'm here to see Bernard," I say tightly.

"Bernard who?" he demands, refusing to budge.

"Bernard Singer?"

"*Mr.* Singer?"

How much longer can this go on? We stare at

each other in a stalemate. He must know he's beat. After all, he can't actually deny that Bernard lives here—or can he?

"I'll ring Mr. Singer," he finally concedes.

He makes a great show of strolling across the marble lobby to a desk containing a huge spray of flowers, a notebook, and a telephone. He presses a few buttons and, while he waits for Bernard to answer, rubs his jaw in aggravation. "Mr. Singer?" he says, into the receiver. "There's a"—he glares at me—"young, er, *person* downstairs asking to see you." His expression changes to one of disappointment as he glances my way. "Yes, thank you, sir. I'll send her right up."

And just when I think I've made it past that guard dog of a doorman, I'm confronted by yet another man in a uniform, who operates the elevator. Being the twentieth century and all, you'd think most people would have figured out how to press the button themselves, but apparently the occupants of Sutton Place are slightly feeble when it comes to technology.

"Can I help you?" he asks.

Not again. "Bernard Singer," I say. As he presses the button for the ninth floor, he clears his throat in disapproval. But at least he's not peppering me with questions.

The elevator doors fold open to reveal a small

hallway, another desk, another spray of flowers, and patterned wallpaper. There are two doors at either end of the corridor, and mercifully, Bernard is standing in one of them.

So this is the lair of a wunderkind, I think, taking a look around the apartment. It's surprising, all right. Not because of what's in it, but because of what isn't.

The living room, with its mullioned windows, cozy fireplace, and stately bookshelves, calls out for well-loved, well-worn furniture, but contains a single beanbag chair. Ditto for the dining room, which is populated by a Ping-Pong table and a couple of folding chairs. Then there's the bedroom: a king-size bed, a king-size television. On the bed itself, a lone sleeping bag.

"I love to watch TV in bed," Bernard says. "I think it's sexy, don't you?"

I'm about to give him a don't-even-try-it look, when I notice his expression. He seems sad.

"Did you just move in?" I ask brightly, searching for an explanation.

"Someone just moved out," he replies.

"Who?"

"My wife."

"You're married?" I shriek. Of all the possibilities, I never considered the one in which he might be hitched. What kind of married man invites a girl he just met to his apartment?

"My *ex*-wife," he corrects. "I keep forgetting we're not married. We got divorced a month ago and I'm still not used to it."

"So you *were* married?"

"For six years. But we were together for two before that."

Eight years? My eyes narrow as I do a quick calculation. If Bernard was in a relationship for that long, it means he has to be at least thirty. Or thirty-one. Or even . . . thirty-five?

When was his first play released? I remember reading about it, so I had to be at least ten. To cover up my ruminations, I quickly ask, "How was it?"

"How was what?"

"Your marriage."

"Well," he laughs. "Not so good. Considering we're divorced now."

It takes me a second to emotionally recalibrate. During the walk over, the far-off reaches of my imagination were constructing visions of Bernard and me together, but nowhere in that picture was there an ex-wife. I always figured my one true love would have only one true love, too—me. The fact of Bernard's previous marriage throws a real monkey wrench into my fantasy.

"And my wife took all the furniture. What about you?" he asks. "Have you ever been married?"

I look at him in astonishment. I'm barely old enough to drink, I nearly say. Instead, I shake my head as if I, too, have been disappointed in love.

"I guess we're both a couple of sad sacks," he says. I go along with his mood. I'm finding him particularly attractive at the moment and I'm hoping he'll put his arms around me and kiss me. I'm longing to be pressed up against that lean chest. I sit in the beanbag chair, instead.

"Why'd she take the furniture?" I ask.

"My wife?"

"I thought you were divorced," I say, trying to keep him on point.

"She's mad at me."

"Can't you make her give it back?"

"I don't think so. No."

"Why not?"

"She stubborn. Oh Lord. She's as stubborn as a mule on race day. Always has been. That's how she got so far."

"Hmmm." I roll around seductively on the beanbag.

My actions have their desired effect, that being why should he think about his ex-wife when he has a lovely young woman—me—to concentrate on instead? Sure enough, in the next second, he asks, "How about you? Are you hungry?"

"I'm always hungry."

"There's a little French place around the corner. We could go there."

"Terrific," I say, leaping to my feet, despite the fact that the word "French" reminds me of the restaurant I used to go to in Hartford with my old boyfriend, Sebastian, who dumped me for my best friend, Lali.

"You like French food?" he asks.

"Love it," I reply. Sebastian and Lali were a long time ago. And besides, I'm with Bernard Singer now, not some mixed-up high school boy.

The "little French place around the corner" turns out to be several blocks away. And it's not exactly "little." It's La Grenouille. Which is so famous, even I've heard of it.

Bernard ducks his head in embarrassment as the maître d'greets him by name. "Bonsoir, Monsieur Singer. We have your usual table."

I look at Bernard curiously. If he comes here all the time, why didn't he say he was a regular?

The maître d' picks up two menus and with an elegant tip of his head, leads us to a charming table by the window.

Then Mr. Monkey-suit pulls out my chair, unfolds my napkin, and places it on my lap. He rearranges my wine glasses, picks up a fork, inspects it, and, the fork having passed muster, replaces it next to my plate. Honestly, all the attention is disorienting. When the maître d' finally retreats, I look to Bernard for help.

He's studying the menu. "I don't speak French. Do you?" he asks.

"*Un peu.*"

"Really?"

"*Vraiment.*"

"You must have gone to a very fancy school. The only foreign language I learned was fisticuffs."

"Ha."

"I was pretty good at it too," he says, making jabbing motions in the air. "Had to be. I was this runt of a kid and everyone's favorite punching bag."

"But you're so tall," I point out.

"I didn't grow until I was eighteen. What about you?"

"I stopped growing when I was six."

"Hahaha. You're funny."

And just as the conversation is about to take off, the maître d' returns with a bottle of white wine. "Your Pouilly-Fuissé, Monsieur Singer."

"Oh, thanks," Bernard says, looking sheepish again. This is very odd. The apartment, the restaurant, the wine—surely Bernard is wealthy. Why, then, does he insist on acting like he's not? Or rather, that it's all a burden which he must somehow endure?

The wine pouring is yet another ritual. When it's over, I breathe a sigh of relief.

"It's annoying, isn't it?" Bernard says, echoing my thoughts.

"Why do you let them do it, then?"

"It makes them happy. If I didn't sniff the cork, they'd be very disappointed."

"You might even lose your special table."

"I've been trying to sit at that table"—he points to an empty table in the back of the room—"for years. But they won't let me. It's Siberia," he adds, in a dramatic whisper.

"Is it colder there?"

"Freezing."

"And what about this table?"

"Right on the equator." He pauses. "And you—you're on the equator too." He reaches out and takes my hand. "I like your gumption," he says.

The chef pulls out all the stops for Bernard. After a stomach-numbing meal of seven courses— including soup, a soufflé, two desserts, and some delicious after-dinner wine that tastes like ambrosia—I look at my watch and discover it's just after midnight. "I ought to go."

"Why? Will you turn into a pumpkin?"

"Something like that," I say, thinking about Peggy.

His next move hangs in the air, spinning like a lazy disco ball. "I suppose I should walk you home," he says finally.

"And ruin all this?" I laugh.

"I haven't done 'this' for a while. What about you?"

"Oh, I'm an expert," I tease.

We walk back to my building, swinging our hands between us.

"Good night, pussycat," he says, stopping in front of my door. We stand awkwardly, until he makes his move. He tilts up my chin and leans in for a kiss. It's gentle and civilized at first, then more and more urgent, ending just before some imaginary line of lust is crossed.

The kiss leaves me swooning. Bernard looks at me longingly, but settles for a gentlemanly peck on the cheek and a squeeze of my hand. "I'll call you tomorrow, okay?"

"Okay." I can barely breathe.

I watch him stroll off into the night. At the corner, he turns and waves. When he's disappeared completely, I slip inside.

I creep down the hallway to the apartment, brushing my fingers against the pea-green wall for support, wondering why anyone would paint a hallway such an ugly color. At the door, I carefully insert my key into the first lock. The bolt drops with an alarming ping.

I hold my breath, wondering if Peggy has heard the sound, and if so, what she'll do. But when I don't hear anything for several seconds, I try the next lock.

It, too, turns easily, which means I should now be able to enter the apartment. I twist the knob and try to ease open the door, but it won't move.

Huh? Maybe Peggy didn't lock the door after all and I've ended up locking it instead. It doesn't seem like something Peggy would do, but I try turning the locks in the opposite direction just to make sure.

No luck. The door moves precisely one-sixteenth of an inch, and then refuses to budge, as if someone has shoved a heavy piece of furniture in front of it.

The dead bolt, I think, with rising panic. It's a metal bar that runs across the door and can only be opened and closed from inside the apartment. We're supposed to use it strictly in an emergency, like a nuclear war or a blackout or a zombie attack. But apparently Peggy has decided to break her own stupid rule and has locked it to teach me a lesson.

Crap. I have to either wake her up or sleep in the hallway.

I scratch on the door. "L'il?" I hiss, hoping L'il is awake and will hear me. "L'il?"

Nothing.

I slump to the floor, resting my back against the wall. Does Peggy really hate me that much? And why? What have I ever done to her?

Another half hour passes, and I give up. I curl into a ball with my Carrie bag nestled between my arms, and try to get some sleep.

And then I guess I do fall asleep, because the next thing I hear is L'il whispering, "Carrie? Are you okay?"

I open my eyes, wondering where the hell I am, and what the hell I'm doing in the hallway.

And then I remember: Peggy and her damn dead bolt.

L'il puts her finger to her lips and motions for me to come inside.

"Thanks," I mouth. She nods as we quietly shut the door. I pause, listening for sounds of Peggy, but there's only silence.

I turn the knob on the bolt and lock us inside.

CHAPTER SIX

The next morning, triumphant, perhaps, in her perceived victory, Peggy sleeps until nine. This allows the Prisoners of Second Avenue a much-needed extra hour of shut-eye.

But once Peggy's up, she's up. And while early-morning silence has never been her forte, this morning she appears to be in an especially good mood.

She's singing show tunes.

I turn over on my cot, and rap quietly on the plywood. L'il raps back, indicating she's awake and has heard the singing as well.

I slide under the sheet and pull the covers up to my nose. Maybe if I lie flat on my bed and put the pillow over my head, Peggy won't notice me.

It was a trick my sisters and I perfected when we were kids. But I'm quite a bit bigger now, and Peggy, with her beady crow eyes, is sure to notice the lumps. Perhaps I could hide under my cot?

This, I decide, is beyond ridiculous.

I won't have it. I'm going to confront Peggy. And full of brio, I hop out of bed and put my ear to the door.

The shower is running, and above that, I can hear Peggy's particularly grating rendition of "I Feel Pretty" from *West Side Story*.

I wait, my hand on the doorknob.

Finally, the water stops. I imagine Peggy toweling herself off and applying creams to her body. She carries her toiletries to and from the bathroom in a plastic shower basket she keeps in her room. It's yet another deliberate reminder that no one is to use her precious possessions on the sly.

When I hear the bathroom door open, I step out into the living room. "Good morning, Peggy."

Her hair is wrapped in a pink towel, and she's wearing a worn chenille robe and fluffy slippers in the shape of bears. At the sound of my voice, she throws up her arms, nearly dropping her basket of toiletries. "You almost scared me to death."

"Sorry," I say. "If you're finished in the bathroom—"

Perhaps Peggy's not such a bad actress after all,

because she immediately recovers. "I need it back in a minute. I have to dry my hair."

"No problem." We stand there, wondering who's going to bring up the locking-out issue first. I say nothing and neither does Peggy. Then she gives me a shrewd, vicious smile and goes into her room.

She's not going to mention it.

On the other hand, she doesn't have to. She made her point.

I trip into the bathroom. If she isn't going to say anything to me, I'm certainly not going to say anything to her.

When I exit, Peggy is standing there with a blow-dryer in her hand. "Excuse me," I say as I wriggle past her.

She goes back into the bathroom and shuts the door.

While the apartment is filled with the buzz of the dryer, I take the opportunity to check in on L'il. She's so tiny, she looks like a doll someone laid under the comforter, her round face as pale as porcelain.

"She's drying her hair," I report.

"You should sneak in there and drop her blow-dryer into the sink."

I tilt my head. The whirring has suddenly ceased, and I skittle back to my cell. I quickly plop myself in the chair in front of my mother's old Royal typewriter.

A few seconds later, Peggy's behind me. I just love the way she insists we respect her privacy, yet doesn't believe we deserve the same, barging into our rooms whenever she feels like it.

She's slurping down her ubiquitous can of Tab. It must be like mother's milk to her—good for any occasion, including breakfast.

"I've got an audition this afternoon, so I'll need quiet in the apartment while I'm practicing." She eyes my typewriter doubtfully. "I hope you're not planning on using that noisy thing. You need to get an electric typewriter. Like everyone else."

"I'd love to, but I can't exactly afford one right now," I reply, trying to keep the sarcasm out of my tone.

"That's not my problem, is it?" she says with more saccharine than an entire six-pack of diet soda.

"It's that *little* itch." Pause. "No. It's *that* little itch.

"Damn. It's that little *itch*."

Yes, it's true. Peggy is auditioning for a hemorrhoid commercial.

"What did you expect?" L'il mouths. "Breck?" She checks her appearance in a hand mirror, carefully dabbing her cheeks with a pot of blush.

"Where are you going?" I hiss in outrage, as if I can't believe she's going to abandon me to Peggy and her little itch.

"Out," she says, mysteriously.

"But where?" And then, feeling like Oliver Twist asking for more grub, I say, "Can I come?"

L'il is suddenly flustered. "You can't. I have to—"

"What?"

"See someone," she says firmly.

"Who?"

"A friend of my mother's. She's very old. She's in the hospital. She can't have visitors."

"How come she can see you?"

L'il blushes, holding up the mirror as if to block my inquiries. "I'm like family," she says, fiddling with her lashes. "What are you doing today?"

"Haven't decided," I grumble, eyeing her suspiciously. "Don't you want to hear about my evening with Bernard?"

"Of course. How was it?"

"Incredibly interesting. His ex-wife took all his furniture. Then we went to La Grenouille."

"That's nice." L'il is annoyingly distracted this morning. I wonder if it's due to Peggy locking me out—or something else entirely. I'm sure she's lying about her mother's sick friend, though. Who puts on blush and mascara to go to a hospital?

But then I don't care, because I get an idea.

I dash into my cubbyhole and come back with my Carrie bag. I rifle through it and pull out a piece of paper. "I'm going to see Samantha Jones."

"Who's that?" L'il murmurs.

"The woman who let me stay at her apartment?" I ask, trying to jog her memory. "Donna LaDonna's cousin? She lent me twenty dollars. I'm going to pay her back." This, of course, is merely an excuse. Both to get out of the apartment and to talk to Samantha about Bernard.

"Good idea." L'il puts down the mirror and smiles, as if she hasn't heard a word I've said.

I open my bag to replace the paper, and find the folded-up invitation to the party at The Puck Building, which I wave in L'il's face. "That party is tonight. We should go." And maybe, if Bernard calls, he could come with us.

L'il looks skeptical. "I'm sure there's a party every night in New York."

"I'm sure there is," I counter. "And I plan to go to every one."

Samantha's steel and glass office building is a forbidding bastion of serious business. The lobby is sharply air-conditioned, with all manner of people rushing about, harassed and irritated. I find the name of Samantha's company—Slovey,

Dinall Advertising—and board an elevator for the twenty-sixth floor.

The elevator ride actually makes me a little queasy. I've never ridden an elevator so high up. What if something happens and we crash to the ground?

But no one else seems the least concerned. Everyone has their eyes turned to the numbers that tick off the floors, their faces intentionally blank, deliberately ignoring the fact that there are at least half a dozen people in the space of a large closet. This must be elevator protocol, and I attempt to copy their demeanor.

But I don't quite get it right, because I actually manage to catch the eye of a middle-aged woman holding a sheaf of folders in front of her chest. I smile, and she quickly looks away.

Then it occurs to me that popping in unexpectedly on Samantha in her place of work might not be the best idea. Nevertheless, when the elevator opens on her floor, I get out and bump around in the softly carpeted hallway until I find two enormous doors with SLOVEY, DINALL ADVERTISING INCORPORATED etched into the glass. On the other side is a large desk behind which sits a small woman with black hair that rises in sharp spikes. She takes in my appearance, and after a beat, says, "Can I help you," in a doubtful, grating tone that sounds like her nose is speaking instead of her mouth.

This is very disconcerting, and in a hesitant voice intended to convey the fact that I hope I'm not bothering her, I say, "Samantha Jones? I just want to—"

I'm about to say I want to leave the twenty dollars for her in an envelope, but the woman waves me to a seat and picks up the phone. "Someone's here for Samantha," she whines into the receiver. Then she asks for my name and nods. "Her assistant will be out to get you," she says wearily. She picks up a paperback book and starts reading.

The reception area is decorated with posters of advertisements, some of which appear to go back to the 1950s. I'm kind of surprised that Samantha Jones has her own assistant. She doesn't look old enough to be anyone's boss, but I guess Donna LaDonna was right when she said her cousin was a "big deal in advertising."

In a few minutes, a young woman appears, wearing a navy suit, a light blue shirt with two straps tied around her neck in a loose bow, and blue running shoes.

"Follow me," she commands. I jump up and trot behind her, through a maze of cubicles, ringing telephones, and the sound of a man shouting.

"Seems like everyone around here is pretty

cranky," I wisecrack.

"That's because we are," she snaps, coming to a halt by the open door of a small office. "Except for Samantha," she adds. "She's *always* in a good mood."

Samantha looks up and waves at the chair in front of her. She's seated behind a white Formica table, wearing an outfit that's nearly identical to her assistant's, with the exception of her shoulder pads, which are much wider. Perhaps the wider your shoulder pads, the more important you are. Her head is cocked against an enormous phone cradle. "Yes, of course, Glenn," she says, making a yakking motion with her hand. "The Century Club is perfect. But I don't see why we have to have flower arrangements in the shape of base-balls. . . . Well, I know it's what Charlie wants, but I've always thought the wedding was supposed to be the bride's day. . . . Yes, of course. . . . I'm sorry, Glenn, but I have a meeting. I really have to go," she continues, with mounting frustration. "I'll call you later. I promise." And with a roll of her eyes, she firmly replaces the receiver, looks up, and tosses her head.

"Charlie's mother," she explains. "We've been engaged for about two minutes and already she's driving me crazy. If I ever get married again, I'm going to skip the engagement completely and go right to City Hall. The minute you get engaged, you become public property."

"But then you wouldn't have the ring," I say awkwardly, suddenly intimidated by Samantha, her office, and her glamorous life.

"I suppose that's true," she concedes. "Now if I could only find someone to sublet my apartment—"

"Aren't you moving in with Charlie?"

"My God. You really are a sparrow. When you have an apartment like mine, rent-controlled and only two hundred and twenty-five dollars a month, you don't ever give it up."

"Why not?"

"Because real estate is impossible in this town. And I might need it back someday. If things don't work out with Charlie. I'm not saying they *won't*, but you never know with men in New York. They're spoiled. They're like kids in a candy store. If you have a good deal—well, naturally, you want to hang on to it."

"Like Charlie?" I ask, wondering if he's a good deal as well.

She smiles. "You catch on quick, Sparrow. As a matter of fact, Charlie is a good deal. Even if he is a baseball freak. He wanted to be a player himself, but of course, his father wouldn't let him."

I nod encouragingly. Samantha seems to be in

a mood to talk, and I'm like a sponge, ready to absorb anything she says. "His father?"

"Alan Tier."

When I look at her blankly, she adds, "The Tiers? The mega real estate family?" She shakes her head as if I'm hopeless. "Charlie is the oldest son. His father expects him to take over the business."

"I see."

"And it's about time. *You* know how it is with men," she says, as if I, too, am some kind of guy expert. "If a man doesn't ask you to marry him—or at least live with him—after two years, he never will. It means he's only interested in having a good time." She folds her arms and puts her feet on the desk. "I'm as interested in having a good time as any man, but the difference between me and Charlie is that my clock is ticking. And his isn't."

Clocks? Ticking? I have no idea what she's talking about, but I keep mum, nodding my head as if I understand.

"He may not have a timetable, but I do." She holds up her hand and ticks off the moments on her fingers. "Married by twenty-five. Corner office by thirty. And somewhere in there—*children*. So when that bachelor story came out, I decided it was time to do something about Charlie. Speed things along."

She pushes aside some papers on her desk to

retrieve a battered copy of *New York Magazine*.

"Here." She holds it out. The headline reads, NEW YORK'S MOST ELIGIBLE BACHELORS, above a photograph of several men standing on bleachers like a sports team in a high school yearbook. "That's Charlie," she says, pointing to a man whose face is partially hidden by a baseball cap. "I told him not to wear that stupid cap, but he wouldn't listen."

"Do people still care about this stuff?" I ask. "I mean, aren't debutantes and eligible bachelors sort of over?"

Samantha laughs. "You really are a rube, kiddo. If only it *didn't* matter. But it does."

"All right—"

"So I broke up with him."

I smile knowingly. "But if you wanted to be with him—"

"It's all about getting the guy to realize he wants to be with *you*." She swings her feet off the desk and comes around to the side. I sit up, aware that I'm about to receive a valuable lesson in man management.

"When it comes to men," she begins, "it's all about their egos. So when I broke up with Charlie, he was furious. Couldn't believe I'd leave him. Giving him no choice but to come crawling after me. Naturally, I resisted. 'Charlie,' I said. 'You know how crazy I am about you, but if I don't respect myself, who will? If you really care about me—I mean me as a person and not just as a lover—then you're going to have to prove it. You're going to have to *make a commitment*.'"

"And did he?" I ask, on the edge of my seat.

"Well, obviously," she says, waving her ringed finger. "And it didn't hurt that the Yankees are on strike."

"The Yankees?"

"Like I said, he's obsessed. You don't know how many baseball games I've had to sit through in the last two years. I'm more of a football girl, but I kept telling myself that someday, it'd be worth it. And it was. With no baseball, Charlie didn't have anything to distract him. And voilà," she says, indicating her hand.

I take the opportunity to mention Bernard. "Did you know Bernard Singer was married?"

"Of course. He was married to Margie Shephard. The actress. Why? Did you see him?"

"Last night," I say, blushing.

"And?"

"We kissed."

"That's it?" She sounds disappointed.

I squirm in my chair. "I only just met him."

"Bernard's a bit of a mess right now. Which is not surprising. Margie walked all over him. Cheated on him with one of the actors in his play."

"You're kidding," I say, aghast.

Samantha shrugs. "It was in all the papers so it's hardly a secret. Not very nice for Bernard, but I always say there's no such thing as bad publicity. Besides, New York is a small town. Smaller than small, if you really think about it."

I nod carefully. Our interview seems to be over. "I wanted to return the twenty dollars you gave me," I say quickly, digging around in my pocket. I pull out a twenty-dollar bill and hand it to her.

She takes the bill and smiles. And then she laughs. I suddenly wish I could laugh like that— knowing and tinkling at the same time.

"I'm surprised," she says. "I wasn't expecting to see you, or my twenty dollars, ever again."

"And I wanted to thank you. For lending me the money. And for taking me to the party. And for introducing me to Bernard. If there's anything I can do—"

"Not a thing," she says, rising to her feet.

She walks me to the door and holds out her hand. "Good luck. And if you need to borrow another twenty sometime—well, you know where to find me."

"Are you sure nobody called?" I ask L'il for the twentieth time.

"I've been here since two. The phone didn't ring once."

"He might have called. While you were visiting your mother's friend. In the hospital."

"Peggy was home then," L'il points out.

"But maybe he did call and Peggy didn't tell me. On purpose."

L'il gives her hair a firm brush. "Why would Peggy do that?"

"Because she hates me?" I ask, rubbing my lips with gloss.

"You only saw him last night," L'il says. "Guys never call the next day. They like to keep you guessing."

"I don't like to be kept guessing. And he said he would call—" I break off as the phone rings. "It's him!" I yelp. "Can you get it?"

"Why?" L'il grumbles.

"Because I don't want to seem too eager. I don't want him to think I've been sitting by the phone all day."

"Even though you have?" But she picks up the phone anyway. I wait in anticipation as she nods and holds out the receiver. "It's your father."

Of course. His timing couldn't be worse. I called him yesterday and left a message with Missy, but he didn't call back. What if Bernard tries to call while I'm talking to my father and it's busy? "Hi, Dad," I sigh.

"Hi, Dad? Is that how you greet your father? Whom you haven't called once since you got to New York?"

"I did call you, Dad." My father, I note, sounds slightly strange. Not only is he in a really good mood, he doesn't seem to remember that I tried to reach him. Which is fine by me. So many things have happened since I've arrived in New York—not all of which my father would consider good—that I've been dreading this conversation. Unnecessarily, it seems.

"I've been really busy," I say.

"I'm sure you have."

"But everything's great."

"Glad to hear it," he says. "Now that I know you're still alive, I can rest easy." And with a quick good-bye, he hangs up.

This really is odd. My father has always been distracted, but he's never been this enthusiastic *and* removed. I tell myself it's only because my father, like most men, hates talking on the phone.

"Are you ready?" L'il demands. "You're the one who wanted to go to this party. And we can't get home too late. I don't want Peggy locking both of us out this time."

"I'm ready," I sigh. I grab my Carrie bag, and with one last, longing look at the phone, follow her out.

A few minutes later, we're strolling down Second Avenue in a flurry of giggles as we do our best Peggy imitations.

"I'm so glad I got you as a roommate," L'il says, taking my arm.

There's a line in front of the entrance to the Puck Building, but by now we've realized that in New York, there's a line for everything. We've already passed three lines on Second Avenue: two in front of movie theaters, and one for a cheese shop. Neither L'il nor I could understand why so many people felt they needed cheese at nine p.m., but chalked it up to yet another fascinating mystery about Manhattan.

We get through the line pretty quick, though, and find ourselves in an enormous room filled with what appears to be every variety of young person. There are rocker types in leather and punk kids with piercings and crazy-colored hair. Tracksuits and heavy gold chains and shiny gold watches. A glittering disco ball spins from the ceiling, but the music is something I've never heard, discordant and haunting and insistent, the kind of music that demands you dance. "Let's get a drink," I shout to L'il. We make our way to the side, where I've spotted a makeshift bar set up on a long plywood table.

"Hey!" a voice exclaims. It's the arrogant blond guy from our class. Capote Duncan. He has his arm around a tall, painfully thin girl with cheekbones like icebergs. Who must be a model, I think, in annoyance, realizing that maybe L'il was right about Capote's ability to get girls.

"I was just saying to Sandy here," he says, in a slight Southern accent, indicating the startled girl next to him, "that this party is like something out of *Swann's Way*."

"Actually, I was thinking Henry James," L'il shouts back.

"Who's Henry James?" the girl named Sandy asks. "Is he here?"

Capote smiles as if the girl has said something charming and tightens his grip around her shoulders. "No, but he could be if you wanted."

Now I know I was right. Capote is an asshole. And since no one is paying attention to me anyway, I figure I'll get a drink on my own and catch up with L'il later.

I turn away, and that's when I spot her. The red-haired girl from Saks. The girl who found my Carrie bag.

"Hi!" I say, frantically waving my arm as if I've

discovered an old friend.

"Hi what?" she asks, put out, taking a sip of beer.

"It's me, remember? Carrie Bradshaw. You found my bag." I hold the bag up to her face to remind her.

"Oh, right," she says, unimpressed.

She doesn't seem inclined to continue the conversation, but for some reason, I do. I suddenly have a desire to placate her. To make her like me.

"Why do you do that, anyway?" I ask. "That protesting thing?"

She looks at me arrogantly, as if she can hardly be bothered to answer the question. "Because it's important?"

"Oh."

"And I work at the battered women's center. You should volunteer sometime. It'll shake you out of your secure little world," she says loudly over the music.

"But . . . doesn't it make you think all men are bad?"

"No. Because I *know* all men are bad."

I have no idea why I'm even having this conversation. But I can't seem to let it—or her—go. "What about being in love? I mean, how can you have a boyfriend or husband knowing this stuff?"

"Good question." She takes another sip of her

beer and looks around the room, glaring.

"I meant what I said," I shout, trying to regain her attention. "About thanking you. Could I buy you a cup of coffee or something? I want to hear more about . . . what you do."

"Really?" she asks, dubious.

I nod enthusiastically.

"Okay," she says, giving in. "I guess you could call me."

"What's your name?"

She hesitates. "Miranda Hobbes. H-o-b-b-e-s. You can get my number from information."

And as she walks away, I nod, making a dialing motion with my finger.

CHAPTER SEVEN

"It's Chinese silk. From the 1930s."

I finger the blue material lovingly and turn it over. There's a gold dragon stitched on the back. The robe is probably way more than I can afford, but I try it on anyway. The sleeves hang at my sides like folded wings. I could really fly in this.

"That looks good on you," the salesman adds. Although "salesman" is probably not the right word for a guy in a porkpie hat, plaid pants, and a black Ramones T-shirt. "Purveyor" might be more appropriate. Or "dealer."

I'm in a vintage clothing store called My Old Lady. The name of which turns out to be startlingly appropriate.

"Where do you get this stuff?" I ask, reluctant

to remove the robe but too scared to ask the price.

The owner shrugs. "People bring things in. Mostly from their old relatives who have died. One man's trash is another one's treasure."

"Or one woman's," I correct him. I screw up my courage. "How much is this, anyway?"

"For you? Five dollars."

"Oh." I slide my arms out of the sleeves.

He wags his head back and forth, considering. "What can you pay?"

"Three dollars?"

"Three fifty," he says. "That old thing's been sitting around for months. I need to get rid of it."

"Done!" I exclaim.

I exit the store still wearing the robe, and head back up to Peggy's.

This morning, when I tried to face the typewriter, I once again drew a blank. *Family.* I thought I could write about my own, but they suddenly felt as foreign to me as French people. French people made me think of La Grenouille, and that made me think about Bernard. And how he still hasn't called. I considered calling him, but told myself not to be weak. Another hour passed, in which I clipped my toenails, braided and unbraided my hair, and scanned my face for blackheads.

"What are you doing?" L'il demanded.

"I've got writer's block."

"There's no such thing as writer's block," she proclaimed. "If you can't write it's because you don't have anything to say. Or you're avoiding something."

"Hmph," I said, squeezing my skin, wondering if maybe I just wasn't a writer after all.

"Don't do that," L'il yelped. "You'll only make it worse. Why don't you go for a walk or something?"

So I did. And I knew exactly where to go. Down to Samantha's neighborhood, where I'd spotted the vintage store on Seventh Avenue.

I catch my reflection in a plate-glass window and stop to admire the robe. I hope it will bring me good luck and I'll be able to write. I'm getting nervous. I don't want to end up in Viktor's 99.9 percent of failed students.

"My Lord!" L'il exclaims. "You look like something the cat dragged in."

"I feel like something the cat dragged in. But look what I got." I spin around to show off my new purchase.

L'il appears doubtful, and I realize how flaky I must seem, shopping instead of writing. Why do I keep evading my work? Is it because I'm afraid of being confronted by my lack of abilities?

I collapse onto the love seat and gently ease off my sandals. "It was about fifty blocks away and my feet are killing me. But it was worth it," I add, trying to convince myself.

"I finished my poem," L'il says casually.

I smile, biting back envy. Am I the only one who has to struggle? L'il doesn't seem to labor at all. But that's probably because she's way more talented.

"And I got some Chinese food, too," she says. "Moo shu pork. There's plenty left over if you want some."

"Oh, L'il. I don't want to eat your food."

"No need to stand on ceremony." She shrugs. "Besides, you've got to eat. How can you work if you're hungry?"

She's right. And it will give me a few more minutes to put off writing.

L'il sits on my bed as I polish off the moo shu pork straight from the carton.

"Don't you ever get scared?" I ask.

"Of what?" she says.

"Of not being good enough."

"You mean at writing?" L'il asks.

I nod. "What if I'm the only one who thinks I can do it and no one else does? What if I'm completely fooling myself—"

"Oh, Carrie." She smiles. "Don't you know

that every writer feels that way? Fear is part of the job."

She picks up her towel to take a long bath, and while she's in the bathroom, I manage to eke out one page, and then two. I type in a title, "Home." I cross it out and write, "My New Home." This somehow reminds me of Samantha Jones. I picture her in her four-poster bed, wearing fancy lingerie and eating chocolates, which, for some strange reason, is how I imagine she spends her weekends.

I push these thoughts out of my head and try to focus, but now the throbbing in my feet is overwhelming and I can't concentrate for the pain.

"L'il?" I knock on the bathroom door. "Do you have any aspirin?"

"I don't think so," she calls out.

"Damn." Peggy must have aspirin somewhere. "Can I come in?" I ask. L'il is in the shallow tub, under a soft pile of bubbles. I check the medicine cabinet. Nothing. I look around, my gaze resting on the closed door to Peggy's bedroom.

Don't do it, I think, remembering Peggy's one final rule. We're not allowed into her room. Ever. Under any circumstances. Her bedroom is strictly verboten.

I carefully open the door.

"What are you doing?" L'il shrieks, jumping out of the tub and grabbing her towel. Remnants of bubbles cling to her shoulders.

I put my finger to my lips to shush her. "I'm only looking for aspirin. Peggy's so cheap, she probably keeps the aspirin hidden in her room."

"What if she realizes some of her aspirin is missing?"

"Even Peggy can't be that crazy." I push the door wider. "You'd have to be really wacky to count your aspirin. Besides," I hiss, "aren't you dying to know what her room's like?"

The blinds are drawn, so it takes a second for my eyes to adjust. When they do, I squeal in horror.

Peggy's bed is covered with bears. Not real bears, of course, but what appears to be every variation on the stuffed animal kind. There are big bears and small bears, bears holding tennis rackets and bears wearing aprons. Bears with pink fur and bears with earmuffs. There's even a bear that appears to be constructed entirely of clothespins.

"That's her big secret?" L'il asks, disappointed. "Bears?"

"She's a middle-aged woman. What kind of middle-aged woman has stuffed animals all over her room?"

"Maybe she collects them," L'il says. "People do, you know."

"Not normal people." I pick up the pink bear

and hold it in front of L'il's face. "Hello," I say, in a funny voice. "My name is Peggy and I'd like to explain a few of my rules. But first I need to put on my rubber suit—"

"Carrie, stop," L'il pleads, but it's too late. We're already in stitches.

"Aspirin," I remind her. "If you were Peggy, where would you keep it?" My eye goes to the top drawer in Peggy's bedside table. Like everything else in the apartment, it's cheap, and when I tug on the knob, the whole drawer flies out, spilling the contents onto the floor.

"Now she's going to kill us for sure," L'il moans.

"We won't tell her," I say, scrambling to pick up the pieces. "Besides, it's only a bunch of pictures." I begin gathering the snapshots when I'm startled by what seems to be an image of a naked breast.

I take a closer look.

Then I scream and drop the picture like it's on fire.

"What is it?" L'il shouts.

I sit down on the floor, shaking my head in disbelief. I pick up the photograph and examine it more closely, still not convinced. But it's exactly what I thought it was. I shuffle through the other photographs, trying to suppress my laughter. They're of Peggy, all right, but in each and every one of them she's buck naked.

And not just any old naked. She's arranged herself like a model in a porn magazine.

Unfortunately, she doesn't exactly look like one. "L'il?" I ask, wanting to delve into this mystery of why Peggy would have posed for these photographs and who might have taken them, but L'il is gone. I hear a faint thud as the door to her room closes, followed by the louder bang of the front door. And before I have a chance to move, Peggy is standing over me.

We both freeze. Peggy's eyes get bigger and bigger as her face turns from red to purple and I wonder if her head is going to explode. She opens her mouth and raises her arm.

The photograph falls from my fingers as I shrink back in fear.

"Get out! Get out!" she screams, swatting at my head. I drop to my hands and knees, and before she can figure out what's happening, crawl between her legs to the hall. I stand up, run to my room, and shut the door.

She immediately yanks it open. "Listen, Peggy—" I begin, but really, what can I say? Besides, she's shouting too much for me to get a word in.

"The minute I laid eyes on you, I knew you were trouble. Who do you think you are, coming into my home and going through my things? Where did you grow up? In a barn? What kind of animal are you?"

"A bear?" I want to say. But she's right. I did violate her privacy. I knew it was wrong and I did it anyway. It was worth it to see those naked photos, though.

"I want you, and your stuff, out of here now!"

"But—"

"You should have thought about your 'buts' before you went into my room," she snaps, which doesn't help much, because after seeing those photographs, all I *can* think about is her butt. Indeed, I'm so absorbed by the image, I hardly notice her segue into how good it will be for me to spend a night or two on the streets.

The next thing I know, she's pulling my suitcase out from under the bed and heaving it onto the mattress. "Start packing," she orders. "I'm going out for twenty minutes and when I get back, you'd better be gone. If you're not, I'm calling the police."

She grabs her purse and storms out.

I stand there in shock. The plywood door opens and L'il comes in, white as a sheet.

"Oh, Lord, Carrie," she whispers. "What are you going to do?"

"Leave," I say, picking up a pile of my clothes

and dumping them into the suitcase.

"But where will you go? This is New York City. It's night and it's dangerous. You can't be out there on your own. What if you're attacked or end up dead? Maybe you could go to the YMCA—"

I'm suddenly angry. At Peggy and her irrationality. "I have plenty of places to go."

"Like where?"

Good question.

I slip on the Chinese robe for good luck and snap my suitcase shut. L'il looks dazed, as if she can't believe I'm going to carry through with my plan. I give her a wan smile and a brief hug. My stomach is clenched in fear, but I'm determined not to back down.

L'il follows me to the street, begging me to stay. "You can't just leave with no place to go."

"Honestly, L'il. I'll be fine," I insist, with way more confidence than I actually feel.

I hold out my arm and hail a cab.

"Carrie! Don't," L'il pleads as I shove my suitcase and typewriter into the backseat.

The cab driver turns around. "Where to?"

I close my eyes and grimace.

Thirty minutes later, stuck outside in the torrential rain of a thunderstorm, I wonder what I was thinking.

Samantha's not home. In the back of my mind, I guess I was figuring if Samantha wasn't there, I could always go to Bernard's and throw myself on his mercy. But now, having splurged on one cab, I don't have enough money for another.

A rivulet of water runs down the back of my neck. My robe is soaked and I'm scared and miserable but I attempt to convince myself that everything is going to be all right. I imagine the rain washing the city clean, and washing Peggy away with it.

But another rumble of thunder changes my mind, and suddenly I'm being attacked by pin-pricks of ice. The rain has turned to hail and I need to find shelter.

I drag my suitcase around the corner, where I spot a small, glass-fronted shop at the bottom of a short flight of steps. At first, I'm not sure it even is a store, but then I see a big sign that reads, NO CHANGE—DO NOT EVEN ASK. I peer through the glass and spot a shelf dotted with candy bars. I pull open the door and go inside.

A strange, hairless man who looks quite a bit like a boiled beet is sitting on a stool behind a Plexiglas barrier. There's a small opening cut into the plastic where you can slide your money across the counter. I'm dripping all over the floor, but the man doesn't seem to mind. "What can I get for you, girlie?" he asks.

I look around in confusion. The store is even tinier on the inside than it looked from the outside. The walls are thin and there's a door in the back that's bolted shut.

I shiver. "How much for a Hershey's bar?"

"Twenty-five cents."

I reach into my pocket and extract a quarter, sliding it through the slot. I pick out a candy bar and start to unwrap it. It's pretty dusty, and I immediately feel sorry for the man. Apparently he doesn't have much business. I wonder how he's able to survive.

Then I wonder if *I'm* going to be able to survive. What if Samantha doesn't come home? What if she goes to Charlie's apartment instead?

No. She has to come home. She just *has to*. I close my eyes and picture her leaning against her desk. *You really are a sparrow*, she says.

And then, as if I've willed it to happen, a cab stops on the corner and Samantha gets out. She's clutching her briefcase across her chest, her head ducked against the rain, when suddenly, she stops, looking defeated. By the weather and, just possibly, by something else.

"Hey!" I yank open the door and race toward her, waving my arms. "It's me!"

"Huh?" She's startled, but quickly regains her

composure. "You," she says, wiping the rain from her face. "What are you doing here?"

I muster up my last ounce of confidence. I shrug, as if I'm used to standing on corners in the rain. "I was wondering—"

"You got kicked out of your apartment," she says.

"How did you know?"

She laughs. "The suitcase and the fact that you're soaked to the skin. Besides, that's what always happens to sparrows. Jesus, Carrie. What am I going to do with you?"

CHAPTER EIGHT

"You're alive!" L'il throws her arms around my neck.

"Of course I am," I say, as if getting kicked out of an apartment happens to me all the time. We're standing in front of The New School, waiting to go in.

"I was worried." She steps back to give me a searching once-over. "You don't look so good."

"Hangover," I explain. "Couldn't be helped."

"Did you finish your story?"

I laugh. My voice sounds like it's been scraped over the sidewalk. "Hardly."

"You'll have to tell Viktor what happened."

"*Viktor?* Since when did you start calling him by his first name?"

"It's his name, isn't it?" She starts into the building ahead of me.

I was beyond relieved when Samantha showed up and rescued me, explaining how she'd decided to give Charlie the night off to keep him guessing. And I was thrilled when I realized Charlie's night off meant Samantha's night out, and that she expected me to accompany her. It wasn't until I discovered that Samantha's night out literally meant *all* night that I began to get worried.

First we went to a place called One Fifth. The inside was a replica of a cruise ship, and even though it was technically a restaurant, no one was eating. Apparently, no one actually eats in trendy restaurants because you're only supposed to be *seen* in them. The bartender bought us drinks, and then two guys started buying us drinks, and then someone decided we should all go to this club, Xenon, where everyone was purple under the black lights. It was pretty funny because no one was acting like they were purple, and just when I was getting used to it, Samantha found some other people who were going to a club called The Saint, so we all piled into taxis and went there. The ceiling was painted like the sky, illuminated by tiny lights over a revolving dance floor that spun like a record, and people kept falling down. Then I got caught up dancing with a bunch of guys who were wearing wigs and lost Samantha but found her again in the bathroom, where you could hear people having sex. I danced on top of a speaker and one of my shoes fell off and I couldn't find it, and Samantha made me leave without it because she said she was hungry, and we were in a taxi again with more people, and Samantha made the driver stop at a twenty-four-hour drugstore in Chinatown to see if they had shoes. Mysteriously, they did but they were bamboo flip-flops. I tried them on along with a pointy hat, which was apparently so hilarious, everyone else had to have bamboo flip-flops and pointy hats as well. Finally, we managed to get back into the taxi, which took us to a metal diner where we ate scrambled eggs.

I think we got home around five a.m. I was too scared to look at my watch, but the birds were singing. Who knew there were so many damn birds in New York? I figured I'd never be able to sleep with the racket, so I got up and started typing. About fifteen minutes later Samantha came out of her room, pushing a velvet sleeping mask onto her forehead.

"Carrie," she said. "What are you *doing*?"

"Writing?"

"Can you please save it for morning?" She groaned in pain. "Plus, I've got terrible cramps. They don't call it 'the curse' for nothing."

"Sure," I said, flustered. The last thing I needed was to annoy her or her cramps.

Now, following L'il's neat head up the stairs to class, I'm racked with guilt. I need to start writing. I have to get serious.

I only have fifty-six days left.

I run after L'il and tap her on the shoulder. "Did Bernard call?"

She shakes her head and gives me a pitying look.

Today we're treated to the pleasure of Capote Duncan's work. It's the last thing I need, considering my condition. I rest my head in my hand, wondering how I'm going to get through this class.

"'She held the razor between her fingers. A piece of glass. A piece of ice. A savior. The sun was a moon. The ice became snow as she slipped away, a pilgrim lost in a blizzard.'" Capote adjusts his glasses and smiles, pleased with himself.

"Thank you, Capote," Viktor Greene says. He's slumped in a chair in the back of the room.

"You're welcome," Capote says, as if he's just done us an enormous favor. I study him closely in an attempt to discover what L'il and, supposedly, hundreds of other women in New York, including models, see in him. He does have surprisingly masculine hands, the kind of hands that look like they'd know how to sail a boat or hammer a nail or pull you up from the edge of a steep rock face. Too bad he doesn't have the personality to match.

"Any comments on Capote's story?" Viktor asks. I turn around to give Capote a dirty look. Yes, I want to say. I have a response. It sucked. I actually feel like I might puke. There's nothing I hate more than some cheesy romantic story about a perfect girl who every guy is in love with and then she kills herself. Because she's so tragic. When in reality, she's just crazy. But, of course, the guy can't see that. All he can see is her beauty. And her sadness.

Guys can be so stupid.

"Who is this girl again?" Ryan asks, with a touch of skepticism that tells me I'm not alone in my thinking.

Capote stiffens. "My sister. I thought that was pretty apparent from the beginning."

"I guess I missed it," Ryan says. "I mean, the way you write about her—she doesn't sound like your sister. She sounds like some girl you're in love with." Ryan's being pretty hard on Capote, especially since they're supposed to be friends. But that's what it's like in this class. When you enter the room, you're a writer first.

"It does sound a little . . . incestuous," I add.

Capote looks at me. It's the first time he's acknowledged my presence, but only because he has to. "That's the point of the story. And if you didn't get the point, I can't help you."

I press on. "But is it really *you*?"

"It's fiction," he snaps. "Of course it's not really me."

"So if it's not really you or your sister, I guess we can criticize her after all," Ryan says as the rest of the class titters. "I wouldn't want to say something negative about a member of your family."

"A writer has to be able to look at everything in their life with a critical eye," L'il says. "Including their own family. They do say the artist must kill the father in order to succeed."

"But Capote hasn't killed anyone. Yet," I say. The class snickers.

"This discussion is totally stupid," Rainbow interjects. It's the second time she's deigned to speak in class, and her tone is world-weary, defiant and superior, designed to put us in our place. Which seems to be somewhere far below hers. "Anyway, the sister is dead. So what difference does it make what we say about her? I thought the story was great. I identified with the sister's pain. It seemed very real to me."

"Thank you," Capote says, as if he and

Rainbow are two aristocrats stranded in a crowd of peasants.

Now I'm sure Rainbow is sleeping with him. I wonder if she knows about the model.

Capote takes his seat, and once again I find myself staring at him with open curiosity. Studied in profile, his nose has character—a distinctive bump of the type passed from one generation to another—"the Duncan nose"—likely the bane of every female family member. Combined with closely spaced eyes, the nose would give the face a rodentlike demeanor, but Capote's eyes are wide-set. And now that I'm really looking at him, a dark inky blue.

"Will L'il read her poem, please?" Viktor murmurs.

L'il's poem is about a flower and its effect on three generations of women. When she's finished, there's silence.

"That was wonderful." Viktor shuffles to the front of the room.

"Anyone can do it," L'il says with cheerful modesty. She might be the only genuine person in this class, probably because she really does have talent.

Viktor Greene stoops over and picks up his knapsack. I can't imagine what's in it besides papers, but the weight tilts him perilously to one side, like a boat listing in the waves. "We reconvene on Wednesday. In the meantime, for those of you who haven't handed in your first story, you need to do so by Monday." He scans the room. "And I need to see Carrie Bradshaw in my office."

Huh? I look to L'il, wondering if she might know the reason for this unexpected meeting, but she only shrugs.

Maybe Viktor Greene is going to tell me I don't belong in this class.

Or *maybe* he's going to tell me I'm the most talented, brilliant student he's ever had.

Or maybe . . . I give up. Who knows what he wants. I smoke a cigarette and make my way to his office.

The door is closed. I knock.

It opens a crack, and the first thing I'm confronted by is Viktor's enormous mustache, followed by his soft sloping face, as if skin and muscle have abandoned any attempt to attach to the skull. He silently swings open the door and I enter a small room filled with a mess of papers and books and magazines. He removes a pile from the chair in front of his desk and looks around helplessly.

"Over there," I say, pointing to a relatively small mound of books perched on the sill.

"Right," he says, plopping the papers on top, where they balance precariously.

I sit down in the chair as he clumsily drops into his seat.

"Well." He touches his mustache.

It's still there, I want to scream, but don't.

"How do you feel about this class?" he asks.

"Good. Really good." I'm pretty sure I suck, but there's no reason to give him ammunition.

"How long have you wanted to become a writer?"

"Since I was a kid, I guess."

"You guess?"

"I *know*." Why do conversations with teachers always go around in circles?

"Why?"

I sit on my hands and stare. There's no good answer to this question. "I'm a genius and the world can't live without my words," is too pretentious and probably untrue. "I love books and want to write the great American novel" is true, but is also what every student wants, because why else would they be in this class? "It's my calling," sounds overly dramatic. On the other hand, why is he even asking me this question? Can't he tell that I *should* be a writer?

In consequence, I end up saying nothing. Instead, I open my eyes as wide as possible.

This has an interesting effect. Viktor Greene suddenly becomes uncomfortable, shifting in his chair and then opening and closing a drawer.

"Why do you have that mustache?" I ask.

"Mmph?" He covers his lips with his tapered, waxy fingers.

"Is it because you think that mustache is a part of you?" I've never talked to a teacher this way, but I'm not exactly in school. I'm in a seminar. And who says Viktor Greene has to be the authority?

"Don't you like the mustache?" he asks.

Hold on. Viktor Greene is *vain*?

"Sure," I say, thinking about how vanity is a weakness. It's a chink in the armor. If you're vain, you should do everything possible to conceal it.

I lean forward slightly to emphasize my admiration. "Your mustache is really, er, great."

"You think so?" he repeats.

Jeez. What a Pandora's box. If he only knew how Ryan and I make fun of that mustache. I've even given it a name: "Waldo." Waldo is not any ordinary mustache, however. He's able to go on adventures without Viktor. He goes to the zoo and Studio 54, and the other day, he even went to Benihana, where the chef mistook him for a piece of meat and accidently chopped him up.

Waldo recovered, though. He's immortal and cannot be destroyed.

"Your mustache," I continue. "It's kind of like

me wanting to be a writer. It's a part of me. I don't know who I'd be if I didn't want to be a writer." I deliver this line with great conviction, and Viktor nods.

"That's fine, then," he says.

I smile.

"I was worried you'd come to New York to become famous."

What?

Now I'm confused. And kind of insulted. "What does my wanting to be a writer have to do with wanting to become famous?"

He wets his lips. "Some people think writing is glamorous. They make the mistake of thinking it's a good vehicle for becoming famous. But it isn't. It's only hard work. Years and years and years of it, and even then, most people don't get what they want out of it."

Like you, I wonder? "I'm not worried, Mr. Greene."

He sadly fingers his mustache.

"Is that it?" I stand up.

"Yes," he says. "That's it."

"Thanks, Mr. Greene." I glare at him, wondering what Waldo would say.

But when I get outside, I'm shaking.

Why shouldn't I? I demand silently. Why

shouldn't I become a famous writer? Like Norman Mailer. Or Philip Roth. And F. Scott Fitzgerald and Hemingway and all those other men. Why can't I be like them? I mean, what is the point of becoming a writer if no one reads what you've written?

Damn Viktor Greene and The New School. Why do I have to keep proving myself all the time? Why can't I be like L'il, with everyone praising and encouraging me? Or Rainbow, with her sense of entitlement. I bet Viktor Greene never asked Rainbow why she wanted to be a writer.

Or what if—I wince—Viktor Greene is right? I'm *not* a writer after all.

I light a cigarette and start walking.

Why did I come to New York? Why did I think I could make it here?

I walk as fast as I can, pausing only to light yet another cigarette. By the time I get to Sixteenth Street, I figure I've probably smoked nearly half a pack.

I feel sick.

It's one thing to write for the school newspaper. But New York is on a whole different level. It's a mountain, with a few successful people like Bernard at the top, and a mass of dreamers and strivers like me at the bottom.

And then there are people like Viktor, who

aren't afraid to tell you that you're never going to reach that peak.

I flick my cigarette butt onto the sidewalk and grind it out in a fury. A fire truck roars down the avenue, horns blaring. "I am pissed off," I scream, my frustration mingling with the wail of the siren.

A couple of people glance my way but don't pause. I'm only another crazy person on the street in New York.

I stomp down the sidewalk to Samantha's building, take the stairs two at a time, unlock the three bolts, and fling myself onto her bed. Which makes me feel, once again, like an interloper. It's a four-poster with a black coverlet and what Samantha calls silk sheets, which, she claims, prevent wrinkles. Except they're really made of some kind of super slippery polyester and I have to push my foot against one of the posts to keep from sliding onto the floor.

I grab a pillow and put it over my head. I think about Viktor Greene and Bernard. I think about how I'm all alone. How I'm constantly having to pull myself up from the depths of despair, trying to convince myself to try one more time. I bury my face deeper into the pillow.

Maybe I should give up. Go back home. And in two months, I'll go to Brown.

My throat closes at the thought of leaving New

York. Am I going to allow what Viktor Greene said to cause me to quit? I have to talk to someone. But who?

That girl. The one with the red hair. The one who found my Carrie bag. She seems like the kind of person who would have something to say about my situation. She hates life, and right now, I do too.

What was her name, again? Miranda. Miranda Hobbes. "H-o-b-b-e-s." I hear her voice in my head.

I pick up the phone and dial information.

CHAPTER NINE

"All men are a disappointment. No matter what anyone says." Miranda Hobbes glares at the cover of *Cosmopolitan*. "'How to Get Him and Keep Him,'" she says, reading the cover line aloud in disgust.

She places the magazine back in the rack. "Even if you could get Him—and why do they always capitalize His name like He's God—I can personally guarantee He wouldn't be worth keeping."

"What about Paul Newman?" I count out four dollars and hand the money to the cashier. "I'm sure he's worth keeping. Joanne Woodward thinks so."

"First of all, no one knows what goes on

between two people in a marriage. And secondly, he's an actor. Which means by definition he's a narcissist." She looks at the package of chicken thighs doubtfully. "Are you sure you know what you're doing?"

I put the chicken thighs, rice, and the tomato into a bag, feigning ignorance about her concerns. Truth is, I'm a little worried about the chicken myself. Besides being minuscule, the supermarket is none too clean. Maybe that's why no one cooks in New York. "Don't you think everyone's a narcissist?" I ask. "I have this theory that all anyone ever really thinks about is themself. It's human nature."

"Is this human nature?" Miranda demands, still absorbed by the rack of magazines. "'How to De-dimple Your Thighs in Thirty Days.' 'Kissable Lips.' 'How to Tell What He's Really Thinking.' I can tell you what he's really thinking. *Nothing*."

I laugh, partly because she's probably right, and partly because I'm in the giddy throes of a new friendship.

It's my second Saturday in New York, and what no one tells you is how the city empties out on the weekends. Samantha goes to the Hamptons with Charlie, and even L'il said she was going to the Adirondacks. I told myself I didn't mind. I'd had enough excitement for the week, and besides, I had to write.

And I did work, for a few hours, anyway. Then I started to feel lonely. I decided there must be a particular kind of lonely in New York, because once you start thinking about all the millions of people out there eating or shopping or going to movies or museums with friends, it's pretty depressing not to be one of them.

I tried calling Maggie, who's spending the summer in South Carolina, but her sister said she was at the beach. Then I tried Walt. He was in Provincetown. I even called my father. But all he said was how much I must be looking forward to Brown in the fall and he'd talk more but he had an appointment.

I wished I could tell him what a hard time I was having with my writing class, but it would have been pointless. He's never been interested in my writing anyway, convinced it's a phase I'll get over when I go to Brown.

Then I looked through Samantha's closet. I found a pair of neon-blue Fiorucci boots that I particularly coveted, and even tried them on, but they were too big. I also discovered an old leather biker jacket that appeared to be from her former life—whatever that was.

I tried Miranda Hobbes again. I'd actually tried her three times since Thursday, but there was no answer.

But apparently she doesn't protest on Saturdays, because she picked up the phone on the first ring.

"Hello?" she asked suspiciously.

"Miranda? It's Carrie Bradshaw."

"Oh."

"I was wondering . . . what are you doing right now? Do you want to get a cup of coffee or something?"

"I don't know."

"Oh," I said again, disappointed.

I guess she felt sorry for me, because she asked, "Where do you live?"

"Chelsea?"

"I'm on Bank Street. There's a coffee shop around the corner. As long as I don't have to take the subway, I guess I could meet you."

We spent two hours at the coffee shop, discovering all kinds of things we had in common. Like we both went to our local high schools. And we both loved the book *The Consensus* as kids. When I told her I knew the author, Mary Gordon Howard, she laughed. "Somehow, I knew you were the type who would." And over yet another cup of coffee, we began to have that magical, unspoken realization that we were going to be friends.

Then we decided we were hungry, but also admitted we didn't have any money. Hence my plan to cook us dinner.

"Why do magazines do this to women?" Miranda complains now, glaring at *Vogue*. "It's all about creating insecurity. Trying to make women feel like they're not good enough. And when women don't feel like they're good enough, guess what?"

"What?" I ask, picking up the grocery bag.

"Men win. That's how they keep us down," she concludes.

"Except the problem with women's magazines is that they're written by women," I point out.

"That only shows you how deep this thing goes. Men have made women coconspirators in their own oppression. I mean, if you spend all your time worrying about leg hair, how can you possibly have time to take over the world?"

I want to point out that shaving your legs takes about five minutes, leaving plenty of time for world-taking-over, but I know she only means it as a rhetorical question.

"Are you sure your roommate won't mind my coming over?" she asks.

"She's not really my roommate. She's engaged. She lives with her boyfriend. She's in the Hamptons anyway."

"Lucky you," Miranda says as we start up the five flights of stairs to the apartment. By the third flight, she's panting. "How do you do this every day?"

"It's better than living with Peggy."

"That Peggy sounds like a nightmare. People like that should be in therapy."

"She probably is, and it's not working."

"Then she needs to find a new shrink," Miranda says, puffing. "I could recommend mine."

"You see a shrink?" I ask, startled, fitting my key into the lock.

"Of course. Don't you?"

"No. Why would I?"

"Because everyone needs to see a shrink. Otherwise you keep repeating the same unhealthy patterns."

"But what if you don't have unhealthy patterns?" I throw open the door and Miranda stumbles in. She flops onto the futon.

"Thinking you don't have unhealthy patterns is an unhealthy pattern in itself. And everyone has something unhealthy from their childhood. If you don't deal with it, it can ruin your life."

I open the cantilevered doors to reveal the small kitchen and place the grocery bag onto the few inches of counter space next to the tiny sink. "What's yours?" I ask.

"My mother."

I find a bent skillet in the oven, pour in some

oil, and light one of the two burners with a match. "How do you know all this stuff?"

"My father's a shrink. And my mother is a perfectionist. She used to spend an hour every morning styling my hair before I went to school. Which is why I cut it and dyed it as soon as I could get away from her. My father says she suffers from guilt. But I say she's a classic narcissist. Everything is about her. Including me."

"But she's your mother," I say, placing the chicken thighs in the hot oil.

"And I hate her. Which is okay, because she hates me, too. I don't fit into her narrow idea of what a daughter should be. What about your mother?"

I pause, but she doesn't seem all that interested in the answer. She's examining the collection of photographs Samantha keeps on the side table, with the zeal of an anthropologist who has suddenly discovered an old piece of pottery. "Is this the woman who lives here? Christ, is she an egomaniac or what? She's in every photograph."

"It *is* her apartment."

"Don't you think it's weird when someone has photographs of themselves all over the place? It's like they're trying to prove they exist."

"I don't know her that well."

"What is she?" Miranda sneers. "An actress? A

model? Who has five photographs of themselves in a bikini?"

"She's in advertising."

"Another business designed to make women feel insecure."

She gets up and comes into the kitchen. "Where'd you learn to cook?"

"I sort of had to."

"My mother tried to teach me, but I refused. I rejected anything that could turn me into a house-wife." She leans over the skillet. "That smells pretty good though."

"It will be," I say, adding two inches of water to the pan. When it boils, I pour in the rice, add the tomato, then turn down the heat and cover the skillet. "And it's cheap. We get a whole meal for four dollars."

"Which reminds me." She reaches into her pocket and pulls out two one-dollar bills. "My share. I hate owing anyone anything. Don't you?"

We go back into the living room and curl up on either end of the couch. We light cigarettes, and I inhale contemplatively. "What if I can't become a writer and I have to get married, instead. What if I have to ask my husband for money? I couldn't do it. I'd hate myself."

"Marriage turns women into whores," Miranda declares. "The whole thing is a sham."

"That's what I think too!" I can hardly believe I've found someone who shares my secret suspicions. "But if you let people know, they want to kill you. They hate the truth."

"That's what happens to women when they go against the system." Miranda fumbles awkwardly with her cigarette. I can tell she's not really a smoker, but maybe, because everyone else in New York smokes, she's trying it out. "And I, for one, plan to do something about it," she continues, coughing.

"What?"

"Haven't decided yet. But I will." She narrows her eyes. "You're lucky you're going to be a writer. You can change people's perceptions. You should write about marriage and what a lie it is. Or even sex."

"Sex?" I grind my cigarette out in the ashtray.

"Sex. It's the biggest sham of all. I mean, your whole life, all you ever hear is how you're supposed to save yourself for marriage. And how it's so special. And then you finally do it. And you're like, *that's it*? This is what everyone's been raving about?"

"You're kidding."

"Come on," she says. "You've done it."

I grimace. "Actually, I haven't."

"Really?" She's surprised. Then pragmatic.

"Well, it doesn't make a bit of difference. You're not missing anything. In fact, if you haven't done it, I would recommend not doing it. Ever." She pauses. "And the worst thing about it? Once you do it, you have to *keep* doing it. Because the guy expects you to."

"Why'd you do it in the first place?" I ask, lighting another cigarette.

"Pressure. I had the same boyfriend all through high school. Although, I have to admit, I was curious."

"And?"

"Everything but 'it' is fine," she says matter-of-factly. "'It' itself is boring as hell. That's what no one tells you. How boring it is. And it hurts."

"I have a friend who did it for the first time and loved it. She said she had an actual orgasm."

"From intercourse?" Miranda yelps. "She's lying. Everyone knows women cannot have an orgasm from intercourse only."

"Then why does everyone do it?"

"Because they have to," she practically screams. "And then you just lie there, waiting for it to be over. The only good thing about it is that it only lasts a minute or two."

"Maybe you have to do it a lot to like it."

"Nope. I've done it at least twenty times, and each time it was as bad as the first." She crosses her arms. "You'll see. And it doesn't matter who you do it with. I did it with another guy six months ago to make sure it wasn't me, and it was just as lousy."

"What about with an older guy?" I ask, thinking about Bernard. "A guy with experience—"

"How old?"

"Thirty?"

"That's even worse," she declares. "His thing could be all wrinkly. There's nothing more disgusting than a wrinkly thing."

"Have you ever seen one?" I ask.

"Nope. And I hope I never have to."

"Well," I say, laughing. "What if I do it and I like it? Then what?"

Miranda snickers, as if this is not a possibility. She jabs her finger at Samantha's photograph. "I bet even she thinks it's boring. She looks like she likes it, but I promise you, she's pretending. Just like every other goddamn woman on the planet."

PART TWO

Bite the Big Apple

CHAPTER TEN

Bernard!

"He called me," I sing to myself like a little bird, skipping down Forty-fifth Street into the Theater District. Apparently, he did call my old apartment and Peggy told him I no longer lived there and she didn't know where I was. And then Peggy had the gall to ask Bernard if she could audition for his new play. Bernard coldly suggested she call his casting director, and suddenly, Peggy's memory as to my whereabouts mysteriously returned. "She's staying with a friend of hers. Cindy? Samantha?"

Just as I'd given up hope of him calling me on his own, Bernard, bless his soul, managed to put two and two together and rang me first.

"Can you meet me at the theater around

lunchtime tomorrow?" he asked.

Bernard sure has some odd ideas about what constitutes a date. But he is a wunderkind, so perhaps he lives outside the rules.

The Theater District is so exciting, even during the day. There are the flashing lights of Broadway, the cute little restaurants, and the seedy theaters promising "LIVE GIRLS," which makes me scratch my head. Would anyone want dead ones?

And then on to Shubert Alley. It's only a narrow street, but I can't help imagining what it would be like to have my own play performed in this theater. If that happened, it would mean everything in my life was perfect.

As per Bernard's instructions, I enter through the stage door. It's nothing special—just a dingy lobby with gray cement walls and peeling linoleum on the floor and a man stationed behind a little window that slides open. "Bernard Singer?" I ask.

The guard looks up from his *Post*, his face a map of veins. "Here to audition?" he asks, taking down a clipboard.

"No, I'm a friend."

"Ah. You're the young lady. Carrie Bradshaw."

"That's right."

"He said he was expecting you. He's out, but

he'll be back soon. He said I should take you on a backstage tour."

"Yes, please," I exclaim. The Shubert Theatre. *A Chorus Line*. Backstage!

"Ever been here before?"

"No!" I can't keep the squeal of excitement out of my voice.

"Mr. Shubert founded the theater in 1913." The guard pulls apart a heavy black curtain to reveal the stage. "Katharine Hepburn performed here in 1939. *The Philadelphia Story*."

"On this very stage?"

"Used to stand right where you are now, every evening, before her first entrance. 'Jimmy,' she'd say, 'how's the house tonight?' And I'd say, 'All the better for you being here, Miss Hepburn.'"

"Jimmy," I plead. "Could I—"

He smiles, catching my enthusiasm. "Only for a second. No one's allowed on that stage who ain't union—"

And before he can change his mind, I'm crossing the boards, looking out at the house. I stride to the footlights and take in row after row of velvet chairs, the balconies, the luxurious boxes on the side. And for a moment, I imagine the theater filled with people, all there to see little ol' me.

I fling out my arms. "Hello, New York!"

"Oh my." I hear a deep, throaty laugh,

followed by the sound of one person clapping. I turn around in horror, and there, in the wings, is Bernard, wearing sunglasses, an open white shirt, and Gucci loafers. Next to him is the clapper, whom I immediately recognize as the actress Margie Shephard. His ex-wife. What the hell is she doing here? And what must she think of me, after witnessing my little performance?

It doesn't take long to find out, because the next thing she says is, "I see a star is born," in a flinty voice.

"Take it easy, Margie," Bernard says, having the sense to at least sound slightly annoyed by her.

"Hello. I'm Carrie." I hold out my hand.

She does me the honor of shaking it, but doesn't provide her own name, confident that I already know who she is. I think I'll always remember what her hand feels like—the long, smooth fingers, the palm, warm and firm. Someday I'll probably even say, "I met Margie Shephard. I shook her hand and she was amazing."

Margie opens her mouth prettily, and emits a sly laugh. "Well, well," she says.

Nobody can say, "Well, well," and get away with it, except Margie Shephard. I can't stop gaping at her. She isn't technically beautiful, but has some kind of inner light that makes you think she's one of the most attractive women you've ever seen.

I totally understand why Bernard married her. What I can't understand is why he isn't *still* married to her.

I don't stand a chance.

"Nice to meet you," Margie says, with a whisper of a wink at Bernard.

"Me too." I stumble over the words. Margie probably thinks I'm an idiot.

She twinkles at Bernard. "We'll continue this discussion later."

"I suggest we don't continue it at all," Bernard mutters. Apparently he isn't as starstruck by her as I am.

"I'll call you." Again, there's the pretty smile, and the eyes that seem to know everything. "Good-bye, Carrie."

"Good-bye." I'm suddenly disappointed to see her go.

Bernard and I watch as she strides through the hallway, one hand caressing the back of her neck—a poignant reminder to Bernard of what he's missing.

I swallow, prepared to apologize for my little show, but instead of being embarrassed, Bernard grabs me under my arms and presses me to him, spinning me around like a child. He kisses me all over my face. "Am I glad to see you, kiddo. You've got great timing. Did anyone ever tell you that?"

"No—"

"You do. If you hadn't been here, I wouldn't have been able to get rid of her. C'mon." He grabs my hand and briskly leads me out the other end of the alley like a madman on a mission. "It's you, baby," he says. "When I saw you, it suddenly made sense."

"Sense?" I ask breathlessly, trying to keep up, confused about his sudden adoration. It's what I'd been hoping for, but now that he actually seems smitten, I'm a bit wary.

"Margie is over. Finished. I'm moving on." We come out on Forty-fourth Street and head to Fifth Avenue. "You're a woman. Where can I buy some furniture?"

"Furniture?" I laugh. "I have no idea."

"Someone's got to know. Excuse me." He accosts a nicely dressed lady in pearls. "Where's the best place to buy furniture around here?"

"What kind of furniture?" she asks, as if this kind of encounter with a stranger is perfectly normal.

"A table. And some sheets. And maybe a couch."

"Bloomingdale's," she says, and moves on.

Bernard looks down at me. "You busy this afternoon? Got time to do some furniture shopping?"

"Sure." It wasn't exactly the romantic lunch I had in mind, but so what?

We jump into a cab. "Bloomingdale's," Bernard directs the driver. "And make it fast. We need to buy sheets."

The cabbie smiles. "You two lovebirds getting married?"

"The opposite. I'm officially getting unmarried," Bernard says, and squeezes my leg.

When we get to Bloomingdale's, Bernard and I run around the fifth floor like two little kids, trying out the beds, bouncing on the sofas, pretending to drink tea from the china display. One of the salesmen recognizes Bernard ("Oh, Mr. Singer. It's an honor. Will you sign this sales slip for my mother?") and follows us around like a puppy.

Bernard buys a dining room set, a brown leather couch and ottoman, an armoire, and a pile of pillows, sheets, and towels. "Can I have it delivered right away?"

"Normally, no," the salesman simpers. "But for you, Mr. Singer, I'll try."

"Now what?" I ask Bernard.

"We go to my apartment and wait."

"I still don't understand why Margie took the furniture," I say as we stroll up Fifty-ninth Street.

"To punish me, I suppose."

"But I thought she was the one who left," I venture, carefully avoiding the word "cheated."

"Chickadee, don't you know anything about women? Fair play doesn't enter into their vocabulary."

"Not all women. I would never be like that. I'd be reasonable."

"That's what's so great about you. You're unspoiled." Still holding hands, we breeze into his building, right past the nasty doorman. Take that, buddy, I think. In the apartment, Bernard puts on a record. Frank Sinatra. "Let's dance," he says. "I want to celebrate."

"I can't dance to this."

"Sure you can." He opens his arms. I rest one hand on his shoulder the way we learned to do in ballroom dancing classes, a million years ago when I was thirteen. He pulls me tighter, his breath scorching my neck. "I like you, Carrie Bradshaw. I really do. Do you think you can like me back?"

"Of course," I giggle. "If I didn't like you, I wouldn't dance with you."

"I don't believe that's true. I think you'd dance with a man and when you got tired of him, you'd dance with another."

"Never." I twist my head to look at his face. His eyes are closed, his expression beatific. I still can't fathom his new attitude. If I didn't know better, I'd think he was falling in love with me.

Or maybe he's falling in love with the idea of falling in love with me. Maybe he wants to be in love with someone and I've ended up in the right place at the right time.

And suddenly, I'm nervous. If Bernard were to fall in love with me, I'd never be able to live up to his expectations. I'd end up being a disappointment. And what am I going to do if he tries to have sex with me?

"I want to know what happened," I say, trying to change the subject. "Between you and Margie."

"I told you what happened," he murmurs.

"I meant this afternoon. What were you arguing about?"

"Does it matter?"

"I guess not."

"The apartment," he says. "We were arguing about the apartment. She wants it back and I said no."

"She wants the apartment, too?" I ask, astounded.

"She might have convinced me if it weren't for you." He takes my hand and twirls me around and around. "When I saw you on that stage, I thought, That's a sign."

"What kind of sign?"

"A sign that I should put my life back together. Buy furniture. Make this place my home again."

He lets go of my hand but I keep spinning and spinning until I collapse to the floor. I lie still as the bare room revolves around me and for a moment I picture myself in an insane asylum, in a white space with no furniture. I close my eyes, and when I open them again, Bernard's face is hovering above mine. He has pretty eyelashes and a crease on either side of his mouth. A small mole is buried in the hair of his right eyebrow. "Crazy, crazy girl," he whispers, before he leans in to kiss me.

I allow myself to be carried away by the kiss. Bernard's mouth envelops mine, absorbing all reality until life seems to consist only of these lips and tongues engaged in a funny dance of their own.

I freeze.

And suddenly, I'm suffocating. I put my hands on Bernard's shoulders. "I can't."

"Something I said?" His lips close back over mine. My heart races. An artery throbs in my neck. I wriggle away.

He sits back on his haunches. "Too intense?"

I fan my face and laugh a little. "Maybe."

"You're not used to guys like me."

"I guess not!" I stand up and brush myself off.

There's a clap of thunder outside. Bernard comes up behind me, pushing my hair aside to mouth my neck. "Have you ever made love in a thunderstorm?"

"Not yet." I giggle, trying to put him off.

"Maybe it's time you did."

Oh no. Right now? Is this the moment? My body trembles. I don't think I can do it. I'm not prepared.

Bernard massages my shoulders. "Relax." He leans in and nibbles my earlobe.

If I do it with him now, he's going to compare me to Margie. I imagine them having sex all the time, in this apartment. I picture Margie kissing Bernard with an intensity that matches his, like in the movies. Then I see myself lying naked on that bare mattress, my arms and legs splayed out stiffly to the side.

Why didn't I do it with Sebastian when I had the chance? At least I'd know how to do it. I never guessed someone like Bernard would come along. A grown man who obviously assumes his girl-friend has sex regularly and wants to do it all the time.

"C'mon," he says gently, pulling at my hand.

I balk and he squints at me. "Don't you want to make love?"

"I do," I say quickly, not wanting to hurt his

feelings. "It's just that—"

"Yes?"

"I forgot my birth control."

"Oh." He drops my hand and laughs. "What do you use? A diaphragm?"

I blush. "Yeah. Sure. Uh-huh." I nod.

"A diaphragm's a pain. And it's messy. With the cream. You use a cream with it, right?"

"Yes." I mentally pedal backward to the health classes we had in high school. I picture the diaphragm, a funny little object that looks like a rubber cap. But I don't recall any mention of cream.

"Why don't you go on the pill? It's so much easier."

"I will. Yes indeed." I agree vigorously. "I keep meaning to get a prescription but—"

"I know. You don't want to take the pill until you know the relationship is serious."

My throat goes dry. Is this relationship serious? Am I ready for it? But in the next second, Bernard is lying on the bed, and has turned on the TV. Is it my imagination, or does he look slightly relieved?

"C'mere, puddy tat," he says, patting the spot next to him. He holds out his hands. "Do you think my nails are too long?"

"Too long for what?" I frown.

"Seriously," he says.

I take his hand in mine, running my fingers over the palm. His hands are lovely and lean, and I can't help thinking about those hands on my body. The sexiest part of a man is his hands. If a man has girlish hands, it doesn't matter what the rest of him is like. "They are, a little."

"Could you cut them and file them for me?" he asks.

What?

"Margie used to do it for me," he explains. My heart softens. He's so sweet. I had no idea a man could be so cozy. But it's not surprising, given my limited experience with romance.

Bernard goes into the bathroom to get clippers and a nail file. I look around the spare bedroom. Poor Bernard, I think, for the hundredth time.

"Primate grooming," he says when he returns. He sits across from me, and I begin carefully clipping his nails. I can hear the rain drumming on the awning below while I file rhythmically, the motion and the rain putting me into a soothing trance. Bernard strokes my arm and then my face as I lean over his hand.

"This is nice, isn't it?" he asks.

"Yes," I reply simply.

"This is what it should be like. No fighting. Or arguing about whose turn it is to walk the dog."

"Did you have a dog?"

"A long-haired dachshund. He was Margie's dog first, but she could never be bothered to pay attention to him."

"Is that what happened to you?"

"Yeah. She stopped paying attention to me, too. It was all about her career."

"That's terrible," I say, filing contentedly. I can't imagine any woman ever losing interest in Bernard.

CHAPTER ELEVEN

I wake up the next morning with an idea.

Maybe it's because of all the time I spent with Bernard, but I'm finally inspired. I know what I have to do: write a play.

This brilliant notion lasts for about three seconds before it's crushed under a million and one reasons why it's impossible. Like Bernard will think I'm copying him. Like I won't be able to do it anyway. Like Viktor Greene won't let me.

I sit on Samantha's bed with my legs crossed, making faces. The fact is, I need to prove I can make it in New York. But how? Maybe I'll get lucky and be discovered. Or maybe it will turn out I have hidden talents even I don't know about. I clutch the silk bedcovers like a survivor clinging to a lifeboat. Despite my fears, it seems my life is starting to take off here—and Brown is less than seven weeks away.

I pluck at a thread. Not that there's anything wrong with Brown, but I've already gotten in there. On the other hand, if New York were a college, I'd still be applying. And if all these other people can make it in New York, why can't I?

I jump out of bed and run around the apartment just for the hell of it, throwing on my clothes while typing the following three sentences: "I will succeed. I must succeed. Damn everyone," and then I grab my Carrie bag and practically slide down all five flights to the lobby.

I beetle up Fourteenth Street, expertly weaving through the crowd, picturing my feet flying a few inches off the ground. I turn right on Broadway and hurl myself into the Strand.

The Strand is a legendary secondhand bookstore where you can find any book for cheap. It's musty and all the salespeople have a very big attitude, like they're the keepers of the flame of high literature. Which wouldn't matter, except the salespeople cannot be avoided. If you're looking for a specific book, you can't find it without help.

I buttonhole a weedy fellow wearing a sweater with elbow patches.

"Do you have *Death of a Salesman*?"

"I should hope so," he says, crossing his arms.

"And *The Importance of Being Earnest*? And maybe *The Little Foxes*? *The Women*? *Our Town*?"

"Slow down. Do I look like a shoe salesman?"

"No," I murmur, as I follow him into the stacks.

After fifteen minutes of searching, he finally finds *The Women*. At the end of the stacks I spot Ryan from class. He's got his nose in *Swann's Way*, scratching his head and jiggling his foot as if overcome by the text.

"Hey," I say.

"Hey." He closes the book. "What are you doing here?"

"Going to write a play." I indicate my small pile of books. "Thought I should read a few first."

He laughs. "Good idea. The best way to avoid writing is by reading. Then you can at least *pretend* you're working."

I like Ryan. He seems okay as a person, unlike his best friend, Capote Duncan.

I pay for my books, and when I turn around, Ryan is still there. He has the air of someone who doesn't quite know what to do with himself. "Want to get a coffee?" he asks.

"Sure."

"I've got a couple of hours to kill before I have to meet my fiancée," he says.

"You're engaged?" Ryan can't be more than twenty-one or two. He seems too young to get married.

"My fiancée's a model." He scratches his cheek, as if he's both proud and ashamed of her profession. "I always find if a woman really, really, really wants you to do something, you should do it. It's easier in the long run."

"So you don't *want* to marry her?"

He smiles awkwardly. "If I sleep with a woman ten times, I think I should marry her. I can't help myself. If she weren't so busy, we'd already be married by now."

We walk down Broadway and go into a hamburger joint. "I wish I could find a guy like that," I say jokingly. "A guy who does everything I want."

"Can't you?" He peers at me in confusion.

"I don't think I'm the man-wrangler type."

"I'm surprised." He absentmindedly picks up his fork and tests the prongs on his thumb. "You're pretty hot."

I grin. Coming from another guy, I'd take this as a pickup line. But Ryan doesn't seem to have an agenda. I suspect he's one of those guys who says exactly what he's thinking and is then stupefied by the consequences.

We order coffee. "How'd you meet her? Your model fiancée?"

He jiggles his leg. "Capote introduced us."

"What is with that guy?" I ask.

"Don't tell me you're interested too."

I give him a dirty look. "Are you kidding? I can't stand him. He's supposedly got all these women after him—"

"I know." Ryan nods in appreciative agreement. "I mean, the guy's not even that good-looking."

"He's like the guy every girl has a crush on in sixth grade. And no one can figure out why."

Ryan laughs. "I always thought *I* was that guy."

"Were you?"

"Kind of, yeah."

I can see it. Ryan at twelve—masses of dark hair, bright blue eyes—a real teen heartthrob. "No wonder you're engaged to a model."

"She wasn't a model when we met, though. She was studying to be a veterinary assistant."

I take a sip of my coffee. "That's like the default profession for girls who don't know what they want to do. But they 'love' animals."

"Harsh but true."

"How'd she become a model?"

"Discovered," Ryan says. "She came to visit me in New York and a guy came up to her in Bergdorf's and gave her his card."

"And she couldn't resist."

"Don't all women want to be models?" he asks.

"No. But all men want to date them."

He chuckles. "You should come to this party tonight. It's a fashion show for some downtown designer. Becky's modeling in it. And Capote's coming."

"Capote?" I scoff. "How can I resist?" But I write down the address on a napkin, anyway.

After Ryan, I pop by Viktor Greene's office to tell him about my exciting new plan to write a play. If I'm really jazzed about it, he'll have to say yes.

Viktor's door is wide open as if he's expecting someone, so I walk right in. He grunts, startled, and pets his mustache.

He doesn't offer me a seat, so I stand in front of his desk. "I've figured out what my project should be."

"Yes?" he asks cautiously, his eyes going past me to the hallway.

"I'm going to write a play!"

"That's fine."

"You don't mind? It's not a short story or a poem—"

"As long as it's about family," he says quickly.

"It will be." I nod. "I'm thinking it should be about this couple. They've been married for a few years and they hate each other—"

Viktor stares at me blankly. It appears he has nothing more to say. I stand awkwardly for a moment then add, "I'll get started right away."

"Good idea." It's now patently clear he wants me out of there. I give him a little wave as I exit.

I run right into L'il. "Carrie!" She flushes.

"I'm going to write a play," I inform her excitedly. "Viktor says it's okay."

"That's perfect for you. I can't wait to read it."

"I've got to write it first."

She steps to the side, trying to get around me.

"What are you doing tonight?" I ask quickly. "Want to have dinner with me and my friend Miranda?"

"I'd love to, but—"

Viktor Greene comes out of his office. L'il glances up at him. "You sure?" I ask, pressing her. "Miranda's really interesting. And we're going to go to one of those cheap Indian places on Sixth Street. Miranda says she knows the best ones—"

L'il blinks as she focuses her attention back on me. "All right. I guess I could—"

"Meet me on Fourteenth and Broadway at eight-thirty. And afterward, we can go to this party," I say over my shoulder.

I leave L'il and Viktor standing there, staring at me like I'm a mugger who has suddenly decided to spare them.

CHAPTER TWELVE

I write three pages of my play. It's all about Peggy and her lover—the guy who took those naughty photos—whom I've named Moorehouse. Peggy and Moorehouse are having an argument about toilet paper. I think it's pretty funny and pretty real—I mean, what couple doesn't argue about toilet paper—and I actually feel satisfied with my work.

At eight o'clock, I pick up Miranda at her house. Miranda's lucky—she has an old aunt who lives in a small, run-down townhouse, consisting of four floors and a basement, where Miranda lives. The basement has its own entrance and two windows just below the sidewalk. It would be perfect but for the fact that it's damp and perpetually dark.

I ring the bell, thinking about how I love the way I can walk to my friends' apartments and how my life has this frenetic, unstructured pace where I never know exactly what's going to happen. Miranda opens the door, her hair still wet from the shower. "I'm not ready."

"That's okay." I stroll past her and plop onto an ancient sofa covered in worn damask. Miranda's aunt used to be rich, about thirty years ago. Then her husband took off with another woman and left her flat broke, except for the house. The aunt worked as a waitress and put herself through school and now she's a professor of Women's Studies at NYU. The apartment is filled with books like *Woman, Culture, and Society* and *Women: A Feminist Perspective*. I always think the best part about Miranda's apartment is the books. The only books Samantha has are astrology, self-help, and *The Kama Sutra*. Other than those, she mostly reads magazines.

Miranda goes into her room to change. I light a cigarette and idly survey the bookshelves, picking out a book by Andrea Dworkin. It falls open and I read the following: "just some wet, ratty, bedraggled thing, semen caked on you, his piss running down your legs . . ."

"What's that?" Miranda asks, peering over my shoulder. "Oh. I love that book."

"Really? I just read this part about semen caked on you—"

"And what about the part when it oozes out and runs down your leg?"

"Says here, it's pee."

"Semen, pee, what's the difference?" Miranda shrugs. "It's all gross." She slings a brown saddlebag over her shoulder. "Did you see that guy after all?"

"'That guy' happens to have a name. Bernard. And yes, I did see him. I'm pretty crazy about him. We went furniture shopping."

"So he's already turned you into his slave."

"We're having fun," I say pointedly.

"Has he tried to get you into bed?"

"No," I say, somewhat defensively. "I need to go on the pill, first. And I've decided I'm not going to sleep with him until my eighteenth birthday."

"I'll be sure to mark it on my calendar. 'Carrie's birthday and lose-her-virginity day.'"

"Maybe you'd like to be there. For moral support."

"Does Bernie have any idea you're planning to use him as a stud service?"

"I believe the word 'stud' only applies if you're planning on reproducing. Which I'm not."

"In that case, 'dud' might be more appropriate."

"Bernard is no dud," I say threateningly. "He's

a famous playwright—"

"Yada yada yada."

"And I'm sure his 'sword' is mightier than his word."

"You'd better hope so," Miranda says. She raises her index finger and slowly lowers it into a crook as we burst out laughing.

"I just love these prices," L'il says, scanning the menu.

"I know." Miranda nods, pleased. "You can get a whole meal for three dollars."

"And a whole beer for fifty cents," I add.

We're seated at a table in the Indian restaurant Miranda kept telling us about, although it wasn't so easy to find. We walked up and down the block three times past nearly identical restaurants until Miranda insisted this was the place, recognizable by the three peacock feathers in a vase in the window. The tablecloths are red-and-white-checkered plastic; the knives and forks tinny. The air is musty and sweet.

"This reminds me of home," L'il says.

"You live in India?" Miranda asks, astonished.

"No, silly. North Carolina." She gestures around the restaurant. "This is exactly like one of those barbecue places tucked off the freeway."

"Freeway?" Miranda queries.

"Highway," I translate.

I hope the whole dinner isn't like this. Miranda and L'il are both intense in their own way, so I assumed they'd like each other. And I need them to get along. I miss having a group of friends. Sometimes it feels like every part of my life is so different, I'm constantly visiting another planet.

"You're a poet?" Miranda asks L'il.

"Indeed," she replies. "What about you?"

I jump in. "Miranda's majoring in Women's Studies."

L'il smiles. "No offense, but what can you do with that?"

"Anything." Miranda glares. She's probably wondering what you can do with a poetry degree.

"Miranda is doing very important work. Protesting against pornography. And she volunteers at a women's shelter," I say.

"You're a feminist." L'il nods.

"I wouldn't consider being anything else."

"I'm a feminist," I volunteer. "I think every woman should be a feminist—"

"But it means you hate men." L'il takes a sip of her beer, and stares straight across the table at Miranda.

"What if I do?" Miranda says.

This is not going well. "I don't hate all men. Just some men," I say, trying to lighten the atmosphere. "Especially men whom I like and they don't like me back."

L'il gives me a sharp look, meaning she's determined to lock horns with Miranda. "If you hate men, how can you ever marry? Have babies?"

"I guess if you truly believe a woman's only purpose in life is to marry and have children—" Miranda breaks off and gives L'il a superior smile.

"I never said that," L'il replies calmly. "Just because you're married and have children doesn't mean it's the only point to your life. You can do all kinds of things and have children."

"Good answer," I say.

"I happen to think it's wrong to bring a child into this patriarchal society," Miranda replies swiftly. And just as the conversation is about to go completely haywire, our samosas arrive.

I quickly grab one of the pastries, dip it into a red sauce, and pop it into my mouth. "Fantastic," I exclaim, as my eyes begin to water and my tongue burns. I frantically wave my hand in front of my face, reaching for a glass of water, as Miranda and L'il laugh. "Why didn't you tell me that sauce was hot?"

"Why didn't you ask?" Miranda giggles. "You dove right in. I figured you knew what you were doing."

"I do!"

"Does that include sex?" Miranda asks wickedly.

"What is it with everyone and sex?"

"It's very exciting," L'il says.

"Ha," I say. "She hates it." I point to Miranda.

"Only the 'intercourse' part." Miranda makes quotation marks with her fingers. "Why do they call it intercourse anyway? It makes it sound like it's some kind of conversation. Which it isn't. It's penetration, pure and simple. There's no give-and-take involved."

Our curries arrive. One is white and creamy. The other two are brown and red, and look dangerous. I take a scoop of the white curry. L'il takes some of the brown and pushes it toward Miranda. "If you know how to do it properly, supposedly it *is* like a conversation," she says.

"How?" Miranda asks, thoroughly unconvinced.

"The penis and vagina communicate."

"No way," I say.

"My mother told me," L'il says. "It's an act of love."

"It's an act of war," Miranda objects, getting heated. "The penis is saying, 'Let me in,' and the vagina is saying, 'Get the hell away from me, creep.'"

"Or maybe the vagina is saying, 'Hurry up,'" I add.

L'il dabs at her mouth, and smiles. "That's the problem. If you think it's going to be terrible, it will be."

"Why?" I dip my fork into the red curry to test it for hotness.

"Tension. If you tense up, it makes it more difficult. And painful. That's why the woman should always have an orgasm first," L'il says nonchalantly.

Miranda finishes her beer and immediately orders another. "That's the dumbest thing I've ever heard. How can you tell if you've even had this supposed orgasm?"

L'il laughs.

"Yeah." I gulp. "How?"

L'il slides back in her chair and puts on a teacherly face. "You're kidding, right?"

"I'm not," I say, looking at Miranda. Her face is closed, as if she doesn't want to hear this.

"You have to know your own body," L'il says cryptically.

"Meaning?"

"Masturbation."

"Eeeeewwww." Miranda puts her hands over ears.

"Masturbation is not a dirty word," L'il scolds. "It's part of a healthy sexuality."

"And I suppose your mother told you this, too?" Miranda demands.

L'il shrugs. "My mother's a nurse. She doesn't believe in mincing words when it comes to health. She says healthy sex is simply a part of a healthy life."

"Well." I'm impressed.

"And she did all that consciousness-raising stuff," L'il continues. "In the early seventies. When the women sit around in a circle with mirrors—"

"Aha." This, I suppose, explains everything.

"She's a lesbian now," L'il says casually.

Miranda's mouth opens as if she's about to speak, but suddenly thinks better of it. For once, she has nothing to say.

After dinner, L'il begs off the party, claiming a headache. Miranda doesn't want to go either, but I point out if she goes home, she'll look like she's sulking.

The party is on Broadway and Seventeenth Street in a building that was once a bank. A security guard tells us to take the elevator to the fourth floor. I figure this must be a big party if the guard is letting people in so easily.

The elevator opens into a white space with crazy art on the walls. As we're taking it in, a small, rotund man with hair the color of butter bustles over, beaming.

"I'm Bobby," he says, extending his hand to me.

"Carrie Bradshaw. And Miranda Hobbes." Miranda gives Bobby a stiff smile while Bobby squints, summing us up.

"Carrie Bradshaw," he says, like he's delighted to meet me. "And what do you do?"

"Why is that always the first question out of everyone's mouth?" Miranda mutters.

I glance at her so she knows I agree, and say boldly, "I'm a playwright."

"A playwright!" Bobby exclaims. "That's good. I love writers. Everyone loves writers. I used to be a writer before I became an artist."

"You're an artist?" Miranda asks, as if this can't possibly be true.

Bobby ignores her. "You must tell me the names of your plays. Perhaps I've seen one—"

"I doubt it," I falter, never expecting he'd assume I'd actually written a play. But now that I've said it, I can't take it back.

"Because she hasn't written any," Miranda blurts out.

"Actually"—I give her a steely look—"I'm in the middle of writing one right now."

"Wonderful," Bobby cheers. "And when it's finished, we can stage it here."

"Really?" This Bobby must be some kind of crazy.

"Of course," he says with a swagger, leading us farther into the room. "I'm doing all kinds of experimental productions. This is a nexus—a nexus," he repeats, savoring the word, "of art, fashion, and photography. I haven't done a play yet, but it seems exactly the right sort of thing. And we can get all kinds of people to come."

Before I can begin to process the idea, Bobby is pawing his way through the crowd, with Miranda and me on his heels. "Do you know Jinx? The fashion designer? We're showing her new collection this evening. You'll love her," he insists, depositing us in front of a scary-looking woman with long, blue-black hair, about a hundred coats of eyeliner, and black lipstick. She's leaning over to light a joint when Bobby interrupts.

"Jinx, darling," he says, which is extremely ironic, as it's clear Jinx is nobody's darling. "This is"—he searches for my name—"Carrie. And her friend," he adds, indicating Miranda.

"Nice to meet you," I say. "I can't wait to see your fashion show."

"Me too," she responds, inhaling the smoke and holding it in her lungs. "If those friggin' models don't get here soon—I hate friggin' models, don't you?" Jinx holds up her left hand, displaying a contraption of metal through which each finger is inserted. "Brass knuckles," she says. "Don't even think about messing with me."

"I won't." I look around, desperate to escape, and spot Capote Duncan in the corner.

"We have to go," I say, nudging Miranda. "I just saw a friend of mine—"

"What friend?" Miranda asks. God, she really is bad at parties. No wonder she didn't want to come.

"Someone I'm very happy to see right now." Which is patently untrue. But as Capote Duncan is the only person I know at this party, I'll take him.

And as we push through the crowd, I wonder if living in New York makes people crazy, or if they're crazy to begin with and New York attracts them like flies.

Capote is leaning against an air conditioner talking to a medium-tall girl with one of those noses that turns up like a little snout. She has masses of blond hair and brown eyes, which gives her an interesting look, and since she's with Capote, I assume she's one of the errant models Jinx was referring to.

"I'll give you a reading list," Capote is saying. "Hemingway. Fitzgerald. And Balzac." I immediately want to puke. Capote is always talking about Balzac, which reminds me of why I can't stand him. He's so pretentious.

"Hel*lo*," I say in a singsong voice.

Capote's head jerks around as if he's anticipating someone special. When he sees me, his face falls. He appears to undergo a brief, internal struggle, as if he'd like to ignore me, but his Southern manners won't let him. Eventually, he manages to summon a smile.

"Carrie Bradshaw," he says, in a slow drawl. "I didn't know you were coming to this."

"Why would you? Ryan invited me."

At the name "Ryan," the modely girl pricks up her ears. Capote sighs. "This is Becky. Ryan's fiancée."

"Ryan's told me so much about you," I say, extending my hand. She takes it limply. Then her face screws up like she's about to cry, and she runs off.

Capote looks at me accusingly. "Nice job."

"What'd I do?"

"She just told me she's planning to dump Ryan."

"That so?" I snicker. "And here I thought you were trying to improve her brain. The reading list?" I point out.

Capote's face tightens. "That wasn't smart, Carrie," he says, pushing past us to follow Becky.

"It's all about being smart with you, isn't it?" I shout after him.

"Nice to meet you, too," Miranda calls out sarcastically.

Unfortunately, the Capote exchange has pushed Miranda over the edge, and she insists on going home. Given Capote's rudeness, I don't really want to stay at the party alone, either.

I'm bummed we didn't get to see the fashion show. On the other hand, I'm glad I met that Bobby character. During the walk home under the salty yellow lights, I keep talking about my play and how it would be so cool to have it performed in Bobby's space, until Miranda finally turns to me and says, "Will you just write the damn thing?"

"Will you come to the reading?"

"Why wouldn't I? Other than the fact that Bobby and all his friends are complete idiots. And what about Capote Duncan? Who the hell does he think he is?"

"He's a big jerk," I say, remembering the expression of fury on his face. I smile. I suddenly realize I enjoy making Capote Duncan angry.

Miranda and I part ways, with me promising to call her tomorrow. When I get inside my building, I swear I can hear Samantha's phone ringing all the way down the stairs. A ringing phone is like a call to arms for me, and I take the steps two at a time. After about the tenth ring, the phone stops, but then it starts again.

I burst through the door and grab it from where it's slid under the couch. "Hello?" I ask breathlessly.

"What are you doing on Thursday night?" It's Samantha herself.

"Thursday night?" I ask dumbly. When is Thursday night? Oh, right, the day after tomorrow. "I have no idea."

"I need you to help me with something. I'm throwing an intimate little dinner party with Charlie at his apartment—"

"I'd love to come," I gush, thinking she's inviting me. "Can I bring Bernard, too?"

"I don't think that's a good idea."

"Why not?"

"Don't take this the wrong way," she purrs. "But I actually need you to cook. You did say you could cook, right?"

I frown. "I might have. But—"

"I can't cook at all. And I don't want Charlie to find out."

"So I'll be in the kitchen all night."

"You'd be doing me an enormous favor," she coos. "And you did say you'd do me a favor someday, if I asked."

"That's true," I admit reluctantly, still not convinced.

"Look," she says, putting on the pressure. "If it's that big a deal, I'll trade you. One night of cooking for any pair of my shoes."

"But your feet are bigger than mine."

"You can put tissue in the toes."

"What about the Fiorucci boots?" I ask craftily.

She pauses, mulling it over. "Oh, why not?" she agrees. "I can always get Charlie to buy me another pair. Especially when he finds out what a wonderful cook I am."

"Right," I mutter as she says good-bye.

How did I get into this mess? Technically, I do know how to cook. But I've only cooked for friends. How many people is she expecting at this intimate dinner? Six? Or sixteen?

The phone rings again. Probably Samantha calling back to discuss the menu. "Samantha?" I ask, cautiously.

"Who's Samantha?" demands the familiar voice on the other end.

"Maggie!" I yip.

"What's going on? I tried calling your number and this nasty woman said you didn't live there anymore. Then your sister said you moved—"

"It's a long story," I say, settling onto the couch for a chat.

"You can tell me tomorrow," she exclaims.

"I'm coming to New York!"

"You *are*?"

"My sister and I are visiting our cousins in Pennsylvania. I'm taking the bus into the city tomorrow morning. I figured I'd stay with you for a couple of nights."

"Oh, Mags, that's fantastic. I can't wait to see you. I have so much to tell you. I'm dating this guy—"

"Maggie?" someone asks in the background.

"Got to go. I'll see you tomorrow. My bus gets in at nine a.m. Can you meet me at Port Authority?"

"Of course." I hang up the phone, thrilled. Then I remember I'm supposed to see Bernard tomorrow night. But maybe Maggie can come with us. I can't wait for her to meet him. She'll probably freak out when she sees how sexy he is.

Full of excitement, I sit down at the typewriter to write a few more pages of my play. I'm determined to take advantage of Bobby's offer to stage a reading in his space. And maybe, just maybe, if the reading is a success, I can stay in New York. I'll have officially become a writer and I won't have to go to Brown at all.

I work like a demon until three a.m., when I force myself to go to bed. I toss and turn with anticipation, thinking about my play and Bernard and all the interesting people I've met. What will Maggie think of my new life?

Surely she has to be impressed.

CHAPTER THIRTEEN

"You actually live here?" Maggie asks, aghast.

"Isn't it great?"

She drops her knapsack on the floor and surveys the apartment. "Where's the bathroom?"

"Right here," I say, pointing to the door behind her. "The bedroom is there. And this is the living room."

She exhales. "It's so small."

"It's big for New York. You should have seen where I was living before."

"But—" She walks to the window and looks out. "It's so dirty. And this building. I mean, it's kind of falling down. And those people in the hallway—"

"The old couple? They've lived here their

whole lives. Samantha keeps hoping they'll die so she can get their apartment," I quip, without thinking. "It has two bedrooms and the rent is cheaper than this place."

Maggie's eyes widen. "That's awful. Wanting someone to die so you can get their apartment. This Samantha sounds like a horrible person. But I'm not surprised, being Donna LaDonna's cousin."

"It's only a joke."

"Well," she says, patting the futon to make sure it's sturdy before she sits down, "I should hope so."

I look at her in surprise. When did Maggie become this prim and proper? She hasn't stopped complaining about New York since I met her at Port Authority. The smell. The noise. The people. The subway terrified her. When we got out on Fourteenth Street and Eighth Avenue, I had to coach her on when to cross the street.

And now she's insulting my apartment? And Samantha? But maybe it's not intentional. Of course she assumes Samantha must be like Donna LaDonna. I would, too, if I didn't know better.

I sit across from her, leaning forward. "I can't believe you're actually here."

"I can't either," she says, full of enthusiasm. We're both trying to recapture our old rapport.

"You look great!"

"Thanks," she says. "I think I lost five pounds. I started windsurfing. Have you ever windsurfed? It's amazing. And the beaches are so beautiful. And there are all these little fishing villages."

"Wow." The thought of fishing villages and long stretches of empty sand suddenly sounds as quaint as living two hundred years ago.

"What about guys?" I ask.

She wriggles her feet out of her tennis shoes, rubbing one heel like she's already developed a blister. "They're gorgeous. Hank—that's this one guy—he's six two and he's on the varsity tennis team at Duke. I swear, Carrie, we should both transfer to Duke. They have the hottest guys."

I smile. "We have lots of hot guys in New York, too—"

"Not like these guys." She sighs dramatically. "Hank would be perfect, except for one thing."

"He has a girlfriend?"

"No." She gives me a pointed look. "I would never date someone who had a girlfriend. Not after Lali."

"Lali." I shrug. Each mention of the past causes my intestines to lurch. Next thing I know, we'll be talking about Sebastian. And I really don't want to. Since I arrived in New York, I've barely thought about Lali or Sebastian or what went on last spring. It feels like all that stuff happened to someone else, not me. "So Hank," I say, attempting to remain in the present.

"He's . . ." She shakes her head, picks up her sneaker, and puts it down. "He's not . . . good in bed. Have you ever had that?"

"I've certainly heard about it."

"You still haven't—"

I try to brush this away as well. "What does that mean, exactly? 'Bad in bed'?"

"He doesn't really do anything. Just sticks it in. And then it's over in like three seconds."

"Isn't it always like that?" I ask, remembering what Miranda's told me.

"No. Peter was really good in bed."

"He was?" I still can't believe that nerdly old Peter was such a big stud.

"Didn't you know? That was one of the reasons I was so angry when we broke up."

"What are you going to do, then?" I ask, twisting my hair into a bun. "About Hank?"

She gives me a secret smile. "I'm not married. I'm not even engaged. So—"

"You're sleeping with another guy?"

She nods.

"You're sleeping with two guys. At the same time?" Now I'm aghast.

She gives me a look.

"Well, I'm sure you don't sleep with both of

157

them at once, but—" I waver.

"It's the eighties. Things have changed. Besides, I'm using birth control."

"You could get a disease."

"Well, I haven't." She glares at me and I drop it. Maggie's always been stubborn. She does what she wants when she wants, and there's no talking her out of it. I absentmindedly rub my arm. "Who's this other guy?"

"Tom. He works at a gas station."

I look at her in consternation.

"What?" she demands. "What is wrong with a guy who works at a gas station?"

"It's such a cliché."

"First of all, he's an incredible windsurfer. And secondly, he's trying to make something of his life. His father has a fishing boat. He could be a fisherman, but he doesn't want to end up like his father. He's going to community college."

"That's great," I say, chastised.

"I know," she agrees. "I kind of miss him." She looks at her watch. "Do you mind if I call him? He's probably back from the beach by now."

"Go ahead." I hand her the phone. "I'm going to take a shower."

I head to the bathroom while I inform her of our itinerary: "Tonight we're going to meet Bernard for a drink at Peartree's, which is this fancy bar near the United Nations. And maybe this afternoon we can go to the White Horse Tavern for lunch. It's where all these famous writers hang out. And in between, we can go to Saks. I'd love you to meet my friend Miranda."

"Sure," she says, as if she's barely heard a word. Her concentration is focused entirely on the phone as she dials her boyfriend's—or should I say "lover's"—number.

Ryan and Capote Duncan are at the White Horse Tavern, seated at a table on the sidewalk. There's a pot of coffee in front them, and they look rough, like they went to bed late and just got up. Ryan's eyes are puffy and Capote is unshaven, his hair still damp from a shower.

"Hey," I say. They're next to the entrance, making it impossible to avoid them.

"Oh. Hi," Capote says wearily.

"This is my friend Maggie."

Ryan immediately perks up at the sight of Maggie's fresh-faced, all-American prettiness. "What are you girls up to?" he asks flirtatiously, which seems to be his default mode with women. "Do you want to join us?"

Capote gives him a frustrated look, but Maggie sits down before either one of us can object. She probably thinks Ryan is cute.

"Where are you from, Maggie?" Ryan asks.

"Castlebury. Carrie and I are best friends."

"Really?" Ryan asks, as if this is supremely interesting.

"Ryan and Capote are in my writing class," I explain.

"I still can't believe Carrie got into that class. And actually came to New York and everything."

Capote raises his eyebrows.

"What do you mean?" I ask, slightly annoyed.

"Well, no one ever really thought you'd become a writer." Maggie laughs.

"That's crazy. I always said I wanted to be a writer."

"But you didn't really write. Until senior year. Carrie worked on the school newspaper," she says to Ryan. She turns back to me. "But even then you didn't actually *write* for the newspaper, did you?"

I roll my eyes. Maggie never figured out I was writing all those stories for the newspaper under a pen name. And I'm not about to tell her now. On the other hand, she's making me sound like a dilettante in front of Capote. Who already seems to believe I don't belong in the class.

Fantastic. Maggie's just added fuel to his fire.

"I've always written a lot. I just didn't show you."

"Sure," Maggie says, grinning as if it's a joke. I sigh. Can't she see how much I've changed? Perhaps it's because she hasn't changed at all. She's the same old Maggie, so she probably assumes I'm the same as well.

"How was the fashion show?" I ask, diverting the conversation away from my supposed lack of writing.

"Great," Capote says listlessly.

"As you can tell, Capote is a man who knows nothing about fashion. He does, on the other hand, know quite a bit about models," Ryan says.

"Aren't models really stupid?" Maggie asks.

Ryan laughs. "That's not really the point."

"Ryan's engaged to a model," I say, wondering if Becky broke up with Ryan after all. He certainly isn't acting like a man who's been dumped. I glance at Capote inquiringly. He shrugs.

"When are you getting married?" Maggie asks politely. She and Ryan seem to have developed a connection and I wonder if she's disappointed he's not available.

"Next year," Ryan says easily. "She went to Paris this morning." Aha. So no need for a formal breakup after all. And poor Ryan, sitting here without a clue. On the other hand, Capote is probably perfectly capable of lying about the situation. He might have told me Becky was going to dump Ryan because he wants Becky for himself.

"Interesting," I say, to no one in particular.

Capote puts five dollars on the table. "I'm taking off."

"But—" Ryan objects. Capote gives a small shake of his head. "I guess I am too," Ryan says reluctantly. "Nice to meet you." He smiles at Maggie. "What are you doing tonight?"

"Carrie's making us have drinks with some guy."

"Bernard Singer is not 'some guy,'" I point out.

Capote pauses. "Bernard Singer? The playwright?"

"He's Carrie's boyfriend," Maggie says dismissively.

Capote's eyes widen behind his glasses. "You're dating Bernard Singer?" he asks, as if it can't be possible someone as esteemed as Bernard Singer would be interested in me.

"Uh-huh," I say, like it's no big deal.

Capote rests his hand on the back of his chair, unsure if he should go after all. "Bernard Singer is a genius."

"I know."

"I'd love to meet Bernard Singer," Ryan says. "Why don't we meet up with you guys for a drink, later?"

"That would be great," Maggie says.

As soon as they're gone, I groan.

"What?" Maggie asks, slightly defensive, knowing she's done something wrong.

"I can't bring them to drinks with Bernard."

"Why not? Ryan is *nice*," she says, as if he's the only normal person she's met so far. "I think he likes me."

"He's engaged."

"And?" Maggie picks up the menu. "You heard him. She's not around."

"He's a big flirt. It doesn't mean anything."

"I'm a flirt too. So it's perfect."

I was wrong. Maggie has changed. She's become a sex addict. And how can I explain about Bernard? "Bernard won't want to meet them—"

"Why not?"

"Because he's older. He's thirty."

She looks at me in horror. "Oh my God, Carrie. *Thirty?* That's disgusting!"

CHAPTER FOURTEEN

Given Maggie's attitude, I decide not to introduce her to Miranda after all. They'd probably
get into a big fight about sex and I'd be stuck in
the middle. Instead, we walk around the Village,
where Maggie has her tarot cards read by a psychic—"I see a man with dark hair and blue eyes."
"Ryan!" Maggie exclaims—and then I take her
to Washington Square Park. There's the usual
assortment of freaks, musicians, drug dealers,
Hare Krishnas, and even two men walking on
stilts, but all she can talk about is how there isn't
any grass. "How can they call it a park if it's all
dirt?"

"There probably was grass, once. And there *are*
trees," I point out.

"But look at the leaves. They're black. Even the squirrels are dirty."

"Nobody notices the squirrels."

"They should," she says. "Did I tell you I'm going to become a marine biologist?"

"No—"

"Hank's a biology major. He says if you're a marine biologist, you can live in California or Florida."

"But you don't like science."

"What are you talking about?" Maggie asks. "I didn't like chemistry, but I loved biology."

This is news to me. When we had to take biology in junior year, Maggie refused to memorize the names of the species and phyla, saying it was the kind of stupid thing that no one would ever use in their real life, so why bother?

We walk around a bit more, with Maggie becoming increasingly distressed about the heat and the odd people and how she thinks she's getting another blister. When I take her back to the apartment, she complains about the lack of effective air-conditioning. By the time we're supposed to leave to meet Bernard, I'm nearly at the end of my rope. Once more, Maggie balks at taking the subway. "I'm not going down there again," she declares. "It stinks. I don't know how you do it."

"It's the best way to get around," I say, trying

to urge her down the stairs.

"Why can't we take a taxi? My sister and brother-in-law told me to take taxis because they're safe."

"They're also expensive. And I don't have the money."

"I have fifty dollars."

What? I wish she'd told me she had money earlier. She could have paid for our hamburgers.

When we're safely in a cab, Maggie reveals her conclusion about why New Yorkers wear black. "It's because it's so dirty here. And black doesn't show dirt. Could you imagine what their clothes would look like if they wore white? I mean, who wears black in the summer?"

"I do," I say, nonplussed, especially as I'm in black. I'm wearing a black T-shirt, black leather pants that are two sizes too big—which I bought for 90 percent off at one of those cheap stores on Eighth Street—and pointy-toed black high heels from the 1950s that I found at the vintage shop.

"Black is for funerals," Maggie says. "But maybe New Yorkers like black because they feel like they've died."

"Or maybe for the first time in their lives they feel like they're *living*."

We get stuck in traffic by Macy's, and Maggie rolls down her window, fanning herself with her hand. "Look at all those people. This isn't living. It's surviving."

I have to admit, she's right about that. New York is about survival.

"Who are we meeting again?" she asks.

I sigh. "Bernard. The guy I'm seeing. The playwright."

"Plays are boring."

"Bernard doesn't agree. So please don't say 'plays are boring' when you meet him."

"Does he smoke a pipe?"

I glare at her.

"You said he was over thirty. I picture him smoking a pipe and wearing slippers."

"Thirty is not *old*. And don't tell him my age, either. He thinks I'm nineteen or twenty. So you have to be nineteen or twenty too. We're sophomores in college. Okay?"

"It's not good when you have to lie to a guy," Maggie says.

I take a deep breath. I want to ask her if Hank knows about Tom, but I don't.

When we finally push through the revolving door at Peartree's, I'm relieved to see Bernard's dark head bent over a newspaper, a glass of scotch in front of him. I still get the jitters when I know I'm going to see him. I count down the hours, reliving the sensation of his soft mouth on mine. As our rendezvous approaches, I get nervous, worried he's going to call and cancel, or not show up at all. I wish I didn't care so much, but I'm glad to have a guy who makes me feel this way.

I'm not sure Bernard feels the same, though. This morning, when I told him I had a friend coming to town unexpectedly, he said, "See your friend, then. We'll get together another time."

I emitted a gasp of disappointment. "But I thought we were going to see each other. *Tonight*."

"I'm not going anywhere. We can see each other when she leaves."

"I told her all about you. I want her to meet you."

"Why?"

"Because she's my best friend. And——" I broke off. I didn't know how to tell him that I wanted to show him off, wanted Maggie to be impressed by him and my astonishing new life. Wanted her to see how far I'd come in such a short time.

I thought he should be able to tell from my voice.

"I don't want to babysit, Carrie," he said.

"You're not! Maggie's nineteen, maybe twenty——" I must have sounded very insistent, because he relented and agreed to meet for a drink.

"But only one drink," he cautioned. "You

should spend time with your friend. She came to see you, not me."

I hate it when Bernard acts all serious.

Then I decided his comment was vaguely insulting. Of course I wanted to spend time with Maggie. But I wanted to see him, too. I thought about calling him back and canceling, just to show him I didn't care, but the reality of not seeing him was too depressing. And I suspected I'd secretly resent Maggie if I couldn't see Bernard because of her.

Things are tense enough with Maggie as it is. Getting ready to go out tonight, she kept saying she couldn't understand why I was "dressing up" to go to a bar. I tried to explain it wasn't that kind of bar, but she only stared at me in incomprehension and said, "Sometimes I really do not get you."

That's when I had a moment of clarity: Maggie is never going to like New York. She's constitutionally unsuited for the city. And when I realized this, my simmering animosity disappeared.

It's okay. It's not Maggie's fault, or mine. It's simply the way we are.

"There's Bernard," I say now, nudging Maggie past the maître d' to the bar. The interior of Peartree's is slick—black walls with chrome sconces, black marble tables, and a mirror along the back wall. Samantha says it's the best pickup place in town: She met Charlie here, and she gets irritated when he comes here without her, thinking he might meet another girl.

"Why is it so dark in here?" Maggie asks.

"It's supposed to be mysterious."

"What's mysterious about not being able to see who you're talking to?"

"Oh, Mags," I say, and laugh.

I creep up behind Bernard and tap him on the shoulder. He starts, grins, and picks up his drink. "I was beginning to think you weren't coming. Thought maybe you'd had a better offer."

"We did, but Maggie insisted we had to meet you first." I briefly touch the back of his hair. It's like a talisman for me. The first time I touched it I was shocked by its delicate softness, so much like a girl's, and I was surprised by how tender it made me feel toward him, as if his hair was a harbinger of his soft, kind heart.

"You must be the friend," he says, crinkling his eyes at Maggie. "Hello, friend."

"Hello," Maggie says cautiously. With her sun-bleached hair and pink cheeks, she's as creamy as a wedding cake, in sharp contrast to Bernard's angles and crooked nose, and the bags under his eyes that make him appear to be a person who spends all of his time inside—in dark caves like Peartree's. I'm hoping Maggie will see the romance of him, but at the moment her expression is one of pure wariness.

"Drink?" Bernard asks, seemingly unaware of the culture clash.

"Vodka tonic," I say.

"I'll have a beer."

"Have a cocktail," I urge.

"I don't want a cocktail. I want a beer," Maggie insists.

"Let her have a beer if she wants one," Bernard says jocularly, the implication being that I'm needlessly giving Maggie a hard time.

"Sorry." My voice sounds hollow. I can already tell this is a mistake. I don't have a clue how to reconcile my past—Maggie—with my present—Bernard.

Two men squeeze in next to Maggie, intent on establishing a place at the bar. "Should we get a table?" Bernard asks. "We could eat. I'd be happy to feed you girls dinner."

Maggie gives me a questioning look. "I thought we were going to meet Ryan."

"We could have dinner. The food's good here."

"It's lousy. But the atmosphere is entertaining." Bernard waves to the maître d' and motions to an empty table near the window.

"Come on." I nudge Maggie and give her a meaningful look. Her stare is slightly hostile, as if she still doesn't understand why we're here.

Nevertheless, she follows Bernard to the table. He even pulls out her chair for her.

I sit next to him, determined to make this work. "How was the rehearsal?" I ask brightly.

"Lousy," Bernard says. He smiles at Maggie to include her in the conversation. "There's always a point in the middle of rehearsals when all the actors seem to forget their lines."

Which is exactly how I feel right now.

"Why is that?" Maggie asks, playing with her water glass.

"I have no idea."

"But they've been saying their lines for at least two weeks, right?" I frown, as if knowing Bernard has given me an inside track on the theater.

"Actors are like children," Bernard says. "They sulk and get their feelings hurt."

Maggie gives him a vacant look.

Bernard smiles tolerantly and opens his menu. "What would you like, Maggie?"

"I don't know. Duck breast?"

"Good choice." Bernard nods. "I'm going to have the usual. Skirt steak."

Why does he sound so formal? Was Bernard always like this and I never noticed before? "Bernard is a creature of habit," I explain to Maggie.

"That's nice," Maggie says.

"What do you always say about being a writer?" I ask him. "You know—about how you have to live a life of habit."

Bernard nods indulgently. "Others have said it better than I can. But the basic idea is that if you're a writer, you need to live your life on the page."

"In other words, your real life should be as uncomplicated as possible," I clarify to Maggie. "When Bernard is working he eats practically the same thing every day for lunch. A pastrami sandwich."

Maggie attempts to look interested. "It sounds kind of boring. But I'm not a writer. I don't even like writing a letter."

Bernard laughs, playfully pointing a finger at me. "I think you need to take more of your own advice, young lady." He shakes his head at Maggie, as if the two of them are in cahoots. "Carrie's an expert at living large. I keep telling her to focus more on the page."

"You've never said that," I reply, indignant. I look down, as if I simply have to readjust my napkin. Bernard's comment brings all of my insecurities about being a writer to the surface.

"I've been meaning to say it." He squeezes my hand. "So there you go. I've said it. Do we want wine?"

"Sure," I say, stung.

"Beaujolais okay for you, Maggie?" he asks politely.

"I like red," Maggie says.

"Beaujolais is red," I comment, and immediately feel like a heel.

"Maggie knew that," Bernard says kindly. I look from one to the other. How did this happen? Why am I the bad guy? It's like Bernard and Maggie are ganging up on me.

I get up to go to the bathroom. "I'll come with you," Maggie says. She follows me down the stairs as I try to compose myself.

"I really want you to like him," I say, parking myself in front of the mirror while Maggie goes into the stall.

"I just met him. How can I know if I like him or not?"

"Don't you think he's sexy?" I ask.

"Sexy?" Maggie says. "I wouldn't call him that."

"But he is. Sexy," I insist.

"If you think he's sexy, that's all that counts."

"Well, I do. And I really, really like him."

The toilet flushes and Maggie comes out. "He doesn't seem very much like a boyfriend," she ventures.

"What do you mean?" I take a lipstick out of

my bag, trying not to panic.

"He doesn't act like he's your boyfriend. He seems like he's more of an uncle or something."

I freeze. "He certainly isn't."

"It just seems like he's trying to help you. Like he likes you and, I don't know—" She shrugs.

"It's only because he's going through a divorce," I say.

"That's too bad," she remarks, washing her hands.

I apply the lipstick. "Why?"

"I wouldn't want to marry a divorced man. It kind of ruins it, doesn't it? The idea that a man has been married to someone else? I wouldn't be able to take it. I'd be jealous. I want a guy who's only ever been in love with me."

"But what if—" I pause, remembering that's what I've always thought I wanted as well. Until now. I narrow my eyes. Maybe it's simply a left-over sentiment from Castlebury.

We get through the rest of dinner, but it's awkward, with me saying things I know make me sound like a jerk, and Maggie being mostly silent, and Bernard pretending to enjoy the food and wine. When our plates are cleared, Maggie runs to the bathroom again, while I scoot my chair closer to Bernard's and apologize for the lousy evening.

"It's fine," he says. "It's what I expected." He

pats my hand. "Come on, Carrie. You and Maggie are in college. We're from different generations. You can't expect Maggie to understand."

"I do, though."

"Then you're going to be disappointed."

Maggie comes back to the table beaming, her demeanor suddenly light and fizzy. "I called Ryan," she announces. "He said he's going over to Capote's and we should meet them there and then maybe we can go out."

I look at Bernard, pleadingly. "But we're already out."

"Go," he says, pushing back his chair. "Have fun with Maggie. Show her the town."

He takes out his wallet and hands me twenty dollars. "Promise me you'll take a cab. I don't want you riding the subway at night."

"No." I try to give back the twenty but he won't take it. Maggie is already at the exit as if she can't get out of there fast enough.

Bernard gives me a quick peck on the cheek. "We can see each other anytime. Your friend is only here for two nights."

"When?" I ask.

"When what?"

"When will I see you again?" I hate myself, sounding like a desperate schoolgirl.

"Soon. I'll call you."

I leave the restaurant in a huff. I'm so mad, I can barely look at Maggie.

A cab pulls up to the curb and a couple gets out. Maggie slides into the backseat. "Are you coming?"

"What choice do I have?" I grumble under my breath.

Maggie has written Capote's address on the back of a napkin. "Green-wich Street?" she asks, pronouncing each syllable.

"It's 'Grenich.'"

She looks at me. "Okay. *Grenich*," she says to the cabbie.

The taxi peels away, throwing me against Maggie. "Sorry," I murmur coldly.

"What's wrong?" she asks.

"Nothing."

"Is it because I didn't like Bernard?"

"How could you not like him." It's not a question.

She folds her arms. "Do you want me to lie to you?" And before I can protest, she continues, "He's too old. I know he's not as old as our parents, but he might as well be. And he's strange. He's not like anyone we grew up with. I just can't see you with him." To soften the blow, she adds kindly, "I'm only telling you this for your own good."

I hate when friends tell you something is "for your own good." How do they know it's for your own good? Do they know the future? Maybe in the future, I'll look back and see that Bernard has actually been "good for me."

"Okay, Mags." I sigh. The taxi is racing down Fifth Avenue, and I study each landmark: Lord & Taylor, the Toy Building, the Flatiron Building, committing each to memory. If I lived here forever, would I ever get tired of these sights?

"Anyway," Maggie says cheerfully, "I forgot to tell you the most important part. Lali's gone to France!"

"Really?" I ask dully.

"You know how the Kandesies have all that land? Well, some big developer came along and bought, like, fifty acres and now the Kandesies are millionaires."

"I bet Lali went to France to meet Sebastian," I say, trying to act like I care.

"That's what I think too," Maggie agrees. "And she'll probably get him back. I always thought Sebastian was one of those guys who used women. He'll probably be with Lali because of her money."

"He has his own money," I point out.

"Doesn't matter. He's a *user*," Maggie says.

And while Maggie natters on, I spend the rest

of the taxi ride thinking about relationships. There must be such a thing as "pure" love. But there also seems to be quite a bit of "impure" love as well. Look at Capote and Ryan with their models. And Samantha with her rich mogul boyfriend. And what about Maggie and her two boyfriends— one for show and one for sex? And then there's me. Maybe what Maggie was hinting at is true. If Bernard wasn't a famous playwright, would I even be interested?

The taxi pulls up in front of a pretty brownstone with chrysanthemums in the window boxes. I grit my teeth. I like to think of myself as a good person. A girl who doesn't cheat or lie or pretend to be something she's not in order to get a guy. But maybe I'm no better than anyone else. Maybe I'm worse.

"Come on," Maggie says gaily, leaping from the cab and hurrying up the steps. "Now we can finally have fun!"

CHAPTER FIFTEEN

Capote's apartment is not what I expected. The furniture consists of soft couches and armchairs, covered in chintz. There's a small dining room with decorative plates on the walls. In the bedroom is an antique armoire; the bedspread is yellow chenille. "It looks like an old lady lives here," I say.

"She does. Or did. The woman who lived here is an old family friend. She moved to Maine," Capote explains.

"Right," I say, dropping onto the couch. The springs are shot and I sink several inches below the cushions. Capote and his "old family friends," I think grumpily. He seems to have an inside track on everything, including apartments. He's one of those people who expect to get things with very little effort, and does.

"Drink?" he asks.

"What do you have?" Maggie says coquettishly.

Huh? I thought she was interested in Ryan. But maybe it's Capote she's after. On the other hand, maybe Maggie flirts with every guy she meets. Every guy except Bernard.

I shake my head. Either way, this situation can lead to no good. How did I get involved in the aiding and abetting of this?

"Anything you want, I have," Capote replies. He doesn't sound particularly flirtatious back. He actually sounds very matter-of-fact, as if he's not exactly thrilled we're here, but has decided to tolerate us nonetheless.

"Beer?" Maggie asks.

"Sure." Capote opens the refrigerator, takes out a Heineken, and hands it to her. "Carrie?"

I'm surprised he's being so polite. Maybe it's his Southern upbringing. Manners trump personal dislikes.

"Vodka?" I get up and follow him into the kitchen. It's a proper kitchen, with a counter that opens into the living room. I'm suddenly a bit envious. I wouldn't mind living here in this charming old apartment with a fireplace and working kitchen. Several pans hang from a rod in the ceiling. "Do you cook?" I ask, with a mixture of sarcasm and surprise.

"I love to cook," Capote says proudly. "Mostly fish. I'm famous for my fish."

"*I* cook," I say, somewhat defiantly, as if I know everything about it and far more than he can possibly comprehend.

"Like what?" He takes two tumblers out of the cabinet and sets them down, adding ice and vodka and a splash of cranberry juice.

"Everything," I say. "Mostly desserts though. I'm really good at Bûche de Noël. It takes two days to make it."

"I'd never want to dedicate that much time to cooking," he says dismissively, raising his glass. "Cheers."

"Cheers."

The buzzer rings and Capote strides to the door, no doubt relieved at the interruption.

Ryan comes in with Rainbow and another girl, who's the size of a twig. She has short dark hair, enormous brown eyes, acne, and is wearing a skirt that barely covers her bottom. For some reason, I'm immediately jealous. Despite the acne, she must be another one of Ryan's model friends. I feel horribly out of place.

Rainbow's eyes scour the room and land on

me. She, too, looks as though she can't imagine what I'm doing here.

"Hi." I wave from the kitchen.

"Oh. Hi." She comes over, while Ryan greets Maggie and plops next to her on the couch. "Are you serving drinks?" she asks.

"I guess so. What do you want? Capote says he has everything."

"Tequila."

I find the bottle and pour some into a glass. Why am I serving *her*? I wonder in annoyance. "So are you and Capote seeing each other?"

"No." Her nose wrinkles. "What makes you say that?"

"You seem so close, is all."

"We're friends." She pauses, looks around again, and seeing that Ryan is still engaged with Maggie and Capote is talking to the strange skinny girl, decides I'm her only option for conversation. "I would never go out with him. I think any girl who dates him is insane."

"Why?" I take a gulp of my drink.

"She'll have her heart broken."

Well. I take another gulp of my drink, and add a little more vodka and ice. I don't feel particularly drunk. In fact, I feel disturbingly sober. And resentful. Of everyone else's life.

I join Maggie and Ryan on the couch. "What

are you guys talking about?"

"You," Ryan says. This is a person who cannot lie.

Maggie blushes. "Ryan!" she scolds.

"What?" he asks, looking from Maggie to me. "I thought you guys were best friends. Don't best friends tell each other everything?"

"You know nothing about women," Maggie giggles.

"At least I try. Unlike most men."

"What *about* me?" I ask.

"Maggie was telling me about you and Bernard." There's a note of admiration in Ryan's voice. Bernard Singer is obviously some kind of hero to both him and Capote. He's exactly what they'd like to be someday. And apparently my association with him elevates my status. But I knew that, didn't I?

"Maggie doesn't like him. She says he's too old."

"I didn't say that. I said he wasn't right for you."

"No man is ever too old," Ryan says, half jokingly. "If Carrie can go out with a guy fifteen years older, it means there's hope for me when I'm in my thirties."

Maggie's face twists in distaste. "You really want to date someone who's seventeen when you're thirty?"

"Maybe not seventeen." Ryan winks. "I'd prefer it if she were legal."

Maggie titters. Ryan's looks and charm seem to have overcome his stupidity about women.

"Anyway, who's seventeen?" he asks.

"Carrie," Maggie says accusingly.

"I'll be eighteen in a month." I glare at her. Why is she doing this to me?

"Does Bernard know you're seventeen?" Ryan asks with too much interest.

"No," Maggie says. "She told me to lie and say she was nineteen."

"Aha. The old lying-up trick," Ryan teases.

The apartment buzzer goes off again. "Reinforcements," Ryan announces as Maggie laughs. Five more people arrive—three scruffy guys and two very serious young women.

"Let's go," I say to Maggie.

Ryan looks at me in surprise. "You can't go," he insists. "The party's just getting started."

"Yeah." Maggie agrees. "I'm having fun." She holds out her empty beer bottle. "Do you mind getting me another?"

"Fine." I get up, annoyed, and go into the kitchen. The new arrivals wander over and ask for drinks. I comply, because I don't have anything better to do and there's really no one I want to talk to at this party.

I spot the phone on the wall next to the refrigerator. Maggie is completely occupied with Ryan, who is now sitting cross-legged on the couch, entertaining her with what appears to be a long and animated story. I tell myself Maggie won't mind if I take off without her. I pick up the phone and dial Bernard's number.

It rings and rings. Where is he? A dozen scenarios run through my head. He went out to a club, but if he did, why didn't he invite Maggie and me? Or he met another girl at Peartree's and he's with her, having sex. Or worse, he's decided he doesn't want to see me anymore and isn't answering his phone.

The suspense is killing me. I call again.

Still no answer. I hang up, rattled. Now I'm really convinced I'm never going to see him again. I can't bear it. I don't care what Maggie says. What if I am in love with Bernard and Maggie just ruined it?

I search the room for her, but she and Ryan have disappeared. Before I can look for them, one of the shaggy guys strikes up a conversation.

"How do you know Capote?"

"I don't," I snap. Then I feel bad and add, "He's in my writing class."

"Ah yes. The fabled New School writing course. Is Viktor Greene still teaching?" he asks in a Boston accent.

"If you'll excuse me," I say, wanting to get away from him, "I have to find my friend."

"What's she look like?"

"Blond. Pretty. All-American?"

"She's with Ryan. In the bedroom."

I scowl at him like it's his fault. "I have to get her out."

"Why?" he asks. "They're two healthy young animals. What do you care?"

I feel even more lost than I did just a few minutes ago. Are all my values and ideals just plain wrong? "I need to use the phone."

"You've got somewhere better to go?" He laughs. "This is where it's all happening."

"I certainly hope not," I mutter, dialing Bernard's number. No answer. I slap down the phone and head to the bedroom.

The music is blaring while one of the serious girls bangs on the door of the bathroom. It finally opens and Capote comes out with Rainbow and the model girl. They're laughing loudly. Normally, I'd love to be at a party like this, but all I can think about is Bernard. And if I can't see him, I want to go home.

I want to crawl into Samantha's bed and pull her slippery sheets over my head and cry.

"Maggie?" I knock briskly on the door.

"Maggie, are you in there?" Silence. "I know you're in there, Maggie." I try the handle, but it's locked. "Maggie, I want to go home," I wail.

Finally, the bedroom door opens. Maggie is flushed, twisting her hair. Behind her, Ryan stands grinning, tugging on his pants. "Jesus, Carrie," Maggie says.

"I need to go home. We have class tomorrow," I remind Ryan, sounding like an old schoolmarm.

"Let's go to your house, then," Ryan suggests.

"No."

Maggie gives me a look. "That's a great idea."

I weigh my options and decide it's the better choice. At least I can get out of here.

We walk to Samantha's building. Upstairs, Ryan extracts a bottle of vodka he pinched from Capote and proceeds to pour us drinks. I shake my head. "I'm tired." While Ryan finds the stereo, I go into Samantha's room and call Bernard.

The phone rings and rings. He's still not there. It's over.

I go out into the living room, where Maggie and Ryan are dancing. "Come on, Carrie." Maggie holds out her arms. What the hell, I think, and join them. Within minutes, though, Maggie and Ryan are making out.

"Hey, guys. Cut it out," I scold.

"Cut what out?" Ryan laughs.

Maggie takes his hand, leading him to the bedroom. "Do you mind? We'll be right out."

"What am *I* supposed to do?"

"Have a drink," Ryan chortles.

They go into the bedroom and close the door. The Blondie album is still playing. "Heart of Glass." That's me, I think. I pick up my vodka and sit at the tiny table in the corner. I light up a cigarette. I try Bernard again.

I know it's wrong. But something alien has taken over my emotions. Having sunk this far, the only place to go is down.

The album stops playing, and from inside the bedroom, I hear panting and the occasional comment, like, "Oh, that's good."

I light another cigarette. Do Maggie and Ryan have any idea how inconsiderate they are? Or do they simply not care?

I ring Bernard once more. Smoke another cigarette. An hour has passed and they're still going at it. Aren't they tired? Then I tell myself to get over it. I shouldn't be so judgmental. I know I'm not perfect. But I would never do what they're doing. I just wouldn't.

I may have suddenly learned something about myself after all. I have what Miranda would call "boundaries."

I should probably bunk down on the futon.

Maggie and Ryan don't sound like they're going to be finished anytime soon. But anger and frustration and fear are keeping me wide awake. I smoke yet another cigarette and dial Bernard.

This time he answers on the second ring. "Hello?" he asks, confused as to who could be calling him at two in the morning.

"It's me," I whisper, suddenly realizing what a bad idea it was to call him.

"Carrie?" he asks sleepily. "What are you doing up?"

"Maggie is having sex," I hiss.

"And?"

"She's doing it with some guy from my class."

"Are they doing it in front of you?"

What a question! "They're in the bedroom."

"Ah," he says.

"Can I come over?" I don't want to sound like I'm begging, but I am.

"Poor thing. You're having a lousy night, aren't you?"

"The worst."

"Coming over here probably won't make it better," he cautions. "I'm tired. I need to sleep. And so do you."

"We could just sleep then. It'd be nice."

"I can't do it tonight, Carrie. I'm sorry. Some other time."

I swallow. "Okay," I say, sounding like a little mouse.

"Good night, kiddo," he says, and hangs up.

I gently replace the receiver. I go to the futon and sit with my knees to my chest, rocking back and forth. My face screws up, and tears trickle out of the corners of my eyes.

Miranda was right. Men do suck.

CHAPTER SIXTEEN

Ryan sneaks out at five in the morning. I keep my eyes squeezed shut, pretending to be asleep, not wanting to look at him or talk to him. I hear his footsteps cross the floor, followed by the squeak of the door. Get over it, I scold myself. It's not a big deal. They had sex. So what? It's not my business. But still. Doesn't Ryan care about his fiancée? And what about Maggie and her two boyfriends? Are there no limits when it comes to sex? Is sex really so powerful it can erase your history and common sense?

I fall into a fitful sleep and then a deeper one. I'm in the middle of a dream in which Viktor Greene is saying he loves me, except that Viktor looks just like Capote, when Maggie startles me awake.

"Hi," she says cheerfully, as if nothing untoward has happened. "Want some coffee?"

"Sure," I say, the whole rotten evening coming back to me. I'm drained and slightly angry again. I light a cigarette.

"You're smoking a lot," Maggie says.

"Ha," I say, thinking about how much she smokes.

"Did you notice I quit?"

Actually, I hadn't. "When?" I defiantly blow a few smoke rings.

"After I met Hank. He said it was disgusting and I realized he was right."

I wonder what Hank would think about Maggie's behavior last night.

She goes into the kitchen, finds the instant coffee and a kettle, and waits for the water to boil. "That was so much fun, wasn't it?"

"Yeah. I had a great time." I can't keep the sarcasm out of my voice.

"What's wrong now?" Maggie says. As if I'm the one who's been constantly complaining.

It's too early for a contentious discussion. "Nothing. But Ryan's in my class—"

"Which reminds me. Ryan is taking me to

a movie. By some Chinese director. *The Seven* something?"

"*The Seven Samurai*. By Kurosawa. He's Japanese."

"How do you know?"

"The guys are always talking about it. It's like six hours or something."

"I don't think we'll last six hours," she says slyly, handing me a mug of coffee.

One night I can excuse. But two? No way. "Listen, Mags. It's not a good idea if Ryan comes here tonight. Samantha might find out—"

"Don't worry." She settles next to me on the futon. "Ryan said we can go to his apartment."

I pick a floating grain of coffee from my brew. "What about his fiancée?"

"He said he thinks she's cheating."

"So that makes it okay?"

"Jesus, Carrie. What's your problem? You're so uptight."

I take a sip of coffee, willing myself not to react. "Uptight" is the one thing I pride myself on not being. But perhaps I don't know myself so well after all.

Class is at one, but I leave the apartment early, claiming errands. Maggie and I were perfectly civil to each other on the surface, but I was walking on eggshells. It took a concerted effort not to bring up Ryan, and even more strength not to mention Bernard. I promised myself I wouldn't talk about him, because if I did, I was afraid I'd accuse Maggie of ruining my relationship. And even to my illogical brain, this seemed a bit extreme.

When Maggie turned on the TV and started doing leg lifts, I made my escape.

There's still an hour before class, so I head over to the White Horse Tavern, where I can load up on decent coffee for a mere fifty cents. To my happy surprise, L'il is there, writing in her journal.

"I'm exhausted," I sigh, sitting across from her.

"You look fine," she says.

"I think I slept about two hours."

She closes her journal and looks at me knowingly. "Bernard?"

"I wish. Bernard dumped me—"

"I'm sorry." She gives me a sympathetic smile.

"Not officially," I say quickly. "But after last night, I think he will." I stir three packets of sugar into my coffee. "And my friend Maggie had sex with Ryan last night."

"That's why you're so pissed off."

"I'm not pissed off. I'm disappointed." She looks unconvinced, so I add, "I'm not jealous, either. Why would I be attracted to Ryan when I have Bernard?"

"Then why are you angry?"

"I don't know." I pause. "Ryan's engaged. And she has two boyfriends. It's wrong."

"The heart wants what the heart wants," she says, somewhat cryptically.

I purse my lips in disapproval. "You'd think the heart would know better."

I keep to myself in class. Ryan tries to engage me with talk about Maggie and how great she is, but I only nod coldly. Rainbow actually says hi, but Capote ignores me, as usual. At least he's still behaving normally.

And then Viktor asks me to read the first ten pages of my play. I'm shocked. Viktor has never asked me to read anything before, and it takes me a minute to adjust. How am I going to read the play alone? There are two parts—a man and a woman. I can't read the man's part too. I'll sound like an idiot.

Viktor has managed to divine this as well. "You'll read the part of Harriet," he says. "And Capote can read Moorehouse."

Capote glances around the room, peeved at the request. "Harriet? *Moorehouse?* What kind of name is Moorehouse?"

"I suppose we'll find out," Viktor says, twirling his mustache.

This is the best thing that's happened to me in at least two days. It might even make up for all the bad.

Clutching my script, I make my way to the front of the room, followed by a red-faced Capote. "What am I playing?" he asks.

"You're a forty-year-old guy who's going through a midlife crisis. And I'm your bitchy wife."

"Figures," he grumbles.

I smile. Is this the reason for his continuing animosity? He thinks I'm a bitch? If he actually thinks I'm a bitch, I'm glad.

We begin reading. By the second page, I'm into the part, focusing on what it must be like to be Harriet, an unhappy woman who wanted to be a success but whose success has been eclipsed by her childish husband.

By the third page, the class gets the idea it's supposed to be funny, and begins snickering. By the fifth page, I hear spurts of actual laughter. When we finish, there's a smattering of applause.

Wow.

I look at Capote, foolishly expecting his approval. But his expression is firm as he studiously avoids my glance. "Good job," he murmurs out of obligation.

I don't care. I go back to my seat floating on air.

"Comments?" Viktor asks.

"It's like a junior version of *Who's Afraid of Virginia Woolf?*," Ryan ventures. I look at him gratefully. Ryan has a loyalty about him that I suddenly appreciate. It's too bad his loyalty ends when it comes to sex. If a guy is a jerk about infidelity, but decent about everything else, is it okay to like him as a person?

"What I found intriguing is the way Carrie was able to make the most banal domestic scene interesting," Viktor says. "I liked that it takes place while the couple is brushing their teeth. It's an everyday activity we all do, no matter who we are."

"Like taking a crap," Capote remarks.

I smile as though I'm far too superior to take offense at his comment. But now it's official, I decide. I hate him.

Viktor pats his mustache with one hand and the top of his head with the other—a gesture that suggests he's attempting to keep all of his hair from running away. "And now, perhaps L'il will grace us with her poem?"

"Sure." L'il stands and goes to the front of the class. "'The Glass Slipper,'" she begins.

" 'My love broke me. As if my body were glass, smashed against the rocks, something used and disposed of. . . .'" The poem continues in this vein for several more lines, and when L'il is finished, she smiles uneasily.

"Thoughts?" Viktor says. There's an unusual edge to his voice.

"I liked it," I volunteer. "The broken glass is a great description of a broken heart." Which reminds me of how I'm going to feel if Bernard ends our relationship.

"It's pedantic and obvious," Viktor says. "Schoolgirlish and lazy. This is what happens when you take your talent for granted."

"Thank you," L'il says evenly, as if she doesn't care. She takes her seat, and when I glance over my shoulder, her head is down, her expression stricken. I know L'il is too strong to cry in class, but if she did, everyone would understand. Viktor can be unkind in his straightforward assessments, but he's never been deliberately mean.

He must be feeling guilty, though, because he's raking at poor Waldo like he's trying to rip him off his face. "To summarize, I'm looking forward to hearing more from Carrie's play. While L'il—" He breaks off and turns away.

This should make me ecstatic, but it doesn't. L'il doesn't deserve the criticism. Which could mean, conversely, that I don't deserve the excessive approval either. Being great isn't so fabulous when it comes at someone else's expense.

I gather my papers, wondering what just happened. Perhaps, when it comes right down to it, Viktor is just another fickle guy. Only instead of being fickle about women, he's fickle about his favorite students. He bestowed his honors on L'il at the beginning, but now he's bored, and I'm the one who's captured his attention.

L'il races out of class. I catch up with her at the elevator, pressing the "close" button before anyone else can get on. "I'm sorry. I thought your poem was wonderful. I truly did," I say profusely, trying to make up for Viktor's critique.

L'il clutches her book bag to her chest. "He was right. The poem sucked. And I do need to work harder."

"You already work harder than anyone in the class, L'il. You work a hell of a lot harder than I do. I'm the one who's lazy."

She gives a little shake of her head. "You're not lazy, Carrie. You're unafraid."

Now I'm confused, given our discussion about my fears as a writer. "I wouldn't say *that*."

"It's true. You're not afraid of this city. Not afraid to try new things."

"You're not either," I say kindly.

We get out of the elevator and step outside. The sun is blazing and the heat is like a slap in the face. L'il squints and puts on a pair of cheap sunglasses, the kind the street vendors sell at every other corner. "Enjoy it, Carrie," she insists. "And don't worry about me. Are you going to tell Bernard?"

"About what?"

"Your play. You should show it to him. I'm sure he'll love it."

I peer at her closely, wondering if she's being cynical, but I can't see any trace of malice. Besides, L'il isn't like that. She's never been jealous of anyone. "Yeah," I say. "Maybe I will."

Bernard. I *should* show him my play. But after last night, is he even speaking to me anymore?

Nothing I can do about it, though. Because now I have to meet Samantha to help her with her crazy dinner party.

CHAPTER SEVENTEEN

"What do we do first?" Samantha asks, clapping her hands in an attempt at enthusiasm.

I look at her like she has to be kidding. "Well, first we buy the food," I say, as if I'm talking to a kindergartner.

"Where do we do that?"

My jaw drops in disbelief. "At a supermarket?" When Samantha said she knew nothing about cooking, I never assumed she meant absolutely nothing, including the fact that "food" is usually made from "ingredients" purchased at a "supermarket."

"And where's the supermarket?"

I want to scream. Instead, I stare at her blankly. She's sitting behind her desk in her office, wearing a low-cut sweater with linebacker shoulders, pearls, and a short skirt. She looks sexy, cool, and collected. I, on the other hand, look ragged and out of place, especially as I'm wearing what is basically some old lady's slip that I've cinched with a cowboy belt. Another great find at the vintage store. "Have you considered takeout?" I ask smartly.

She emits her tinkling laugh. "Charlie thinks I can cook. I don't want to disabuse him of the fact."

"And why, pray tell, does he think that?"

"Because I told him, Sparrow," she says, becoming slightly irked. She stands up and puts her hands on her hips. "Haven't you heard the expression 'Fake it till you make it'? I'm the original fake-it girl."

"Okay." I throw up my hands in defeat. "I'll need to see Charlie's kitchen first. See what kind of pans he has."

"No problem. His apartment is spectacular. I'll take you there now." She picks up a giant Kelly bag, which I've never seen before.

"Is that new?" I ask, half in admiration and half in envy.

She strokes the soft leather before she slings it over her shoulder. "It's nice, isn't it? Charlie bought it for me."

"Some people have quite the life."

"Play your cards right, and you'll have quite the life too, Sparrow."

"How's this grand scheme of yours going to go down?" I ask. "What if Charlie finds out—"

She waves this away. "He won't. The only time Charlie's been in the kitchen is when we have sex on the counter."

I make a face. "And you honestly expect me to prepare food on it?"

"It's clean, Carrie. Haven't you ever heard of maids?"

"Not in my universe."

We're interrupted by the entry of a short man with sandy brown hair who looks exactly like a tiny Ken doll. "Are you leaving?" he says sharply to Samantha.

A flash of annoyance crosses her face before she quickly composes herself. "Family emergency," she says.

"What about the Smirnoff account?" he demands.

"Vodka has been around for over two hundred years, Harry. I daresay it will still be here tomorrow. My sister, on the other hand," she says, indicating me, "may not."

As if on cue, my entire body floods in embarrassment, rendering me bright red.

Harry, however, isn't buying it. He scrutinizes me closely—apparently, he needs glasses but is too vain to wear them. "Your sister?" he asks. "When did you get a sister?"

"Really, Harry." Samantha shakes her head.

Harry stands aside to let us pass, then follows us down the hall. "Will you be back later?"

Samantha stops and slowly turns around. Her lips curl into a smile. "My goodness, Harry. You sound just like my father."

This does the trick, all right. Harry turns about fifteen shades of green. He's not much older than Samantha, and I'm sure the last thing he expected was to be compared to someone's old man.

"What was that about?" I ask, when we're out on the street.

"Harry?" she says, unconcerned. "He's my new boss."

"You talk to your new boss like that?"

"Have to," she says. "Considering how he talks to me."

"Meaning?"

"Well, let's see," she says, pausing at the light. "On his first day of work, he comes into my office and says, 'I've heard you're highly competent at everything you put your mind to.' Sounds like a compliment, right? But then he adds, 'Both in and out of the office.'"

"Can he actually get away with that?"

"Of course." She shrugs. "You've never worked in an office, so you have no idea. But eventually, sex always comes up. When it does, I give it right back to them."

"But shouldn't you tell someone?"

"Who?" she says. "His boss? Human Resources? He'll either say he was joking or I came on to him. What if I'm fired? I don't plan to sit at home all day, popping out babies and baking cookies."

"I don't know about your mothering skills, but considering your cooking abilities, it's probably not a good idea."

"Thank you," she says, having made her point.

Samantha may have lied to Charlie about her culinary knowledge, but she wasn't kidding about the apartment. His building is on Park Avenue in Midtown, and it's gold. Not real gold, of course, but some kind of shiny gold metal. And if I thought the doormen in Bernard's building were sharp, the doormen in Charlie's building have them beat. Not only are they wearing white gloves, they're sporting caps with gold braid. Even their uniforms have loops of gold braid hanging from the shoulders. It's all pretty tacky. But impressive.

"You really live here?" I ask in a whisper as we cross the lobby. It's marble and it echoes.

"Of course," she says, greeting a doorman who is politely holding the elevator. "It's very me, don't you think? Glamorous yet classy."

"I guess that's one way to look at it," I murmur, taking in the smoky mirrored walls that line the interior of the lift.

Charlie's apartment is, not surprisingly, enormous. It's on the forty-fifth floor with floor-to-ceiling windows, a sunken living room, another wall of smoky mirrors, and a large Plexiglas case filled with baseball memorabilia. I'm sure it has several bedrooms and bathrooms, but I don't get to see them because Samantha immediately directs me to the kitchen. It, too, is enormous, with marble countertops and gleaming appliances. It's new all right. Too new.

"Has anyone ever cooked in here?" I ask, opening the cabinets to look for pots and pans.

"I don't think so." Samantha pats me on the shoulder. "You'll figure it out. I have faith in you. Now wait till you see what I'm going to wear."

"Great," I mutter. The kitchen is practically bare. I find a roll of aluminum foil, some muffin tins, three bowls, and a large frying pan.

"Ta-da!" She says, reappearing in the doorway in a French maid's outfit. "What do you think?"

"If you're planning to work on Forty-second Street, it's just peachy."

"Charlie loves it when I wear this."

"Look, sweetie," I say, between gritted teeth. "This is a dinner party. You can't wear that."

"I know," she says, exasperated. "God, Carrie, can't you take a joke?"

"Not when I have to prepare an entire meal with three bowls and a roll of aluminum foil. Who's coming to this shindig anyway?"

She holds up her hand. "Me, Charlie, some really boring couple who Charlie works with, another really boring couple, and Charlie's sister, Erica. And my friend Cholly, to liven things up."

"Cholly?"

"Cholly Hammond. You met him at the same party where you met Bernard."

"The seersucker guy."

"He runs a literary magazine. You'll like him."

I wave the aluminum foil in her face. "I won't get to see him, remember? I'll be in here, cooking."

"If cooking makes you this neurotic, you really shouldn't do it," Samantha says.

"Thanks, sweetie. But I believe this was your idea, remember?"

"Oh, I know," she says airily. "C'mon. I need you to help me pick out something to wear.

Charlie's friends are very conservative."

I follow her down a carpeted hallway and into a large suite with a walk-in closet and his-and-her bathrooms. I gawk at the splendor of it all. Imagine having this much space in Manhattan. No wonder Samantha's so eager to get hitched.

When we enter the closet, I nearly fall over in a dead faint. The closet alone is the size of Samantha's entire apartment. On one side are racks and racks of Charlie's clothing, arranged by type and color. His jeans are ironed and folded over hangers. Stacks of cashmere sweaters in every color are piled neatly on the shelves.

At the other end is Samantha's section, made obvious not only by her work suits and high-heeled pumps and the slinky dresses she loves to wear, but by its relative meagerness. "Hey, sister, looks like you've got some catching up to do," I point out.

"I'm working on it," she laughs.

"What's this?" I ask, indicating a bouclé suit with white piping. "Chanel?" I look at the price tag, which is still on the sleeve, and gasp. "Twelve hundred dollars?"

"Thank you." She removes the hanger from my hands.

"Can you afford that?"

"I can't not afford it. If you want the life, you

have to look the part." She frowns. "I would think you of all people would understand. Aren't you obsessed with fashion?"

"Not at these prices. This lovely garment I'm wearing cost two bucks."

"It looks it," she says, taking off the French maid's outfit and dropping it onto the floor.

She slides into the Chanel suit and considers her image in the full-length mirror. "What do you think?"

"Isn't that what all those ladies wear? The ones who lunch? I know it's Chanel, but it's not really you."

"Which makes it perfect for an up-and-coming Upper East Side lady."

"But you're not one," I object, thinking about all those crazy nights we've spent together.

She puts her finger to her lips. "I am now. And I will be, for as long as I need to be."

"And then what?"

"I'll be independently wealthy. Maybe I'll live in Paris."

"You're planning to divorce Charlie before you've even married him? What if you have kids?"

"What do you think, Sparrow?" She kicks the French maid's uniform into the closet and looks at me pointedly. "I believe someone has some cooking to do."

Four hours later, despite the fact that the oven is going and two burners are lit, I'm shivering with cold. Charlie keeps the apartment cooled to the temperature of a refrigerated truck. It's probably ninety degrees outside, but I sure could use one of his cashmere sweaters right now.

How can Samantha take it? I wonder, stirring the pan. But I suppose she's used to it. If you marry one of these mogul types, you kind of have to do what they want.

"Carrie?" Samantha asks, coming into the kitchen. "How's it going?"

"The main course is almost ready."

"Thank God," she says, taking a gulp of red wine from a large goblet. "I'm going insane out there."

"What do you think I'm doing in here?"

"At least you don't have to talk about window treatments."

"How do you 'treat' a window? Do you send it to a doctor?"

"Decorator," she sighs. "Twenty thousand dollars. For curtains. I don't think I can do it."

"You'd better do it. I'm freezing my butt off in here so you can look good. I still don't understand why you didn't hire a caterer."

"Because Superwoman doesn't hire a caterer.

She does everything herself."

"Here," I say, handing her two finished plates. "And don't forget your cape."

"What are we having, anyway?" She looks at the plates in consternation.

"Lamp chops with a mushroom cream sauce. The green stuff is asparagus. And those brown things are potatoes," I say sardonically. "Has Charlie figured out I'm back here cooking?"

"Doesn't have a clue." She smiles.

"Good. Then just tell him it's French."

"Thanks, Sparrow." She wheels out. Through the open door, I hear her exclaim, "Voilà."

Unfortunately, I can't see the guests, because the dining room is around the corner. I caught a glimpse of it though. The table was also Plexiglas. Apparently Charlie has a love of plastic.

I get to work on the mini chocolate soufflés. I'm about to put them into the oven when a voice exclaims, "Aha! I knew it was too good to be true."

I jump a mile, nearly dropping the muffin pan. "Cholly?" I hiss.

"Carrie Bradshaw, I presume," he says, strolling purposefully into the kitchen and opening the freezer. "I was wondering what became of you. Now I know."

"Actually, you don't," I say, gently closing the oven door.

"Why is Samantha keeping you hidden back here?"

I open my mouth to explain, then catch myself. Cholly seems like the gossipy type—he'll probably run out and spill the beans that it's me doing the cooking. I'm just like Cyrano, except I don't think I'm going to get the guy at the end.

"Listen, Cholly—"

"I get it," he says with a wink. "I've known Samantha for years. I doubt she can boil an egg."

"Are you going to tell?"

"And spoil the fun? No, little one," he says, kindly. "Your secret's safe with me."

He goes out, and two minutes later, Samantha comes running back in. "What happened?" she asks in a panic. "Did Cholly see you? That meddling old man. I knew I shouldn't have invited him. And it was going so well. You could practically see the steam coming out of the other women's ears, they were so jealous." She grits her teeth in frustration and puts her hands over her face. It's the first time I've seen her genuinely distraught, and I wonder if her fabulous relationship with Charlie is everything she says it is.

"Hey," I say, touching her shoulder. "It's okay. Cholly promised he wouldn't tell."

"Really?"

"Yes. And I think he'll keep his word. He

seems like a pretty nice old guy."

"He is," she says in relief. "And those women out there, they're like snakes. During cocktails, one of them kept asking me when we were planning to have children. When I said I didn't know, she got all superior and told me I'd better get on it right away before Charlie changed his mind about marrying me. And then she asked me when I was planning to quit my job."

"What'd you say?" I ask, in indignation.

"I said, 'Never. Because I don't consider my work a job. I consider it a career. And you don't quit a career.' That shut her up for a minute. Then she asked where I went to college."

"And?"

Samantha straightens. "I lied. Said I went to a little school in Boston."

"Oh, sweetie."

"What difference does it make? I'm not going to risk losing Charlie because some uptight society matron doesn't approve of where I went to school. I've gotten this far, and I don't plan to go back."

"Of course not," I say, touching her shoulder. I pause. "Maybe I should go. Before anyone else wanders in."

She nods. "That's a good idea."

"The soufflés are in the oven. All you have to do is take them out in twenty minutes, turn them over onto a plate, and put a scoop of ice cream on top."

She looks at me gratefully, and envelops me in a hug. "Thanks, Sparrow. I couldn't have pulled this off without you."

She takes a step back and smoothes her hair. "Oh, and Sparrow?" she adds carefully. "Would you mind going out the service entrance?"

CHAPTER EIGHTEEN

Where is everybody? I think in annoyance as I bang down the phone for the millionth time.

When I got home last night, I kept wondering about Samantha and Charlie. Was that the way to a happy relationship? Turning yourself into what the man wanted?

On the other hand, it seemed to be working. For Samantha, anyway. And in comparison, my own relationship with Bernard was sorely lacking. Not only in sex, but in the simple fact that I still wasn't sure I was ever going to see him again. I guess the best thing about living with a guy is that you know you're going to see him again. I mean, he has to come home at some point, right?

Unfortunately, the same can't be said of Bernard. And it's all Maggie's fault. If she hadn't been so rude, if she hadn't insisted on tracking down Ryan and seducing him . . . And she's still *with* Ryan, having a mini affair, while I've got nothing. I've become a handmaiden to other people's relationships. Aiding and abetting. And now *I'm* all alone.

Thank God for Miranda. I'll always have her. Miranda will never have a relationship. So where the hell is she?

I pick up the phone and try her again. No answer. Strange, as it's raining, which means she can't be marching around in front of Saks. I try Bernard again too. No answer there either. Feeling thoroughly pissed off, I call Ryan. Jeez. Even he's not picking up. Figures. He and Maggie are probably holed up having sex for the twentieth time.

I give up. I stare at the rain. Drip, drip, drip. It's depressing.

At last the buzzer goes off. Two short toots, followed by a long one, like someone's leaning on the button. *Maggie*. Great friend she is. She came to New York to see me, but spent all her time with stupid old Ryan. I go out into the hallway and lean over the stairs, prepared to give her a piece of my mind.

Instead I see the top of Miranda's head. The

rain has flattened her bright red hair into a neat cap.

"Hey," I exclaim.

"It's pissing out there. Thought I'd stop off here till it lets up."

"C'mon in." I hand her a towel and she rubs her hair, the damp strands standing up from her head like the crest on a rooster. Unlike me, she appears to be full of good cheer. She goes into the kitchen, opens the refrigerator, and peers in. "Got anything to eat in this place?"

"Cheese."

"Yum. I'm starving." She grabs a small knife and attacks the brick of cheddar. "Hey. Have you noticed how you haven't heard from me for two days?"

Actually, I haven't. I've been too busy with Maggie and Samantha and Bernard. "Yeah," I say. "Where were you?"

"Guess." She grins.

"You went to a rally? In Washington?"

"Nope. Guess again."

"I give up." I wander to the futon and flop down, gazing out the window. I light a cigarette, thinking about how I'm not in the mood for games.

She balances on the arm of the futon, munching her cheese. "Having sex."

"Huh?" I stub out the cigarette.

"Having sex," she repeats. She slides onto the cushion. "I met a guy and we've been having non-stop sex for the last two days. And the worst thing about it? I couldn't poop. I honestly could not poop until he finally left this morning."

"Hold on. *You* met a guy?"

"Yes, Carrie. *I* did. Believe it or not, there are some men who find me attractive."

"I never said there weren't. But you always say—"

"I know." She nods. "Sex sucks. But this time, it didn't."

I stare at her wide-eyed and slightly jealous, not knowing where to begin.

"He's a law student at NYU," she says, settling into the couch. "I met him in front of Saks. At first, I didn't want to talk to him because he was wearing a bow tie—"

"*What?*"

"And it was yellow. With black polka dots. He kept walking by and I kept trying to ignore him, but he signed the petition, so I thought I'd try to be polite. Turns out he's been studying all these cases about free speech and pornography. He says the porn industry was the first to use the printing press. Did you know that? It wasn't because every-one wanted to read all this great literature. It was because men wanted to look at dirty pictures!"

"Wow," I bleat, trying to get into the spirit of things.

"We were talking and talking, and then he said why don't we continue this discussion over dinner? I wasn't really attracted to him, but he seemed like an interesting guy and I thought maybe we could be friends. So I said yes."

"Fantastic." I force a smile. "Where did you go?"

"Japonica. This Japanese restaurant on University. And it wasn't cheap, by the way. I tried to split it with him but he wouldn't."

"You let a man pay for you?" This isn't at all like Miranda.

She smiles awkwardly. "It goes against everything I believe in. But I told myself that maybe this once, I could let it go. I kept thinking about that night with you and your friend L'il. About how her mother was a lesbian. I kept wondering if maybe I was a lesbian, but if I am, how come I'm not attracted to women?"

"Maybe you haven't met the right one," I joke.

"Carrie!" she says, but she's in too good a mood to be offended. "I've always been attracted to guys. I just wish they were more like women. But with Marty—"

"That's his name? Marty?"

"He can't help his name. I mean, you don't

exactly get to name yourself, do you? But I was kind of worried. Because I wasn't sure I could even kiss him." She lowers her voice. "He's not the best-looking guy. But I told myself that looks aren't everything. And he really *is* smart. Which can be a turn-on. I've always said I'd rather be with a smart, ugly guy than a good-looking dumb guy. Because what are you going to talk about with a dumb guy?"

"The weather?" I ask, wondering if Bernard thinks the same thing about me. Maybe I'm not smart enough for him and that's why he hasn't called.

"So then," Miranda continues, "we're walking through the Mews—that cute little cobblestoned street—and suddenly he pushes me up against the wall and starts making out with me!"

I shriek while Miranda bobs her head. "I couldn't believe it myself," she titters. "And the crazy thing about it was that it was totally sexy. We made out every five seconds on the street and when we got to my house, we ripped off our clothes and we did it!"

"Amazing," I say, lighting another cigarette. "Absolutely amazing."

"We did it three times that night. And the next morning, he took me to breakfast. I was worried it was a one-night stand, but he called in the afternoon and came over and we had sex again and he spent the night and we've seen each other practically every minute since then."

"Hold on," I say, waving my cigarette. "Every minute?" And another one bites the dust. Miranda is going to have some big romance with this guy she just met, and I'll never see her again either.

"I hardly know him," she giggles, "but so what? If it's right, it's right, don't you think?"

"I guess so," I say grudgingly.

"Can you believe it? Me? Having nonstop sex? Especially after all those things I told you. And now that I've finally had good sex, I'm thinking it might give me a new perspective on life. Like all men aren't necessarily horrible after all."

"That's great," I say weakly, feeling sorry for myself.

And then it happens. My eyes well up with tears.

I quickly brush them away, but Miranda catches me. "What's wrong?"

"Nothing."

"Why are you crying?" Her face screws up with worry. "You're not mad because I have a boyfriend now, are you?"

I shake my head.

"Carrie. I can't help you unless you tell me what's wrong," she says gently.

I spill the whole story, starting with the disastrous dinner with Bernard and how Maggie insisted we go to a party and how she ended up with Ryan and how Bernard hasn't called me and now it's probably over. "How did this happen to me?" I wail. "I should have slept with Bernard when I had the chance. Now it will never happen. I'll be a virgin for the rest of my life. Even L'il isn't a virgin. And my friend Maggie is sleeping with three guys. At once! What's wrong with me?"

Miranda puts her arms around my shoulders. "Poor baby," she says soothingly. "You're having a bad day."

"Bad day? More like bad week," I sniffle. But I'm grateful for her kindness. Miranda is usually so prickly. I can't help but wonder if maybe she's right and two days of great sex have awakened her maternal instinct.

"Not everyone is the same," she says firmly. "People develop at different times."

"But I don't want to be the last."

"Lots of famous people are late bloomers. My father says it's an advantage to be a late bloomer. Because when good things start happening, you're ready for it."

"Like you were finally ready for Marty?"

"I guess so." She nods. "I liked it, Carrie. Oh my God. I really liked it." She covers her mouth in horror. "If I like sex, do you think it means I can't be a feminist?"

"No." I shake my head. "Because being a feminist—I think it means being in charge of your sexuality. You decide who you want to have sex with. It means not trading your sexuality for . . . other things."

"Like marrying some gross guy who you're not in love with just so you can have a nice house with a picket fence."

"Or marrying a rich old geezer. Or a guy who expects you to cook him dinner every night and take care of the children," I say, thinking of Samantha.

"Or a guy who makes you have sex with him whenever he wants, even if you don't," Miranda concludes.

We look at each other in triumph, as if we've finally solved one of the world's great problems.

CHAPTER NINETEEN

At about seven, when Miranda and I have taken a few swigs from the bottle of vodka and have proceeded to interpretive-dance our way through Blondie, the Ramones, The Police, and Elvis Costello, Maggie arrives.

"Magwitch!" I exclaim, throwing my arms around her, determined to forgive and forget.

She takes in Miranda, who has picked up a candle and is singing into it like it's a microphone. "Who *is* that?"

"Miranda!" I shout. "This is my friend Maggie. My best friend from high school."

"Hi." Miranda waves the candle at her.

Maggie spots the vodka, storms toward it, and proceeds to pour half the bottle down her throat.

"Don't worry," she snaps, catching my expression. "I can buy more. I'm eighteen, remember?"

"So?" I say, wondering what this has to do with anything. She glares at Miranda and drops onto the futon.

"Ryan stood me up," she snarls.

"Huh?" I'm puzzled. "Haven't you been with him for the last twenty-four hours?"

"Yes. But the minute I let him out of my sight, he disappeared."

I can't help it. I start laughing.

"It isn't funny. We were at some coffee shop getting breakfast at six in the evening. I went into the bathroom, and when I came out, he was gone."

"He ran away?"

"Sure sounds like it, doesn't it?"

"Oh, Mags." I'm trying to be sympathetic. But I can't quite get there. It's all too ridiculous. And not terribly surprising.

"Could you turn that thing off?" Maggie shouts at Miranda. "It's hurting my ears."

"Sorry," I say, to both Maggie and Miranda, as I scurry across the room to lower the volume on the stereo.

"What's her problem?" Miranda asks. She sounds put out, which I know she doesn't intend. She's just a bit soused.

"Ryan ran out of the coffee shop while she

was in the bathroom."

"Ah," Miranda says with a smile.

"Mags?" I ask, making a cautious approach. "There's nothing Miranda likes more than guy troubles. Mostly because she hates all men." I hope this introduction will make Maggie and Miranda appreciate each other. After all, guy troubles, along with clothing and body parts, are a major source of bonding among women.

But Maggie isn't having it. "Why didn't you tell me he was a dick?" she demands.

This isn't fair. "I thought I did. You knew he was engaged."

"You're dating a guy who's engaged?" Miranda asks, not liking the sound of this.

"He isn't really engaged. He *says* he's engaged. She made him get engaged so she could string him along." Maggie takes another swig of vodka. "That's what I think, anyway."

"It's a good thing he left," I say. "Now at least you know his true nature."

"Here, here," Miranda adds.

"Hey. Miranda just got a new boyfriend," I tell Maggie.

"Lucky you." Maggie scowls, unimpressed.

"Maggie has two boyfriends," I say to Miranda, as if this is something to be admired.

"That's something I've never understood.

How do you handle it? I mean, they're always saying you should date two or three guys at once, but I've never seen the point," Miranda says.

"It's fun," Maggie retorts.

"But it goes both ways, right?" Miranda counters. "We hate guys who date more than one woman at a time. I've always believed that what's unacceptable in one sex should, by definition, be unacceptable in the other."

"Excuse me." Maggie sounds a warning note. "I hope you're not calling me a slut."

"Of course not!" I jump in. "Miranda's only talking about feminism."

"Then you shouldn't have any problem with women having sex with as many men as they want," Maggie says pointedly. "To me, that's feminism."

"You can do anything you want, sweetie," I reassure her. "No one's judging you."

"All I'm saying is that men and women are the same. They should be held to the same standards," Miranda insists.

"I totally disagree. Men and women are completely different," Maggie replies obstinately.

"I kind of hate when people say men and women are different," I interject. "It sounds like an excuse. Like when people say, 'Boys will be boys.' It makes me want to scream."

"It makes me want to sock someone," Miranda agrees.

Maggie stands up. "All I can say is that you two deserve each other." And while Miranda and I look at her in bewilderment, Maggie runs into the bathroom and slams the door.

"Was it something I said?" Miranda asks.

"It's not you. It's me. She's mad at me. About something. Even though I should be mad at her."

I knock on the bathroom door. "Mags? Are you okay? We were just having a conversation. We weren't saying anything bad about you."

"I'm taking a shower," she shouts.

Miranda gathers her things. "I'd better go."

"Okay," I demur, dreading being left alone with Maggie. Once she gets angry, she can carry a grudge for days.

"Marty's coming over anyway. After he finishes studying." She waves and hurries down the stairs.

Lucky her.

The shower is still going full blast. I straighten up my desk, hoping the worst is not to come.

Eventually Maggie comes out of the bathroom toweling her hair. She begins picking up her things, stuffing clothing into her duffel bag.

"You're not leaving, are you?"

"I think I should," she grumbles.

"C'mon, sweetie. I'm sorry. Miranda is just very adamant about her views. She doesn't have anything against you. She doesn't even know you."

"You can say that again."

"Since you're not seeing Ryan, maybe we could go to a movie?" I ask hopefully.

"There's nothing I want to see." She looks around. "Where's the phone?"

It's under the chair. I grab it and hand it over reluctantly. "Listen, Mags," I say, trying not to be confrontational. "If you don't mind, could you not call South Carolina? I have to pay for the long distance calls, and I don't have that much money."

"Is that all you're about now? Money?"

"No—"

"As a matter of fact, I'm calling the bus."

"You don't have to go," I say, desperate to make up. I don't want her visit to end in a fight.

Maggie ignores me, looking at her watch as she nods into the receiver. "Thanks." She hangs up. "There's a bus that leaves for Philadelphia in forty-five minutes. Do you think I can make it?"

"Yes. But, Maggie—" I break off. I really don't know what to say.

"You've changed, Carrie," she says, zipping up her bag with a snap.

"I still don't know why you're so angry.

Whatever I've done, I'm sorry."

"You're a different person. I don't know who you are anymore." She punctuates this with a shake of her head.

I sigh. This confrontation has likely been brewing since the moment Maggie turned up at the apartment and declared it a slum. "The only thing that's different about me is that I'm in New York."

"I know. You haven't stopped reminding me of the fact for two days."

"I do live here—"

"You know what?" She picks up her bag. "Everyone here is crazy. Your roommate Samantha is crazy. Bernard is a creep, and your friend Miranda is a freak. And Ryan is an asshole." She pauses while I cringe, imagining what's coming next. "And now you're just like them. You're crazy too."

I'm stunned. "Thanks a lot."

"You're welcome." She starts for the door. "And don't worry about taking me to the bus station. I can get there myself."

"Fine." I shrug.

She exits the apartment, banging the door behind her. For a moment, I'm too shaken to move. How dare she attack me? And why is it always about her? The whole time she was here, she barely had the decency to ask me how I was doing. She could have tried to understand my situation instead of criticizing everything about it.

I take a deep breath. I yank open the door and run after her. "Maggie!"

She's already outside, standing on the curb, her arm raised to hail a taxi. I hurry toward her as a taxi pulls up and she opens the door.

"Maggie!"

She spins around, her hand on the handle. "What?"

"Come on. Don't leave this way. *I'm sorry.*"

Her face has turned to stone. "Good." She crawls into the backseat and shuts the door.

My body sags as I watch the taxi weave into traffic. I tilt my head back, letting the rain's drizzle soothe my hurt feelings. "Why?" I ask aloud.

I stomp back into the building. Damn Ryan. He *is* an asshole. If he hadn't stood Maggie up, we wouldn't have had this fight. We'd still be friends. Sure, I'd be a little pissed off with her for sleeping with Ryan, but I would have ignored it. For the sake of our friendship.

Why can't she extend the same courtesy to me?

I bang around in the apartment a while, all churned up about Maggie's disastrous visit. I hesitate, then pick up the phone and call Walt.

While it rings, I remember how I've neglected

Walt all summer and how he's probably pissed at me too. I shudder, thinking about what a bad friend I've been. I'm not even sure Walt is still living at home. When his mother picks up, I say, "It's Carrie," in the sweetest voice possible. "Is Walt there?"

"Hello, Carrie," Walt's mother says. "Are you still in New York?"

"Yes, I am."

"I'm sure Walt will be very happy to hear from you," she adds, sticking another knife into the wound. "Walt!" she calls out. "It's Carrie."

I hear Walt coming into the kitchen. I picture the red Formica table crowded with chairs. The dog's bowl slopped over with water. The toaster oven where Walt's mother keeps the sugar so ants won't get it. And, no doubt, the look of confusion on Walt's face. Wondering why I've decided to call him now, when I've forgotten him for weeks.

"Hello?" he asks.

"Walt!" I exclaim.

"Is this *the* Carrie Bradshaw?"

"I guess so."

"What a surprise. I thought you were dead."

"Oh, Walt." I giggle nervously, knowing I deserve a hard time.

Walt seems ready to forgive, because the next thing he asks is, "Well, *qué pasa*? How's Nuevo?"

"*Bueno. Muy bueno*," I reply. "How are you?" I lower my voice. "Are you still seeing Randy?"

"*Mais oui!*" he exclaims. "In fact, my father has decided to look the other way. Thanks to Randy's interest in football."

"That's great. You're having a real relationship."

"It appears so, yes. Much to my surprise."

"You're lucky, Walt."

"What about you? Anyone special?" he asks, putting a sarcastic spin on "special."

"I don't know. I've been seeing this guy. But he's older. Maggie met him," I say, getting to my underlying reason for the call. "She hated him."

Walt laughs. "I'm not surprised. Maggie hates everyone these days."

"Why?"

"Because she has no idea what to do with her life. And she can't stand anyone who does."

Thirty minutes later, I've told Walt the whole story about Maggie's visit, which he finds immensely entertaining. "Why don't you come to visit me?" I ask, feeling better. "You and Randy. You could sleep in the bed."

"A bed's too good for Randy," Walt says jokingly. "He can sleep on the floor. In fact, he can sleep anywhere. If you take him to a store, he'll fall asleep standing up."

I smile. "Seriously, though."

"When are you coming home?" he asks.

"I don't know."

"You know about your father, of course," he says smoothly.

"No."

"Oops."

"Why?" I ask. "What's going on?"

"Hasn't anyone told you? Your father has a girlfriend."

I clutch the phone in disbelief. But it makes sense. No wonder he's been acting so strange lately.

"I'm sorry. I figured you knew," Walt continues. "I only know because my mother told me. She's going to be the new librarian at the high school. She's like twenty-five or something."

"My father is dating a twenty-five-year-old?" I shriek.

"I thought you'd want to know."

"Damn right," I say, furious. "I guess I'll be coming home this weekend after all."

"Great," Walt says. "We could use some excitement around here."

CHAPTER TWENTY

"This will never do," Samantha says, shaking her head.

"It's luggage." I, too, glare at the offending suitcase. It's ugly, but still, the sight of that suitcase makes me insanely jealous. I'm going back to boring old Castlebury while Samantha is headed for Los Angeles.

Los Angeles! It's a very big deal and she only found out yesterday. She's going to shoot a commercial and stay at the Beverly Hills Hotel, which is where all the movie stars hang out. She bought enormous sunglasses and a big straw hat and a Norma Kamali bathing suit that you wear with a white T-shirt underneath. In honor of the occasion, I tried to find a palm tree at the party store, but all they had were some green paper leafy things that I've wrapped around my head.

There are clothes and shoes everywhere. Samantha's enormous green plastic Samsonite suitcase lies open on the living room floor.

"It's not luggage, it's baggage," she complains.

"Who's going to notice?"

"Everyone. We're flying first-class. There'll be porters. And bellhops. What are the bellhops going to think when they discover Samantha Jones travels with Samsonite?"

I love it when Samantha does that funny thing and talks about herself in the third person. I tried it once myself, but there was no way I could pull it off. "Do you honestly think the bellhops are going to be more interested in Samsonite than Samantha Jones?"

"That's just it. They'll expect my luggage to be glamorous as well."

"I bet that jerky Harry Mills carries American Tourister. Hey," I say, swinging my legs off the back of the couch. "Did you ever think that someday you'd be traveling with a man you hardly knew? It's kind of weird, isn't it? What if your suitcase opens by accident and he sees your Skivvies?"

"I'm not worried about my lingerie. I'm worried about my image. I never thought I'd have this life when I bought that." She frowns at the suitcase.

"What *did* you think?" I hardly know anything about Samantha's past, besides the fact that she comes from New Jersey and seems to hate her mother. She never mentions her father, so these tidbits about her early life are always fascinating.

"Only about getting away. Far, far away."

"But New Jersey's just across the river."

"Physically, yes. Metaphorically, no. And New York wasn't my first stop."

"It wasn't?" Now I'm really intrigued. I can't imagine Samantha living anywhere but New York.

"I traveled all around the world when I was eighteen."

I nearly fall off the couch. "How?"

She smiles. "I was a groupie. To a very famous rock 'n' roll guy. I was at a concert and he picked me out of the crowd. He asked me to travel with him and I was stupid enough to think I was his girlfriend. Then I found out he had a wife stashed away in the English countryside. That suitcase has been all around the world."

I wonder if Samantha's hatred of her luggage is actually due to a bad association with the past. "And then what happened?"

She shrugs, picking out lingerie from the pile and

folding the pieces into little squares. "He dumped me. In Moscow. His wife suddenly decided to join him. He woke up that afternoon and said, 'Darling, I'm afraid it's over. You're binned.'"

"Just like that?"

"He was English," she says, laying the squares into the bottom of the suitcase. "That's what Englishmen do. When it's over, it's over. No phone calls, no letters, and especially no crying."

"Did you? Cry?" I can't picture it.

"What do you think? I was all alone in Moscow with nothing but this stupid suitcase. And a plane ticket to New York. I was jumping up and down for joy."

I can't tell if she's kidding or not.

"In other words, it's your runaway suitcase," I point out. "And now that you don't need to run anymore, you need something better. Something permanent."

"Hmmm," she says cryptically.

"What's it like?" I ask. "When you pass a record store and see the rock 'n' roll guy's face on a poster? Does it make you feel weird to think you spent all that time with him?"

"I'm grateful." She grabs a shoe and looks around for its partner. "Sometimes I think if it weren't for him, I wouldn't have made it to New York at all."

"Didn't you always want to come here?"

She shrugs. "I was a wild child. I didn't know what I wanted. I only knew I didn't want to end up a waitress and pregnant at nineteen. Like Shirley."

"Oh."

"My mother," she clarifies.

I'm not surprised. There's an underlying pulse of determination in Samantha that has to come from somewhere.

"You're lucky." She finds the matching shoe and pushes it into the corner of the suitcase. "At least you have parents who will pay for college."

"Yeah," I say vaguely. Despite her confessions about her past, I'm not ready to tell her about my own. "But I thought you went to college."

"Oh, Sparrow." She sighs. "I took a couple of night courses when I arrived in New York. I got a job through a temp agency. The first place they sent me was Slovey, Dinall. I was a secretary. They didn't even call them 'assistants' back then. Anyway, it's boring."

Not to me. But the fact that she's come so far from nothing puts my own struggles to shame. "It must have been hard."

"It was." She presses down on the top of the suitcase. There's practically her whole closet in there, so naturally, it won't shut. I kneel on the cover as she clicks the locks into place.

The phone rings as we're dragging the suitcase to the door. Samantha ignores the insistent ringing, so I make a move to grab it. "Don't answer," she warns. But I've already picked it up.

"Hello?"

"Is Samantha still there?"

Samantha frantically shakes her head. "Charlie?" I ask.

"Yeah." He doesn't sound terribly friendly. I wonder if he found out it was me doing the cooking after all.

I hold out the receiver. Samantha rolls her eyes as she takes it. "Hello, darling. I'm about to walk out the door." There's an edge of annoyance in her tone.

"Yes, I know," she continues. "But I can't make it." She pauses and lowers her voice. "I told you. I have to go. I don't have a choice," she adds, sounding resigned. "Well, life's inconvenient, Charlie." And she hangs up the phone.

She briefly closes her eyes, inhales, and forces a smile. "Men."

"Charlie?" I ask, perplexed. "I thought you guys were so happy."

"Too happy. When I told him I suddenly had to go to LA, he freaked out. Said he'd made plans for us to have dinner with his mother tonight. Which he somehow neglected to tell me. As if I don't have a life of my own."

"Maybe you can't have it both ways. His life *and* your life. How do you put two lives together, anyway?"

She gives me a look as she picks up her suitcase. "Wish me luck in Hollywood, Sparrow. Maybe I'll be discovered."

"What about Charlie?" I hold open the door as she bangs the suitcase down the stairs. It's a good thing it is a Samsonite. Most suitcases probably couldn't take the abuse.

"What about him?" she calls out.

Boy. She must really be angry.

I run to the window and lean out over the parapet to catch a glimpse of the street below. An enormous limousine is idling at the curb. A uniformed driver stands next to the passenger door. Samantha emerges from the building as the driver hurries forward to take her suitcase.

The passenger door opens, and Harry Mills gets out. He and Samantha have a brief exchange as he lights up a cigar. Samantha slides past him and gets into the car. Harry takes a big puff on the cigar, looks up and down the street, and follows. The door closes and the limo pulls away, a puff of cigar smoke drifting from the open window.

Behind me, the phone rings. I approach it cautiously, but curiosity gets the better of me and I pick it up. "Is Samantha there?" It's Charlie. Again.

"She just left," I say politely.

"Damn," he shouts, and hangs up.

Damn you, too, I think, quietly replacing the receiver.

I retrieve my own Hartmann suitcase from under Samantha's bed. The phone rings some more, but I know better than to answer it.

After a while, the caller gives up. Then the buzzer goes off. "Yes?" I ask brusquely, into the intercom.

"It's Ryan," comes back the garbled reply.

I click open the door. Ryan. I'm working myself up to give him what-for about Maggie, when he appears at the top of the stairs holding a lone rose. The stem is limp and I briefly wonder if he picked it up off the street.

"You're too late," I say accusingly. "Maggie left last night."

"Rats. I knew I fucked up."

I should probably tell him to go away, but I'm not finished. "Who runs out of a diner while their date is in the bathroom?"

"I was tired," he says helplessly, as if this is a legitimate excuse.

"You're kidding. Right?"

He gives me a hangdog look. "I couldn't figure out how to say good-bye. I was exhausted. And I'm not Superman. I try to be, but somewhere along the line I seem to have encountered kryptonite."

I smile in spite of myself. Ryan is one of those guys who can always joke himself out of the bad books. I know he knows it, and I know it's disloyal, but I can't stay mad at him. After all, he didn't stand me up.

"Maggie was really, really hurt," I scold.

"I figured she would be. That's why I came by. To make it up to her."

"With that rose?"

"It is pretty sad, isn't it?"

"It's pathetic. Especially since she took her anger out on me."

"On you?" He's surprised. "Why would she take it out on you? It wasn't your fault."

"No. But somehow I got lumped in with your bad behavior. We got into a fight."

"Was there hair pulling?"

"No, there was not," I say, indignant. "Jesus, Ryan."

"I'm sorry." He grins. "Guys love girl fights. What can I say?"

"Why don't you just admit you're an asshole?"

"Because that would be too easy. Capote's an asshole. I'm just a jerk."

"Nice way to talk about your best friend."

"Just because we're friends doesn't mean I have

to lie about his personality," he says.

"I suppose that's true," I unwillingly agree, wondering why women are so judgmental of each other. Why can't we say, "Hey, she's kind of messed up, but I love her anyway?"

"I came by to ask Maggie to Rainbow's father's art opening. It's tonight. There's a dinner afterward. It's going to be really cool."

"I'll go," I volunteer, wondering why no one invites me to these glamorous parties.

"You?" Ryan asks, unsure.

"Why not? Am I chopped liver or something?"

"Not at all," he says, backpedaling. "But Maggie said you were obsessed with Bernard Singer."

"I don't have to see Bernard every night." I fudge, unwilling to admit that Bernard and I are probably over.

"Okay, then," he gives in. "I'll meet you at the gallery at eight."

Yippee, I think, when he's gone. I've been hearing about this art opening for weeks, wondering if Rainbow would ask me, and if not, how I could wrangle an invitation. I kept telling myself it was only a stupid party, while secretly knowing it was an event I didn't want to miss.

And since Bernard hasn't called, why not? I'm certainly not going to put my life on hold for him.

CHAPTER TWENTY-ONE

The gallery is in SoHo, a deserted patch of run-down blocks with cobblestoned streets and enormous buildings that were once factories. It's hard to imagine Manhattan as a center of industrialism, but apparently they used to make everything here, from clothing to lightbulbs to tools. A metal ramp leads to the gallery's entrance, the railing decorated with all manner of chic, downtown types, smoking cigarettes and discussing what they did the night before.

I push my way through the crowd. It's packed inside, a mass of patrons forming a bottleneck by the entrance as everyone seems to have run into someone they know. The air is filled with smoke and the damp smell of sweat, but there's the familiar buzz of excitement that indicates this is the place to be.

I take refuge along a wall, avoiding the circle of well-wishers gathered around a portly man with a goatee and hooded eyes. He's dressed in a black smock and embroidered slippers, so I assume this is the great Barry Jessen himself, the most important artist in New York and Rainbow's father. Indeed, Rainbow is standing behind him, looking, for the first time, lost and rather insignificant, despite the fact that she's wearing a bright green fringed dress. Next to Barry, and towering over him by at least a head, is the model Pican.

She has the deliberately unself-conscious look of a woman who's aware she's exceptionally beautiful and knows you know it too, but is determined not to make her beauty the main attraction. She holds her head cocked slightly to the side and leaning toward her husband, as if to say, "Yes, I know I'm beautiful, but this night is all about him." It is, I suppose, the ultimate indication of true love.

Either that, or it's very good acting.

I don't see Ryan or Capote yet, so I pretend to be extremely interested in the art. You'd think other people would be curious as well, but the spaces in front of the paintings are mostly empty, as if socializing is what an opening is really about.

And maybe for good reason. I can't decide

what I think about the paintings. They're black and gray, with stick figures that appear to be victims of terrible violence or purveyors of injury. Hellish drops of blood drip from every angle. The stick figures are pierced with knives and needles while claws rip their ankles. It's all very disturbing and quite unforgettable, which may be the point.

"What do you think?" asks Rainbow, coming up behind me. I'm surprised she's lowered herself to solicit my opinion, but so far I'm the only person here who's remotely close to her age.

"Powerful," I say.

"I think they're creepy."

"You do?" I'm surprised she's so honest.

"Don't tell my father."

"I won't."

"Ryan said he's bringing you to the dinner," she says, twirling a piece of fringe. "I'm glad. I would have invited you myself, but I didn't have your number."

"That's okay. I'm happy to be here."

She smiles and drifts away. I go back to staring at the paintings. Maybe New York isn't so complicated after all. Perhaps belonging is simply a matter of showing up. If people see you enough, they assume you're part of their group.

❖ ✳ C_B ✳ ❖

Eventually, Ryan and Capote appear, already in their cups. Ryan is weaving slightly and Capote is jovial, greeting everyone he sees like they're an old friend.

"Carrie!" he says, kissing me on both cheeks as if he couldn't be more pleased to see me.

A secret signal pulses through the crowd, and several people glide to the exit. These, apparently, are the chosen ones—chosen to attend the dinner, anyway.

"C'mon," Ryan says, jerking his head toward the door. We follow the select group onto the street as Ryan runs his hands through his hair.

"Man, that was terrible," he exclaims. "You've got to wonder what the world is coming to when we call that 'art.'"

"You're a philistine," Capote says.

"You can't tell me you actually liked that shit."

"I did," I say. "I thought it was disturbing."

"Disturbing, but not in a good way," Ryan says.

Capote laughs. "You can take the boy out of the suburbs but you can't take the suburbs out of the boy."

"I take serious offense to that comment," Ryan cracks.

"*I'm* from the suburbs," I say.

"Of course you are," Capote says, with a certain amount of disdain.

"And you're from someplace better?" I challenge him.

"Capote's from an old Southern family, darlin'," Ryan says, imitating Capote's accent. "His grandmother fought off the Yankees. Which would make her about a hundred and fifty years old."

"I never said my grandmother fought the Yankees. I said she told me never to *marry* one."

"I guess that lets me out," I comment, while Ryan snickers in appreciation.

The dinner is being held at the Jessens' loft. It seems like ten years ago when L'il laughed at me for thinking the Jessens lived in a building without running water, but my early assessment isn't far off. The building is a little scary. The freight elevator has a door that slides open manually, followed by one of those clanging wire gates. Inside is a crank to move the elevator up and down.

The operation of said elevator is a source of consternation. When we get in, five people are discussing the alternate possibility of finding the stairs.

"It's terrible when people live in these places," says a man with yellow hair.

"It's cheap," Ryan points out.

"Cheap shouldn't mean dangerous."

"What's a little danger when you're the most

important artist in New York?" Capote says, with his usual arrogance.

"Oh my. You're so macho," the man replies. The lighting in the elevator is dim and when I turn around to take a closer look, I discover the speaker is none other than Bobby. The Bobby from the fashion show. Who promised me a reading in his space.

"Bobby," I nearly shout.

He doesn't recognize me at first. "Hello, yes, great to see you again," he replies automatically.

"It's me," I insist. "Carrie Bradshaw?"

He suddenly remembers. "Of course! Carrie Bradshaw. The playwright."

Capote snorts and, since no one else seems either capable or interested, takes over the operation of the crank. The elevator lurches upward with a sickening jolt that throws several of the occupants against the wall.

"I'm so happy I didn't eat anything today," remarks a woman in a long silver coat.

Capote manages to get the elevator reasonably close to the third story, meaning the doors open a couple of feet above the floor. Ever the gentleman, he hops out and extends his hand to the lady in the silver coat. Ryan gets out on his own, followed by Bobby, who jumps and falls to his knees. When it's my turn, Capote hesitates, his arm poised midair.

"I'm fine," I say, rejecting his offer.

"Come on, Carrie. Don't be a jerk."

"In other words, try being a lady," I murmur, taking his hand.

"For once in your life."

I'm about to continue this argument, when Bobby inserts himself and links his arm through mine. "Let's get a drink and you can tell me all about your new play," he gushes.

The huge open space has been hastily remodeled into something resembling an apartment by the addition of Sheetrock walls. The area near the windows is as big as a skating rink; along one side is a table, covered with a white cloth, that probably seats sixty. In front of the ceiling-high windows is a grouping of couches and armchairs draped with sailcloth. The wooden floor is worn, scuffed by the feet of hundreds of factory workers. In a few places, it's actually black, as if someone set a small fire, thought better of it, and extinguished the flames.

"Here you go," Bobby says, handing me a plastic cup filled with what turns out to be cheap champagne. He takes my hand. "Who do you want to meet? I know everyone."

I want to extract my hand, but it seems rude. And besides, I'm sure Bobby is only being friendly. "Barry Jessen?" I ask boldly.

"Don't you know him?" Bobby asks, with such genuine surprise it makes me laugh. I can't imagine why Bobby would think I knew the great Barry Jessen, but apparently he assumes I get around quite a bit. Which only reinforces my theory: if people see you enough, they think you're one of them.

Bobby marches me straight up to Barry Jessen himself, who is engaged in conversation with several people at once, and pulls me into the circle. My sense of belonging dissipates like a mist but Bobby seems immune to the hostile glances. "This is Carrie Bradshaw," he announces to Barry. "She's dying to meet you. You're her favorite artist."

Not one word of this is true, but I don't dare contradict him. Especially as Barry Jessen's expression changes from irritation to mild interest. He isn't immune to flattery—just the opposite. He expects it.

"Is that so?" His black eyes lock on mine and I suddenly have the eerie sensation of staring into the face of the devil.

"I loved your show," I say awkwardly.

"Do you think others will love it as well?" he demands.

His intensity unnerves me. "It's so powerful, how can anyone not love it?" I blurt out, hoping he won't question me further.

He doesn't. Having received his kudos, he abruptly turns away, addressing himself to the lady in the silver coat.

Unfortunately, Bobby doesn't get the message. "Now, Barry," he begins insistently. "We have to talk about Basil," at which point I seize the opportunity to escape. The thing about famous people, I realize, is that just because you can meet them doesn't make you a famous person yourself.

I skitter down a little hallway and past a closed door, from which I hear laughter and hushed whisperings, then past another door that's probably the bathroom because several people are lined up beside it, and right on through to an open door at the end of the corridor.

I pull up short, startled by the decor. The room is completely different from the rest of the loft. Oriental rugs are strewn across the floor and an ornate antique Indian bed covered with silk pillows sits in the center.

I figure I've wandered in the Jessens' bedroom by accident, but it's Rainbow who's resting on the bed, talking to a guy wearing a knit Jamaican cap perched over dreadlocks.

"Sorry," I murmur quickly, as the guy looks up in surprise. He's shockingly handsome, with chiseled features and beautiful black eyes.

Rainbow whips around, startled, worried

she's been caught out, but when she sees me, she relaxes. "It's only Carrie," she says. "She's cool."

"Only Carrie" ventures a step closer. "What are you guys doing?"

"This is my brother, Colin," Rainbow says, indicating the guy with the dreadlocks.

"You get high?" Colin asks, holding up a small marijuana pipe.

"Sure." Somehow, I don't think being a little stoned at this party is going to be a problem. Half the people here already seem like they're on something.

Rainbow makes space for me on the bed. "I love your room," I say, admiring the luxurious furnishings.

"You do?" She takes the pipe from Colin, leaning forward as he flicks the bowl with a gold lighter.

"It's very anti-Barry," Colin says, in a clipped accent. "That's what's so great about it."

I take a hit from the pipe and pass it to Colin. "Are you English?" I ask, wondering how he can be English while Rainbow seems so American.

Rainbow giggles. "He's Amhara. Like my mother."

"So Barry isn't your father?"

"Lord, no!" Colin exclaims. He and Rainbow exchange a secretive look.

"Does anyone actually like their father?" Rainbow asks.

"I do," I murmur. Maybe it's the dope, but I'm suddenly feeling sentimental about my old man. "He's a really good guy."

"You're lucky," Colin says. "I haven't seen my real father since I was ten."

I nod as though I understand, but honestly, I don't. My father might not be perfect, but I know he loves me. If something bad happened, he'd be there for me—or would try to be, anyway.

"Which reminds me," Colin says, reaching into his pocket and extracting a small aspirin bottle that he shakes in Rainbow's face. "I found these in Barry's stash."

"Oh, Colin. You didn't," Rainbow squeals.

Colin pops open the top and shakes out three large round pills. "I did."

"What if he notices they're gone?"

"He won't. By the end of the night, he'll be too high to notice anything."

Rainbow plucks one of the pills out of Colin's hand and washes it down with a gulp of champagne.

"You want one, Carrie?" Colin offers me a pill.

I don't ask what it is. I don't want to know. I already feel like I've found out more than I should. I shake my head.

"They're really fun," Colin urges, popping the pill into his mouth.

"I'm good," I say.

"If you change your mind, you know where to find me. Just ask for an aspirin," he says as he and Rainbow fall onto the cushions, laughing.

Back in the main room, there's the usual frenetic energy of people jabbering and shouting into one another's faces to be heard above the din. Cigarette and marijuana smoke waft through the air, while Pican and some of her model friends lounge indolently on the couches with half-closed eyes. I walk past them to the open window for some fresh air.

I remind myself that I'm having a good time.

Bobby spots me and begins waving frantically. He's talking to a middle-aged woman in a skin-tight white dress that looks like it's made of bandages. I wave back and hold up my cup, indicating I'm on my way to the bar, but he won't be deterred. "Carrie," he shouts. "Come meet Teensie Dyer."

I put on my best game face and saunter over.

Teensie looks like someone who eats small children for breakfast. "This is Carrie Bradshaw," Bobby crows. "You should be her agent. Did you know she's written a play?"

"Hello," she says, giving me a narrow smile.

Bobby puts his arm around my shoulder, trying to press me closer as I stiffly resist. "We're going to perform Carrie's new play in my space. You must come."

Teensie flicks her cigarette ash on the floor. "What's it about?"

Damn Bobby, I think, as I wriggle out of his grasp. I'm not about to talk about my play to a complete stranger. Especially as I hardly know what it's about myself.

"Carrie won't say." Bobby pats my arm. And leaning into my ear, adds in a stage whisper, "Teensie's the biggest agent in town. She represents everyone. Including Bernard Singer."

The smile freezes on my face. "That's nice."

There must be something in my expression that sets off a warning bell because Teensie deigns to finally look me in the eye.

I glance away, hoping to steer the conversation in another direction. Something tells me this Teensie person will be none too pleased to discover her biggest client is dating little ol' me. Or was dating little ol' me, anyway.

The music stops.

"Dinner is served!" shouts Barry Jessen from the top of a ladder.

CHAPTER TWENTY-TWO

As if the night couldn't get any weirder, I find myself seated next to Capote.

"You again?" I ask, squeezing past him onto my folding chair.

"What's your problem?" he says.

I roll my eyes. Where to begin? With the fact that I miss Bernard and wish he were here? Or that I'd prefer to be sitting next to someone else? I settle on: "I just met Teensie Dyer."

He looks impressed. "She's a big agent."

Figures he'd say that. "She seemed like a bitch to me."

"That's stupid, Carrie."

"Why? It's the truth."

"Or your perspective."

"Which is?"

"This is a hard city, Carrie. You know that."

"So?" I say.

"You want to end up hard too? Like most of these people?"

I look at him in disbelief. Doesn't he realize he's one of them? "I'm not worried," I retort.

A bowl of pasta comes our way. Capote grabs it and politely serves me, then himself. "Tell me you're not really going to do your play at Bobby's."

"Why not?"

"Because Bobby is a joke."

I give him a nasty smile. "Or is it because he hasn't asked you to perform your great work?"

"I wouldn't do it even if he did. It's not the way to do things, Carrie. You'll see."

I shrug. "I guess that's the difference between you and me. I don't mind taking chances."

"Do you want me to lie to you? Like everyone else in your life?"

I shake my head, mystified. "How do you know people lie to me? More likely they lie to you. But the biggest liar in your life? *Yourself.*" I take a gulp of wine, hardly believing what I just said.

"Fine," he says, as if I'm hopeless.

He turns to the woman on his other side. I follow his cue and smile at the man on my left.

I breathe a sigh of relief. It's Cholly. "Hello," I say brightly, determined to forget about my encounter with Teensie and my hatred of Capote.

"Little one!" he exclaims. "My goodness. You certainly do get around. Is New York turning out to be everything you hoped?"

I glance around the table. Rainbow is slumped in her chair, eyes half closed, while Capote is pontificating about his favorite topic again—Proust. I spot Ryan, who has had the good luck to be seated next to Teensie. He's making eyes at her, no doubt hoping she'll take him on as a client. Meanwhile, Bobby is standing behind Barry Jessen, desperately trying to engage him while Barry, now sweating profusely, angrily wipes his face with a napkin.

I experience one of those bizarre moments where the universe telescopes and everything is magnified: the movement of Pican's lipsticked mouth, the stream of red wine Bobby pours into his glass, the gold signet ring on Teensie's right finger as she raises her hand to her temple.

I wonder if Maggie was right. Maybe we are all crazy.

And suddenly, everything goes back to normal. Teensie gets up. Barry makes room for Bobby next to him. Ryan leans over to Rainbow and whispers something in her ear.

I turn back to Cholly. "I think it's fantastic."

He seems interested, so I start telling him about my adventures. How I got kicked out of Peggy's. And how I named Viktor Greene's mustache Waldo. And how Bobby wants me to do a reading of my play when I haven't even finished it yet. When I'm done, I have Cholly in stitches. There's nothing better than a man who's a good audience.

"You should come to a soiree at my house sometime," he says. "I have this wonderful little publication called *The New Review*. We like to pretend it's literary, but every so often it requires a party."

I'm writing my phone number on a napkin for him when Teensie approaches. At first I think I'm her target, but it's Cholly she's after.

"Darling," she says, aggressively inserting a chair between Cholly and me, therefore effectively cutting me off. "I've just met the most charming young writer. Ryan somebody. You ought to meet him."

"Love to," Cholly says. And with a wink, he leans around Teensie. "Have you met Carrie Bradshaw? She's a writer too. She was just telling me—"

Teensie abruptly changes the subject. "Have you seen Bernard, lately?"

"Last week," Cholly says dismissively, indicating

he has no interest in talking about Bernard.

"I'm worried about him," Teensie says.

"Why?" Cholly asks. Men are never concerned about each other the way women are.

"I heard he's dating some young girl."

My stomach clenches.

"Margie says Bernard's a mess," Teensie continues, with a sidelong glance my way. I try to keep my face disinterested, as if I hardly know who she's talking about. "Margie said she met her. And frankly, she's concerned. She thinks it's a very bad sign that Bernard is seeing someone so young."

I pour myself more wine while pretending to be fascinated by something at the other end of the table. But my hand is shaking.

"Why would Margie Shephard care? She's the one who left him," Cholly says.

"Is that what he told you?" Teensie asks slyly.

Cholly shrugs. "Everyone knows she cheated on him. With an actor in his play."

Teensie snickers. "Sadly, the reverse is true. Bernard cheated on her."

A wire wraps around my heart and squeezes tight.

"In fact, Bernard cheated on Margie several times. He's a wonderful playwright, but a lousy husband."

"Really, Teensie. What does it matter?" Cholly remarks.

Teensie puts a hand on his arm. "This party is giving me an awful headache. Could you ask Barry for some aspirin?"

I glare at her. Why can't she ask Barry herself? Damn her and what she said about Bernard and me. "Colin has aspirin," I interject helpfully. "Pican's son?"

Teensie's eyebrows rise in suspicion, but I give her an innocent smile.

"Well, thank you." She gives me a sharp look and goes off to find Colin.

I hold my napkin to my face and laugh.

Cholly laughs along with me. "Teensie's a very silly woman, isn't she?"

I nod, speechless. The thought of the evil Teensie on one of Colin's pills is just too funny.

Of course, I don't really expect Teensie to take the pill. Even I, who know nothing about drugs, was smart enough to realize Colin's big white pill wasn't an aspirin. I don't give it much thought until an hour later, when I'm dancing with Ryan.

Swaying precariously on bended knees, Teensie appears in the middle of the floor, clutching Bobby's shoulder for support. She's giggling madly while attempting to remain upright. Her legs are like rubber. "Bobby!" she screams. "Did I ever tell you how much I love you?"

"What the hell?" Ryan asks.

I'm overcome by hysteria. Apparently, Teensie took the pill after all, because she's lying on her back on the floor, laughing. This goes on for several seconds until Cholly swoops in, pulls Teensie to her feet, and leads her away.

I keep on dancing.

Indeed, everyone keeps dancing until we're interrupted by a loud scream followed by several shouts for help.

A crowd gathers by the elevator. The door is open, but the shaft appears to be empty.

Cries of "What happened?" "Someone fell!" "Call 911," echo through the loft. I rush forward, fearing it's Rainbow and that she's dead. But out of the corner of my eye I see Rainbow hurrying to her room, followed by Colin. I push in closer. Two men have jumped into the shaft, so the elevator must be a mere foot or two below. A limp woman's hand reaches out and Barry Jessen grabs it, hauling a disheveled and dazed Teensie out of the hole.

Before I can react, Capote elbows me. "Let's go."

"Huh?" I'm too startled to move.

He jerks my arm. "We need to get out of here. *Now.*"

"What about Teensie?"

"She's fine. And Ryan can take care of himself."

"I don't understand," I protest as Capote propels me to the exit.

"Don't ask questions." He flings open the door and starts down the stairs. I pause on the landing, baffled. "Carrie!" He turns around to make sure I'm following him. When he sees I'm not, he hops up the stairs and practically pushes me down in front of him. "Move!"

I do as he says, hearing the urgent thump of his feet after me. When we get to the lobby, he bangs through the door and yanks me out after him. "Run!" he shouts.

He races to the corner as I struggle to keep up in the Fiorucci boots Samantha gave me. Seconds later, two police cars, lights flashing and sirens wailing, pull up to the Jessens' building. Capote slings his arm around my shoulders. "Act normal. Like we're on a date or something."

We cross the street, my heart exploding in my chest. We walk like this for another block until we get to West Broadway and Prince Street. "I think there's a cool bar around here," Capote says.

"A 'cool' bar? Teensie just fell down the elevator shaft, and all you can think about is a 'cool' bar?"

He releases me from his grasp. "It's not my fault, is it?"

No, but it is mine. "We should go back. Aren't you worried about Teensie?"

"Look, Carrie," he says, exasperated. "I just saved your life. You should be grateful."

"I'm not sure what I'm supposed to be grateful for."

"You want to end up in the papers? Because that's what would have happened. Half the people there were on drugs. You think the police aren't going to notice? And the next day it's all over Page Six. Maybe you don't care about your reputation. But I happen to care about mine."

"Why?" I ask, unimpressed by his self-importance.

"Because."

"Because why?" I taunt.

"I have a lot of people counting on me."

"Like who?"

"Like my family. They're very upright, good people. I would never want them to be embarrassed. On account of my actions."

"You mean like if you married a Yankee."

"Exactly."

"What do all these Yankee girls you date think? Or do you just not tell them?"

"I figure most women know what they're

getting into when they date me. I never lie about my intentions."

I look down at the sidewalk, wondering what I'm doing standing on a corner in the middle of nowhere, arguing with Capote Duncan. "I guess I should tell you the truth too. I'm the one who's responsible for Teensie's accident."

"You?"

"I knew Colin had pills. He said they were aspirin. So I told Teensie to get an aspirin from him."

It takes a moment for Capote to process this information. He rubs his eyes while I worry he's going to turn me in. But then he tips back his head and laughs, his long curls falling over his shoulders.

"Pretty funny, huh?" I boast, preening in his approval. "I never thought she'd actually take the damn thing—"

Without warning, he cuts me off with a kiss.

I'm so surprised, I don't respond at first as his mouth presses on mine, pushing eagerly at my lips. Then my brain catches up. I'm confounded by how nice and natural it feels, like we've been kissing forever. Then I get it: this is how he gets all those women. He's a pouncer. He kisses a woman when she least expects it and once he's got her off-balance, he maneuvers her into bed.

Not going to happen this time, though. Although a terrible part of me wishes it would.

"No." I push him away.

"Carrie," he says.

"I can't." Have I just cheated on Bernard?

Am I even with Bernard?

A lone taxi snakes down the street, light on. It's available. I'm not. I flag it down.

Capote opens the door for me.

"Thanks," I say.

"See ya," he replies, as if nothing at all just happened.

I sag into the backseat, shaking my head.

What a night. Maybe it's a good time to get out of Dodge after all.

CHAPTER TWENTY-THREE

"Oh," my youngest sister, Dorrit, says, looking up from a magazine. "You're home."

"Yes, I am," I say, stating the obvious. I drop my bag and open the refrigerator, more out of habit than hunger. There's an almost-empty container of milk and a package of moldy cheese. I take out the bottle of milk and hold it up. "Doesn't anyone bother to shop around here?"

"No," Dorrit says sullenly. Her eyes go to my father, but he seems oblivious to her displeasure.

"I've got all my girls home!" he exclaims, overcome with emotion.

That's one thing that hasn't changed about my father: his excessive sentimentality. I'm glad there's still a remnant of my old father left. Because otherwise, he appears to have been taken over by an alien.

First off, he's wearing jeans. My father has never worn jeans in his life. My mother wouldn't allow it. And he's sporting Ray-Ban sunglasses. But most bewildering of all is his jacket. It's by Members Only and it's orange. When I stepped off the train, I barely recognized him.

He must be going through a midlife crisis.

"Where's Missy?" I ask now, trying to ignore his strange getup.

"She's at the conservatory. She learned to play the violin," my father says proudly. "She's composing a symphony for an entire orchestra."

"She learned to play the violin in one month?" I ask, astounded.

"She's very talented," my father says.

What about me?

"Yeah, right, Dad," Dorrit says.

"You're okay too," my father replies.

"C'mon, Dorrit," I say, picking up my suitcase. "You can help me unpack."

"I'm busy."

"Dorrit!" I insist meaningfully, with a glance at my father.

She sighs, closes her magazine, and follows me upstairs.

My room is exactly how I left it. For a moment,

I'm filled with memories, going to the shelves and touching the old books my mom gave me as a kid. I open my closet door and peek inside. I could be mistaken, but it looks like half my clothes are missing. I spin around and glare at Dorrit accusingly. "Where are my clothes?"

She shrugs. "I took some. And Missy. We figured that since you were in New York, you wouldn't be needing them."

"What if I do?"

She shrugs again.

I let it go. It's too early in my visit to get into a fight with Dorrit—although given her sulky attitude, there's sure to be an altercation by the time I leave on Monday. In the meantime, I need to probe her for information about my father and this supposed girlfriend of his.

"What's up with Dad?" I ask, sitting cross-legged on the bed. It's only a single and suddenly feels tiny. I can't believe I slept in it for so many years.

"He's gone crazy. Obviously," Dorrit says.

"Why is he wearing jeans? And a Members Only jacket? It's hideous. Mom would never let him dress like that."

"Wendy gave it to him."

"Wendy?"

"His girlfriend."

"So this girlfriend thing is true?"

"I guess so."

I sigh. Dorrit is so blasé. There's no getting through to her. I only hope she's given up the shoplifting. "Have you met her?"

"Yeah," Dorrit says, noncommittally.

"And?" I nearly scream.

"Eh."

"Do you hate her?" This is a stupid question. Dorrit hates everyone.

"I try to pretend she doesn't exist."

"What does Dad think?"

"He doesn't notice," she says. "It's disgusting. When she's around, he only pays attention to her."

"Is she pretty?"

"*I* don't think so," Dorrit replies. "Anyway, you can see for yourself. Dad's making us go to dinner with her tonight."

"Ugh."

"And he has a motorcycle."

"What?" This time I really do scream.

"Didn't he tell you? He bought a motorcycle."

"He hasn't told me anything. He hasn't even told me about this Wendy person."

"He's probably afraid," Dorrit says. "Ever since he met her, he's become totally whipped."

Great, I think, unpacking my suitcase. This is going to be a terrific weekend.

A little bit later, I find my father in the garage, rearranging his tools. I immediately suspect that Dorrit is right—my father is avoiding me. I've been home for less than an hour, but already I'm wondering why I came back at all. No one seems the least bit interested in me or my life. Dorrit ran off to a girlfriend's house, my father has a motorcycle, and Missy is all caught up with her composing. I should have stayed in New York.

I spent the entire train ride mulling over last night. The kiss with Capote was a terrible mistake and I'm horrified I went along with it, if only for a few seconds. But what does it mean? Is it possible I secretly like Capote? No. He's probably one of those "love the one you're with" guys—meaning he automatically goes after whatever woman happens to be around when he's feeling horny. But there were plenty of other women at the party, including Rainbow. So why'd he pick me?

Feeling lousy and hungover, I bought some aspirin and drank a Coke. I kept torturing myself with all the unfinished business I was leaving behind, including Bernard. I even considered getting off the train in New Haven and taking the next train back to New York, but when I thought about how disappointed my family would be, I couldn't do it.

Now I wish I had.

"Dad!" I intone in annoyance.

He turns, startled, a wrench in his hand. "I was just cleaning out my workbench."

"I can see that." I peer around for this notorious motorcycle and spot it next to the wall, partly hidden behind my father's car. "Dorrit said you bought a motorcycle," I say craftily.

"Yes, Carrie, I did."

"Why?"

"I wanted to."

"But why?" I sound like a woeful girl who's just been dumped. And my father's acting like a jerky boy who doesn't have any answers.

"Do you want to see it?" he asks finally, unable to keep his obvious enthusiasm in check.

He wheels it out from behind the car. It's a motorcycle, all right. And not just any old motorcycle. It's a Harley. With enormous handlebars and a black body decaled with flames. The kind of motorcycle favored by members of the Hells Angels.

My father rides a Harley?

On the other hand, I'm impressed. It's no wussie motorcycle, that's for sure.

"What do you think?" he asks proudly.

"I like it."

He seems pleased. "I bought it off this kid in

town. He was desperate for money. I only paid a thousand dollars."

"Wow." I shake my head. Everything about this is so unlike my father—from his sentence construction to the motorcycle itself—that for a moment I don't know what to say. "How'd you find this kid?" I ask.

"He's Wendy's cousin's son."

My eyes bug out of my head. I can't believe how casually he's mentioned her. I go along with the game. "Who's Wendy?"

He brushes the seat of the motorcycle with his hand. "She's my new friend."

So that's how he's going to play it. "What kind of friend?"

"She's very nice," he says, refusing to catch my eye.

"How come you didn't tell me about her?"

"Oh, Carrie." He sighs.

"Everyone says she's your girlfriend. Dorrit and Missy and even Walt."

"Walt knows?" he asks, surprised.

"Everyone knows, Dad," I say sharply. "Why didn't you tell *me*?"

He slides onto the seat of the motorcycle, playing with the levers. "Do you think you could cut me some slack?"

"Dad!"

"This is all very new for me."

I bite my lip. For a moment, my heart goes out to him. In the past five years, he hasn't shown an ounce of interest in any woman. Now he's apparently met someone he likes, which is a sign that he's moving forward. I should be happy for him. Unfortunately, all I can think about is my mother. And how he's betraying her. I wonder if my mother is up in heaven, looking down at what he's become. If she is, she'd be horrified.

"Did Mom know her? This Wendy friend of yours?"

He shakes his head, pretending to study the instrument panel. "No." He pauses. "I don't think so, anyway. She's a little bit younger."

"How young?" I demand.

I've suddenly pushed too hard, because he looks at me defiantly. "I don't know, Carrie. She's in her late twenties. I've been told it's rude to ask a woman her age."

I nod knowingly. "And how old does she think you are?"

"She knows I have a daughter who's going to Brown in the fall."

There's a sharpness in his tone I haven't heard since I was a kid. It means, *I'm in charge. Back off.*

"Fine." I turn to go.

"And Carrie?" he adds. "We're having dinner

with her tonight. I'm going to be very disappointed if you're rude to her."

"We'll see," I mutter under my breath. I head back to the house, convinced my worst fears have been confirmed. I already hate this Wendy woman. She has a relative who's a Hells Angel. And she lies about her age. I figure if a woman is willing to lie about her own birth date, she's willing to lie about pretty much anything.

I start to clean out the refrigerator, tossing out one scientific experiment after another. That's when I remember that I've lied about my age as well. To Bernard. I pour the last of the sour milk down the drain, wondering what my family is coming to.

"Don't you look special?" Walt quips. "Though a mite overdressed for Castlebury."

"What does one wear to a restaurant in Castlebury?"

"Surely not an evening gown."

"Walt," I scold. "It's not an evening gown. It's a hostess gown. From the sixties." I found it at my vintage store and I've been wearing it practically nonstop for days. It's perfect for sweaty weather, leaving my arms and legs unencumbered, and so far, no one has commented on my unusual garb except to say they liked it. Odd clothing is expected in New York. Here, not so much.

"I'm not going to change my style for Wendy. Did you know she has a cousin who's a Hells Angel?"

Walt and I are sitting on the porch, sipping cocktails while we wait for the notorious Wendy to arrive. I begged Walt to join us for dinner, but he declined, claiming a previous engagement with Randy. He did, however, agree to come by for a drink, so he could see the Wendy person in the flesh.

"Maybe that's the point," he says now. "She's completely different."

"But if he's interested in someone like Wendy, it calls into question his whole marriage to my mother."

"I think you're taking the analogy too far," Walt responds, acting as the voice of reason. "Maybe the guy's just having fun."

"He's my father." I scowl. "He shouldn't be allowed to have fun."

"That's mean, Carrie."

"I know." I stare out the screen at the neglected garden. "Did you talk to Maggie?"

"Yup," Walt says, enigmatically.

"What did she say? About New York?"

"She had a great time."

"What did she say about *me*?"

"Nothing. All she talked about was some guy you introduced her to."

"Ryan. Whom she immediately bonked."

"That's our Maggie," Walt says with a shrug.

"She's turned into a sex fiend."

"Oh, let her," he says. "She's young. She'll grow out of it. Anyway, why do you care?"

"I *care* about my *friends*." I swing my Fiorucci boots off the table for emphasis. "I just wish my friends cared about me."

Walt stares at me blankly.

"I mean, even my family hasn't asked me about my life in New York. And frankly, my life is so much more interesting than anything that's happening to them. I'm going to have a play produced. And I went to a party last night at Barry Jessen's loft in SoHo—"

"Who's Barry Jessen?"

"Come on, Walt. He's like the most important artist in America right now."

"As I said, 'Aren't you special?'" Walt teases.

I fold my arms, knowing I sound like a jerk. "Doesn't anyone care?"

"With your big head?" Walts jokes. "Careful, it might explode."

"Walt!" I give him a hurt look. Then my frustration gets the better of me. "I'm going to be a famous writer someday. I'm going to live in a big, two-bedroom apartment on Sutton Place. And I'm going to write Broadway plays. And then everyone will have to come and visit *me*."

"Ha-ha-ha," Walt says.

I stare down at the ice cubes in my glass.

"Look, Carrie," Walt says. "You're spending one summer in New York. Which is great. But it's hardly your life. And in September, you're going to Brown."

"Maybe I'm not," I say suddenly.

Walt smiles, sure I can't be serious. "Does your father know? About this change of plans?"

"I just decided. This minute." Which is true. The thought has been fluttering around the edges of my consciousness for weeks now, but the reality of being back in Castlebury has made it clear that being at Brown will only be more of the same. The same kinds of people with exactly the same attitudes, just in a different location.

Walt smiles. "Don't forget I'll be there too. At RISD."

"I know." I sigh. I sound as arrogant as Capote. "It'll be fun," I add, hopefully.

"Walt!" my father says, joining us on the porch.

"Mr. Bradshaw." Walt stands up, and my father embraces him in a hug, which makes me feel left out again.

"How you doin', kid?" my father asks. "Your

hair's longer. I barely recognized you."

"Walt's always changing his hair, Dad." I turn to Walt. "What my father means is that you probably didn't recognize him. He's trying to look *younger*," I add, with enough bantering in my voice to prevent this statement from coming across as nasty.

"What's wrong with looking younger?" my father declares in high spirits.

He goes into the kitchen to make cocktails, but takes his time about it, going to the window every second or so like a sixteen-year-old girl waiting for her crush to arrive. It's ridiculous. When Wendy does turn up, a mere five minutes later, he runs out of the house to greet her.

"Can you believe this?" I ask Walt, horrified by my father's silly behavior.

"He's a man. What can I say?"

"He's my *father*," I protest.

"He's still a man."

I'm about to say, "Yeah, but my father isn't supposed to act like other men," when he and Wendy come strolling up the walk, holding hands.

I want to gack. This relationship is obviously more serious than I'd thought.

Wendy is kind of pretty, if you like women with dyed blond mall hair and blue eye shadow rimmed around their eyes like a raccoon.

"Be nice," Walt says warningly.

"Oh, I'll be perfectly nice. I'll be nice if it kills me." I smile.

"Shall I call the ambulance now or later?"

My father opens the screen door and urges Wendy onto the porch. Her smile is wide and patently fake. "You must be Carrie!" she says, enveloping me in a hug as if we're already best friends.

"How could you tell?" I ask, gently extracting myself.

She glances at my father, her face full of delight. "Your dad has told me all about you. He talks about you constantly. He's so proud of you."

There's something about this assumed intimacy that immediately rubs me the wrong way. "This is Walt," I say, trying to get her off the topic of myself. What can she possibly know about me anyway?

"Hello, Walt," Wendy says too eagerly. "Are you and Carrie—"

"Dating?" Walt interjects. "Hardly." We both laugh.

She tilts her head to the side, as if unsure how to proceed. "It's wonderful the way men and women can be friends these days. Don't you think?"

"I guess it depends on what you call 'friends,'" I murmur, reminding myself to be pleasant.

"Are we ready?" my father asks.

"We're going to this great new restaurant. Boyles. Have you heard of it?" Wendy asks.

"No." And unable to stop myself, I grumble, "I didn't even know there were restaurants in Castlebury. The only place we ever went was the Hamburger Shack."

"Oh, your father and I go out at least twice a week," Wendy chirps on, unperturbed.

My father nods in agreement. "We went to a Japanese restaurant. In Hartford."

"That so," I say, unimpressed. "There are tons of Japanese restaurants in New York."

"Bet they're not as good as the one in Hartford, though," Walt jokes.

My father gives him a grateful look. "This restaurant really is very special."

"Well," I say, just for the hell of it.

We troop down the driveway. Walt gets into his car with a wave of his hand. "Ta-ta, folks. Have fun."

I watch him go, envious of his freedom.

"So!" Wendy says brightly when we're in the car. "When do you start at Brown?"

I shrug.

"I'll bet you can't wait to get away from New York," she enthuses. "It's so dirty. And loud." She puts her hand on my father's arm and smiles.

❖ ✳ C_B ✳ ❖

Boyles is a tiny restaurant located in a damp patch off Main Street where our renowned Roaring Brook runs under the road. It's highfalutin for Castlebury: the main courses are called pasta instead of spaghetti, and there are cloth napkins and a bud vase on each table containing a single rose.

"Very romantic," my father says approvingly as he escorts Wendy to her chair.

"Your father is such a gentleman," Wendy says.

"He is?" I can't help it. He and Wendy are totally creeping me out. I wonder if they have sex. I certainly hope not. My father's too old for all that groping around.

My father ignores my comment and picks up the menu. "They have the fish again," he says to Wendy. And to me: "Wendy loves fish."

"I lived in Los Angeles for five years. They're much more health-conscious there," Wendy explains.

"My roommate is in Los Angeles right now," I say, partly to get the conversation away from Wendy. "She's staying at the Beverly Hills Hotel."

"I had lunch there once," Wendy says, with her unflappable cheeriness. "It was so exciting. We sat next to Tom Selleck."

"You don't say," my father replies, as if Wendy's

momentary proximity to a television actor raises her even further in his eyes.

"I met Margie Shephard," I interject.

"Who's Margie Shephard?" My father frowns.

Wendy winks at me, as if she and I possess a secret intimacy regarding my father's lack of knowledge regarding popular culture. "She's an actress. Up-and-coming. Everyone says she's beautiful, but I don't see it. I think she's very plain."

"She's beautiful in person," I counter. "She sparkles. From within."

"Like you, Carrie," Wendy says suddenly.

I'm so surprised by her compliment, I'm temporarily disabled in my subtle attack. "Well," I say, picking up the menu. "What were you doing in Los Angeles?"

"Wendy was a member of an—" My father looks to Wendy for help.

"Improv group. We did improvisational theater."

"Wendy's very creative." My father beams.

"Isn't that one of those things where you do mime, like Marcel Marceau?" I ask innocently, even though I know better. "Did you wear white greasepaint and gloves?"

Wendy chuckles, amused by my ignorance. "I studied mime. But mostly we did comedy."

Now I'm completely baffled. Wendy was an

actress—and a comedic one at that? She doesn't seem the least bit funny.

"Wendy was in a potato chip commercial," my father says.

"You shouldn't tell people that," Wendy gently scolds. "It was only a local commercial. For State Line potato chips. And it was seven years ago. My big break." She rolls her eyes with appropriate irony.

Apparently Wendy doesn't take herself too seriously after all. It's another check in her "pluses" column. On the other hand, it might only be a show for my benefit. "It must be a drag to be in Castlebury. After Los Angeles."

She shakes her head. "I'm a small-town girl. I grew up in Scarborough," she says, naming the town next door. "And I love my new job."

"But that's not all." My father nudges her. "Wendy's going to be teaching drama, too."

I wince as Wendy's life story becomes clear to me: local girl tries to make it big, fails, and crawls home to teach. It's my worst fear.

"Your father says you want to be a writer," Wendy continues blithely. "Maybe you should write for the *Castlebury Citizen*."

I freeze. The *Castlebury Citizen* is our small-town newspaper, consisting mostly of the minutes from zoning board meetings and photographs of

Pee Wee baseball teams. Steam rises from behind my eyes. "You think I'm not good enough to make it in New York?"

Wendy frowns in confusion. "It's just so difficult in New York, isn't it? I mean, don't you have to do your laundry in the basement? A friend of mine lived in New York and she said—"

"My building doesn't have a laundry." I look away, trying to contain my frustration. How dare Wendy or her friend presume anything about New York? "I take my dirty clothes to a Laundromat." Which isn't exactly true. Mostly I let them pile up in a corner of the bedroom.

"Now, Carrie. No one is making any assumptions about your abilities—" my father begins, but I've had enough.

"No, they're not," I say spitefully. "Because no one seems to be interested in me at all." And with that, I get up, my face burning, and zigzag around the restaurant in search of the restroom.

I'm furious. At my father and Wendy for putting me in this position, but mostly at myself, for losing my temper. Now Wendy will come across as kind and reasonable, while I'll appear jealous and immature. This only inflames my anger, causing me to recall everything I've always hated about my life and my family but refused to admit.

I go into the stall and sit on the toilet to think.

What really galls me is the way my father has never taken my writing seriously. He's never given me a word of encouragement, never said I was talented, has never even given me a compliment, for Christ's sake. I might have lived my entire life without noticing, if it weren't for the other kids at The New School. It's pretty obvious that Ryan and Capote and L'il and even Rainbow have grown up praised and encouraged and applauded. Not that I want to be like them, but it wouldn't hurt to have some belief from my own parent that I had something special.

I dab at my eyes with a piece of toilet paper, reminding myself that I have to go back out there and sit with them. I need to come up with a strategy, pronto, to explain my pathetic behavior.

There's only one choice: I'm going to have to pretend my outburst never happened. It's what Samantha would do.

I raise my chin and stride out.

Back at the table, Missy and Dorrit have arrived, along with a bottle of Chianti set in a woven straw basket. It's the kind of wine I'd be embarrassed to drink in New York.

And with an ugly pang, I realize how average it all is. My father, the middle-aged widower, inappropriately dressed and going through a midlife crisis by taking up with a somewhat desperate younger woman, who, against the plain backdrop of Castlebury, probably appears interesting and different and exciting. And my two sisters, a punk and a nerd. It's like some lousy sitcom.

If they're so ordinary, does it mean I am too? Can I ever escape my past?

I wish I could change the channel.

"Carrie!" Missy cries out. "Are you okay?"

"Me?" I ask with feigned surprise. "Of course." I take my place next to Wendy. "My father says you helped him find his Harley. I think it's so interesting that you like motorcycles."

"My father is a state trooper," she responds, no doubt relieved that I've managed to get ahold of myself.

I turn to Dorrit. "You hear that, Dorrit? Wendy's father is a state trooper. You'd better be careful—"

"Carrie." My father looks momentarily distraught. "We don't need to air our dirty laundry."

"No, but we do need to wash it."

No one gets my little joke. I pick up my wine glass and sigh. I'd planned to go back to New York on Monday, but there's no way I can possibly last that long. Come tomorrow, I'm taking the first train out of here.

CHAPTER TWENTY-FOUR

"I do love you, Carrie. Just because I'm with Wendy—"

"I know, Dad. I *like* Wendy. I'm only leaving because I have this play to write. And if I can get it done, it's going to be performed."

"Where?" my father asks. He's clutching the wheel of the car, absorbed in changing lanes on our little highway. I'm convinced he doesn't really care, but I try to explain anyway.

"At this space. That's what they call it—'a space.' It's really a kind of loft thing at this guy's apartment. It used to be a bank—"

I can tell by his glance into the rearview mirror that I've lost him.

"I admire your tenacity," he says. "You don't

give up. That's good."

Now he's lost *me*. "Tenacity" isn't the word I was hoping for. It makes me sound like someone clinging to a rock face.

I slump down in the seat. Why can't he ever say something along the lines of "You're really talented, Carrie, of course you're going to succeed." Am I going to spend the rest of my life trying to get some kind of approval from him that he's never going to give?

"I wanted to tell you about Wendy before," he says, swerving into the exit lane that leads to the train station. Now's my opportunity to tell him about my struggles in New York, but he keeps changing the subject back to Wendy.

"Why didn't you?" I ask hopelessly.

"I wasn't sure about her feelings."

"And you are now?"

He pulls into a parking spot and kills the engine. With great seriousness, he says, "She loves me, Carrie."

A cynical puff of air escapes my lips.

"I mean it. She really loves me."

"Everyone loves you, Dad."

"You know what I mean." He nervously rubs the corner of his eye.

"Oh, Dad." I pat his arm, trying to understand. The last few years must have been terrible for him. On the other hand, they've been terrible for me, too. And Missy. And Dorrit.

"I'm happy for you, Dad, I really am," I say, although the thought of my father in a serious relationship with another woman makes me shaky. What if he marries her?

"She's a lovely person. She—" He hesitates. "She reminds me of Mom."

This is the cherry on the crap sundae. "She's not anything like Mom," I say softly, my anger building.

"She is. When Mom was younger. You wouldn't remember because you were just a baby."

"Dad." I pause deliberately, hoping the obvious falseness of his statement will sink in. "Wendy likes motorcycles."

"Your mother was very adventurous when she was young too. Before she had you girls—"

"Just another reason why I'll never get married," I say, getting out of the car.

"Oh, Carrie." He sighs. "I feel sorry for you, then. I worry that you'll never find true love."

His comment stops me. I stand rigid on the sidewalk, about to explode, but something prevents me. I think of Miranda and how she'd interpret this situation. She'd say it was my father who was worried about never finding true love again, but because he's too scared to admit it, he pins his fears on me.

I grab my suitcase from the backseat.

"Let me help you," he says.

I watch as my father lugs my suitcase through the wooden door that leads into the ancient terminal. I remind myself that my father isn't a bad guy. Compared to most men, he's pretty great.

He sets down my suitcase and opens his arms. "Can I have a hug?"

"Sure, Dad." I hug him tightly, inhaling a whiff of lime. Must be a new cologne Wendy gave him.

A yawning emptiness opens up inside me.

"I want the best for you, Carrie. I really do."

"I know, Dad." Feeling like I'm a million years old, I pick up my suitcase and head to the platform. "Don't worry, Dad," I say, as if to convince myself as well. "Everything is going to be *fine*."

The moment the train pulls out of the station, I start to feel better. Nearly two hours later, when we're passing the projects in the Bronx, I'm positively giddy. There's the brief, magical view of the skyline—the Emerald City!—before we plunge into the tunnel. No matter where I might travel—Paris, London, Rome—I'll always be thrilled to get back to New York.

Riding the elevator in Penn Station, I make

an impromptu decision. I won't go straight to Samantha's apartment. Instead, I'll surprise Bernard.

I have to find out what's going on with him before I can proceed with my life.

It takes two separate subway trains to get near his place. With each stop, I become more and more excited about the prospect of seeing him. I arrive at the Fifty-ninth Street station under Bloomingdale's, the heat coursing through my blood threatening to scald me from the inside.

He has to be home.

"Mr. Singer's out, miss," the doorman says, with, I suspect, a certain amount of relish. None of the doormen in this building particularly like me. I always catch them looking at me sideways as if they don't approve.

"Do you know when he'll be back?"

"I'm not his secretary, miss."

"Fine."

I scan the lobby. Two leather-clad armchairs are stationed in front of a faux fireplace, but I don't want to sit there with the doorman's eyes on me. I spin out the door and park myself on a pretty bench across the street. I rest my feet on my suitcase, as if I have all the time in the world.

I wait.

I tell myself I'll only wait for half an hour,

and then I'll go. Half an hour becomes forty-five minutes, then an hour. After nearly two hours, I begin to wonder if I've fallen into a love trap. Have I become the girl who waits by the phone, hoping it will ring, who asks a friend to dial her number to make sure the phone is working? Who eventually picks up a man's dry cleaning, scrubs his bathroom, and shops for furniture she'll never own?

Yup. And I don't care. I can be that girl, and someday, when I've got it all figured out, I won't be.

Finally, at two hours and twenty-two minutes, Bernard comes strolling up Sutton Place.

"Bernard!" I say, rushing toward him with unbridled enthusiasm. Maybe my father was right: I am tenacious. I don't give up that easily on anything.

Bernard squints. "Carrie?"

"I just got back," I say, as if I haven't been waiting for nearly three hours.

"From where?"

"Castlebury. Where I grew up."

"And here you are." He slings his arm comfortably around my shoulders.

It's like the dinner with Maggie never happened. Nor my series of desperate phone calls. Nor his not calling me the way he promised. But maybe, because he's a writer, he lives in a slightly different reality, where the things that seem earth-shattering to me are nothing to him.

"My suitcase," I murmur, glancing back.

"You moving in?" he laughs.

"Maybe."

"Just in time, too," he teases. "My furniture finally arrived."

I spend the night at Bernard's. We sleep in the crisp new sheets on the enormous king-size bed. It's so very, very comfortable.

I sleep like a baby and when I wake up, darling Bernard is next to me, his face buried in his pillow. I lie back and close my eyes, enjoying the luxurious quiet while I mentally review the events of the evening.

We started by fooling around on the new couch. Then we moved into the bedroom and fooled around while we watched TV. Then we ordered Chinese food (why does sex always seem to make people hungry?) and fooled around some more. We finished off with a bubble bath. Bernard was very gentle and sweet, and he didn't even try to put in the old weenie. Or at least I'm pretty sure he didn't. Miranda says the guy really has to jam it in there, so I doubt I could have missed it.

I wonder if Bernard secretly knows I'm a

virgin. If there's something about me that flashes "undefiled."

"Hiya, butterfly," he says now, stretching his arms toward the ceiling. He rolls over and smiles, and moves in for a kiss, morning breath and all.

"Have you gotten the pill yet?" Bernard asks, making coffee in the spiffy new machine that gurgles like a baby's belly.

I casually light a cigarette and hand him one. "Not yet."

"Why not?"

Good question. "I forgot?"

"Pumpkin, you can't neglect these kinds of things," he chastises gently.

"I know. But it's just that—with my father and his new girlfriend—I'll take care of it this week, I promise."

"If you did, you could spend the night more often." Bernard sets two cups of coffee on the sleek dining room table. "And you could get a small valise for your things."

"Like my toothbrush?" I giggle.

"Like whatever you need," he says.

A valise, huh? The word makes spending the night sound planned and glamorous, as opposed to last-minute and smutty. I laugh. A valise sounds very expensive. "I don't think I can afford a *valise*."

"Oh well then." He shrugs. "Something nice. So the doormen won't be suspicious."

"They'll be suspicious if I'm carrying a plastic grocery bag but not if I'm carrying a valise?"

"You know what I mean."

I nod. With a valise, I wouldn't look so much like a troubled teenager he'd picked up at Penn Station. Which reminds me of Teensie.

"I met your agent. At a party," I say easily, not wanting to ruin the mood.

"Did you?" He smiles, clearly unconcerned about the incident. "Was she a dragon lady?"

"She practically ripped me to shreds with her claws," I say jokingly. "Is she always like that?"

"Pretty much." He rubs the top of my head. "Maybe we should have dinner with her. So the two of you can get to know each other."

"Whatever you want, Mr. Singer," I purr, climbing into his lap. If he wants me to have dinner with his agent, it means our relationship is not only back on track, but speeding forward like a European train. I kiss him on the mouth, imagining I'm a Katharine Hepburn character in a romantic black-and-white movie.

CHAPTER TWENTY-FIVE

Later, on my way downtown, I pass a store for medical supplies. In the window are three mannequins. Not the pretty kind you see in Saks or Bergdorf's, where they make the mannequins from molds of actual women, but the scary cheap ones that look like oversized dolls from the 1950s. The dolls are wearing surgical scrubs, and it suddenly hits me that scrubs would make the perfect New York uniform. They're cheap, washable, and totally cool.

And they come neatly packaged in cellophane. I buy three pairs in different colors, and remember what Bernard said about a valise.

The only good thing about going to my father's this weekend was that I found an old binoculars case that belonged to my mother, which I pur-loined to use as a handbag. Perhaps other items can be similarly repurposed as well. When I trip by a fancy hardware store, I spot the perfect carryall.

It's a carpenter's tool bag, made of canvas with a real leather bottom, big enough for a pair of shoes, a manuscript, and a change of scrubs. And it's only six dollars. A steal.

I buy the tool bag and stick my purse and scrubs into it, grab my suitcase, and head to the train.

It's been humid the past few days, and when I enter Samantha's apartment there's a closed-in smell, as if every odor has been trapped. I breathe deeply, partly due to relief at being back, and partly because this particular smell will always remind me of New York and Samantha. It's a mixture of old perfume and scented candles, cigarette smoke and something else I can't quite identify: a sort of comforting musk.

I put on the blue scrubs, make a cup of tea, and sit down at the typewriter. All summer I've been terrified about facing the blank page. But maybe because I went home and realized I have worse things to worry about—like not making it and ending up like Wendy—that I'm actually excited. I have hours and hours stretching before me in which to write. Tenacity, I remind myself. I'm going work until I finish this play. And I will not answer the phone. In an effort to make good on my promise, I even unplug it.

I write for four hours straight, until hunger forces me out in search of food. I wander dazedly into the deli, the characters still in my head, yapping away as I buy a can of soup, heat it up, and place it next to my typewriter so I can eat and work. I beetle on for quite a while, and when I finally feel finished for the day, I decide to visit my favorite street.

It's a tiny, brick-paved path called Commerce Street—one of those rare places in the West Village that you can never find if you're actually looking for it. You have to sneak up on it by using certain landmarks: the junk store on Hudson Street. The sex shop on Barrow. Somewhere near the pet store is a small gate. And there it is, just on the other side.

I stroll slowly down the sidewalk, wanting to memorize each detail. The tiny, charming town houses, the cherry trees, the little neighborhood bar where, I imagine, all the patrons know one another. I take several turns up and down the street, pausing in front of each house, picturing how it would feel to live there. As I gaze up at the tiny windows on the top floor of a red-brick carriage house, it dawns on me that I've changed. I used to worry that my dream of becoming a writer was just that—a dream. I had no idea how to do it, where to begin and how to continue. But lately, I'm beginning to feel that I *am* a writer. This is me. Writing and wandering the Village in my scrubs.

And tomorrow, if I skip class, I'll have another day like this one, all to myself. I'm suddenly overcome with joy. I run all the way back to the apartment, and when I spot my pile of plays on the table, I'm can't believe how happy I am.

I settle in to read, making notes with a pencil and underlining especially poignant bits of dialogue. I can do this. Who cares what my father thinks? For that matter, who cares what anyone thinks? Everything I need is in my head, and no one can take that away.

At eight o'clock, I fall into one of those rare, deep sleeps where your body is so exhausted, you wonder if you'll ever wake up. When I finally wrench myself out of bed, it's ten a.m.

I count the hours I slept—fourteen. I must have been really tired. So tired, I didn't even know how shattered I was. At first, I'm groggy from all the sleep, but when the grogginess dissipates, I feel terrific. I put on my scrubs from the day before, and without bothering to brush my teeth, go straight to the typewriter.

My powers of concentration are remarkable.

I write without stopping, without noticing the time, until I type the words "THE END." Elated and a little woozy, I check the clock. It's just after four. If I hurry, I can get the play photocopied and into Viktor Greene's office by five.

I leap into the shower, my heart pounding in triumph. I slide into a clean pair of scrubs, grab my manuscript, and run out the door.

The copy place is on Sixth Avenue, just around the corner from the school. For once, it's my lucky day—there's no line. My play is forty pages long and copying is expensive, but I can't risk losing it. Fifteen minutes later, one copy of my play tucked neatly into a manila envelope, I gallop to The New School.

Viktor is in his office, slumped over his desk. At first I think he's asleep, and when he doesn't move, I wonder if he actually is dead. I knock on the door. No response. "Viktor?" I ask in alarm.

Slowly, he lifts his head, as if he has a cement block on the back of his neck. His eyes are puffy, the lower lids turned out, defiantly exposing their red-rimmed interior. His mustache is ragged as if rent by despairing fingers. He props up his cheeks with his hands. His mouth falls open. "Yes?"

Normally, I would ask what's wrong. But I don't know Viktor well enough, and I'm not sure I want to know anyway. I take a step closer, holding the manila envelope aloft. "I finished my play."

"Were you in class today?" he asks mournfully.

"No. I was writing. I wanted to get my play finished." I slide the envelope across his desk. "I thought maybe you could read it tonight."

"Sure." He stares at me as if he barely remembers who I am.

"So, uh, thanks, Mr. Greene." I turn to go, glancing back at him in concern. "I'll see you tomorrow, then?"

"Mmmm," he replies.

What the hell's the matter with him? I wonder, bounding down the stairs. I walk briskly for several blocks, buy a hot dog from a vendor, and ponder what to do next.

L'il. I haven't seen her for ages. Not properly, anyway. She's the one person who I can really talk to about my play. Who will actually understand. And if Peggy's there—so what? She's already kicked me out once. What can she do to me now?

I hike up Second Avenue, enjoying the noise, the sights, the people scurrying home like cockroaches. I could live here forever. Maybe even become a real New Yorker someday.

Seeing my old building on Forty-seventh Street brings back all kinds of memories—Peggy's nude pictures, her collection of bears, and those tiny little rooms with the awful camp beds—and

I wonder how I managed to last even three days. But I didn't know better then. Didn't know what to expect and was willing to take anything.

I've come a long way.

I press impudently on the buzzer like I mean business. Eventually, a small voice answers. "Yes?" It's not L'il or Peggy, so I assume it's my replacement.

"Is L'il there?" I ask.

"Why?"

"It's Carrie Bradshaw," I say loudly.

Apparently L'il is home, because the buzzer goes off and the locks click open.

Upstairs, the door to Peggy's apartment widens a crack, just enough for someone to peek out while keeping the chain latched. "Is L'il here?" I ask into the crack.

"Why?" asks the voice again. Perhaps "why" is the only word she knows.

"I'm a friend of hers."

"Oh."

"Can I come in?"

"I guess so," the voice says nervously. The door creaks open, just enough for me to push through.

On the other side is a plain young woman with unfortunate hair and the remnants of teen-age acne. "We're not supposed to have visitors," she whispers in fear.

"I know," I say dismissively. "I used to live here."

"You did?" The girl's eyes are as big as eggs.

I stride past her. "You can't let Peggy run your life." I yank open the door to the tiny bedrooms. "L'il?"

"What are you doing?" the girl bleats, right on my heels. "L'il isn't here."

"I'll leave her a note then." I fling open the door to L'il's bedroom and halt in confusion.

The room is empty. The camp bed has been stripped of its linens. Gone is the photograph of Sylvia Plath that L'il used to keep on her desk, along with her typewriter, ream of paper, and all her other belongings.

"Did she move?" I ask, perplexed. Why wouldn't she tell me?

The girl backs out of the room and sits on her own bed, pressing her lips together. "She went home."

"What?" This can't be true.

The girl nods. "On Sunday. Her father drove up and got her."

"Why?"

"How should I know?" the girl says. "Peggy was really pissed off, though. L'il only told her that morning."

My voice rises in alarm. "Is she coming back?"

The girl shrugs.

"Did she leave an address or anything?"

"Nope. Just said she had to go home is all."

"Yeah, well, thanks," I say, realizing I won't get anything more out of her.

I leave the apartment and walk blindly downtown, trying to make sense of L'il's departure. I rack my brain for everything she told me about herself and where she was from. Her real name is Elizabeth Reynolds Waters, so that's a start. But what town is she from specifically? All I know is that she's from North Carolina. And she and Capote knew each other before, because as L'il said once, "people from the South all know each other." If L'il left on Sunday, she must have reached home by now, even if she was driving.

I narrow my eyes, determined to find her.

CHAPTER TWENTY-SIX

Without knowing exactly where I'm going, I realize I'm on Capote's street. I recognize his building right away. His apartment is on the second floor, and the yellow old-lady curtains are clearly visible through the window.

I hesitate. If I ring his bell and he's home, no doubt he'll think I've come back for more. He might even presume that his kiss was so wonderful, I've fallen head over heels for him. Or maybe he'll be annoyed, assuming I've come to yell at him for his inappropriate behavior.

What the hell? I can't live my life worrying about what stupid Capote thinks. I press hard on his buzzer.

After a few seconds, the window flies open and

Capote sticks his head out. "Who's there?"

"It's me." I wave.

"Oh. Carrie." He doesn't look particularly happy to see me. "What do you want?"

I open my arms in a gesture of exasperation. "Can I come up?"

"I've only got a minute."

"I've only got a minute too." Jeez. What a jerk.

He disappears for a moment, and reappears, jangling some keys in his hand. "The buzzer isn't working," he says, tossing the set down to me.

The buzzer is probably worn out from all his female guests, I think, as I trudge upstairs.

He's waiting in the entry in a ruffled white shirt and black tuxedo pants, fumbling with a shiny bow tie. "Where are you off to?" I ask, snickering at his getup.

"Where do you think?" He steps back so I can pass. If he has any memory of our kiss, he certainly isn't acting like it.

"I wasn't expecting to find you in a monkey suit. I never figured you for the type."

"Why's that?" he asks, somewhat offended.

"The right end goes under the left," I say, indicating his bow tie. "Why don't you use one of those clip-on things?"

As expected, my question rattles him. "It isn't proper. A gentleman never wears a clip-on bow tie."

"Right." I insolently run my finger over the pile of books on his coffee table as I make myself comfortable on the squishy couch. "Where are you headed?"

"To a gala." He frowns disapprovingly at my actions.

"For what?" I idly pick up one of the books and flip through it.

"Ethiopia. It's a very important cause."

"How big of you."

"They don't have any food, Carrie. They're starving."

"And you're going to a fancy dinner. For starving people. Why don't you just send them the food instead?"

That's it. Capote jerks on the ends of his bow tie, nearly choking himself. "Why are you here?"

I lean back against the cushions. "What's the name of the town L'il comes from?"

"Why?"

I roll my eyes and sigh. "I need to know. I want to get in touch with her. She left New York, in case you don't know."

"As a matter of fact, I do know. Which you would have known as well if you bothered to come to class today."

I sit up, eager for information. "What happened?"

"Viktor made an announcement that she'd left. To pursue other interests."

"Don't you find that strange?"

"Why?"

"Because L'il's only interest is writing. She'd never give up class."

"Maybe she had family issues."

"You're not even curious?"

"Look, Carrie," he snaps. "Right now my only concern is not being late. I've got to pick up Rainbow—"

"All I want is the name of L'il's hometown," I say, becoming officious.

"I'm not sure. It's either Montgomery or Macon."

"I thought you knew her," I say accusingly, although I suspect my disdain might actually be about Rainbow. I guess he's seeing her after all. I know I shouldn't care, but I do.

I rise. "Have fun at the gala," I add, with a dismissive smile.

Suddenly, I hate New York. No, scratch that. I don't *hate* New York. I only hate some of the people in it.

There are listings for three Waterses in Montgomery County and two in Macon. I start with Macon, and get L'il's aunt on the first try. She's nice as can be, and gives me L'il's number.

L'il is shocked to hear my voice, and not, I suspect, altogether pleased, although her lack of enthusiasm could be due to embarrassment at having abandoned New York. "I went by your apartment," I say, my voice filled with concern. "The girl there said you moved back home."

"I had to get away."

"Why? Because of Peggy? You could have moved in with me." No response. "You're not sick, are you?" I ask, my voice pitched with worry.

She sighs. "Not in the traditional sense, no."

"Meaning?"

"I don't want to talk about it," she whispers.

"But L'il," I insist. "What about writing? You can't just quit New York."

There's a pause. Then she says stiffly, "New York is not for me." I hear a muffled sob as if she's put her hand over the receiver. "I have to go, Carrie."

And suddenly, I put two and two together. I don't know why I didn't see it before. It was so obvious. I simply never imagined that anyone could be attracted to him.

I feel sick. "Is it Viktor?"

"No!" she cries.

"It *is* Viktor. Why didn't you tell me? What happened? Were you seeing him?"

"He broke my heart."

I'm stunned. I still can't believe L'il was having

an affair with Viktor Greene and his ridiculous mustache. How could anyone even kiss the guy with that big bushy Waldo in the way? And on top of it, to have him break your heart?

"Oh, L'il. How awful. You can't let him force you out of class. Plenty of women have affairs with their professors. It's never a good idea. But sometimes the best thing to do is to pretend it didn't happen," I add in a rush, thinking briefly about Capote and how we're both behaving as if we never kissed.

"It's more than that, Carrie," she says ominously.

"Of course it is. I mean, I'm sure you thought you were in love with him. But really, L'il, he's not worth it. He's just some weird loser guy who happened to win a book award," I ramble on. "And six months from now when you've published more poems in *The New Yorker* and won awards yourself, you won't even remember him."

"Unfortunately, I will."

"Why?" I ask dumbly.

"I got pregnant," she says.

That shuts me up.

"Are you there?" she asks.

"With Viktor?" My voice trembles.

"Who else?" she hisses.

"Oh, L'il." I crumple in sympathy. "I'm

sorry. So, so sorry."

"I got rid of it," she says harshly.

"Oh." I hesitate. "Maybe it's for the better."

"I'll never know, will I?"

"These things happen," I say, trying to soothe her.

"He made me get rid of it."

I squeeze my eyes shut, feeling her agony.

"He didn't even ask if I wanted it. There was no discussion. He just assumed. He assumed—" She breaks off, unable to continue.

"L'il," I whisper.

"I know what you're thinking. I'm only nineteen. I shouldn't have a child. And I probably would have . . . taken care of it. But I didn't have a choice."

"He forced you to have an abortion?"

"Pretty much. He made the appointment at the clinic. He took me there. Paid for it. And then he sat in the waiting room while I had it done."

"Oh my God, L'il. Why didn't you run out of there?"

"I didn't have the guts. I knew it was the right thing to do, but—"

"Did it hurt?" I ask.

"No," she says simply. "That was the weirdest thing. It didn't hurt and afterward, I felt fine. Like I was back to my old self. I was *relieved*. But then

I started thinking. And I realized how terrible it was. Not the abortion necessarily, but the way he'd behaved. Like it was a foregone conclusion. I realized he couldn't have loved me at all. How can a man love you if he won't even consider having a baby with you?"

"I don't know, L'il—"

"It's black-and-white, Carrie," she says, her voice rising. "You cannot even pretend anymore. And even if I could, we'd always have this thing between us. Knowing that I was pregnant with his child and *he didn't want it*."

I shudder. "But maybe after a while . . . you could come back?" I ask carefully.

"Oh, Carrie." She sighs. "Don't you get it? I'm never coming back. I don't even want to *know* people like Viktor Greene. I wish I'd never come to New York in the first place." And with a painful cry, she hangs up.

I sit there twisting the phone cord in despair. Why L'il? She's not the type of person I'd imagine this happening to, but on the other hand, who is? There's a terrible finality about her actions that's frightening.

I put my head in my hands. Maybe L'il is right about New York. She came here to win and the city beat her. I'm terrified. If this could happen to L'il, it could happen to anyone. Including myself.

CHAPTER TWENTY-SEVEN

I sit tapping my feet in annoyance.

Ryan is at the front of the class, reading his short story. It's good. Really good—about one of his crazy late nights at a club where some girl with a shaved head tried to have sex with him. It's so good, I wish I'd written it myself. Unfortunately I can't give it my full attention. I'm still reeling from my conversation with L'il and the perfidy of Viktor Greene.

Although "perfidy" isn't a strong enough word. Heinous? Egregious? *Invidious?*

Sometimes there are no words to describe the treachery of men in relationships.

What is wrong with them? Why can't they be more like women? Someday I'm going to write a book called *World Without Men*. There would be no Viktor Greenes. Or Capote Duncans, either.

I try to focus on Ryan, but L'il's absence fills the room. I keep glancing over my shoulder, thinking she'll be there, but there's only an empty desk. Viktor has taken up residence in the back of the room, so I can't study him without boldly turning around in my seat. I did, however, do a little reconnaissance on my own before class.

I got to school twenty minutes early and headed straight for Viktor's office. He was standing by the window, watering one of those stupid hanging plants that are all the rage, the idea being that they will somehow provide extra oxygen in this nutrient-starved city.

"Yop?" he said, turning around.

Whatever I thought I was going to say got caught in my throat. I gaped, then smiled awkwardly.

Viktor's mustache was gone. Waldo had been thoroughly eradicated—much like, I couldn't help thinking, his unborn child.

I waited to see what he would do with his hands, now that Waldo was gone.

Sure enough, they went right to his upper lip, patting the skin in panic, like someone who's lost a limb and doesn't know it's gone until they try to use it.

"Errrrr," he said.

"I was wondering if you'd read my play," I asked, regaining my equilibrium.

"Mmmm?" Having concluded Waldo was, indeed, no more, his hands dropped limply to his sides.

"I finished it," I said, enjoying his discomfort. "I dropped it off yesterday, remember?"

"I haven't gotten to it yet."

"When will you get to it?" I demanded. "There's this man who's interested in doing a reading—"

"Sometime this weekend, I imagine." He nodded his head briefly in confirmation.

"Thanks." I skittled down the hallway, convinced, somehow, that he knew I was onto him. That he knew I knew what he'd done.

Capote's laughter brings me back to the present. It's like nails on a chalkboard, for all the wrong reasons. I actually like his laugh. It's one of those laughs that makes you want to say something funny so you can hear it all over again.

Ryan's story is apparently very amusing. Lucky him. Ryan is one of those guys whose talent will always outshine his flaws.

Viktor ambles to the front of the room. I stare at the bare patches of skin around his mouth and shudder.

Flowers. I need flowers for Samantha. And toilet paper. And maybe a banner. "Welcome Home." I wander through the flower district on Seventh Avenue, dodging puddles of water on which float wanton petals. I remember reading somewhere about the society ladies on the Upper East Side who send their assistants each morning to buy fresh flowers. I wish, briefly, that I could be that kind of person, concerned with the details of fresh flowers, but the effort feels overwhelming. Will Samantha send someone for flowers when she marries Charlie? He seems like the type who would expect it. And suddenly, the whole idea of flowers is so depressingly dull I'm tempted to abort my quest.

But Samantha will appreciate them. She's coming back tomorrow and they'll make her feel good. Who doesn't like flowers? But what kind? Roses? Doesn't seem right. I duck into the smallest shop, where I try to buy a lily. It's five dollars. "How much do you want to spend?" the salesgirl asks.

"Two dollars? Maybe three?"

"For that you'll get baby's breath. Try the deli down the street."

At the deli, I settle on a hideous bunch of multicolored flowers in unnatural hues of pink, purple, and green.

Back home, I put the flowers in a tall glass and place them next to Samantha's bed. The flowers may make Samantha happy, but I can't shake my own feeling of dread. I keep thinking about L'il and how Viktor Greene ruined her life.

At loose ends, I look doubtfully at the bed. Although not much has happened in it recently, besides the consumption of crackers and cheese, I should wash the sheets. The Laundromat's creepy, though. All kinds of crimes take place between the washers and dryers. Muggings and stolen clothes and fisticuffs over possession of the machines. Nevertheless, I dutifully strip the bed, stuffing the black sheets into a pillowcase that I sling over my shoulder.

The Laundromat is harshly lit but not crowded. I buy a package of soap from a vending machine and tear it open, the sharp particles of detergent making me sneeze. I stuff the sheets into the washer and sit on top, staking my claim.

What is it about the Laundromat that's so depressing?

Is it the simple reality of literally exposing your dirty laundry to strangers as you shove it quickly in and out of the washer, hoping no one will notice your ragged underpants and polyester sheets? Or is it a sign of defeat? Like you never managed to make it into a building with its own basement laundry room.

Maybe Wendy had a point about New York, after all. No matter what you think you *can* be, when you're forced to stop and look at where you actually are, it's pretty depressing.

Sometimes there's no escaping the truth.

Two hours later, when I'm hauling my clean laundry up the steps to the apartment, I discover Miranda on the landing, crying into a copy of the *New York Post*.

Oh no. Not again. What is it about the last two days? I put down my sack. "Marty?"

She nods once and lowers the newspaper in shame. On the floor next to her, the top of an open bottle of vodka juts from a small paper bag. "I couldn't help it. I had to," she says, explaining the alcohol.

"You don't have to apologize to *me*," I say, unlocking the door. "Bastard."

"I didn't know where else to go." She gets up and takes a brave step before her face crumples in pain. "Oh God. It hurts, Carrie. Why does it hurt so much?"

"I don't understand. I thought everything was great," I say, lighting a cigarette as I prepare to bring my best powers of relationship analysis to the situation.

"I thought we were having fun." Miranda chokes back tears. "I've never had fun with a guy before. And then, this morning when we got up, he was acting strange. He had this kind of sick smile on his face while he was shaving. I didn't want to say anything because I didn't want to be one of those girls who are always asking, 'What's wrong?' I was trying to do everything *right*, for once."

"I'm sure you were—"

Outside, there's a rumble of thunder.

She wipes her cheek. "Even though he wasn't really my type, I thought I was making progress. I told myself I was breaking the pattern."

"At least you tried," I say soothingly. "Especially since you don't even like guys. When I met you, you didn't want to have anything to do with them, remember? And it was cool. Because when you really think about it, guys are kind of a big waste of time."

Miranda sniffs. "Maybe you're right." But in the next second, a fresh round of tears clouds her eyes. "I used to be strong. But then I was taken in by . . ." She struggles to find the words. "I was betrayed by . . . my own beliefs. I guess I thought I was tougher than I am. I thought I could spot a creep a mile away."

A crack of lightning makes us both jump.

"Oh, sweetie." I sigh. "When a guy wants to get you in bed, he's always on his best behavior. On the other hand, he did want to be with you all the time. So he must have really been crazy about you."

"Or maybe he was using me for my apartment. Because my apartment is bigger than his. And I don't have any roommates. He had this one roommate, Tyler. Said he was always farting and calling everyone a 'fag.'"

"But it doesn't make sense. If he was using you for your apartment, why would he break up with you?"

"How should I know?" She pulls her knees to her chest. "Last night, when we were having sex, I should have known something was wrong. Because the sex was very . . . strange. Nice, but strange. He kept stroking my hair. And looking into my eyes with this sad expression. And then he said, 'I want you to know that I care about you, Miranda Hobbes. I really do.'"

"He used your full name like that? 'Miranda Hobbes'?"

"I thought it was romantic," she snivels. "But this morning, after he'd finished showering, he came out holding his razor and shaving cream and asked me if I had a shopping bag."

"What?"

"For his stuff."

"Ouch."

She nods dazedly. "I asked him why he wanted it. He said he realized it wasn't going to work out between us and we shouldn't waste each other's time."

My jaw drops. "Just like that?"

"He was so . . . clinical about it. Official. Like he was in court or something and I was being sentenced to jail. I didn't know what to do, so I gave him the damn shopping bag. And it was from Saks. One of those big red expensive ones, too."

I sit back on my heels. "Aw, sweetie. You can always get another shopping bag—"

"But I can't get another Marty," she wails. "It's me, Carrie. There's something wrong with me. I drive guys away."

"Now listen. This has nothing to do with you. There's something wrong with *him*. Maybe he was afraid you were going to dump him so he broke up with you first."

She lifts her head. "Carrie. I ran down the street after him. Yelling. When he saw me coming, he started running. Into the subway. Can you believe that?"

"Yes," I say. Given what happened to L'il, I'd believe just about anything right now.

She blows hard into a wad of toilet paper.

"Maybe you're right. Maybe he does think I'm too good for him." And just as I'm beginning to hope I've gotten through to her, a stubborn, closed look comes over her face. "If I could just see him. Explain. Maybe we can get back together."

"No!" I yelp. "He's already run away once. Even if you do get back together, he'll do the same thing. It's his *pattern*."

She lowers the toilet paper and gives me a doubtful look. "How do you know?"

"Trust me."

"Maybe I can change him." She reaches for the phone, but I yank the cord before she can grab it.

"Miranda." I clutch the phone in my arms. "If you call Marty, I will lose all respect for you."

She glares. "If you do not hand over that phone, I will have a very hard time considering you a friend."

"That stinks," I say, grudgingly passing her the phone. "Putting a guy before your friends."

"I'm not putting Marty before you. I'm trying to find out what happened."

"You *know* what happened."

"He owes me a proper explanation."

I give up. She picks up the phone and frowns into the receiver. She presses down on the hook a few times, and looks at me accusingly. "You did this on purpose. Your phone's out of order."

"Really?" I ask in surprise. I take the phone from her and try it myself. Nothing. Not even air. "I'm pretty sure I used it this morning."

"Maybe you didn't pay the bill."

"Maybe Samantha didn't pay the bill. She went to LA."

"Shhhh." Miranda holds up a finger as her eyes dart around the room. "What do you hear?"

"Nothing?"

"That's right. Nothing." She jumps up and starts flipping switches. "The air conditioner's off. And the lights aren't working."

We run to the window. The traffic on Seventh Avenue is in a snarl. Horns honk as several sirens go off at once. People are getting out of their cars, waving their arms and pointing at the traffic lights.

My eyes follow their gestures. The lights swaying over Seventh Avenue are dark.

I look uptown. Smoke is billowing from somewhere near the river.

"What's happening?" I scream.

Miranda crosses her arms and gives me a tangled, triumphant smile. "It's a blackout," she declares.

CHAPTER TWENTY-EIGHT

"Okay. Let me get this straight," I say. "The lining from the uterus migrates to other parts of the body, and when you get your period, it bleeds?"

"And sometimes, you can't get pregnant. Or if you do, the fetus can actually develop outside the uterus," Miranda says, proudly displaying her knowledge.

"Like in your stomach?" I ask in horror.

She nods. "Or in your butt. My aunt had a friend who couldn't poop. Turns out there was a baby growing in her lower intestine."

"No!" I exclaim, and light another cigarette. I puff on it thoughtfully. The conversation is getting out of hand, but I'm enjoying the perversity.

I figure it's a special day—a day that's outside of all other days and is therefore exempt from the normal rules.

The entire city is without power. The subways aren't running and the streets are a mess. Our stairwell has been plunged into darkness. And there's a hurricane outside. Which means Samantha, Miranda, and I are stuck. For the next few hours, anyway.

Samantha arrived unexpectedly minutes after the blackout began. There was a lot of shouting in the stairwell, and people coming out of their apartments to compare notes. Someone said the ancient telephone building was struck by lightning, while another resident claimed the storm knocked down the phone lines and all the air conditioners caused a power outage. Either way, there are no lights and no phone service. Enormous black clouds rolled over the city, turning the sky an eerie grayish green. The wind picked up and the sky flashed with lightning.

"It's like Armageddon," Miranda declared. "Someone is trying to tell us something."

"Who?" Samantha asked with her usual sarcasm.

Miranda shrugged. "The Universe?"

"My uterus my Universe," Samantha said, and

that's how the whole conversation began.

Turns out Samantha has endometriosis, which is why she's always in so much pain when she gets her period. But it wasn't until she got to LA that the pain became unbearable and she started throwing up, right in the middle of a photography shoot. When the photographer's assistant found her nearly passed out on the bathroom floor, they insisted on calling an ambulance. She had to have her insides scraped out, and then they sent her back to New York, to rest.

"I'm going to be scarred for life," Samantha moans now. She pulls down the top of her jeans to reveal two large Band-Aids on either side of her ridiculously flat stomach, and peels away the adhesive. Underneath is a large red welt with four stitches. "Look," she commands.

"That's awful," Miranda concurs, her eyes shining with strange admiration. I was worried that Miranda and Samantha would hate each other, but instead, Miranda appears to have accepted Samantha's position as top dog. She's not only impressed with Samantha's worldliness, but is doing her level best to get Samantha to like her. Which consists of agreeing with everything Samantha says.

Putting me in the position of being the disagreer. "I don't care about scars. I think they add character." I can never understand why women get so worked up about these tiny imperfections.

"Carrie," Miranda scolds, shaking her head in accordance with Samantha's distress.

"As long as Charlie never finds out," Samantha says, leaning back against the cushions.

"Why should he care?" I ask.

"Because I don't want him to know I'm not perfect, Sparrow. And if he calls, I need you to pretend I'm still in LA."

"Fine." It seems weird to me, but then again, the whole situation is weird, with the blackout and all. Perhaps it's even Shakespearean. Like in *As You Like It* when everyone takes on different personas.

"Sparrow?" Miranda asks, jokingly.

I give her a dirty look as Samantha starts talking about my sex life with Bernard. "You have to admit, it's odd," she says, propping her feet on the pillows.

"He must be gay," Miranda says from the floor.

"He's not gay. He was *married*." I get up and pace around in the flickering candlelight.

"All the more reason to be horny," Samantha laughs.

"No guy dates a girl for a whole month without trying to have sex with her," Miranda insists.

"We've had sex. We just haven't had inter-course."

"Honey, that ain't sex. That's what you do in sixth grade." Samantha.

"Have you even seen it?" Miranda asks, gig-gling.

"As a matter of fact, I have." I point my ciga-rette at her.

"It's not one of those bendy ones, is it?" Miranda asks as she and Samantha chortle.

"No, it's not. And I'm insulted," I say, in faux outrage.

"Candles. And sexy lingerie. That's what you need," Samantha coos.

"I've never understood sexy lingerie. I mean, what's the point? The guy's only going to take it off," I object.

Samantha flicks her eyes in Miranda's direc-tion. "That's the trick. You don't take it off right away."

"You mean you run around his apartment in your underwear?" Me.

"You wear a fur coat. With sexy lingerie underneath."

"I can't afford a fur." Miranda.

"Then wear a trench coat. Do I have to teach you guys everything about sex?"

"Yes, please," I say.

"Especially since Carrie's still a virgin," Miranda screams.

"Honey, I knew that. I knew it the moment she walked in."

"Is it that obvious?" I ask.

"What I can't understand is why you're still one," Samantha says. "I got rid of mine when I was fourteen."

"How?" Miranda hiccups.

"The usual way. Boone's Farm Strawberry Hill and the back of a van."

"I did it on my parents' bed. They were away at a conference."

"That is sick," I say, pouring myself another drink.

"I know. I'm a very sick puppy," Miranda says.

When is this blackout going to end?

1:45 a.m.

"Babies! That's all it's about. Who ever knew the world would be all about babies?" Samantha shouts.

"Every time I see a baby, I swear, I want to throw up," Miranda says.

"I did throw up once." I nod eagerly. "I saw a filthy bib, and that was it."

"Why don't these people just get cats and a litter box?" Samantha asks.

2:15 a.m.

"I will never call a guy. Never ever." Samantha.

"What if you can't help it?" Me.

"You have to help it."

"It's all about low self-esteem." Miranda.

"You really should tell Charlie. About the procedure," I say, feeling wobbly.

"Why should I?" Samantha asks.

"Because it's what real people do."

"I didn't come to New York to be real."

"Didja come here to be fake?" I slur.

"I came here to be new," she says.

"I came here to be myself," Miranda adds. "I couldn't be, back home."

"Me neither." The room is spinning. "My mother died," I murmur, just before I pass out.

When I come to, light is streaming into the apartment.

I'm lying on the floor under the coffee table. Miranda is curled up on the couch, snoring, which immediately makes me wonder if this was secretly the reason Marty broke up with her. I try to sit up, but my head feels like it weighs a million pounds. "Ow," I say, putting it back down again.

Eventually I'm able to roll onto my stomach and crawl to the bathroom, where I take two aspirin and wash them down with the last of the bottled water. I stumble into Samantha's bedroom and crumple up on the floor.

"Carrie?" she says, awoken by my banging.

"Yer?"

"What happened last night?"

"Blackout."

"Damn."

"And endometriosis."

"Double damn."

"And Charlie."

"I didn't call him last night, did I?"

"Couldn't. Phones don't work."

"Are the lights still off?"

"Mmmm."

Pause.

"Did your mother really die?"

"Yep."

"I'm sorry."

"Me, too."

I hear her rustling around in those black silk sheets. She pats the side of the bed. "There's plenty of room here."

I heave myself onto the mattress and promptly fall into a greasy sleep.

CHAPTER TWENTY-NINE

"Hey, I found some food," Miranda exclaims. She places a box of Ritz crackers on the bed and we dive in.

"I think we should walk up to Charlie's." I brush my cracker crumbs off the sheet. "He's got the biggest apartment." And we've been stuck here for hours. I don't know how much longer I can last.

"No," Samantha says adamantly. "I'd rather starve then let him see me like this. My hair's dirty."

"Everyone's hair is dirty. Including Charlie's," I point out.

"Listen. What we talked about last night, we don't ever tell anyone, right?" Miranda says.

"I still can't believe Marty only has one testicle." I take another cracker. "That should have been a tip-off."

"I think it's a plus," Samantha says. "It made him work harder as a lover."

I feel around in the box for another cracker. It's empty. "We need supplies."

"I'm not moving." Samantha yawns luxuriously. "No power, no work. No Harry Mills trying to look up my skirt."

I sigh and change into my last clean pair of scrubs.

"Have you decided to become a doctor now?" Samantha asks.

"Where's your stethoscope?" Miranda hoots.

"They're very chic," I insist.

"Since when?"

"Since now." Hrmph. Apparently neither my sexual experiences nor my sartorial choices are much appreciated around here.

Miranda leans toward Samantha, and with an excited squeal demands, "Okay, what's the *worst* sex you've ever had?"

I throw up my hands. When I slip out of the apartment, the two of them are howling with laughter about something they've dubbed "The Pencil Problem."

❖ ✳ C_B ✳ ❖

I wander aimlessly around the Village, and when I spot the open door of the White Horse Tavern, I go inside.

In the dim light, I discover a few people sitting at the bar. My first reaction is one of relief that I've found someplace that's open. My second is dismay when I realize who's sitting there: Capote and Ryan.

I blink. It can't be. But it is. Capote's head is thrown back and he's laughing loudly. Ryan is hanging on to his bar stool. Clearly, they're both severely inebriated.

What the hell are they doing here? Capote's apartment is only a couple of blocks away, and it's possible he and Ryan got stuck at Capote's place when the power went out. But I'm surprised to see them, considering Capote's extensive alcohol collection. Judging from the looks of them, I guess they ran out.

I shake my head in disapproval, gearing up for the inevitable encounter. But secretly, I'm awfully glad to see them.

"Is this bar stool taken?" I ask, sliding in next to Ryan.

"Huh?" His eyes uncross as he stares at me in surprise. Then he falls upon me, embracing me in a bear hug. "Carrie Bradshaw!" He looks to

Capote. "Speak of the devil. We were just talking about you."

"You were?"

"Weren't we?" Ryan asks, confused.

"I think that was about twelve hours ago," Capote says. He's soused, but not nearly as plastered as Ryan. Probably because he thinks it's "ungentlemanly" to appear drunk. "We've moved on from there."

"Hemingway?" Ryan asks.

"Dostoyevsky," Capote replies.

"I can never keep those damn Russians straight, can you?" Ryan asks me.

"Only when I'm sober," I quip.

"Are you sober? Oh no." Ryan takes a step backward and nearly lands in Capote's lap. He slaps his hand on the bar. "Can't be sober in a blackout. Not allowed. Barkeep, get this lady a drink!" he demands.

"Why are *you* here?" Capote asks.

"I'm foraging for supplies." I look at the two of them doubtfully.

"We were too." Ryan slaps his forehead. "And then something happened and we got trapped here. We tried to leave, but the cops kept accusing Capote of being a looter, so we were driven back to this lair." He breaks up with laughter, and suddenly, I do too. Apparently, we've got a serious case of cabin fever because we fall all over each other, holding our stomachs and pointing at Capote and laughing even harder. Capote shakes his head, as if he can't understand how he ended up with the two of us.

"Seriously, though," I hiccup. "I need supplies. My two girlfriends—"

"You're with women?" Ryan asks eagerly. "Well, let's go." He stumbles out of the bar with Capote and me running after him.

I'm not exactly sure how it happened, but an hour later, Capote, Ryan, and I are bumbling up the stairs to Samantha's apartment. Ryan is clutching the handrail while Capote encourages him forward. I look at the two of them and sigh. Samantha is going to kill me. Or not. Maybe nothing really matters after twenty-four hours without electricity.

In any case, I'm not returning empty-handed. Besides Ryan and Capote, I have a bottle of vodka and two six-packs of beer, which Capote managed to cadge from the bartender. Then I found a church basement where they were handing out jugs of water and ham-and-cheese sandwiches. Then Ryan decided to take a leak in an empty doorway. Then we got chased by a cop on a motorcycle, who yelled at us and told us to go home.

This, too, was extremely funny, although I suspect it shouldn't have been.

Inside the apartment, we discover Samantha bent over the coffee table, writing out a list. Miranda is next to her, battling several expressions, from consternation to admiration to out-and-out horror. Finally, admiration wins. "That's twenty-two," she exclaims. "And who's Ethan? I hate that name."

"He had orange hair. That's basically all I can remember."

Oh dear. It seems they've resorted to the vodka bottle as well.

"We're home," I call out.

"*We?*" Samantha's head snaps around.

"I brought my friend Ryan. And his friend Capote."

"Well," Samantha purrs, rising to her feet as she takes in my stray cats with approval. "Are you here to rescue us?"

"More like we're rescuing them," I say belligerently.

"Welcome." Miranda waves from the couch.

I look at her in despair, wondering what I've done. Maybe what they say about danger is true. It heightens the senses. And apparently makes everyone seem much more attractive than they are under normal circumstances. Probably has something to do with the survival of the species. But if that's true, Mother Nature couldn't have chosen a more unreliable bunch.

I head into the kitchen with my sack of supplies and start unwrapping the sandwiches.

"I'll help you," Capote says.

"There's nothing to do," I say sharply, cutting the sandwiches in half to save the rest for later.

"You shouldn't be so rigid, you know?" Capote flips open a can of beer and pushes it toward me.

"I'm not. But someone needs to keep a level head."

"You worry too much. You always act like you're going to get into trouble."

I'm flabbergasted. "Me?"

"You get this sour, disapproving look on your face." He opens a can of beer for himself.

"And what about the arrogant, disapproving look on yours?"

"I'm not arrogant, Carrie."

"And I'm Marilyn Monroe."

"What do you have to worry about, anyway?" he asks. "Aren't you going to Brown in the fall?"

Brown. I'm paralyzed. Despite the blackout and our paltry supplies and the presence of Capote Duncan, it's the last place I think I'll ever want to be. The whole idea of college suddenly feels irrelevant. "Why?" I ask, defensively. "Are you trying to get rid of me?"

He shrugs and takes a sip of beer. "Nah. I'd probably miss you."

He goes back to join the others while I stand there in shock, holding the plate of sandwiches in my hands.

7:00 p.m.

Strip poker.

9:00 p.m.

More strip poker.

10:30 p.m.

Wearing Samantha's bra on my head.

2:00 a.m.

Have constructed tent from old blanket and chairs. Capote and I under tent.

Discussing Emma Bovary.

Discussing L'il and Viktor Greene.

Discussing Capote's views on women: "I want a woman who has the same goals as I do. Who wants to do something with her life."

I'm suddenly shy.

Capote and I lie down under the tent. It's nice but tense. What would it be like to do it with *him*, I wonder. I shouldn't even think about it though, not with Miranda and Samantha and Ryan out there, still playing cards.

I stare up at the blanket. "Why did you kiss me

that night?" I whisper.

He reaches out, finds my hand, and curls his fingers around mine. We stay like that, silently holding hands for what feels like an eternity.

"I'm not a good boyfriend, Carrie," he says finally.

"I know." I untangle my hand from his. "We should try to get some sleep."

I close my eyes, knowing sleep is impossible. Not when every nerve ending is jumping with electricity, like my electrons are determined to communicate with Capote's across the barren space between us.

Too bad we can't use it to turn on the lights.

Then I must fall asleep, because the next thing I know, we're being woken by a terrific jangling, which turns out to be the phone.

I climb out of the tent as Samantha runs out of her bedroom with a sleeping mask on her head.

"What the—" Ryan sits up and bangs his head on the coffee table.

"*Could someone please answer that phone,*" Miranda shrieks.

Samantha makes a frantic slicing motion across her neck.

"If no one's going to answer it, I will," Ryan says, crawling toward the offending instrument.

"No!" Samantha and I shout at once.

I rip the receiver from Ryan's hand. "Hello?" I ask cautiously, expecting Charlie.

"Carrie?" asks a concerned male voice.

It's Bernard. The blackout's over.

PART THREE

Departures and Arrivals

CHAPTER THIRTY

My birthday's coming!

It's nearly here. I can't stop reminding everyone. My birthday! In less than two weeks, I'll be eighteen.

I'm one of those people who loves her birthday. I don't know why, but I do. I love the date: August 13. I was actually born on Friday the thirteenth, so even though it's bad luck for everyone else, it's good luck for me.

And this year, it's going to be huge. I'm turning eighteen, I'm going to lose my virginity, and I'm having my reading at Bobby's that night. I keep reminding Miranda that it's going to be a doubleheader: my first play and my first lay.

"Play and lay—get it?" I say, tickled by the

rhyme. Miranda is, understandably, quite sick of my little joke, and every time I say it, she puts her hands over her ears and claims she wishes she'd never met me.

I've also become incredibly neurotic about my birth control pills. I keep looking into the little plastic container, checking to make sure I've taken the pill and haven't accidentally lost any. When I went to the clinic, I considered getting a diaphragm, too, but after the doctor showed it to me, I decided it was too complicated. I kept thinking about cutting two holes in the top and making it into a hat for a cat. I wonder if anyone's done that yet.

Naturally, the clinic reminded me of L'il. I still feel guilty about what happened to her. I sometimes wonder if I feel bad because it didn't happen to me, and I'm still in New York and have a play reading and a smart, successful boyfriend who hasn't ruined my life—yet. If it weren't for Viktor Greene, L'il would still be here, strolling the gritty streets in her Laura Ashley dresses and finding flowers in the asphalt. But then I wonder if it's *all* Viktor's fault. Perhaps L'il was right: New York simply isn't for her. And if Viktor hadn't driven her out, maybe something else would have.

Which reminds me of what Capote said to me during the blackout. About not having to worry because I was going to Brown in the fall. That makes me nervous as well, because with each passing day, I want to go to Brown less and less. I'd miss all my friends here. Besides, I already know what I want to do with my life. Why can't I just continue?

Plus, if I go to Brown, I won't, for instance, get free clothes.

A couple of days ago a little voice in the back of my head told me to look up that designer, Jinx, at her shop on Eighth Street. The store was empty when I walked in, so I figured Jinx was in the back, polishing her brass knuckles. Sure enough, when she heard the sound of moving hangers, she emerged from behind a curtain, looked me up and down, and said, "Oh. You. From Bobby's."

"Yes," I said.

"Have you seen him?"

"Bobby? I'm doing a play reading in his space." I said it casually, like I was having play readings all the time.

"Bobby is weird," she said, twisting her mouth. "He is really one effed up mother-effer."

"Mmm," I agreed. "He certainly does seem a little . . . randy."

This cracked her up. "Harharhar. That's a good word for him. Randy. That's exactly what he is. Randy with no candy."

I wasn't exactly sure what she was talking about, but I went along with it.

In the light of day, Jinx looked less sinister and more, dare I say, normal. I could see she was one of those women who wore lots of makeup not because she was trying to frighten anyone, but because she had bad skin. And her hair was very dry, due to the black henna. And I imagined she didn't come from a very nice home and maybe had a father who was a drunk and a mother who yelled all the time. I knew Jinx had talent though, and I suddenly appreciated the efforts it must have taken her to get here.

"So you need something to wear. For Bobby's," she said.

"Yes." I hadn't actually gotten around to thinking about what to wear to the reading, but once she said it, I realized it was all I should have been worrying about.

"I've got just the thing." She went into the back and came out holding a white vinyl jumpsuit with black piping along the sleeves. "I didn't have enough money for fabric, so I had to make it really small. If it fits, it's yours."

I wasn't expecting such generosity. Especially when I ended up walking out with an armload of clothes. Apparently I'm one of the few people in New York who is actually willing to wear a white vinyl jumpsuit or a plastic dress or red rubber pants.

It was like Cinderella and that damn slipper.

And just in time, too. I've gotten awfully sick of my ratty blue silk robe and my hostess dress and my surgical scrubs. It's like Samantha always says: If people keep seeing you in the same old outfits, they start to think you haven't any prospects.

Samantha, meanwhile, has gone back to chez Charlie. She says they're bickering about china patterns and crystal decanters and the pluses and minuses of a raw bar at their reception. She can't believe her life has been reduced to this, but I keep reminding her that come October, the wedding will be over and she won't have to worry about her life ever again. This caused her to make one of her notorious deals with me: She would help with the guest list for the play reading if I agreed to go shopping with her for a wedding dress.

That's the problem with weddings. They're contagious.

In fact, they're so contagious Donna LaDonna and her mother are coming to New York to participate in the ritual. When Samantha mentioned they were coming, I realized I'd become so caught up in my New York life, I'd actually forgotten that Donna is Samantha's cousin.

The idea of seeing Donna again made me a

little uneasy, but not as jumpy as giving Bernard my play.

Last night I screwed up my courage and finally presented Bernard with the manuscript. I literally delivered it to him on a silver platter. We were in his apartment and I found a silver platter that Margie had overlooked, and I tied a big red ribbon around it, and I served it to him while he was watching MTV. All the while, of course, thinking I should have been on that silver platter myself.

Now I wish I hadn't given it to him at all. The thought of Bernard reading my play and not liking it has made me frantic with worry. I've been pacing the apartment all morning, waiting for him to call, praying he will call before I have to meet Samantha and Donna LaDonna at Kleinfeld.

I haven't heard from Bernard, but I've had plenty of contact with Samantha. She keeps calling to remind me of the appointment. "It's at noon sharp. If we're not there on the dot of twelve, we lose the room."

"What are you? Cinderella? Will your taxi turn into a pumpkin as well?"

"Don't be funny, Carrie. This is my wedding."

And now it's almost time to meet Samantha, and Bernard still hasn't called to tell me whether he likes my play or not.

My whole life is hanging by one tulle thread.

The phone rings. Must be Bernard. Samantha has to have run out of dimes by now.

"Carrie?" Samantha practically shrieks into the phone. "Why are you still at home? You should be on your way to Kleinfeld."

"I'm just leaving." I glare at the phone, jump into my new jumpsuit, and careen down the stairs.

Kleinfeld is miles away, in Brooklyn. It takes about five subways to get there, and when I change trains, I give in to my trembling paranoia and call Bernard. He's not home. He's not at the theater. At the next station, I try him again. Where the hell is he? When I get off the train in Brooklyn, I rush right to a phone booth on the corner. The phone rings and rings. I hang up, destroyed. I'm sure Bernard is avoiding my calls on purpose. He must have read my play and hated it and he doesn't want to tell me.

I arrive at the temple of holy matrimony disheveled and disturbingly sweaty. Vinyl is not the thing to wear on a humid August day in New York, even if it is white.

Kleinfeld is nothing to look at from the outside, being one of those enormous soot-stained buildings with windows like sad, streaky eyes, but inside, it's another story. The decor is pink, plush, and hushed like the petals of a flower. Ageless saleswomen with put-on faces and soft demeanors glide through the waiting room. The Jones party has its own suite, complete with dressing room, raised platform, and 360-degree mirrors. It also contains a pitcher of water, a pot of tea, and a plate of cookies. And, thank heavens, a phone.

Samantha isn't there, though. Instead, I find a pretty, middle-aged woman sitting stiffly on a velvet settee, legs crossed demurely at the ankles, hair smoothed into a perfect helmet. This must be Charlie's mother, Glenn.

Seated next to her is another woman, who could be Glenn's polar opposite. She's in her mid-twenties, dressed in a lumpy navy suit without a lick of makeup. She's not inherently unattractive, but given her messy hair and an expression that indicates she's used to making the best of things, I suspect she tries to deliberately make herself homely.

"I'm Glenn," the first woman says, holding out a long, bony hand with a discreet platinum watch clasped around her thin wrist. She must be left-handed, because left-handed people always wear their watches on their right wrist so everyone will know they're left-handed and, therefore, possibly more interesting and special. She indicates the young woman next to her. "This is my daughter, Erica."

Erica gives me a firm, no-nonsense handshake.

There's something refreshing about her, like she knows how ridiculous her mother is and how this whole scene is kind of silly.

"Hi," I say, warmly, and take a seat on the edge of a small, decorative chair.

Samantha told me Glenn had a face-lift, so while Glenn smoothes her hair and Erica eats a cookie, I surreptitiously study Glenn's face, looking for signs of the surgery. On closer inspection, they're not hard to find. Glenn's mouth is stretched and tucked up like the grin of the Joker, although she's not smiling. Her eyebrows are dangerously close to her hairline. I'm peering at her so hard she can't help but sense my staring. She turns to me and, with a little flutter of her hand, says, "That's quite an interesting outfit you're wearing."

"Thank you," I say. "I got it for free."

"I should hope so."

I can't tell if she's being deliberately rude or if this is simply her usual demeanor. I take a cookie, and feel a little sad. I can't fathom why Samantha has insisted on my presence. Surely she isn't planning to include me on her journey into the future. I can't imagine where I would fit in.

Glenn shakes her arm and peers at her watch. "Where's Samantha?" she asks, with a quiet sigh of annoyance.

"Maybe she's caught in traffic," I suggest.

"It's terribly rude, being late for your own dress fitting," Glenn murmurs, in a low, warm voice intended to take the sting out of the insult. There's a knock on the door and I jump up to open it.

"Here she is," I chirp, expecting Samantha but finding Donna LaDonna and her mother, instead.

There's no sign of Samantha. Nevertheless, I'm so relieved not to be alone with Glenn and her daughter, I go too far. "Donna!" I shout.

Donna is all sexed up in a slouchy top with shoulder pads and leggings. Her mother is wearing a sad imitation of Glenn's real Chanel suit. What will Glenn think of Donna and her mother? I can already tell she's none too impressed by me. And suddenly, I'm a tad embarrassed for Castlebury.

Donna, of course, doesn't notice. "Hi, Carrie," she says, like she just saw me yesterday.

She and her mother go to Glenn, who shakes hands nicely and pretends to be thrilled to meet them.

While Donna and her mother coo over the room, Glenn's suit, and the future wedding plans, I sit back and observe. I always thought Donna was one of the most sophisticated girls in our school, but seeing her in New York, on my turf, I wonder what I ever found so intriguing about her. Sure, she's pretty, but not as pretty as Samantha.

And she's not the least bit stylish in that *Flashdance* getup. She's not even very interesting, babbling to me about how she and her mother got their nails done and bragging about how they shopped at Macy's. Jeez. Even I know only tourists shop at Macy's.

And then Donna blurts out her own very exciting news. She, too, is getting married. She holds out her hand, revealing a solitaire diamond chip.

I lean over to admire it, although you practically need a magnifying glass to see the damn thing. "Who's the lucky guy?"

She gives me a brief smile as if she's surprised I haven't heard. "Tommy."

"Tommy? Tommy *Brewster*?" The Tommy Brewster who basically made my life hell merely because I had the bad luck to sit next to him in assembly for four years of high school? The big dumb jock who was Cynthia Viande's serious boyfriend?

The question is apparently written all over my face, because Donna immediately explains that Cynthia broke up with him. "She's going to BU and she didn't want to take Tommy with her. She actually thought she could do better," Donna smirks.

No kidding, I want to say.

"Tommy's going into the military. He's going

to be a pilot," Donna adds boastfully. "He'll be traveling a lot and it'll be easier if we're married."

"Wow." Donna LaDonna engaged to Tommy Brewster? How could this happen? If I'd had to place bets in high school, I would have wagered that Donna LaDonna was the one who was on her way to bigger and better things. She was the last person I imagined would be the first to become a housewife.

Having dispatched this information, Donna veers the conversation onto the topic of babies.

"I was always a hands-on mom," Glenn says, nodding. "I breast-fed Charlie for nearly a year. Of course, it meant I could barely leave the apartment. But it was worth every minute. The scent of his little head . . ."

"The smell of his poopy diaper," Erica mutters under her breath. I give her a grateful look. She's been so quiet, I'd forgotten she was there.

"I think it's one of the reasons Charlie turned out so well," Glenn continues, ignoring her daughter as she directs her comments to Donna. "I know breast-feeding isn't very popular, but I think it's terribly rewarding."

"I've heard it can make the kid smarter," Donna says.

I stare at the plate of cookies, wondering what Samantha would think of this discussion. Does she know Glenn is planning to turn her into a baby-making machine? The thought gives me the willies. What if what Miranda said about endometriosis is true, and Samantha can't get pregnant right away—or at all? And what if she does, and the baby is born in her intestine?

Where the hell is Samantha, anyway?

Boy, this is really making me uncomfortable. I've got to get out of here. "Can I use the phone?" I ask, and without waiting for permission, pick up the receiver and dial Bernard's number. He's still not there. I hang up, fuming, and decide to call him every thirty minutes until I reach him.

When I turn back to the room, the conversation has flagged. So much so that Donna actually asks how my summer is going.

Now it's my turn to brag.

"I'm having a play reading next week."

"Oh," Donna says, clearly unimpressed. "What's a play reading?"

"Well, I wrote this play, and my professor really loved it and then I met this guy, Bobby, who has a sort of performance space in his apartment, and I have a boyfriend who actually *is* a playwright—Bernard Singer, maybe you've heard of him—not that I'm not an actual writer but . . ." My voice gets smaller and smaller until it trails off into a painful little nothingness.

And where is Samantha in all this?

Glenn taps her watch impatiently.

"Oh, she'll show up," Mrs. LaDonna gushes. "We LaDonnas are always late," she says proudly, as if this is a plus. I look at her and shake my head. She's no help at all.

"I think your play sounds very exciting," Erica says, tactfully changing the subject.

"It is," I agree, praying Samantha will arrive at any moment. "It's kind of a big deal. Being my first play and all."

"I always told Erica she should become a writer," Glenn says, giving her daughter a disapproving look. "If you're a writer, you can stay at home with your children. If you actually decide to have children."

"Mother, please," Erica says, as if she's had to tolerate this discussion many times before.

"Instead Erica's decided to become a public defender!" Glenn exclaims grimly.

"A public defender," Mrs. LaDonna says, attempting to look impressed.

"What's that?" Donna asks, examining her manicure.

"It's a special kind of lawyer," I answer, wondering how Donna cannot know this.

"It's all about choice, Mother," Erica says firmly. "And I choose not to be chosen."

Glenn gives her a stiff little smile. She probably can't move her muscles too much due to the face-lift. "It all sounds so terribly sad."

"But it isn't sad at all," Erica replies evenly. "It's freeing."

"I don't believe in choice," Glenn announces, addressing the room. "I believe in destiny. And the sooner you accept your destiny, the better. It seems to me you young girls waste a terrible amount of time trying to choose. And all you end up with is nothing."

Erica smiles. And turning to me, she explains, "Mother's been trying to marry Charlie off for years. She's pushed every debutante in the Blue Book in his direction, but of course, he never liked any of them. Charlie's not that dumb."

There's an audible gasp from Mrs. LaDonna as I peer around in shock. Donna and her mother look like they've had face-lifts as well. Their expressions are as frozen as Glenn's.

The phone rings and I automatically reach for it, wondering if it's Bernard, having somehow managed to track me down at Kleinfeld.

I'm such a dummy sometimes. It's Samantha.

"Where are you?" I whisper urgently. "Everyone's here. Glenn and Erica—"

"Carrie." She cuts me off. "I'm not going to be able to make it."

"What?"

"Something came up. A meeting I can't get out of. So if you wouldn't mind telling Glenn . . ."

Actually, I would mind. I'm suddenly tired of doing her dirty work. "I think you should tell her yourself." I hand Glenn the phone.

While Glenn speaks to Samantha, a saleswoman peeks into the room, beaming with excitement, pulling an enormous rack of wedding dresses behind her. The atmosphere explodes as Donna and her mother rush toward the dresses, pawing and fondling the garments like they're sugary confections.

I've had enough. I dive into the rack of wedding dresses and fight my way through to the other side.

Weddings are like a train. Once you get on, you can't get off.

Sort of like the subway.

The train is stopped, again, somewhere in the dark catacombs between Forty-second and Fifty-ninth streets. It's been stuck for twenty minutes now, and the natives are getting restless.

Including myself. I yank open the door between the cars and step out onto the tiny platform, leaning over the edge in an attempt to discover the cause of the holdup. It's useless, of course. It always is. I can just make out the walls of the tunnel until they disappear into darkness.

The train lurches unexpectedly and I nearly tip off the platform. I grab the handle of the door just in time, reminding myself that I need to be more careful. It's hard to be careful, though, when you feel indestructible.

My heart does that jackhammer thing that happens whenever I get all anticipatory about the future.

Bernard read my play.

The minute I escaped from Kleinfeld, I ran to a phone booth and finally reached him. He said he was in the middle of casting. I could tell by his voice that he didn't want me to come by, but I kept insisting and finally he relented. He could probably tell by *my* voice that I was in one of those nothing-is-going-to-stop-me moods.

Not even the subway.

The train screeches to a halt just inside the platform at Fifty-ninth Street.

I bang though the cars until I reach the head compartment, then I do the dangerous thing again and leap from the train onto the concrete. I run up the escalator, zoom through Bloomingdale's, and race up to Sutton Place, sweating like a mad thing in the white vinyl.

I catch Bernard in front of his building, hailing

a cab. I spring up behind him.

"You're late," he says, jangling his keys. "And now I'm late too."

"I'll ride with you to the theater. Then you can tell me how much you loved my play."

"It's not the best time, Carrie. My mind's not focused." He's being all business. I hate it when he's like this.

"I've been waiting all day," I plead. "I'm going crazy. You *have* to tell me what you thought."

I don't know why I'm in such a frenzy. Maybe it's because I just came from Kleinfeld. Maybe it's because Samantha didn't show up. Or maybe it's because I don't ever want to have to marry a man like Charlie and have a mother-in-law like Glenn. Which means I *have* to succeed at something else.

Bernard grimaces.

"Oh my God. You didn't like it." I can feel my knees buckling beneath me.

"Take it easy, kid," he says, hustling me into the cab.

I perch on the seat next to him like a bird about to take flight. I swear I see a look of pity cross his face, but it's immediately gone and I tell myself I must have imagined it.

He smiles and pats my leg. "It's good, Carrie. Really."

"Good? Or really good?"

He shifts in his seat. "Really good."

"Honestly? Do you mean it? You're not just humoring me?"

"I said it was really good, didn't I?"

"Say it again. *Please*."

"It's really good." He smiles.

"Yippee!" I shout.

"Can I go to my casting now?" he asks, extracting the manuscript from his briefcase and holding it out to me.

I suddenly realize I've been clutching his arm in fear. "Cast away," I say gallantly. "Castaways. Ha-ha. Get it?"

"Sure, kiddo." He leans over to give me a quick kiss.

But I hold on to him. I put my hands around his face and kiss him hard. "That's for liking my play."

"I guess I'll have to like your plays more often," he jokes, getting out of the cab.

"Oh, you will," I say from the open window.

Bernard goes into the theater as I throw back my head in relief. I wonder what I was so worked up about. And then it hits me: If Bernard didn't like my play, if he didn't like my writing, would I still be able to like *him*?

Luckily, that's one question I don't have to answer.

CHAPTER THIRTY-ONE

"And she has the nerve to tell Samantha I've got a big head."

"Well—" Miranda says cautiously.

"A big fat swollen head. Like a basketball," I say, leaning into the mirror to apply more lipstick. "And meanwhile, she's marrying this stupid jock—"

"Why do you care so much?" Miranda asks. "It's not like you have to see them again."

"I know. But couldn't they have been a little impressed? I'm doing so much more with my life than they ever will."

I'm talking, of course, about Donna LaDonna and her mother. After her no-show at Kleinfeld, Samantha took the LaDonnas to Benihana as a consolation prize. When I asked Samantha if Donna mentioned me, she said Donna told her I'd become completely full of myself and obnoxious. Which really pissed me off.

"Did Samantha find a dress?" Miranda asks, fluffing her hair.

"She never showed up. She had an important meeting she couldn't get out of. But that's not the point. What bugs me is that this girl, who thought she was such a big deal in high school—" I break off, wondering if I have become a monster. "You don't think I have a big head, do you?"

"Oh, Carrie. I don't know."

Which means yes. "Even if I do, I don't care," I insist, trying to justify my attitude. "Maybe I do have a bit of an ego. So what? Do you know how long it's taken me to even get an ego? And I'm still not sure it's fully developed. It's more of an 'egg' than an 'ego.'"

"Uh-huh." Miranda looks dubious.

"Besides, men have egos all the time and no one says they're full of themselves. And now that I have this tiny little bit of self-esteem, I don't intend to let it go."

"Good," she says. "Don't."

I march past her into the bedroom, where I snake my legs into a pair of fishnet stockings and slip the white plastic dress with the clear plastic cut-outs over my head. I pull on the bright blue Fiorucci boots and check my appearance in the full-length mirror.

"Who are these people again?" Miranda eyes me with a worried expression.

"Bernard's agent—Teensie Dyer. And her husband."

"Is that what you're supposed to wear to the Hamptons?"

"It's what *I* wear to the Hamptons."

True to his word, Bernard has actually come through on his promise to introduce me to Teensie. In fact, he's gone above and beyond his call to duty and invited me to the Hamptons to stay with Teensie and her husband. It's only for Saturday night, but who cares? It's the Hamptons! All summer, I've been dying to go. Not just to find out why they're such a big deal, but to be able to say, "I went to the Hamptons," to people like Capote.

"Do you really think you should be wearing plastic?" Miranda asks. "What if they think you're wearing a garbage bag?"

"Then *they're* stupid."

Yep, I'm full of myself all right.

I toss a bathing suit, the Chinese robe, my new red rubber pants, and the hostess gown into my carpenter's bag. The bag reminds me of how Bernard said I needed a valise. Which leads me to wonder if Bernard is finally going to demand I have sex with him. I've been taking the pill, so I suppose there's no reason not to, but I'm pretty adamant about waiting for my eighteenth birthday. I want the event to be special and memorable, something I'll remember for the rest of my life.

Of course, the thought of finally doing it also makes me queasy.

Miranda must pick up on my mood, because she looks at me curiously. "Have you slept with him yet?"

"No."

"How can you go away with him and not sleep with him?"

"He respects me."

"No offense, but it sounds weird. Are you *sure* he's not gay?"

"Bernard is not gay!" I nearly shout.

I go out into the living room and pick up my play, wondering if I should bring it with me in case I have a chance to slip it to Teensie. But that might be too obvious. Instead, I have another idea.

"Hey," I say, holding up the manuscript. "*You* should read my play."

"Me?" Miranda asks, taken aback.

"Why not?"

"Didn't Bernard read it? I thought he liked it. He's the expert."

"But you're the audience. And you're smart. If you like it, it means other people will too."

"Oh, Carrie," she says, pulling at her lip. "I don't know anything about plays."

"Don't you *want* to read it?"

"I'm going to hear you read it on Thursday. At Bobby's."

"But I want *you* to read it, first."

"Why?" She looks hard at me, but then relents. Perhaps she can see how, underneath the bravado, I'm a nervous wreck. She holds out her hand for the manuscript. "If you really want me to—"

"I do," I say firmly. "You can read it this weekend and give it back to me on Monday. And sweetie? If you don't like it, can you please pretend you do?"

Bernard went out to the Hamptons on Friday, so I take the Jitney by myself.

I don't mind. From the sound of it, I kept picturing the Jitney as some kind of old-fashioned cable car, but it turns out to be a regular bus.

It chugs along a crowded highway until eventually we turn off and start going through little beach towns. At first they're tacky, with bars and clam shacks and car dealerships, but then every-thing becomes more green and marshy, and when we cross a bridge and drive past a log cabin with totem poles on the front and a sign reading CIGARETTES $2 CARTON, the landscape changes completely. Old oaks and manicured hedges line the street, behind which I glimpse enormous shin-gled mansions.

The bus snakes into a picture-perfect town. Neatly painted white shops with green awnings pop-ulate the streets. There's a bookstore, a tobacconist, Lilly Pulitzer, a jewelry store, and an old-fashioned movie theater where the bus pulls over.

"Southampton," the driver announces. I pick up my carpenter's bag and get out.

Bernard is waiting for me, leaning against the hood of a small bronze Mercedes, his smooth bare feet pushed into Gucci loafers. Miranda was right: the plastic dress and Fiorucci boots that were per-fect for the city feel out of place in this quaint little town. But Bernard doesn't care. He takes my bag, pausing for a kiss. His mouth is sublimely familiar. I love the way I can feel one of his incisors under his top lip.

"How was the trip?" he asks, smoothing my hair.

"Great," I say breathlessly, thinking about how much fun we're going to have.

He holds open the door and I slide onto the front seat. The car is old, from the 1960s, with a polished wooden steering wheel and shiny nickel dials. "This your car?" I ask, teasingly.

"It's Peter's."

"Peter?"

"Teensie's husband." He starts the engine, puts the car into gear, and pulls away from the curb with a jolt.

"Sorry," he laughs. "I'm a tad distracted. Don't take this the wrong way, but Teensie's insisted on giving you your own room."

"Why?" I frown in annoyance, but secretly, I'm relieved.

"She kept asking me how old you were. I told her it was none of her damn business, and that's when she got suspicious. You are over eighteen, aren't you?" he asks, half jokingly.

I sigh, as if the question is beyond ridiculous. "I told you. I'm a sophomore in college."

"Just checking, kitten," he says, giving me a wink. "And don't be afraid to stand up to Teensie, okay? She can be a bully, but she's got an enormous heart."

In other words, she's an absolute bitch.

We swing into a long gravel drive and park in front of a shingled house. It's not quite as large as I imagined, given the enormity of the houses I saw along the way, but it's still big. What was once a regular-sized house is attached to a soaring barnlike structure.

"Nice, huh?" Bernard says, gazing up at the house from behind the windshield. "I wrote my first play here."

"Really?" I ask, getting out of the car.

"Rewrote it, actually. I'd written the first draft during the day when I was working the night shift at the bottling plant."

"That's so romantic."

"It wasn't at the time. But in hindsight, yeah, it does sound romantic."

"With a touch of cliché?" I ask, razzing him.

"I went to Manhattan one night with my buddies," he continues, opening the trunk. "Stumbled across Teensie at a club. She insisted I send her my play, said she was an agent. I didn't even know what an agent was back then. But I sent her my play anyway, and the next thing I know, she opened her house to me for the summer. So I could write. Undisturbed."

"And were you?" I ask, trying to keep the apprehension out of my voice. "Undisturbed?"

He laughs. "When I was disturbed, it wasn't unpleasant."

Crap. Does that mean he slept with Teensie?

And if he did, why didn't he tell me? He could have warned me, at least. I hope I won't discover any other unpleasant facts this weekend.

"Don't know where I'd be without Teensie," he says, slinging his arm across my shoulders.

We're almost at the house when Teensie herself appears, strolling briskly up a flagstone path. She's wearing tennis whites, and while I can't speak for her heart, there's no mistaking the fact that her breasts are enormous. They strain against the cloth of her polo shirt like two boulders struggling to erupt from a volcano. "There you are!" she exclaims pleasantly, shielding her eyes from the sun.

She plants herself in front of me, and in a rush, says, "I'd shake hands but I'm sweaty. Peter's inside somewhere, but if you want a drink, ask Alice." She turns around and trots back to the courts, waggling her fingers in the air.

"She seems nice," I say, in an effort to like her. "And she has really big breasts," I add, wondering if Bernard has seen them in the flesh.

Bernard hoots. "They're fake."

"*Fake?*"

"Silicone."

So he has seen them. How else would he know all about them? "What else is plastic?"

"Her nose, of course. She likes to think of

herself as Brenda. In *Goodbye, Columbus*. I always tell her she's more Mrs. Robinson than Miss Patimkin."

"What does her husband think?"

Bernard grins. "Pretty much whatever she tells him to, I imagine."

"I mean about the *silicone*."

"Oh," he says. "I don't know. He spends a lot of his time hopping."

"Like a bunny?"

"More like the White Rabbit. All he's missing is the pocket watch." Bernard opens the front door and calls out, "Alice," like he owns the place.

Which, given his history with Teensie, I suppose he does.

We've entered the barn part of the house, which has been fashioned into a gigantic living room filled with couches and stuffed chairs. There's a stone fireplace and several doors that lead to unseen corridors. One of the doors flies open and out pops a small man with longish hair and what was likely once a girlishly pretty face. He's on his way to another door when he spots us and beetles over.

"Anyone seen my wife?" he inquires, in an English accent.

"She's playing tennis," I say.

"Ah, *right*." He smacks his forehead. "Very

observant of you. Yes, very observant. That infernal game." He tumbles on without pause: "Well, make yourselves at home. You know the drill, Bernard, all very casual, *mi casa es su casa* and all that—we've got the president of Bolivia for dinner tonight, so I thought I might brush up on my *Español*."

"*Gracias*," I say.

"Oh, you speak Spanish," he exclaims. "Excellent. I'll tell Teensie to put you next to *el presidente* at dinner." And before I can demur, he scurries out of the room as Teensie herself reappears.

"Bernard, darling, will you be a gentleman and carry Cathy's suitcase to her room?"

"Cathy?" Bernard asks. He looks around. "Who's Cathy?"

Teensie's face twists in annoyance. "I thought you said her name was Cathy."

I shake my head. "It's Carrie. Carrie Bradshaw."

"Who can keep track?" she says helplessly, implying that Bernard has had such an endless parade of girlfriends, she can't keep their names straight.

She leads us up the stairs and down a short hallway in the original part of the house. "Bathroom here," she says, opening a door to reveal a powder-blue sink and narrow glassed-in shower. "And

Carrie's in here." She opens another door to reveal a small room with a single bed, a patchwork quilt, and a shelf of trophies.

"My daughter's room," Teensie says smugly. "It's above the kitchen, but Chinita loves it because it's private."

"Where is your daughter?" I ask, wondering if Teensie has decided to kick her own daughter out of her room for the sake of propriety.

"Tennis camp. She's graduating from high school next year and we're hoping she'll get into Harvard. We're all so terribly proud of her."

Meaning this Chinita is practically my age.

"Where do *you* go to school?" Teensie asks.

"Brown." I glance at Bernard. "I'm a sophomore."

"How interesting," Teensie replies, in a tone that makes me wonder if she's seen through my lie. "I should put Chinita in touch with you. I'm sure she'd love to hear all about Brown. It's her *safety* school."

I ignore the insult and lob one of my own. "I'd love to, Mrs. Dyer."

"Call me Teensie," she says, with a flash of resentment. She turns to Bernard and, determined not to let me get the better of her, says, "Why don't we let your friend unpack."

❖ ✳ ᶜ𝐁 ✳ ❖

A short while later, I'm sitting on the edge of the bed, wondering where the phone is and if I should call Samantha to ask for advice on how to deal with Teensie, when I remember Teensie on the floor of the Jessens' and smile. Who cares if she hates me? I'm in the Hamptons! I jump up, hang my clothes, and slip into a bikini. The room is a bit stuffy, so I open the window and take in the view. The bright green lawn ends at a mani-cured hedge, and beyond are miles of fields fuzzy with short leafy plants—potato fields, Bernard explained on the way over. I inhale the sweet, humid air, which means the ocean can't be far away.

Above the gentle sound of the surf, I hear voices. I lean out the window and discover Teensie and another woman seated at a metal table on a small patio, sipping what appear to be Bloody Marys. I can hear their conversation as clearly as if I were sitting across from them.

"She's barely older than Chinita," Teensie exclaims. "It's outrageous."

"How young *is* she?"

"Who knows? She looks like she's barely out of high school."

"Poor Bernard," says the second woman.

"It's just so pathetically textbook," Teensie adds.

"Well, after that horrible summer with Margie—didn't they get married here?"

"Yes." Teensie sighs. "You'd think he'd have the sense not to bring this young twit—"

I gasp, then quickly shut my mouth in the perverse desire not to miss a word.

"It's obviously subconscious," the second woman says. "He wants to make sure he'll never get hurt again. So he chooses someone young and wide-eyed, who worships him and will never leave him. He controls the relationship. As opposed to Margie."

"But how long can it possibly last?" Teensie moans. "What can they have in common? What do they talk about?"

"Maybe they don't. *Talk*," the second woman says.

"Doesn't this girl have parents? What kind of parent lets their daughter go away with a man who's clearly ten or fifteen years older?"

"It *is* the eighties," the second woman sighs, trying to be conciliatory. "The girls are different now. They're so bold."

Teensie gets up to go into the kitchen. I practically crawl out the window, hoping to hear the rest of their conversation, but I can't.

Numb with shame, I flop back on the bed. If what they said is true, it means I'm merely a pawn in Bernard's play. The one he's acting out in his real life to help him get over Margie.

Margie. Her name gives me the willies.

Why did I think I could compete with her for Bernard's affections? Apparently, I can't. Not according to Teensie.

I throw the pillow against the wall in rage. Why did I come here? Why would Bernard subject me to this? Teensie must be right. He *is* using me. He might not be aware of it, but it's no secret to everyone else.

There's only one way to save face. I have to leave. I'll ask Bernard to drive me to the bus stop. I'll say good-bye and never see him again. And then, after I have my reading and I'm the toast of the town, he'll realize what a mistake he made.

I'm tossing clothes into my carpenter's bag, when I catch the sound of his voice. "Teensie?" he calls. I peer over the windowsill.

He's striding across the lawn, looking concerned and a bit peeved. "Teensie?" he calls again as Teensie appears on the patio.

"Yes, darling?"

"Have you seen Carrie?" he asks.

I detect a slight drop of disappointment in her shoulders. "No, I haven't."

"Where is she?" Bernard demands, looking around.

Teensie throws up her hands. "I'm not her keeper."

They both disappear into the house as I bite my lip in triumph. Teensie was wrong. Bernard does care about me. She knows it too, and it's driving her mad with jealousy.

Poor Bernard, I think. It's my duty to save him from the Teensies of the world.

I quickly pick up a book and arrange myself on the bed. Sure enough, a minute later Bernard knocks on my door.

"Come in!"

"Carrie?" He pushes open the door. "What are you doing? I've been waiting for you at the pool. We're having lunch."

I put down my book and smile. "I'm sorry. No one told me."

"Silly goose," he says, coming toward me and kissing the top of my head. He lies down next to me. "Love the bikini," he murmurs.

We fool around frantically until we hear Teensie calling our names. This cracks me up and causes Bernard to guffaw as well. And that's when I decide to break my own rule. I *will* have Bernard. Tonight. I'll sneak into his room and we'll finally do it. Right under Teensie's little bobbed nose.

CHAPTER THIRTY-TWO

At dinner, Teensie's husband, Peter, makes good on his threat and I'm seated next to the Bolivian president. He's a pockmarked thug of a man, with a heavy, self-important demeanor that frightens me. Knowing nothing about Bolivia or its politics, I'm determined not to say the wrong thing. I have a feeling if I do, I may possibly be eliminated.

Luckily, *el presidente*, as Peter keeps calling him, has absolutely no interest in me. We've barely unfolded our napkins and placed them on our laps when he takes one look at me, sums me up as being of no importance, and immediately turns to the woman on his left. At the other end of the table, Teensie has placed Bernard to her right. I'm too far away to hear their conversation, but

Teensie, who is laughing and gesturing, appears to be keeping her little group engaged. Ever since the first guests began to arrive, Teensie's become a different person. There's no trace of the subtle, calculated nastiness she displayed this afternoon.

I take a bite of my fish, determined not to betray the fact that I'm becoming mortifyingly bored. The only thing that's keeping me going is the thought of Bernard, and how we can be together, later.

I idly wonder if Teensie's husband, Peter, knows about Teensie and Bernard. I take a sip of my wine and sigh quietly. I cut another piece of fish and stare at my fork, wondering if it's worth hazarding another mouthful. The fish is dry and plain, as if someone decided food should be a punishment instead of a pleasure.

"Don't like the fish?" Peter's voice comes from my left.

"Actually, I don't." I smile, relieved someone is talking to me.

"That bad, eh?" He pushes the fish to the side of his plate. "It's this newfangled diet my wife has going. No butter, no salt, no skin, no fat, and no spices. All part of a misguided attempt to live forever."

I giggle. "I'm not sure living forever is a good idea."

"Not sure?" Peter declares. "It's a bloody awful idea. How'd you get thrown in with this lot anyway?"

"I met Bernard, and—"

"I mean, what do you do in New York?"

"Oh. I'm a writer," I say simply. I sit up a little straighter, and add, "I'm studying at The New School, but I'm having my first play reading next week."

"Well done," he says, sounding impressed. "Have you talked to my wife?"

I look down at my plate. "I don't think your wife is interested in me or my writing." I glance across the table at Teensie. She's been drinking red wine, and her lips are a ghastly shade of purple. "On the other hand, I don't need your wife's good opinion in order to succeed."

That's the egg part of my ego rising to the surface.

"You're quite a confident young lady," Peter remarks. And then, as if to emphasize the fact that I've gone too far, he gives me one of those devastatingly polite smiles that could probably put the queen of England in her place.

I sit frozen in disgrace. Why couldn't I keep my mouth shut? Peter was only trying to be friendly, and now I've insulted his wife. In addition to committing the supposed sin of arrogance.

It's acceptable in a man, but not in a woman. Or not in this crowd, anyway.

I tap Peter on the arm.

"Yes?" He turns. There's no sharpness in his tone, merely a deadening disinterest.

I'm about to ask him if I were a man, would I be judged so harshly, but his expression stops me. "Could you pass the salt?" I ask, adding quietly, "Please?"

I manage to make it through the rest of the dinner by pretending to be interested in a long story about golfing in Scotland, with which Peter regales our end of the table. When the plates are cleared, I hope Bernard and I can escape, but instead we're ushered onto the terrace for coffee and dessert. This is followed by chess in the living room. Bernard plays with Peter, while I perch on the edge of Bernard's chair, pretending to play dumb. The truth is, anyone who's halfway good at math can play chess, and after enduring several bad moves by Bernard, I begin quietly giving him advice. Bernard starts winning and a small crowd gathers to witness the spectacle.

Bernard gives me all the credit, and at last, I can see my esteem rising slightly in their eyes. Maybe I'm a contender after all.

"Where'd you learn to play chess?" he asks,

fixing us another round of drinks from a wicker cart in the corner.

"I've always played. My father taught me."

Bernard regards me, bemused. "You've just made me realize I don't know a thing about you."

"That's because you forgot to ask," I say playfully, my equilibrium restored. I look around the room. "Don't any of these people ever go to bed?"

"Are you tired?"

"I was thinking—"

"Plenty of time for that later," he says, brushing the back of my hair with his lips.

"You two lovebirds." Teensie waves from the couch. "Come over here and join the discussion."

I sigh. Bernard may be willing to call it an evening, but Teensie is determined to keep us downstairs.

I endure another hour of political discussions. Finally, Peter's eyes close, and when he falls asleep in his chair, Teensie murmurs that perhaps we should all go to bed.

I give Bernard a meaningful look and scurry to my room. Now that the moment has arrived, I'm shaking with fear. My body trembles in anticipation. What will it be like? Will I scream? And what if there's blood?

I slip on my negligee and brush my hair a hundred times. When thirty minutes have passed and the house is quiet, I slip out, creep across the living room, and up the other set of stairs, which leads to Bernard's room. It's at the end of a long hall, located conveniently next to Teensie and Peter, but, like all the rooms in the new wing, it has its own en suite bathroom.

En suite. My, what a lot of things I've learned this weekend. I giggle as I turn the knob on Bernard's door.

He's in bed, reading. Under the soft light of the lamp, he looks sleek and mysterious, like something out of a Victorian novel. He puts his finger to his lips as he slides back the covers. I fall silently into his arms, close my eyes, and hope for the best.

He turns off the light and rearranges himself under the sheets. "Good night, kitten."

I sit up, perplexed. "Good night?"

I lean over and turn on the light.

He grabs my hand. "What are you doing?"

"You want to *sleep*?"

"Don't you?"

I pout. "I thought we could—"

He smiles. "Here?"

"Why not?"

He turns off the light. "It's rude."

I turn it back on. "Rude?"

"Teensie and Peter are in the next room." He turns off the light again.

"So?" I say in the dark.

"I don't want them to hear us. It might make them . . . uncomfortable."

I frown in the darkness, my arms crossed over my chest. "Don't you think it's time Teensie got over the fact that you've moved on? From her *and* Margie?"

"Oh, Carrie." He sighs.

"I'm serious. Teensie needs to accept that you're seeing other people now. That you're seeing me—"

"Yes, she does," he says softly. "But we don't need to rub it in her face."

"I think we do," I reply.

"Let's go to sleep. We'll figure it out in the morning."

This is my cue to flounce out of the room in anger. But I figure I've done enough flouncing for the evening. Instead, I lie silently, mulling over every scene, every conversation, fighting back tears and the gnawing realization that somehow, I haven't necessarily managed to come out on top this weekend, after all.

CHAPTER THIRTY-THREE

"I'm so glad you came to see me," Bobby proclaims as he opens the door. "This is a very nice surprise. Yes, a very nice surprise," he patters on, taking my arm.

I shift my bag from one side to the other. "It's really not a surprise, Bobby. I called you, remember?"

"Oh, but it's always a surprise to see a friend, don't you think? Especially when the friend is so attractive."

"Well," I say, frowning, wondering what this has to do with my play.

Bernard and I returned to the city late Sunday afternoon, hitching a ride with Teensie and Peter in the old Mercedes. Teensie drove, while Bernard and Peter talked about sports and I sat quietly, determined to be on my best behavior. Which wasn't difficult, as I didn't have much to say anyway. I kept wondering if Bernard and I stayed together, if this was what our life would be. Weekends with Teensie and Peter. I didn't think I could take it. I wanted Bernard, but not his friends.

I went back to Samantha's, vowing to get my life in order, which included calling Bobby and scheduling an appointment to discuss the reading. Unfortunately, Bobby doesn't seem to be taking it as seriously as I am.

"Let me show you around the space," he says now, with irritating insistence, especially as I saw the space when I was at his party. That night feels like ages ago, an uncomfortable reminder that while time is racing on, my own time may be running out.

The reading may be my last chance to establish a toehold in New York. A firm grip on the rock of Manhattan from which I cannot be removed.

"We'll set up chairs here." Bobby indicates the gallery space. "And we'll serve cocktails. Get the audience liquored up. Should we have white wine or vodka or both?"

"Oh, both," I murmur.

"And are you planning on having real actors? Or will it just be a reading?"

"I think maybe just a reading. For now," I say, envisioning the bright lights of Broadway. "I'm planning to read the whole play myself." After the class reading with Capote, it seemed easier not to get anyone else involved.

"Better that way, yes?" Bobby nods. His nodding—his unbridled enthusiasm—is starting to get to me. "We should have some champagne. To celebrate."

"It's barely noon," I object.

"Don't tell me you're one of those time Nazis," he intones, urging me down a short hallway that leads to his living quarters. I follow him uncertainly, a warning bell chiming in my head. "Artists can't live like other people. Schedules and all that—kills the creativity, don't you think?" he asks.

"I guess so." I sigh, wishing I could escape. But Bobby's doing me an enormous favor, staging a reading of my play in his space. And with this thought I accept a glass of champagne.

"Let me show you around the rest of the place."

"Honestly, Bobby," I say in frustration. "You don't have to."

"I want to! I've cleared my whole afternoon for you."

"But why?"

"I thought we might want to get to know each other better."

Oh for goodness' sake. He can't possibly be trying to seduce me. It's too ridiculous. For one thing, he's shorter than I am. And he has jowls, meaning he must be over fifty years old. And he's gay. Isn't he?

"This is my bedroom," he says, with a flourish. The decor is minimalist and the room is spotless, so I imagine he has a maid to pick up after him.

He plunks himself on the edge of the neatly made bed and takes a sip of champagne, patting the spot next to him.

"Bobby," I say firmly. "I really should go." In demonstration of my intentions, I place my glass on the windowsill.

"Oh, don't put it there," he cries. "It will leave a ring."

I pick up the glass. "I'll put it back in the kitchen, then."

"But you can't go," he clucks. "We haven't finished talking about your play."

I roll my eyes, but I don't want to completely offend him. I figure I'll sit next to him for a moment and then leave.

I perch gingerly on the side of the bed, as far away from him as possible. "About the play—"

"Yes, about the play," he agrees. "What made you want to write it?"

"Well, I . . ." I fumble for the words but I take

too long and Bobby becomes impatient.

"Hand me that photograph, will you?" And before I can protest, he's scooted next to me and is pointing at the picture with a manicured finger. "My wife," he says, followed by a giggle. "Or should I say my ex-wife?"

"You were married?" I ask as politely as possible, given those alarm bells are now clanging away like a bell tower.

"For two years. Annalise was her name. She's French, you see?"

"Uh-huh." I peer more closely at the image. Annalise is one of those beauties who looks absolutely insane, with a ridiculous pouty mouth and wild, scorching black eyes.

"You remind me of her." Bobby puts his hand on my leg.

I unceremoniously remove it. "I don't look a thing like her."

"Oh, but you do. To me," he murmurs. And then, in hideous slow motion, he purses his lips and pushes his face toward mine for a kiss.

I quickly turn away and wrestle free from his grasping fingers. Ugh. What kind of man gets manicures anyway?

"Bobby!" I pick up my glass from the floor and start out of the room.

He follows me into the kitchen, wagging his

tail like a chastened puppy. "Don't go," he pleads. "There's nearly a whole bottle of champagne left. You can't expect me to drink it myself. Besides, it doesn't keep."

The kitchen is tiny, and Bobby has stationed himself in the doorway, blocking my exit.

"I have a boyfriend," I say fiercely.

"He doesn't have to know."

I'm about to flee, when he changes his tack from sly to hurt. "Really, Carrie. It's going to be very hard to work together if I think you don't like me."

He has to be kidding. But maybe Samantha was right. Doing business with men is tricky. If I reject Bobby, is he going to cancel my play reading? I swallow and try to summon a smile. "I do like you, Bobby. But I have a boyfriend," I repeat, figuring the emphasis of this fact is probably my best tactic.

"Who?" he demands.

"Bernard Singer."

Bobby breaks into a glass-shattering peal. "Him?" He moves closer and tries to take my hand. "He's too old for you."

I shake my head in wonder.

The momentary lull gives Bobby another chance to attack. He wraps his arms around my neck and attempts to mouth me again.

There's a kind of tussle, with me trying to maneuver around him and him trying to push me against the sink. Luckily, Bobby not only looks like a butter ball, but has the consistency of one as well. Besides, I'm more desperate. I duck under his outstretched arms and hightail it for the door.

"Carrie! Carrie," he cries, clapping his hands as he skitters down the hall after me.

I reach the door, and pause, breathless. I'm about to tell him what a scumball he is and how I don't appreciate being taken in under false pretenses—all the while seeing my future crumble before me—when I catch his pained expression.

"I'm sorry." He hangs his head like a child. "I hope—"

"Yes?" I ask, rearranging my hair.

"I hope this doesn't mean you hate me. We can still do your reading, yes?"

I do my best to look down my nose at him. "How can I trust you? After this."

"Oh, forget about it," he says, waving his hands in front of his face as though encased in a swarm of flies. "I didn't mean it. I'm too forward. Friends?" he asks sheepishly, holding out his hand.

I straighten my shoulders and take it. Quick as a wink, he's clutched my hand and is lifting it to his mouth.

I allow him to kiss it before I jerk it back.

"What about your play?" he pronounces. "You have to allow me to read it before Thursday. Since you won't let me kiss you, I need to know what I'm getting into."

"I don't have it. I'll drop it off tomorrow," I say hastily. Miranda has it, but I'll get it from her later.

"And invite some of your friends to the reading. The pretty ones," he adds.

I shake my head and walk out the door. Some men never give up.

Nor some women. I fan myself in relief as I ride down the elevator. At least I still have my reading. I'll probably be fighting Bobby off all night, but it seems like a small price to pay for impending fame.

CHAPTER THIRTY-FOUR

"Who is this creep, exactly?" Samantha asks, tearing the top off a pink package of Sweet'N Low and pouring the powdered chemicals into her coffee.

"He's some kind of art dealer. He's the guy with the space. I went to the fashion show there?" I gather the tiny strips of pink paper from the middle of the table, fold them neatly, and wrap them in my napkin. I can't help it. Those damn leavings from fake sugar packages drive me crazy. Mostly because you can't go two feet without finding one.

"The space guy," Samantha says, musingly.

"Bobby. Do you know him?" I ask, thinking she must. She knows everyone.

We're at the Pink Tea Cup, this very famous

restaurant in the West Village. It's pink all right, with twee wrought-iron chairs and ancient table-cloths printed with cabbage roses. They're open twenty-four hours, but they only serve breakfast, so if you time it right, you get to see Joey Ramone eating pancakes at five in the afternoon.

Samantha has left work early, claiming she's still in pain from the operation. But it can't be too bad, since she's managed to make it out of the apartment. "Is he short?" she asks.

"He had to stand on his tippy-toes when he tried to kiss me." The memory of Bobby's attempted assault causes a fresh round of irritation, and I pour way too much sugar into my cup.

"Bobby Nevil." She nods. "Everyone knows him. He's infamous."

"For jumping young girls?"

Samantha makes a face. "That would garner him no notoriety at all." She lifts her cup and tastes her coffee. "He tried to attack Michelangelo's *David*."

"The sculpture?" Oh, great. Just my luck. "He's a criminal?"

"More like an art revolutionary. He was trying to make a statement about art."

"Meaning what? Art sucks?"

"Who sucks?" Miranda demands, arriving at the table with her knapsack and a black Saks shopping bag slung over her shoulder. She grabs a handful of napkins from the dispenser and mops her brow. "It's ninety degrees out there." She waves at the waitress and asks for a glass of ice.

"Are we talking about sex again?" She looks at Samantha accusingly. "I hope I didn't come all the way down here for another conversation about Kegel exercises. Which I tried, by the way. They made me feel like a monkey."

"Monkeys do Kegel exercises?" I ask, surprised.

Samantha shakes her head. "You two are hopeless."

I sigh. I'd walked away from Bobby's thinking I could handle his underhanded behavior, but the more I thought about it, the more incensed I became. Was it wrong to assume that when I finally got a break, it would be based on my own merits, as opposed to the random horniness of some old coot? "Bobby tried to jump me," I inform Miranda.

"That little thing?" She's not impressed. "I thought he was gay."

"He's one of those guys no one wants on their team. Gay or straight," Samantha says.

"Is that an actual thing?" Miranda asks.

"They're called the lost boys of sexual orientation. Come on, guys," I say. "This is serious."

"There was a professor at my school," Miranda says. "Everyone knew if you slept with him he'd give you an A."

I glare at her. "Not helping."

"Well, come on, Carrie. This is nothing new. Every bar I've worked in has an unspoken rule that if you have sex with the manager, you'll get the best shifts," Samantha says. "And every office I've worked in—same thing. There's always some guy coming on to you. And most of them are married."

I groan. "And do you—?"

"Have sex with them? What do you think, Sparrow?" she asks sharply. "I don't *need* to have sex with some guy to get ahead. On the other hand, I'm not ashamed of anything I've done. Shame is a useless emotion."

Miranda's face contorts into an expression that signifies she's about to say something inappropriate. "If that's true, why won't you tell Charlie about the endometriosis? If you're not ashamed, why can't you be honest?"

Samantha's lips curl into a patronizing smile. "My relationship with Charlie is none of your business."

"Why do you talk about it all the time, then?" Miranda asks, refusing to back down.

I put my head in my hands, wondering why

we're all so worked up. It must be the heat. It curdles the brain.

"So should I have my play reading at Bobby's or not?" I ask.

"Of course," Samantha says. "You can't let Bobby's stupid little pass make you question your talents. Then he'll have won."

Miranda has no choice but to agree. "Why should you let that squat little toad define who you are or what you can do?"

I know they're right, but for a moment, I feel defeated. By life and the never-ending struggle to make something of it. Why can't things just be easy?

"Did you read my play?" I ask Miranda.

She reddens. And in a voice that's too high, says, "I meant to. But I was so busy. I promise I'll read it tonight, okay?"

"Can't," I say sharply. "I need it back. I have to give it to Bobby first thing tomorrow."

"Don't get testy—"

"I'm not."

"It's right here," she says, opening her knapsack and riffling through it. She looks inside in confusion, then picks up the shopping bag and dumps the contents onto the table. "It must have gotten mixed up with my flyers."

"You took my play to Saks?" I ask, incredulous,

as Miranda paws frantically through her papers.

"I was going to read it when things got slow. Here it is," she says in relief, holding up a few pages.

I quickly flip through them. "Where's the rest? This is only the first third."

"Has to be here," she mutters as I join her in going through each piece of paper one by one. "Oh my God." She sits back in her chair. "Carrie, I'm sorry. This guy got in my face yesterday. Grabbed a bunch of flyers and ran. The rest of your play must have been mixed up with them—"

I stop breathing. I have one of those terrible premonitions that my life is about to fall apart.

"You must have another copy," Samantha says soothingly.

"My professor has one."

"Well, then," Miranda chirps, as if everything's all right.

I grab my bag. "I've got to go," I squeak, just before my mouth goes completely dry.

Damn. Crap! And every other expletive I can think of.

If I don't have my play, I don't have anything. No reading, no life.

But surely Viktor has a copy. I specifically remember the day I gave it to him. And what kind of teacher throws out their students' work?

I run through the Village, barging through traffic and nearly knocking over several passersby on my route to The New School. I arrive heaving, take the stairs two at a time, and throw myself on Viktor's door.

It's locked.

I wheel around in a frenzy, trip down the stairs, and run all the way back to Samantha's place.

She's lying in bed with a pile of magazines. "Carrie? Can you believe what Miranda said to me? About Charlie? I thought it was very uncalled for—"

"Yeah," I say as I search the kitchen for the white pages.

"Did you find your play?"

"No!" I scream, flipping through the phone book.

I pat my heart, trying to get a grip. There it is: Viktor Greene. With an address in the Mews.

"Carrie?" Samantha asks, on my way back out. "Could you pick me up something to eat? Maybe Chinese? Or pizza. With pepperoni. And not too much cheese. Be sure to tell them no extra cheese—"

Argh!!!!!!

I haul myself back to the Mews, every muscle in my body screaming with pain from the exertion. I walk up and down the cobblestoned street twice before I find Viktor's place, tucked behind a portcullis and hidden by ivy. I bang on the door several times, and when I can't rouse him, plop down on the stoop.

Where the hell is he? Viktor's always around. He has no life, apart from the school and his occasional affair with one of his students. The bastard. I get up and kick the door, and when there's still no answer, I peek in the window.

The tiny carriage house is dark. I sniff the air, convinced I can catch a whiff of decay.

It's not surprising. Viktor is a pig.

Then I notice three days' worth of newspapers strewn next to the door. What if he's gone away? But where would he go? I snuffle around the window again, wondering if the smell is an indication that he's dead. Maybe he had a heart attack and, since he doesn't have any friends, no one's thought to look for him.

I bang on the window, which is totally useless. I look around for something to break it with, loosening a brick from the edge of the cobblestones. I raise it above my head, ready to attack.

"Looking for Viktor?" comes a voice from behind me.

I lower the brick and turn around.

The speaker is an elderly lady with a cat on

a leash. She walks cautiously forward and bends down painstakingly to scoop up the papers. "Viktor's gone," she informs me. "I told him I'd save his newspapers. Lots of crooks around here."

I surreptitiously drop the brick. "When is he coming back?"

She squints. "Friday? His mother died, poor thing. He's gone to the Midwest to bury her."

"Friday?" I take a step and nearly trip on the brick. I grab a vine of ivy to steady myself.

"That's what he said. Friday." The old woman bobs her head.

The reality of my situation hits me like a truckload of cement. "That's too late!" I cry, as I let go of the vine and collapse to the ground in despair.

"Sparrow?" Samantha asks, coming into the living room. "What are you doing?"

"Huh?"

"You've been sitting there for over an hour with your mouth hanging open. It's not very attractive," she scolds. When I don't respond, she stands over me and knocks on my head. "Hello? Anyone home?"

I unhinge my eyes from a blank spot on the wall and swivel my head around to look at her.

She shakes a sheaf of newspaper pages in my

face. "I thought we could have some fun. Work on my engagement announcement for *The New York Times*. You're a writer. This should be a snap for you."

"I'm not a writer. Not anymore," I respond dully.

"Don't be ridiculous. You've had one small setback." She settles in next to me with the pile of papers on her lap. "I've been collecting these since May. The wedding and engagement announcements in *The New York Times*. Also known as the 'women's sports pages.'"

"Who cares?" I lift my head.

"Everyone who's anyone in New York, Sparrow," she explains, as if talking to a child. "And it's especially important because the *Times* won't take just any old announcement. The man has to be Ivy League. And both parties need to come from the right sort of families. Old money is best, but new money will do. Or fame. If, for instance, the bride has a famous father, like an actor or a sculptor or a composer, she'll definitely get in."

"Why can't you just get married?" I rub my cheeks. My skin is cold, as if I've lost all circulation.

"Where's the fun in that?" Samantha asks.

"Why get married in New York if you're going to be a nobody? You might as well have stayed home. A wedding in New York is all about taking your proper place in society. It's why we're getting married at the Century Club. If you get married there, it's a statement."

"Meaning?"

She pats my leg. "You belong, Sparrow."

"But what if you don't? Belong."

"For God's sake, Sparrow. You *act* like you do. What is wrong with you? Have you forgotten everything I've taught you?"

And before I can protest, she goes to the typewriter, rolls a piece of paper into the carriage, and points at the chair. "You write. I'll dictate."

My shoulders slump, but I follow her order and place my hands on the keys, more out of rote than of conscious action.

Samantha plucks a page from her pile and scans the announcements. "Here's a good one. 'Miss Barbara Halters from Newport, Rhode Island, known to her friends as Horsie . . .'"

If she's joking, it's completely lost on me. "I thought you were from Weehawken."

"Who wants to be from there? Put down 'Short Hills.' Short Hills is acceptable."

"But what if someone checks—"

"They *won't*. Can we please continue? Miss Samantha Jones—"

"What about 'Ms.'?"

"Okay. Ms. Samantha Jones, of Short Hills, New Jersey, attended . . ." She pauses. "What college is near Short Hills?"

"I don't know."

"Just say 'Princeton' then. It's close enough. Princeton," she continues, satisfied with her choice. "And I graduated with a degree in . . . English literature."

"No one's going to believe that," I protest, beginning to come to life. "I've never seen you read anything other than a self-help book."

"Okay. Skip the part about my degree. It doesn't matter anyway," she says with a wave. "The tricky part is my parents. We'll say my mother was a homemaker—that's neutral—and my father was an international businessman. That way I can explain why he was never around."

I take my hands off the keys and fold them in my lap. "I can't do this."

"Why not?"

"I can't lie to *The New York Times*."

"You're not the one who's lying. I am."

"Why do *you* have to lie?"

"Carrie," she says, becoming frustrated. "Everyone lies."

"No, they don't."

"You lie. Didn't you lie to Bernard about your age?"

"That's different. I'm not marrying Bernard."

She gives me a cold smile, as if she can't believe I'm challenging her. "Fine. I'll write it myself."

"Be my guest." I get up as she sits down in front of the typewriter.

She bangs away for several minutes while I watch. Finally, I can't take it anymore. "Why can't you tell the truth?"

"Because the truth isn't good enough."

"That's like saying you're not good enough."

She stops typing. She sits back and folds her arms. "I am good enough. I've never had any doubt in my mind—"

"Why don't you be yourself, then?"

"Why don't *you*?" She jumps up. "You're worried about *me*? Look at you. Sniveling around the apartment because you lost half your play. If you're such a great writer, why don't you write another one?"

"It doesn't work that way," I scream, my throat raw. "It took me a whole month to write that play. You don't just sit down and write a whole play in three days. You have to think about it. You have to—"

"Fine. If you want to give up, that's your

problem." She starts toward her room, pauses, and spins around. "But if you want to act like a loser, don't you dare criticize me," she shouts, banging the door behind her.

I put my head in my hands. She's right. I'm sick of myself and my failure. I might as well pack my bags and go home.

Like L'il. And all the millions of other young people who came to New York to make it and failed.

And suddenly, I'm furious. I run to Samantha's room and pound on the door.

"What?" she yells as I open it.

"Why don't *you* start over?" I shout, for no rational reason.

"Why don't you?"

"I will."

"Good."

I slam the door.

As if in a trance, I go to my typewriter and sit down. I rip out Samantha's phony announcement, crumple it into a ball, and throw it across the room. I roll a fresh piece of paper into the carriage. I look at my watch. I have seventy-four hours and twenty-three minutes until my reading on Thursday. And I'm going to make it. I'm going to write another play if it kills me.

❖ ✳ C_B ✳ ❖

My typewriter ribbon breaks on Thursday morning. I look around at the empty candy wrappers, the dried tea bags, and the greasy pizza crusts.

It's my birthday. I'm finally eighteen.

CHAPTER THIRTY-FIVE

My hands shake as I step into the shower.

The bottle of shampoo slips from my fingers, and I manage to catch it just before it breaks on the tiles. I take a deep breath, tilting my head back against the spray.

I did it. I actually did it.

But the water can't erase how I really feel: red-eyed, weak, and rattled.

I'll never know what would have happened if Miranda hadn't lost my play and I hadn't had to rewrite it. I don't know if it's good or bad. I don't know if I'll be celebrated or disdained. But I did it, I remind myself. I *tried*.

I get out of the shower and towel off. I peer into the mirror. My face looks drawn and hollow, as I've barely slept for three days. This is not how I was expecting to make my debut, but I'll take it. I don't have a choice.

I put on the red rubber pants, my Chinese robe, and Samantha's old Fiorucci boots. Maybe someday I'll be like Samantha, able to afford my own shoes.

Samantha. She went back to work on Tuesday morning and I haven't heard from her since. Ditto for Miranda, who hasn't called either. Probably too scared I'll never forgive her.

But I will. And I hope Samantha can forgive me as well.

"Here you are," Bobby says gaily. "And right on time."

"If you only knew," I mumble.

"Excited?" He bounces on his toes.

"Nervous." I smile weakly. "Is it true you attacked *David*?"

He frowns. "Who told you that?"

I shrug.

"It's never a good idea to dwell on the past. Let's have some champagne."

I follow him to the kitchen, keeping my carpenter's bag between us so he can't try any of his funny business. If he does, I swear, I really will hit him this time.

I needn't have worried though, because the guests start arriving and Bobby scurries to the door to greet them.

I remain in the kitchen, sipping my champagne. The hell with it, I think, and drain the whole glass. I pour myself another.

Tonight's the night, I think grimly. My reading and Bernard.

I narrow my eyes. He'd better be prepared to do it this time. Tonight he'd better not have any excuses.

I shake my head. What kind of attitude is that to take about losing your virginity? Not good.

I'm about to pour myself more champagne when I hear, "Carrie?" I nearly drop the bottle as I turn around and find Miranda.

"Please don't be mad," she implores.

My body sags in relief. Now that Miranda's here, maybe everything really will be okay.

After Miranda's arrival, I can't exactly describe the party because I'm everywhere at once: greeting guests at the door, worrying about when to set up the chairs, fending off Bobby, and trying to come up with something impressive to say to Charlie, who has shown up, unexpectedly, with Samantha.

If Samantha is mad at me from the other night,

she's doing her best not to show it, complimenting me on my pants while holding on to Charlie's arm as if she owns him. He's a large man, almost handsome, and slightly gawky, as if he doesn't know what to do with his limbs. He immediately starts talking about baseball, and when some other people chime in, I slip away to find Bernard.

He's in the corner with Teensie. I can't believe he brought her after that disastrous weekend, but apparently, either he doesn't care or Teensie never bothered to give him an earful about me. Maybe because it's my night, Teensie is all smiles, at least on the surface.

"When Bernard told me about this event, I couldn't believe it," she says, leaning forward to whisper loudly in my ear. "I said I simply had to see it for myself."

"Well, thank you," I reply modestly, smiling at Bernard. "I'm so glad you could make it."

Capote and Ryan wander over with Rainbow in tow. We talk about class and how Viktor disappeared and how we can hardly believe the summer is nearly over. There's more drinking and schmoozing, and I feel like a jewel, whirling in the center of all the attention, remembering my first night in New York with Samantha, and how far I've come since then.

"Hello, little one." It's Cholly Hammond in his

usual seersucker uniform. "Have you met Winnie Dieke?" he asks, gesturing toward a young woman with a sharp face. "She's from the *New York Post*. If you're very nice to her, she might write about the event."

"Then I'll be very nice. Hello, Winnie," I say smoothly, holding out my hand.

By ten thirty, the party is packed. Bobby's space is a regular stop for revelers out on the town. It's got free booze, shirtless bartenders, and a hodge-podge of crazy characters to shake things up. Like the old lady on roller skates, and the homeless man named Norman, who sometimes lives in Bobby's closet. Or the Austrian count and the twins who claim to be du Ponts. The model who slept with everyone. The young socialite with the silver spoon around her neck. And in the middle of this great spinning carnival is little old me, standing on my tiptoes in an effort to be heard.

When another half hour passes, I remind Bobby that there is, indeed, entertainment, and Bobby tries to shuffle people into the seats. He stands on a chair, which collapses underneath him. Capote turns down the music as Bobby manages to right himself, and straddling two chairs instead of one, Bobby calls for everyone's attention.

"Tonight we have the world premiere of a play by this very charming young writer, Carrie

Bradshaw. The name of the play is . . . uh . . . I don't really know but it doesn't matter—"

"*Ungrateful Bastards*," Miranda calls out the title.

"Yes, ungrateful bastards—the world is full of them," Bobby squawks. "And now, without further ado—"

I take a deep breath. My heart seems to have migrated to my stomach. There's a grudging round of applause as I take my place at the front of the room.

I remind myself that this is really no different from reading in front of the class, and I begin.

They say that people in stressful situations can lose their perception of time, and that's what happens to me. In fact, I seem to lose all my senses, because at first I have no awareness of sight or sound. Then I become conscious of a few chuckles from the front row, which consists of Bernard, Miranda, Samantha and Charlie, Rainbow, Capote, and Ryan. Then I notice people getting up and leaving their seats. Then I realize the laughter is not due to my play, but to something funny someone said in the back of the room. Then someone turns up the music.

I try to ignore it, but my face flames with heat and my voice cracks. I'm dying up here. In the back of the room, people are dancing. I'm reduced to a mumble, a murmur, an afterthought.

Will this ever end?

Miraculously, it does. Bernard jumps to his feet, clapping. Miranda and Samantha yell their approval. But that's all. Not even Bobby is paying attention. He's by the bar, fawning over Teensie.

That's it? I think wildly. It's *over*? What was that? What just happened?

I thought there'd be cheering.

I thought there'd be applause.

I did all this work for nothing?

The truth begins to dawn on me, although "dawn" isn't the most accurate word. "Dawn" implies something pleasant. Hope. A better day. A new beginning. This is no beginning. This is an end. A disgrace. An embarrassment.

I suck.

Capote and my father and everyone else were right: I have no talent. I've been chasing a dream I made up in my head. And now it's over.

I'm shaking. What should I do? I look around the room, imagining the people turning to leaves, red and then brown and then crumbling to pieces onto the ground. How can I . . . what can I . . . ?

"I thought it was really good." Bernard moves toward me, his grin like the smile of the clown in a jack-in-the-box. "Quite refreshing."

"It was great," Miranda says, giving me a hug.

"I don't know how you stood up in front of all those people. I would have been so frightened."

I look to Samantha, who nods. "It was fun, Sparrow."

This is one of those situations where no one can help you. Your need is so great, it's like a black hole sucking the life out of everyone around you. I stumble forward, blindly.

"Let's get a drink," Bernard says, taking my hand.

"Yes, let's all have a drink," Samantha agrees. This is too much. Even Samantha, who's my biggest cheerleader, knows my play is a disaster.

I'm like Typhoid Mary. No one wants to be around me.

Bernard hurries to the bar, and, as if shedding a virus, deposits me next to Teensie, of all people, who is now talking to Capote.

I smile awkwardly.

"Well," Teensie says, with a dramatic sigh.

"You must have worked on it," Capote says. "Since class. I thought it was better than what you read in class."

"I had to completely rewrite it. In three days." And suddenly, I realize Capote was right. About what he said at the Jessens' dinner. Bobby *is* a joke. And a reading in his space wasn't the right way to get my work noticed. Why didn't I listen? The summer's over and the only thing I've managed to achieve is making a complete and utter fool of myself.

The blood drains from my face.

Capote must understand my distress, because he pats my shoulder and says, "It's good to take chances, remember?"

And as he wanders away, Teensie moves in for the kill. "I thought it was amusing. Very, very amusing," she purrs. "But look at *you*, dear. You're a mess. You look exhausted. And you're way too thin. I'm sure your parents must be very worried about you."

She pauses, and with a glittering smile asks, "Don't you think it's time to go *home*?"

CHAPTER THIRTY-SIX

I am trying to get drunk and not succeeding.

I'm a total failure. I can't even win at inebriation.

"Carrie," Bernard cautions.

"What?" I ask, lifting a purloined bottle of champagne to my lips. I snuck it out of the party in my carpenter's bag. I knew that bag would come in handy someday.

"You could hurt yourself." Bernard wrenches the bottle away from me. "The cab could stop short and you could knock out your teeth."

I pull the bottle back, clinging to it tightly. "It's my birthday."

"I know."

"Aren't you going to say happy birthday?"

"I have. Several times. Maybe you didn't hear me."

"Did you get me a present?"

"Yes. Now look," he says becoming stern. "Maybe I should drop you at your apartment. There's no reason to do this tonight."

"But I want my present," I wail. "And it's my birthday. It has to be done on the day or it doesn't count."

"Technically, it's not your birthday anymore. It's after two."

"Technically my birthday didn't start until after two last night. So it still counts."

"It's going to be okay, kiddo." He pats my leg.

"You didn't like it, did you?" I take another swig and look out the open window, feeling the stinky summer air whooshing across my face.

"Like what?" he asks.

Jeez. What does he think I'm talking about? Is he really that thick? Is everyone this thick and I just never noticed before? "My *play*. You said you liked it but you didn't."

"You said you rewrote it."

"Only because I had to. If Miranda—"

"Come on, kiddo," he says, reassuringly. "These things happen."

"To me. Only to me. Not to you or anyone else."

It seems Bernard has had enough of my histri-onics. He folds his arms.

His gesture scares some sense into me. I can't lose him, too. Not tonight. "Please," I say. "Let's not fight."

"I didn't know we *were* fighting."

"We're not." I put down the bottle and cling to him like a limpet.

"Awwww, kiddo." He strokes my cheek. "I know you had a rough night. But that's the way it is when you put something out there."

"Really?" I sniff.

"It's all about rewriting. You'll rework the play, and it'll be great. You'll see."

"I hate rewriting," I grumble. "Why can't the world come out right the first time?"

"What would be the fun in that?"

"Oh, Bernard." I sigh. "I love you."

"Yeah, I love you, too, kitten."

"Honest? At two in the morning? On Madison Avenue? You love me?"

He smiles.

"What's my present?" I coo.

"If I told you, it wouldn't be a present, now, would it?"

"I'm giving you a present," I slur.

"You don't have to give me a present."

"Oh, but I do," I say cryptically. Even if my

play was a disaster, losing my virginity could salvage it.

"Here!" Bernard says, triumphantly, handing me a perfectly wrapped box in shiny black paper complete with a big black bow.

"Oh my God." I sink to my knees on the carpet in his living room. "Is it really what I think it is?"

"I hope so," he says nervously.

"I already love it." I look at him with shining eyes.

"You don't know what it is yet."

"Oh, but I do," I cry out in excitement, tearing away the paper and fingering the raised white lettering on the box. CHANEL.

Bernard looks slightly uncomfortable with my overwhelming demonstrance. "Teensie thought you'd like it."

"Teensie? You asked Teensie what to get me? I thought she hated me."

"She said you needed something nice."

"Oh, Bernard." I lift the cover from the box and gently open the tissue paper. And there it is: my first Chanel handbag.

I lift it out and cradle it in my arms.

"Do you like it?" he asks.

"I love it," I say solemnly. I hold it for a few

seconds more, savoring the soft leather. With sweet reluctance, I slip it back into its cotton pouch and carefully replace it in the box.

"Don't you want to use it?" Bernard asks, perplexed by my actions.

"I want to save it."

"Why?" he says.

"Because I always want it to be . . . *perfect*." Because nothing ever is. "Thank you, Bernard." I wonder if I'm going to cry.

"Hey, puddy tat. It's only a purse."

"I know, but—" I get up and curl next to him on the couch, stroking the back of his neck.

"Eager little beaver, aren't you?" He kisses me and I kiss him back and as we're starting to get into it, he takes my hand and leads me to the bedroom.

This is it. And suddenly, I'm not so sure I'm ready.

I remind myself that this should not be a big deal. We've done everything but. We've spent the entire night together a dozen times. But knowing what's to come makes it feel different. Even kissing is awkward. Like we barely know each other.

"I need a drink," I say.

"Haven't you had enough?" Bernard looks worried.

"No—I mean a drink of water," I lie. I grab one of his shirts to cover myself and race into the kitchen. There's a bottle of vodka on the counter. I close my eyes, brace myself, and take a gulp. I quickly rinse my mouth with water.

"Okay. I'm ready," I announce, standing in the doorway.

I feel all jumbly again. I'm trying to be sexy, but I don't know how. Everything feels so false and artificial, including myself. Maybe you have to learn how to be sexy in the bedroom. Or maybe it's something you have to be born with. Like Samantha. Sexiness comes naturally to her. With me, it would be easier to be a plumber right now.

"Come here," Bernard laughs, patting the bed. "And don't get any ideas about stealing that shirt. Margie used to take my shirts."

"Margie?"

"Let's not talk about her, okay?"

We start making out again, but now it feels like Margie is in the room. I try to banish her, telling myself that Bernard is mine now. But it only makes me feel more diminished in comparison. Maybe after we get it over with, it'll be better. "Let's just do it, okay?" I say.

He raises his head. "Don't you like this?"

"No. I love it. But I just want to do it."

"I can't just—"

"Bernard. *Please.*"

Miranda was right. This is terrible. Why didn't I get this over with a long time ago? At least I'd know what to expect.

"Okay," he murmurs. He lies on top of me. He wriggles around a bit. Then he wriggles some more.

"Has it happened?" I'm confused. Boy, Miranda wasn't kidding. It really is nothing.

"No. I—" He breaks off. "Look. I'm going to need you to help me a little."

Help him? What is he talking about? No one told me "help" was part of the program.

Why can't he just do it?

And there we are, naked. Naked in our skins. But naked mostly in our emotions. I wasn't prepared for *this*. The raw, unfortunate intimacy.

"Could you just—?" he asks.

"Sure," I say.

I do my best, but it isn't enough. Then he tries. Then it seems he's finally ready. He gets on top of me. Okay, let's go, buddy, I think. He makes a few thrusting motions. He puts his hand down there to help himself.

"Is it supposed to be like this?" I ask.

"What do you think?" he says.

"I don't know."

"What do you mean, you don't know?"

"I've never done it before."

"What!" He draws back in shock.

"Don't be mad at me," I plead, clinging to his leg as he leaps off the bed. "I never met the right guy before. There has to be a first time for everyone, right?"

"Not with me." He darts around the room, snatching up my things.

"What are you doing?"

"You need to get dressed."

"Why?"

He pulls at his hair. "Carrie, you cannot stay here. We cannot do this. I'm not that guy."

"Why *not*?" I ask, my obstinance turning to panic.

"Because I'm not." He stops, takes a breath, gets ahold of himself. "I'm an adult. And you're a kid—"

"I'm not a kid. I'm eighteen."

"I thought you were a sophomore in college." More horror.

"Oops," I say, trying to make a joke of it.

His jaw drops. "Are you insane?"

"No, I don't think so. I mean, the last time I checked I seemed to be fairly normal—" Then I lose it. "It's me, isn't it? You don't want me. That's why you couldn't do it. You couldn't get it up. Because—" As soon as the words are out of my mouth, I realize this is just about the worst thing you can say to a guy. Ever. Because I can promise you, he's none too happy about it himself.

"I can't do this," he wails, more to himself than to me. "I cannot do this. What am I doing? What's happened to my life?"

I try to remember everything I've read about impotence. "Maybe I *can* help you," I falter. "Maybe we can work on it—"

"I don't want to have to work on my sex life," he roars. "Don't you get it? I don't want to have to work on my marriage. I don't want to have to work on my relationships. I want them to just happen, without effort. And if you weren't such an asshole all the time, maybe you'd understand."

What? For a moment, I'm too stung to react. Then I draw back in hurt and indignation. I'm an asshole? Can women even be assholes? I must really be terrible if a man calls me an asshole.

I shut my mouth. I pick up my pants from where he's dropped them on the bed.

"Carrie," he says.

"What?"

"It's probably best if you go."

"No kidding."

"And we . . . probably shouldn't see each other anymore."

"Right."

"I still want you to have the purse," he says,

trying to make nice.

"I don't want it." This, however, is very much a lie. I do want it. Badly. I want to get something out of this debacle of a birthday.

"Take it, please," he says.

"Give it to Teensie. She's just like you." I want to slap him. It's like one of those dreams where you try to hit a guy and keep missing.

"Don't be a jerk," he says. We're dressed and at the door. "Take it, for Christ's sake. You know you want it."

"That's just gross, Bernard."

"Here." He tries to shove the bag into my hands but I yank open the door, hit the elevator button, and cross my arms.

Bernard rides down in the lift with me. "Carrie," he says, trying not to make a scene in front of the elevator man.

"No." I shake my head.

He follows me outside and raises his hand to hail a cab. Why is it that whenever you don't want a taxi, there's one right there? Because half of me is still hoping this isn't actually happening, and a miracle will occur and everything will go back to normal. But then Bernard is giving the driver my address and ten dollars to get me home.

I get into the backseat, fuming.

"Here," he says, offering me the bag again.

"I told you. I don't want it," I scream.

And as the cab pulls away from the curb, he yanks open the door and tosses it inside.

The bag lands at my feet. For a moment, I think about throwing it out the window. But I don't. Because now I'm crying hysterically. Great, heaving sobs that feel like they're going to rip me apart.

"Hey," the taxi driver says. "Are you cryin'? You're cryin' in my cab? You want sumpin to cry about, lady, I'll give you sumpin. How about them Yankees then? How about that goddamned baseball strike?"

Huh?

The cab pulls up in front of Samantha's building. I stare at it helplessly, unable to move for my tears.

"Hey, lady," the driver growls. "You gonna get out? I don't have all night."

I wipe my eyes as I make one of those rash and ill-advised decisions everyone tells you not to. "Take me to Greenwich Street."

"But—"

"Greenwich Street."

I get out at the phone booth on the corner. My fingers are trembling as I search for a dime and drop it into the slot. The phone rings several times. A sleepy voice says, "Yeah?"

"Capote?"

"Yeah?" He yawns.

"It's me. Carrie Bradshaw."

"Yeah, Carrie. I know your last name."

"Can I come up?"

"It's four in the morning."

"Please?"

"All right." The light goes on in his window. His shadow moves back and forth, back and forth. The window opens and he throws down the keys.

I catch them neatly in the palm of my hand.

CHAPTER THIRTY-SEVEN

I open one eye and close it. Open it again. Where the hell am I? This must be one of those bad dreams when you think you're awake but you're still actually asleep.

I don't feel asleep, though.

Besides, I'm naked. And it kind of hurts down there.

But that's because . . . I smile. It happened. I am officially no longer a virgin.

I'm in Capote Duncan's apartment. I'm in his bed. The bed with the plaid sheets his mother bought him. And the two foam pillows (why are guys so chintzy about pillows?), and the scratchy army blanket that belonged to his grandfather. Who got it from his father, who fought in the

Civil War. Capote is very sentimental. I can hear Patsy Cline still crooning softly on the stereo. "I Fall to Pieces." From now on, every time I hear that song, I'll think of Capote and the night we spent together. The night he kindly took my virginity.

I guess I'm lucky, because it was pretty much the way I'd always hoped it would be. And while we were doing it, I honestly felt like I was in love with him. He kept telling me how beautiful I was. And how I shouldn't be afraid. And how happy he was to be with me. And how he'd wanted to be with me from the beginning, but he thought I couldn't stand him. And then, when I started dating Bernard, how he figured he'd lost his chance. And when I actually managed to write a play, he decided I'd think he wasn't "good enough." Because he hadn't managed to write much of anything.

Yow. Guys can be so insecure.

Naturally, I told him he'd gotten me all wrong, although it is true—which I didn't tell him—that I didn't find him terribly attractive at the beginning.

Now, of course, I think he's the most gorgeous creature on earth.

I peek at him. He's still asleep, lying on his back, his face so peaceful and relaxed, I actually think

I can detect a slight smile on his lips. Without his glasses, he looks shockingly vulnerable. Last night, after we kissed for a bit and he did the sexy librarian thing and took off his specs, we stared and stared into each other's eyes. I felt like I could see his entire history in his pupils.

I could know everything about him in a way I'd never known anyone before.

It was a little eerie, but also kind of profound.

I guess that's what I found most surprising about sex: the knowing. How you can understand a person completely and vice versa.

I lean over the edge of the bed, searching for my Skivvies. I want to get out while Capote's still asleep. A deal's a deal, and I said I'd leave first thing in the morning.

I raise myself slowly, sliding carefully off the bed so as not to jiggle the mattress. The mattress itself is about a hundred years old, left here by the original owners. I wonder how many people have had sex on this bed. I hope a lot. And I hope it was as good for them as it was for me.

I find my clothes splayed around the couch. The Chanel bag is by the door, where I dropped it when Capote grabbed my face and backed me up against the wall, kissing me like crazy. I practically tore his clothes off.

But I'm never going to see him again, so it

doesn't matter. And now I have to face the future: Brown.

Maybe, after four years of college, I'll try again. I'll storm the gates of the Emerald City, and this time, I'll succeed.

But for now, I'm too tired. Who knew eighteen could be so exhausting?

I sigh and wriggle my feet into my shoes. I had a good run. Sure, I messed up a few times, but I managed to survive.

I tiptoe back to the bedroom for one last look at Capote. "Good-bye, lover," I murmur quietly.

His mouth pops open and he wakes, pounding his pillow in confusion. He sits up and squints at me. "Huh?"

"Sorry," I whisper, picking up my watch. "I was just—" I indicate the door.

"Why?" He rubs his eyes. "Didn't you like it?"

"I loved it. But—"

"Why are you leaving then?"

I shrug.

He feels for his glasses and puts them on, blinking behind the thick lenses. "Aren't you going to at least allow me the pleasure of giving you breakfast? A gentleman never lets a lady leave without feeding her, first."

I laugh. "I'm perfectly capable of feeding myself. Besides, you make me sound like a bird."

"A bird? More like a tiger," he chuckles. "C'mere." He opens his arms. I crawl across the bed and fall into them.

He strokes my hair. He's warm and snuggly and smells a little. Of man, I suppose. The scent is strangely familiar. Like toast.

He pulls back his head and smiles. "Did anyone ever tell you how pretty you look in the morning?"

At about two in the afternoon, we manage to make it to the Pink Tea Cup for breakfast. I wear one of Capote's shirts over my rubber pants and we eat pancakes and bacon with real maple syrup and drink about a gallon of coffee and smoke cigarettes and talk shyly and eagerly about nothing. "Hey," he says, when the check comes. "Want to go to the zoo?"

"The zoo?"

"I hear they have a new polar bear."

And suddenly, I do want to go to the zoo with Capote. In my two months in New York, I haven't done one touristy thing. I haven't been to the Empire State Building. Or the Statue of Liberty. Or Wollman Rink or the Metropolitan Museum or even the Public Library.

I've been sorely remiss. I can't leave New York without going on the Circle Line.

"I need to do one thing first," I say.

I get up and head to the restroom. There's a pay phone on the wall outside the door.

Miranda picks up after the first ring. "Hello?" she asks urgently, as if she's expecting bad news. She always answers the phone like that. It's one of the things I love about her.

"I did it!" I squeal triumphantly.

"Carrie? Is that you? Oh my God. What happened? How was it? Did it hurt? How was Bernard?"

"I didn't do it with Bernard."

"What?" She gasps. "Who *did* you do it with? You can't go out there and pick up some random stranger. Oh no, Carrie. You didn't. You didn't pick up some guy at a bar—"

"I did it with Capote," I say proudly.

"That guy?" I can hear her jaw drop. "I thought you hated him."

I glance back at Capote. He casually tosses a few bills onto the table. "Not anymore."

"But what about Bernard?" she demands. "I thought you said Bernard was The One."

Capote stands up. "Change of plans," I say quickly. "He couldn't do it. I had to abort the mission and find another rocket."

"Carrie, that's disgusting. Did Samantha tell you to say that? You sound just like her. Oh my

God. This is insane. What are you going to do now?"

"Visit the polar bear," I say, laughing. I gently hang up before she can ask any more questions.

Have I ever been in love? Really in love? And why is it that with each new guy I think I'm more in love with him than the last? I think briefly of Sebastian and smile. What on earth was I doing with him? Or Bernard? I lean over the wall to get a better view of the polar bear. Poor Bernard. He turned out to be even more messed up than I am.

"What are you laughing about?" Capote asks, wrapping his arms around me from behind. We haven't been able to take our hands off each other, leaning into each other on the subway, walking arm in arm as we strolled up Fifth Avenue, and kissing at the entrance to the zoo. My body has turned to butter. I can't believe I wasted the whole summer pursuing Bernard instead of Capote.

But maybe Capote wouldn't like me so much if I hadn't.

"I'm always laughing," I say.

"Why?" he asks sweetly.

"Because life is funny."

At the zoo, we buy hot dogs and polar bear baseball caps. We run down Fifth Avenue, past the old man who sells pencils in front of Saks, which reminds me of the first time I met Miranda. We join a line of tourists inside the Empire State Building and ride the elevator to the top. We look through viewfinders and make out until we're breathless. We take a taxi back to Capote's.

We have sex again, and don't stop until we both realize we're starving. We go to Chinatown and eat Peking duck, which I've never had before, and we wander through SoHo and laugh about how Teensie took a pill at Barry Jessen's opening and all the other crazy things that have happened to us during the summer. It's pretty late by now—after midnight—so I figure I'll spend one more night with him and go home in the morning.

But when morning comes, we still can't manage to tear ourselves apart. We go back to my place and make love on Samantha's bed. I change my clothes, stick my toothbrush and a change of underwear into my carpenter's bag, and we head out to be tourists again. We do the Circle Line and the Statue of Liberty, climbing all the way to the top and laughing about how small it is once you finally get up to the crown, then we go back to Capote's.

We eat hamburgers at the Corner Bistro and pizza at John's. I have my first orgasm.

The hours pass in a fuzzy, dreamlike way, mingled with a thread of despair. This can't last forever. Capote starts a job at a publishing company after Labor Day. And I have to go to Brown.

"Are you sure?" he murmurs.

"I don't have a choice. I was hoping something would happen with my play and I'd be able to convince my father to let me go to NYU instead."

"Why don't you tell him you changed your mind?"

"I'd need a pretty big excuse."

"Like you met a guy you're crazy about and want to be with him?"

"He'd have a heart attack. I wasn't raised to base my decisions on a guy."

"He sounds like a tough old nut."

"Nah. You'd like him. He's a genius. Like you." Three days with Capote have taught me that what I thought was Capote's arrogance was simply due to his deep knowledge of literature. Like me, he has a searing belief that books are sacred. They might not be to other people, but when you have a passion, you hold on to it. You defend it. You don't pretend it isn't important at the risk of offending others.

And suddenly it's Wednesday morning. Our last class is today. I'm so weak with sadness I can barely lift my arm to brush my teeth. I'm dreading facing the class. But like so much in life, it turns out I needn't have worried.

No one really cares.

Ryan and Rainbow are chatting outside the building when Capote and I arrive together. I drop Capote's hand, thinking it's not a good idea for people to know about us, but Capote has no such compunction. He takes back my hand and drapes my arm over his shoulder.

"Ho, ho, are you guys an item now?" Ryan asks.

"I don't know." I look to Capote for confirmation.

He answers by kissing me on the mouth.

"Gross," Rainbow declares.

"I was wondering how long it would take for you two to get together," Ryan says.

"There's a new club opening on the Bowery," Rainbow remarks.

"And a reading at Cholly Hammond's," Ryan says. "I've heard he throws a great party."

"Anyone want to go to Elaine's next week?" Capote asks.

And on and on they go, with no mention of the fact that I won't be around. Or of my play. They've probably forgotten it by now anyway.

Or, like me, they're too embarrassed to mention it.

When in doubt, there's always plan C: If something really horrible happens, ignore it.

I follow the group inside, trudging my feet. What was it all for, anyway? I made friends with people I'll probably never see again, dated a man who turned out to be a dud, found a love that can't be sustained, and spent all summer writing a play that no one will ever see. As my father would say, I didn't use my time "constructively."

CHAPTER THIRTY-EIGHT

"What's going to happen with you and Capote?" Miranda demands. "Do you actually think you're going to have a long-distance relationship? Sounds like a case of the deliberate subconscious—"

"If it's deliberate, how can it be subconscious?"

"You know what I mean. You choose the end of the summer to fall in love with this guy because secretly, *you don't want it to last*."

I fold the white vinyl jumpsuit and press it into my suitcase. "I don't think my subconscious is capable of being that conniving."

"Oh, but it is," Miranda says. "Your subconscious can make you do all kinds of things. For instance, why are you still wearing his shirt?"

I glance down at the light blue shirt I took from him after our first night. "I forgot I was wearing it."

"You see?" Miranda says victoriously. "That's why it's so important to have analysis."

"How do you explain Marty, then?"

"Subconscious again." She flicks her shoulders in dismissal. "I finally realized he wasn't for me. Even though my conscious was trying to break the pattern, my unconscious knew it wouldn't work. Plus, I couldn't go to the bathroom the whole time I was with him."

"Sounds like your intestines were the problem and not your subconscious." I yank open a drawer and remove three pairs of socks. Which I haven't seen since I put them there two months ago. Socks! What was I thinking? I throw them into the suitcase as well.

"Let's face it, Carrie," Miranda sighs. "It's *all* hopeless."

Men, or the fact that I have to leave New York? "Isn't that what they call wish fulfillment?"

"I'm a realist. Just because you had sex once doesn't mean you have to fall in love," she mutters. "And I never thought you and Samantha would turn out to be those dopey types who moon over their wedding dresses and the smell of their man's shirt."

"First of all, Samantha didn't even show up for her wedding dress. And secondly—" I break off. "Do you think you'll visit me in Providence?"

"Why would I want to go there? What do they have in Providence that we don't have in New York?"

"Me?" I ask mournfully.

"You can visit me anytime," Miranda says firmly. "You can sleep on the couch if you don't mind the springs."

"You know me. I don't mind anything."

"Oh, Carrie," she says sadly.

"I know."

"Got anything to eat in this place? I'm starving," she asks.

"Maybe some peanut butter crackers left over from the blackout."

Miranda goes into the kitchen and returns with the last of the blackout food. "Remember that night?" she asks, tearing open the package.

"How can I forget?" If only I'd known then what I do now. I could have started seeing Capote. We could have been together for two weeks by now.

"What's Samantha going to do with this place anyway? Now that you're leaving and she's getting married?"

"Dunno. Probably find someone like me to rent it."

"Well, it's a shame," Miranda says. I'm not sure if she's referring to my leaving, or the fact that Samantha wants to hang on to her apartment when she has somewhere much better to live. She munches thoughtfully on a cracker while I continue to pack. "Hey," she says finally. "Did I tell you about this course I'm going to take? Patriarchial Rituals in Contemporary Life."

"Sounds interesting," I say, without much enthusiasm.

"Yeah. We study weddings and stuff like that. Did you know that everything leading up to the wedding—the showers and the registering and picking the ugly bridesmaid dresses—was solely designed to give women something to do back in the days when they didn't have careers? And also to brainwash them into thinking that they had to get married too?"

"Actually, I didn't. But it makes sense."

"What are you going to do? At Brown?" Miranda asks.

"Dunno. Study to be a scientist, I guess."

"I thought you were going to become some big writer."

"Look how that turned out."

"The play wasn't that bad," Miranda says, brushing crumbs from her lips. "Have you noticed that ever since you lost your virginity, you've been acting like someone died?"

"When my career died, I died along with it."

"Bullshit," Miranda declares.

"Why don't you try standing in front of a room full of people while they laugh at you?"

"Why don't you stop acting like you're the biggest thing since sliced bread?"

I gasp.

"Fine," Miranda says. "If you can't take constructive criticism—"

"Me? What about you? Half the time your 'realism' is just another word for bitterness—"

"At least I'm not a Pollyanna."

"No, because that would imply that something good might happen—"

"I don't know why you think everything should be handed to you."

"You're just jealous," I snap.

"Of Capote Duncan?" Her eyes narrow. "That's beneath even you, Carrie Bradshaw."

The phone rings.

"You'd better get it," Miranda says tightly. "It's probably *him*. About to declare his undying *love*." She goes into the bathroom and slams the door.

I take a breath. "Hello?"

"Where the hell have you been?" Samantha shrieks.

This is very unlike her. I hold the phone away from my ear. "Were you worried? You're going to be so proud of me. I lost my virginity."

"Well, good for you," she says briskly, which is not the reaction I was expecting. "I'd love to celebrate, but unfortunately, I've got a crisis of my own on my hands. I need you to get over to Charlie's place immediately."

"But—"

"Just come, okay? Don't ask questions. And bring Miranda. I need all the help I can get. And could you pick up a box of garbage bags on the way? Make sure they're the big ones. The kind those pathetic people in the suburbs use for leaves."

"Enjoy it," Samantha says, gesturing to her face as she opens the door to Charlie's apartment. "This is the only time you're ever going to see me cry."

"Is that a promise?" Miranda says tartly. We're still a bit edgy from our almost-fight. If it weren't for Samantha's crisis call, we'd probably be at each other's throats.

"Look," Samantha says, dabbing her eye and holding out her finger for inspection. "That is an actual tear."

"Could have fooled me," I say.

Miranda looks around in awe. "Wow. This place is *nice*."

"Check out the view," Samantha says. "It's the last time you'll see it, too. I'm leaving."

"*What?*"

"That's right," she says, strolling to the sunken living room. There's a stunning vista of Central Park. You can practically see right into the duck pond. "The wedding's off," she declares. "Charlie and I are *over*."

I look at Miranda and roll my eyes. "Surely, this too shall pass," I murmur, heading to the window for a better view.

"Carrie, I'm serious," Samantha says. She goes to a glass tray on wheels, picks up a crystal decanter, and pours herself a healthy dose of whiskey. "And I have you to thank for it." She slugs back her drink and turns on us. "Actually, I have both of you to thank."

"Me?" Miranda asks. "I've hardly even met the guy."

"But you're the one who told me to tell him."

"Tell him what?" Miranda says, mystified.

"About my condition."

"Which is?"

"You know. The thing," Samantha hisses. "The lining . . ."

"Endometriosis?" I ask.

Samantha holds up her hands. "I don't want to hear that word. Ever again."

"Endometriosis is hardly a 'condition,'" Miranda remarks.

"Try telling that to Charlie's mother."

"Oh boy." I realize I could use a drink too. And a cigarette.

"I don't get it." Miranda goes to the Plexiglas case that contains Charlie's collection of sports memorabilia. She leans closer. "Is that a real baseball?"

"What do you think? And yes, that really is Joe DiMaggio's signature," Samantha snaps.

"I thought you were picking out China patterns," Miranda says, as Samantha gives her a look and disappears down the hallway.

"Hey, I just figured something out. You know how Samantha always says Charlie wanted to be a baseball player and his mother wouldn't let him?" I ask. "Maybe Charlie secretly thinks he's Joe DiMaggio and Samantha is Marilyn Monroe."

"That's right. And remember how Joe DiMaggio always resented Marilyn's sexuality and tried to turn her into a housewife? It's practically textbook."

Samantha returns with a pile of clothes in her arms, which she dumps onto the Ultrasuede couch as she glares at me. "And you're as much to blame as Miranda. You were the one who told me to be a little more real."

"I didn't mean it though. I never thought—"

"Well, here's what real gets you in New York." She runs back to the bedroom and returns with another pile, which she drops at our feet. Then she grabs the box of garbage bags, rips one open, and begins frantically shoving clothes into the bag. "This is what it gets you," she repeats, her voice rising. "A kick in the teeth and fifty cents for the subway."

"Whoa. Are you serious?" I ask.

She pauses for a moment and thrusts out her arm. "See this?" She indicates a large gold Rolex encrusted with diamonds.

"Is that real too?" Miranda gasps.

"Hold on," I caution. "Why would someone who's breaking up with you give you a giant Rolex?"

"You could probably buy a small country with that," Miranda adds.

Samantha rocks back on her heels. "Apparently, it's a tradition. When you break off an engagement, you give your ex-fiancée a watch."

"You should get engaged more often."

In a fury, Samantha rips off the watch and throws it against the Plexiglas case, where it bounces off harmlessly. Some things are simply indestructible. "How did this happen to me? I had it all figured out. I had New York by the balls. Everything was working. I was so good at being someone else."

If only we could all put our hearts in a Plexiglas case, I think, as I kneel down next to her. "You weren't so good about showing up at Kleinfeld," I say gently.

"That was an exception. One slipup. And I made up for it by telling Glenn I'd be happy to use her decorator to redo the apartment. Even if it meant living with chintz. What's wrong with a few flowers here and there? I can do roses if I have to—" And suddenly, she bursts into tears. Only this time, they're real.

"Don't you get it?" she sobs. "I've been rejected. For having faulty fallopian tubes."

In the annals of dating, being rejected for your fallopian tubes has got to be right up there with—well, you name it, I suppose. But maybe dating in New York really is like what Samantha always says: everything counts, even the things you can't see.

And what you *can* see is usually bad enough.

I mentally count the number of garbage bags strewn around Charlie's apartment. Fourteen. I had to run out and get another box. Two years in a relationship and you can really accumulate a lot of stuff.

"Baggage," Samantha says, kicking one of the bags out of the way. "All baggage."

"Hey!" I exclaim. "There are Gucci shoes in that one."

"Halston, Gucci, Fiorucci? Who cares?" She throws up her hands. "What's the difference when your entire life has been ripped away?"

"You'll find someone else," Miranda says nonchalantly. "You always do."

"But not someone who will marry me. Everyone knows the only reason a man in Manhattan ever says 'I do' is because he wants children."

"But you don't know that you can't have children," Miranda points out. "The doctor said—"

"Who cares what he said? It's always going to be the same old story."

"You don't know that," I insist. I grab a bag and pull it toward the door. "And do you really want to spend the rest of your life pretending to be someone you're not?" I take a breath and gesture at the Plexiglas furnishings. "Surrounded by *plastic*?"

"All men are jerks. But you knew that." Miranda retrieves the watch from under the coffee table. "I guess that's the last of it," she says, holding out the Rolex. "Don't want to leave this behind."

Samantha carefully weighs the watch in the palm of her hand. Her face scrunches in agony. She takes a deep breath. "Actually, I do."

She places the watch on the table as Miranda and I look at each other in bewilderment.

"Where's the bag with the Gucci shoes?" she orders.

"There?" I ask, wondering what's come over her.

She rips open the bag and dumps out two pairs of loafers. "And the Chanel suit. Where's that?"

"I think it's in here," Miranda says cautiously, pushing a bag into the center of the room.

"What are you doing?" I ask anxiously, as Samantha extracts the Chanel suit and places it on the table next to the watch.

"What do you think I'm doing?"

"I have no idea." I look to Miranda for help, but she's as mystified as I am.

Samantha finds a tennis dress, and holds it up, laughing. "Did I tell you Charlie wanted me to take tennis lessons? So I could play with Glenn. In Southampton. As if I would actually enjoy hitting balls with that mummy. She's sixty-five years old and she says she's fifty. Like anyone's going to believe *that*."

"Well—" I sneak another glance at Miranda, who shakes her head, stupefied.

"Do you want this, Sparrow?" Samantha tosses me the tennis dress.

"Sure," I say hesitantly.

I'm wondering what to do with it, when Samantha suddenly changes her mind and rips it out of my hands. "On second thought, *no*," she shouts, hurling the dress onto the pile. "Don't take it. Don't make the same mistake I did."

She continues on in this vein, tearing through the bags and removing every item of clothing from her life with Charlie. The pile gets bigger and bigger, while Miranda and I watch in concern. I bite my lip. "Are you really going to leave all this stuff?"

"What do you think, Sparrow?" she says. She pauses and takes a deep breath, hands on her hips. She tilts her head, and gives me a fierce smile.

"It's baggage. And even if I'm not the most real person in the world, I'll tell you one thing about Samantha Jones. She can't be bought. At *any* price."

"Remember when I first moved here and you made me pour that carton of milk down the drain because you said the smell made you sick?" I ask, rearranging myself on the futon. It's two a.m.

and we're finally back at Samantha's apartment. All the packing and unpacking has me beat.

"Did she really do that?" Miranda asks.

"Oh yeah." I nod.

"Adults shouldn't drink milk anyway." Samantha exhales as she throws back her head in relief. "Thank God that's over. If these fallopian tubes could talk—"

"Luckily, they can't." I get up and go into the bedroom. I look at my own meager belongings, and with a sigh, open my suitcase.

"Sparrow?" Samantha calls. "What are you doing?"

"Packing," I say loudly. "I'm leaving tomorrow, remember?" I stand in the doorway. "And after this summer, I really don't think I'm a sparrow anymore. Haven't I graduated by now?"

"You have indeed," Samantha agrees. "I now declare you a pigeon. The official bird of New York City."

"The *only* bird in New York City," Miranda giggles. "Hey, it's better than being a rat. Did you know that in China, rats are good luck?"

"I love the Chinese." Samantha smiles. "Did you know they invented pornography?"

CHAPTER THIRTY-NINE

"Stanford White," Capote says. "He designed the original Pennsylvania Station. It was one of the most beautiful buildings in the world. But in 1963 some idiot sold the air rights and they tore it down to put up this monstrosity."

"That is so sad," I murmur, riding down the escalator behind him. "I wonder if it smelled as bad then as it does now."

"What?" he asks loudly, over the hubbub.

"Nothing."

"I always wish I could have lived in New York at the turn of the century," he says.

"I'm glad I was able to live here at all."

"Yeah. I don't think I'd ever be able to leave

New York," he adds, his words causing another jolt of despair.

All morning we've been saying the wrong things to each other, when we've managed to say anything at all.

I've been studiously trying to bring up the future, while Capote keeps studiously avoiding it.

Hence the history lesson about Penn Station.

"Listen," I begin.

"Look at the time," he says quickly, nodding at the clock. "You don't want to miss your train."

If I didn't know better, I'd think he was trying to get rid of me.

"That was fun, wasn't it?" I venture, shuffling in line to buy my ticket.

"Yeah. It was great." For a moment he yields, and I see the little boy in him.

"You could come and visit me in Providence—"

"Sure," he says. I can tell by the way his eyes dart to the side that it's never going to happen, though. He'll have found another girl by then. But if I weren't leaving, maybe I could have been The One.

He has to find her someday, right?

I purchase my ticket. Capote picks up my suitcase as I buy copies of *The New York Times* and the *Post*. I won't be doing that for a while, I think sourly. We find the escalator to my gate. As we descend, I'm filled with a blinding emptiness. This is it, I think. The End.

"All aboard," the conductor shouts.

I place one foot on the step and pause. If only Capote would rush forward, grab my arm, and pull me back to him. If only there was a sudden blackout. If only something would happen—anything—to prevent me from getting on that train.

I look back over my shoulder and find Capote in the crowd.

He waves.

The trip to Hartford is three hours. For the first hour, I'm a puddle of misery. I can't believe I've left New York. I can't believe I've left Capote. What if I never see him again?

It isn't right. It's not the way it's *supposed* to be. Capote should have declared his undying love.

"Should," I suddenly recall myself saying to Samantha and Miranda, "is the worst word in the English language. People always think things 'should' be a certain way, and when they're not, they're disappointed."

"What happened to you?" Samantha asked. "You had sex and now you know everything?"

"I not only had sex, I had an orgasm," I said proudly.

"Oh, honey, welcome to the club," Samantha exclaimed. And then she turned to Miranda. "Don't worry. Someday you'll have one too."

"How do you know I haven't?" Miranda shrieked.

I close my eyes and lean my head back against the seat. Maybe it's okay about Capote. Just because something doesn't last forever, it doesn't mean it wasn't meaningful while it did last. It doesn't mean it wasn't important.

And what's more important than your first guy? Hey, I could have done a lot worse.

And suddenly, I feel free.

I shuffle through my newspapers and open the *New York Post*. And that's when I spot my name.

I frown. It can't be. Why is my name in Page Six? Then I look at the title of the piece: "Disaster and Plaster."

I drop the paper like I've been bitten.

When the train pulls into New Haven for a twenty-minute layover, I race out of my compartment and run to the nearest phone booth. I catch Samantha in her office, and shaking and spluttering manage to ask if she's seen the *Post*.

"Yes, Carrie, I did. And I thought it was terrific."

"What?" I scream.

"Calm down. You can't take these things so personally. There's no such thing as bad publicity."

"They said my reading was the worst thing they've seen since their high school Christmas pageant."

"Who cares?" she purrs. "They're probably jealous. You got a mention for your first play in New York City. Aren't you excited?"

"I'm *mortified*."

"That's too bad. Because Cholly Hammond called. He's been trying to get in touch with you for days. He wants you to call him immediately."

"Why?"

"Oh, Sparrow," she sighs. "How should I know? But he said it was important. I've got to go. I've got Harry Mills in my office—" And she hangs up.

I stare at the phone. Cholly Hammond? What can he want?

I count out more change. Normally, the cost of making a long-distance call from a pay phone would be a problem, but I happen to be kind of flush right now. In the spirit of Samantha, I sold my brand-new, never used Chanel bag to the nice man at the vintage shop for two hundred and fifty dollars. I knew the money wasn't near what it was worth, but I wouldn't need the bag at Brown. And besides, I was kind of happy to get rid of it.

Baggage.

I drop several quarters into the slot. The phone is answered by a bright young thing.

"Is Cholly there?" I ask, giving my name.

Cholly immediately gets on the line.

"Little one!" he exclaims, like I'm his long-lost friend.

"Cholly!" I reply.

"I saw your mention in the *Post* and found it very intriguing," he enthuses. "Especially as I've been thinking about you for weeks. Ever since I sat next to you at Barry Jessen's opening."

My heart sinks. Here we go again. Another old geezer who wants to get into my pants.

"I kept musing about our oh-so-amusing conversation. Pun intended."

"Is that so?" I ask, trying to recall what I might have said that could be so memorable.

"And since I'm always on the lookout for something new, I thought, wouldn't it be interesting to try to get some younger readers to *The New Review*? And who better to capture them than a young woman herself? In a sort of column, if you will. New York through the eyes of an ingenue."

"I don't know how good it would be. Given how badly my play went over."

"Goodness gracious," he exclaims. "But that's the whole point. If it *had* been a swimming success,

I wouldn't be calling you. Because the whole idea behind this enterprise is that Carrie Bradshaw never wins."

"Excuse me?" I gasp.

"Carrie never wins. That's the fun of it, don't you see? It's what keeps her going."

"But what about love? Does she ever win at love?"

"Especially not at love."

I hesitate. "That sounds like a curse, Cholly."

He laughs loud and long. "You know what they say: One man's curse is another man's opportunity. So what do you say? Can we meet in my office this afternoon at three?"

"In New York?"

"Where else?" he says.

Whoo-hooo, I think, swaying through the first-class cabin on the train headed back to the city. The seats are enormous and covered in red velvet and there's a paper napkin on each headrest. There's even a special compartment where you can stash your suitcase. It's a heck of a lot nicer than coach.

"Always go first-class." I hear Samantha's voice in my head.

"But only if you can pay for it yourself," Miranda counters.

Well, I am paying for it myself. Via Bernard and his lovely gift. But what the hell? I deserve it.

Maybe I'm not a failure after all.

I don't know how long I'll stay in New York, or what my father will do when I tell him. But I'll worry about that later. For the moment, all I care about is one simple fact: I'm going back.

I teeter up the aisle, looking for a place to sit and someone decent to sit next to. I pass a balding man, and a lady who's knitting. Then I spot a pretty girl with a luxurious mane of hair, flipping through a copy of *Brides* magazine.

Brides. She's got to be kidding. I take the seat next to her.

"Oh hi!" she says eagerly, moving her bag. I smile. She's just as sweet as I thought she'd be, given that gorgeous hair.

"I'm so glad to get you as a seatmate," she whispers intimately, looking around. "The last time I took the train to New York, this creepy guy sat right next to me. He actually tried to put his hand on my leg. Can you believe it? I had to move my seat three times."

"That's terrible," I say.

"I know." She nods, wide-eyed.

I smile. "Getting married?" I ask, indicating her magazine.

She blushes. "Not exactly. I mean, not yet. But

I hope to be engaged in a couple of years. My boyfriend works in New York. On Wall Street." She ducks her head prettily. "My name's Charlotte, by the way."

"Carrie," I say, holding out my hand.

"What about you? Do you have a boyfriend?"

I burst out laughing.

"What's so funny?" she says, confused. "They say Paris is romantic, but I think New York is romantic too. And the men—"

I laugh even harder.

"Well, really," she says primly. "If you're going to laugh the whole way to New York . . . I don't see what's so funny about going to New York to find love."

I howl.

"Well?" she demands.

I wipe away my tears. I sit back and cross my arms. "Do you really want to know about love in New York?"

"Yes, I do." Her tone is curious and a little bit cautious.

The train toots its horn as I lean forward in my seat.

"Sweetie," I say, with a smile. "Have I got a story for *you*."